The Prose Works

of

Sir Philip Sidney

In Four Volumes

Volume I

SIR PHILIP SIDNEY

Born 1554
Died 1586

THE
COVNTESSE
OF PEMBROKES
ARCADIA,

WRITTEN BY SIR PHILIPPE
SIDNEI.

LONDON
Printed for William Ponsonbie.
Anno Domini, 1590.

Title-page of the Editio Princeps

SIR PHILIP SIDNEY

THE
COUNTESSE OF PEMBROKES
ARCADIA

EDITED BY

ALBERT FEUILLERAT

CAMBRIDGE
AT THE UNIVERSITY PRESS
1965

PUBLISHED BY
THE SYNDICS OF THE CAMBRIDGE UNIVERSITY PRESS

Bentley House, 200 Euston Road, London, N.W. 1
American Branch: 32 East 57th Street, New York, N.Y. 10022

First printed 1912
Reprinted 1962
1963
1965

First printed in Great Britain at the University Press, Cambridge
Reprinted by offset-lithography by
Lowe & Brydone (Printers), Ltd., London, N.W. 10

PUBLISHER'S NOTE

FEUILLERAT'S edition of the complete works of Sir Philip Sidney has long been out of print, but has continued to be in demand by scholars. Bibliographical research has shown that Feuillerat did not work from the best copy-texts, and that many of his readings are corrupt. Further, three more manuscripts of Sidney have been discovered since Feuillerat's edition was printed. It may, however, be many years before a new and definitive edition is published, and it has therefore been decided to reissue with minor corrections the complete prose works in Feuillerat's edition. The publisher gratefully acknowledges the advice of Professor R. W. Zandvoort and Mrs Jean Bromley in connection with this reprint.

The prose works are divided among the four volumes as follows: vol. I, *Arcadia*, 1590; vol. II, *Arcadia*, 1593 and *The Lady of May*; vol. III, *The Defence of Poesie*, Political Discourses, Correspondence and Translation; vol. IV, *Arcadia* (original version). These volumes combine with Professor Ringler's newly edited *Complete Poems* to make all Sidney's works available again.

The parts of Feuillerat's prefatory notes which are not relevant to this reprint have been removed; the remaining parts are set out below.

*　　*　　*

In accordance with the method adopted in the first volume, the text given is that of the earliest edition. Thus, the last part of *Arcadia* is printed from the folio of 1593 and *The Lady of May* from the folio of 1598.

PREFATORY NOTE

The fact that such an important author should have had to wait so long for his due is probably referable to the difficulties with which a modern editor has to struggle in choosing an authentic text. Sir Philip Sidney was blessed with a most charming and most talented sister; but this fascinating lady made no scruple to revise and, as she probably thought, to better the writings of her deceased brother. Hence, the danger of printing, as Sir Philip's, passages which fell from the pen of Mary. In many cases, it is hopeless to determine how much is due to her collaboration; in others, unauthorised editions fortunately permit us to escape the effects of her revisory spirit. For this reason, my principle has been—whenever this was possible—to choose as a basis of the text the earliest editions known, even when these, from a literary point of view, are inferior to "amended" texts.

As regards the present volume, my choice has proved simple enough. Two forms of *Arcadia* have been preserved. The earlier, known as "the old Arcadia," contained five books and was circulated in manuscript, several copies of which still exist, three having been discovered by Mr B. Dobell. With this first form, the author, it appears, was not satisfied and he set about revising it; or, rather, he enlarged it by the addition of several new stories dovetailed into the principal one, after the manner of Spanish romances. At the time of his death, Sidney had not proceeded further than a portion of the third Book, and thus his manuscript was left unfinished. This manuscript, having come to the hands of Ponsonby, was printed and published in a quarto volume, in 1590. Three years later, another edition in folio, pretending to wipe away "those spottes wherewith the beauties" of *Arcadia* "were unworthely blemished," appeared with rearrangements and additions said to have been worked up from "severall loose sheets" sent by the author to the Countess of Pembroke. As a matter of fact, the editor of this new edition—as I shall show in due course—contented himself with slightly modifying the text of the quarto and completing the story from that "old Arcadia" already mentioned, thus giving the unnatural combination of a rejected work and of a work which represented the final form adopted by the author. Such being the case, I have thought it best to give in a separate volume—the first—the text of the

PREFATORY NOTE

quarto of 1590, reserving for the second volume that part of the original *Arcadia* which was added in 1593. Thus, the incongruity of blending two incompatible forms has been avoided without omitting what is, after all, an interesting part of Sir Philip Sidney's works.

In accordance with the scheme of *The Cambridge English Classics*, the text adopted is printed without any deviations from the original[1] in the matter of spelling and punctuation, save those recorded in the list found on page 520. These exceptions consist of evident misprints which it has been thought useless to preserve. In the Notes, I have given the variant readings supplied by all the editions published from 1593 down to 1674[2]. These are fourteen in number, or, rather, twelve, for the 1623 and 1629 folios are duplicates of the 1621 and 1627 editions respectively. This long and self-imposed task has been, I need not say, tedious and has involved sacrifices of many sorts. To some, it may even seem foolish to have wasted so much time upon mere collation. Yet I do not regret my pains, for it is now possible to solve most of the bibliographical problems which present themselves, that of the Edinburgh edition amongst others.

[1] In the British Museum (Press Mark: G. 10440).
[2] The manuscripts of "the old Arcadia" have not been collated; to include their variants would have meant practically printing the whole of the earlier form. It also goes without saying that I have not recorded differences in spelling. In the Notes, the spelling given is that of the earliest edition where the difference appears.

CONTENTS

	PAGE
The Countesse of Pembrokes Arcadia . . .	1
List of Misprints in the Quarto which have been corrected	520
Notes (variants)	522
Appendix (the Eclogues as printed in 1593) . .	563
Alphabetical Table of the Personages in *Arcadia* .	567
Index of First Lines of Poems	571

THE
COUNTESSE
OF PEMBROKES
ARCADIA,

WRITTEN BY SIR PHILIPPE
SIDNEI.

LONDON
Printed for William Ponsonbie.
Anno Domini, 1590.

TO MY DEARE LADIE
AND SISTER, THE COUN-
TESSE OF PEMBROKE.

HEre now have you (most deare, and most worthy to be most deare Lady) this idle worke of mine : which I fear (like the Spiders webbe) will be thought fitter to be swept away, then worn to any other purpose. For my part, in very trueth (as the cruell fathers among the Greekes, were woont to doo to the babes they would not foster) I could well find in my harte, to cast out in some desert of forgetfulnes this child, which I am loath to father. But you desired me to doo it, and your desire, to my hart is an absolute commandement. Now, it is done onelie for you, onely to you: if you keepe it to your selfe, or to such friendes, who will weigh errors in the ballaunce of good will, I hope, for the fathers sake, it will be pardoned, perchance made much of, though in it selfe it have deformities. For indeede, for severer eyes it is not, being but a trifle, and that triflinglie handled. Your deare selfe can best witnes the maner, being done in loose sheetes of paper, most of it in your presence, the rest, by sheetes, sent unto you, as fast as they were done. In summe, a young head, not so well stayed as I would it were, (and shall be when God will) having many many fancies begotten in it, if it had not ben in some way delivered, would have growen a monster, & more sorie might I be that they came in, then that they gat out. But his chiefe safetie, shalbe the not walking abroad; & his chiefe protection, the bearing the liverye of your name; which (if much much good will do not deceave me) is worthy to be a sāctuary for a greater offender. This say I, because I knowe the vertue so; and this say I, because it may be ever so; or to say better, because it will be ever so. Read it then at your idle tymes, and the follyes your good judgement wil finde in it, blame not, but laugh at. And so, looking for no better stuffe, then, as in an Haberdashers shoppe, glasses, or feathers, you will continue to love the writer, who doth excedinglie love you; and most most hartelie praies you may long live, to be a principall ornament to the familie of the Sidneis.

Your loving Brother

Philip Sidnei.

*T*He division and summing of the Chapters was not of Sir Philip Sidneis *dooing,* but adventured by the over-seer of the print, for the more ease of the Readers. He therfore submits himselfe to their judgement, and if his labour answere not the worthines of the booke, desireth pardon for it. As also if any defect be found in the Eclogues, which although they were of Sir Phillip Sidneis writing, yet were they not perused by him, but left till the worke had bene finished, that then choise should have bene made, which should have bene taken, and in what manner brought in. At this time they have bene chosen and disposed as the over-seer thought best.

4

THE COUNTESSE OF
PEMBROKES ARCADIA WRIT-
TEN BY SIR PHILIP
SIDNEI.

THE FIRST BOOKE.

CHAP. 1.

[1] *The sheperdish complaints of the absented lovers* Strephon *and* Claius. [2] *The second shipwrack of* Pyrocles *and* Musidorus. *Their strange saving,* [3] *enterview, and* [4] *parting.*

IT *was in the time* that the earth begins to put on her new 1
aparrel against the approch of her lover, and that the Sun
rũning a most evẽ course becums an indifferent arbiter betweene
the night and the day; when the hopelesse shepheard *Strephon*
was come to the sandes, which lie against the Island of Cithera;
where viewing the place with a heavy kinde of delight, and
sometimes casting his eyes to the Ileward, he called his friendly
rivall, the pastor *Claius* unto him, and setting first downe in
his darkened countenance a dolefull copie of what he would
speake: O my *Claius*, said he, hether we are now come to pay
the rent, for which we are so called unto by over-busie Remembrance, Remembrance, restlesse Remembrance, which
claymes not onely this dutie of us, but for it will have us
forget our selves. I pray you when wee were amid our flocke,
and that of other shepheardes some were running after their
sheep strayed beyond their bounds, some delighting their eyes
with seeing them nibble upon the short and sweete grasse,
some medicining their sicke ewes, some setting a bell for an
ensigne of a sheepish squadron, some with more leasure invent-
ing new games of exercising their bodies & sporting their wits:
did Remembrance graunt us any holiday, eyther for pastime

or devotion, nay either for necessary foode or naturall rest? but that still it forced our thoughts to worke upõ this place, where we last (alas that the word last should so long last) did gaze our eyes upon her ever florishing beautie: did it not still crie within us? Ah you base minded wretches, are your thoughts so deeply bemired in the trade of ordinary worldlings, as for respeƈt of gaine some paultry wooll may yeeld you, to let so much time passe without knowing perfeƈtly her estate, especially in so troublesome a season? to leave that shore unsaluted, from whence you may see to the Island where she dwelleth? to leave those steps unkissed wherein *Urania* printed the farewell of all beautie? Wel then, Remembraunce commaunded, we obeyed, and here we finde, that as our remembrance came ever cloathed unto us in the forme of this place, so this place gives newe heate to the feaver of our languishing remembrance. Yonder my *Claius, Urania* lighted, the verie horse (me thought) bewayled to be so disburdned: and as for thee, poore *Claius,* when thou wentst to help her downe, I saw reverence and desire so devide thee, that thou didst at one instant both blushe and quake, and in stead of bearing her, weart ready to fall downe thy selfe. There shee sate, vouchsafing my cloake (then most gorgeous) under her: at yonder rising of the ground she turned her selfe, looking backe toward her woonted abode, and because of her parting bearing much sorrow in hir eyes, the lightsomnes whereof had yet so naturall a cherefulnesse, as it made even sorrow seeme to smile; at that turning she spake unto us all, opening the cherrie of hir lips, & Lord how greedily mine eares did feed upon the sweete words she uttered? And here she laide her hand over thine eyes, when shee saw the teares springing in them, as if she would conceale them from other, and yet her selfe feele some of thy sorrow: But woe is me, yonder, yonder, did she put her foote into the boate, at that instant as it were deviding her heavenly beautie, betweene the Earth and the Sea. But when she was imbarked, did you not marke how the windes whistled, & the seas daunst for joy, how the sailes did swel with pride, and all because they had *Urania?* O *Urania,* blessed be thou *Urania,* the sweetest fairenesse and fairest sweetnesse: with that worde his voice brake so with sobbing, that he could say no further; and *Claius* thus answered. Alas my *Strephon* (said he) what

needes this skore to recken up onely our losses? What doubt
is there, but that the light of this place doth call our thoughtes
to appeare at the court of affection, held by that racking
steward, Remembraunce? Aswell may sheepe forget to feare
when they spie woolves, as wee can misse such fancies, when
wee see any place made happie by her treading. Who can
choose that saw her but thinke where she stayed, where she
walkt, where she turned, where she spoke? But what is all
this? truely no more, but as this place served us to thinke of
those thinges, so those thinges serve as places to call to memorie
more excellent matters. No, no, let us thinke with consideration, and consider with acknowledging, and acknowledge with
admiration, and admire with love, and love with joy in the
midst of all woes: let us in such sorte thinke, I say, that our
poore eyes were so inriched as to behold, and our low hearts so
exalted as to love, a maide, who is such, that as the greatest
thing the world can shewe, is her beautie, so the least thing that
may be praysed in her, is her beautie. Certainely as her eye-
lids are more pleasant to behold, then two white kiddes climing
up a faire tree, and browsing on his tendrest braunches, and yet
are nothing, compared to the day-shining starres contayned in
them; and as her breath is more sweete then a gentle South-
west wind, which comes creeping over flowrie fieldes and
shaddowed waters in the extreeme heate of summer, and yet is
nothing, compared to the hony flowing speach that breath doth
carrie: no more all that our eyes can see of her (though when
they have seene her, what else they shall ever see is but drie
stuble after clovers grasse) is to bee matched with the flocke of
unspeakeable vertues laid up delightfully in that best builded
folde. But in deede as wee can better consider the sunnes
beautie, by marking how he guildes these waters, and mountaines them by looking upon his owne face, too glorious for our
weake eyes: so it may be our conceits (not able to beare her
sun-stayning excellencie) will better way it by her workes upon
some meaner subject employed. And alas, who can better
witnesse that then we, whose experience is grounded upon
feeling? hath not the onely love of her made us (being silly
ignorant shepheards) raise up our thoughts above the ordinary
levell of the worlde, so as great clearkes do not disdaine our
conference? hath not the desire to seeme worthie in her eyes

made us when others were sleeping, to sit vewing the course of heavens? when others were running at base, to runne over learned writings? when other marke their sheepe, we to marke our selves? hath not shee throwne reason upon our desires, and, as it were given eyes unto *Cupid?* hath in any, but in her, love-fellowship maintained friendship betweene rivals, and beautie taught the beholders chastitie? He was going on with his praises, but *Strephon* bad him stay, & looke: & so they both perceaved a thing which floted drawing nearer and nearer to the banke; but rather by the favourable working of the Sea, then by any selfe industrie. They doubted a while what it should be; till it was cast up even hard before thẽ: at which time they fully saw that it was a man: Wherupon running for pitie sake unto him, they found his hands (as it should appeare, constanter frends to his life then his memorie) fast griping upon· the edge of a square small coffer, which lay all under his breast: els in him selfe no shew of life, so as the boord seemed to bee but a beere to carry him a land to his Sepulchre. So drew they up a young man of so goodly shape, and well pleasing favour, that one would think death had in him a lovely countenance; and, that though he were naked, nakednes was to him an apparrell. That sight increased their compassion, and their compassion called up their care; so that lifting his feete above his head, making a great deale of salt water to come out of his mouth, they layd him upon some of their garments, and fell to rub and chafe him, till they brought him to recover both breath the servant, & warmth the companion of living. At length, opening his eyes, he gave a great groane, (a dolefull note but a pleasaunt dittie) for by that, they found not onely life, but strength of life in him. They therefore continued on their charitable office, until (his spirits being well returned,) hee (without so much as thanking them for their paines) gate up, and looking round about to the uttermost lymittes of his sight, and crying upon the name of *Pyrocles*, nor seeing nor hearing cause of comfort: what (said he) and shall *Musidorus* live after *Pyrocles?* therewithall hee offered wilfully to cast destruction & himselfe againe into the sea: a strange sight to the shepheards, to whom it seemed, that before being in apparance dead had yet saved his life, and now comming to his life, shoulde be a cause to procure his death; but they ranne unto him, and

pulling him backe, (then too feeble for them) by force stickled
that unnatural fray. I pray you (said he) honest men, what
such right have you in me, as not to suffer me to doe with my
self what I list? and what pollicie have you to bestow a benefite
where it is counted an injury? They hearing him speake in
Greek (which was their naturall language) became the more
tender hearted towards him; and considering by his calling and
looking, that the losse of some deare friend was great cause of
his sorow; told him they were poore men that were bound by
course of humanitie to prevent so great a mischiefe; and that
they wisht him, if opinion of some bodies perishing bred such
desperate anguish in him, that he should be comforted by his
owne proofe, who had lately escaped as apparant danger as any
might be. No, no (said hee) it is not for me to attend so high
a blissefulnesse: but since you take care of mee, I pray you
finde meanes that some Barke may be provided, that will goe
out of the haven, that if it be possible we may finde the body
farre farre too precious a foode for fishes: and for the hire (said
he) I have within this casket, of value sufficient to content
them. *Claius* presently went to a Fisherman, & having agreed
with him, and provided some apparrell for the naked stranger,
he imbarked, and the Shepheards with him: and were no sooner
gone beyond the mouth of the haven, but that some way into
the sea they might discerne (as it were) a stayne of the waters
colour, and by times some sparkes and smoke mounting thereout.
But the young man no sooner saw it, but that beating his brest,
he cried, that there was the beginning of his ruine, intreating
them to bend their course as neere unto it as they could:
telling, how that smoake was but a small relique of a great fire,
which had drivẽ both him & his friend rather to committe
themselves to the cold mercie of the sea, then to abide the hote
crueltie of the fire: and that therefore, though they both had
abandoned the ship, that he was (if any where) in that course
to be met withall. They steared therefore as neere thetherward as they could: but when they came so neere as their
eies were ful masters of the objeƈt, they saw a sight full of
piteous strangenes: a ship, or rather the carkas of the shippe,
or rather some few bones of the carkas, hulling there, part
broken, part burned, part drowned: death having used more
then one dart to that destruƈtion. About it floted great store

of very rich thinges, and many chestes which might promise
no lesse. And amidst the precious things were a number of
dead bodies, which likewise did not onely testifie both elemēts
violence, but that the chiefe violence was growen of humane
inhumanitie: for their bodies were ful of grisly wounds, &
their bloud had (as it were) filled the wrinckles of the seas
visage: which it seemed the sea woulde not wash away, that
it might witnes it is not alwaies his fault, when we condemne
his crueltie: in summe, a defeate, where the conquered kept both
field and spoile: a shipwrack without storme or ill footing: and
a wast of fire in the midst of water.

But a litle way off they saw the mast, whose proude height
now lay along; like a widdow having lost her make of whom
she held her honor: but upon the mast they saw a yong man
(at least if he were a man) bearing shew of about 18. yeares of
age, who sate (as on horsback) having nothing upon him but
his shirt, which being wrought with blew silk & gold; had a
kind of resemblance to the sea: on which the sun (then neare
his Westerne home) did shoote some of his beames. His haire
(which the young men of Greece used to weare very long) was
stirred up & down with the wind, which seemed to have a
sport to play with it, as the sea had to kisse his feet; himselfe
full of admirable beautie, set foorth by the strangenes both of
his seate & gesture: for, holding his head up full of unmoved
majestie, he held a sworde aloft with his faire arme, which often
he waved about his crowne as though he would threaten the
world in that extremitie. But the fishermen, when they came
so neere him, that it was time to throwe out a rope, by which
hold they might draw him, their simplicity bred such amasement, & their amasement such a superstitiõ, that (assuredly
thinking it was some God begotten betweene *Neptune* and
Venus, that had made all this terrible slaughter) as they went
under sayle by him, held up their hands, and made their
prayers. Which when *Musidorus* sawe, though he were almost
as much ravished with joy, as they with astonishment, he lept
to the Mariner, and tooke the rope out of his hande and (saying,
doest thou live, and arte well? who answered, thou canst tell
best, since most of my well beyng standes in thee,) threwe it
out, but alreadie the shippe was past beyond *Pyrocles*: and
therefore *Musidorus* could doo no more but perswade the

Mariners to cast about againe, assuring them that hee was but a man, although of most divine excellencies, and promising great rewardes for their paine.

And now they were alreadie come upon the staies; when one of the saylers descried a Galley which came with sayles and oares directlie in the chase of them; and streight perceaved it was a well knowne Pirate, who hunted not onely for goodes but for bodies of menne, which hee imployed eyther to bee his Galley slaves, or to sell at the best market. Which when the Maister understood, he commaunded forthwith to set on all the canvasse they could, and flie homeward, leaving in that sort poore *Pyrocles* so neere to be reskewed. But what did not *Musidorus* say? what did he not offer to perswade them to venture the fight? But feare standing at the gates of their eares, put back all perswasions: so that hee had nothing to accompanie *Pyrocles*, but his eyes; nor to succour him, but his wishes. Therefore praying for him, and casting a long look that way he saw the Galley leave the pursuite of them, & turne to take up the spoiles of the other wrack: and lastly he might well see them lift up the yong man; and alas (said he to himselfe) deere *Pyrocles* shall that bodie of thine be enchayned? shall those victorious handes of thine be commaunded to base offices? shall vertue become a slave to those that be slaves to viciousnes? Alas, better had it bene thou hadst ended nobly thy noble daies: what death is so evill as unworthy servitude? But that opinion soone ceased when he saw the gallie setting upon an other ship, which held long and strong fight with her: for then he began a fresh to feare the life of his friende, and to wish well to the Pirates whome before he hated, least in their ruyne hee might perish. But the fishermen made such speed into the haven, that they absented his eyes from beholding the issue: where being entred, he could procure neither them nor any other as then to put themselves into the sea: so that beyng as full of sorrow for being unable to doe any thing, as voide of counsell how to doe any thing, besides, that sicknesse grew something upon him, the honest shepheards *Strephon* and *Claius* (who being themselves true friends, did the more perfectly judge the justnesse of his sorrowe) advise him, that he should mitigate somwhat of his woe, since he had gotten an amendment in fortune, being come from assured persuasion of his death, to have no cause to dispaire of his life: as one that had lamented the death of his sheepe, should after know they were but strayed, would receive pleasure though readily hee knew not where to finde them.

CHAP. 2.

[1] *The pastors comfortes to the wracked* Musidorus. [2] *His passage into* Arcadia. *The descriptions of* [3] *Laconia,* [4] *Arcadia,* Kalanders [5] *person,* [6] *house, and* [7] *entertainement to* Musidorus, *now called* Palladius. *His* [8] *sicknes, recovery,* [9] *and perfections.*

1 NOw sir (saide they) thus for our selves it is. Wee are in profession but shepheards, and in this countrie of Laconia little better then strangers, and therefore neither in skill, nor habilitie of power greatly to stead you. But what we can present unto you is this: Arcadia, of which countrie wee are, is but a little way hence, and even upon the next confines.

5 There dwelleth a Gentleman, by name *Kalander,* who vouchsafeth much favour unto us: A man who for his hospitalitie is so much haunted, that no newes sturre, but comes to his eares ; for his upright dealing so beloved of his neighbours, that he hath many ever readie to doe him their uttermost service, and by the great good will our Prince beares him, may soone obtaine the use of his name and credit, which hath a principall swaie, not only in his owne Arcadia but in al these coūtries of *Peloponnesus :* and (which is worth all) all these things give him not so much power, as his nature gives him will to benefit : so that it seemes no Musicke is so sweet to his eare as deserved thankes. To him we will bring you, & there you may recover againe your helth, without which you cănot be able to make any diligent search for your friend : and therefore but in that respect, you must labour for it. Besides, we are sure the cōfort of curtesie, & ease of wise counsell shall not be wanting.

2 *Musidorus* (who besides he was meerly unacquainted in the coūtrie had his wits astonished with sorow) gave easie consent

to that, frō which he saw no reason to disagree : & therefore
(defraying the Mariners with a ring bestowed upon thē) they
tooke their journey together through *Laconia* ; *Claius* & *Stre-phon* by course carying his chest for him, *Musidorus* only bearing
in his coūtenance evidēt marks of a sorowfulmind supported
with a weak bodie, which they perceiving, & knowing that the
violence of sorow is not at the first to be strivē withal : (being
like a mighty beast, soner tamed with folowing, thā overthrowē
by withstāding) they gave way unto it for that day & the next ;
never troubling him, either with asking questions, or finding
fault with his melācholie, but rather fitting to his dolor dolorous
discourses of their own & other folks misfortunes. Which
speeches, thogh they had not a lively entrāce to his sēces shut
up in sorow, yet like one half asleep, he toke hold of much of
the matters spoken unto him, so as a man may say, ere sorow
was aware, they made his thoughts beare away something els
beside his own sorow, which wrought so in him, that at lēgth
he grew cōtent to mark their speeches, then to marvel at such
wit in shepheardes, after to like their company, & lastly to
vouchsafe conferēce : so that the 3. day after, in the time that
the morning did strow roses & violets in the heavenly floore
against the cōming of the Sun, the nightingales (striving one
with the other which coulde in most dainty variety recount
their wrong-caused sorow) made thē put of their sleep, &
rising frō under a tree (which that night had bin their paviliō)
they went on their jorney, which by & by welcomed *Musidorus*
eyes (wearied with the wasted soile of Laconia) with delightfull
prospeċts. There were hilles which garnished their proud 4
heights with stately trees: hūble valleis, whose base estate
semed cōforted with refreshing of silver rivers : medows,
enameld with al sorts of ey-pleasing floures : thickets, which
being lined with most pleasāt shade, were witnessed so to by
the chereful depositiō of many wel-tuned birds : each pasture
stored with sheep feeding with sober security, while the prety
lābs with bleting oratory craved the dams cōfort : here a shep-heards boy piping, as though he should never be old : there a
yong shepherdesse knitting, and withall singing, & it seemed
that her voice cōforted her hands to work, & her hāds kept
time to her voices musick. As for the houses of the coūtry
(for many houses came under their eye) they were all scattered,

no two being one by th'other, & yet not so far off as that it barred mutual succour: a shew, as it were, of an accõpanable solitarines, & of a civil wildnes. I pray you (said *Musidorus*, then first unsealing his long silent lips) what coũtries be these we passe through, which are so divers in shew, the one wãting no store, th'other having no store but of want.

3   The country (answered *Claius*) where you were cast a shore, & now are past through, is Laconia, not so poore by the barrennes of the soyle (though in it selfe not passing fertill) as by a civill warre, which being these two yeares within the bowels of that estate, betweene the gentlemen & the peasants (by them named *Helots*) hath in this sorte as it were disfigured the face of nature, and made it so unhospitall as now you have found it: the townes neither of the one side nor the other, willingly opening their gates to strangers, nor strangers willingly entring for feare of being mistaken.

4   But this countrie (where now you set your foote) is Arcadia: and even harde by is the house of *Kalander* whether we lead you: this countrie being thus decked with peace, and (the childe of peace) good husbandrie. These houses you see so scattered are of men, as we two are, that live upon the commoditie of their sheepe: and therefore in the division of the Arcadian estate are termed shepheards; a happie people, wanting litle, because they desire not much. What cause then, said *Musidorus*, made you venter to leave this sweete life, and put your selfe in yonder unpleasant and dangerous realme? Garded with povertie (answered *Strephon*) & guided with love: But now (said *Claius*) since it hath pleased you to aske any thing of us whose basenes is such as the very knowledge is darknes: geve us leave to know somthing of you, & of the young man you so much lament, that at least we may be the better instructed to enforme *Kalander*, and he the better know how to proportion his entertainment. *Musidorus* (according to the agreement betweene *Pyrocles* and him to alter their names) answered, that he called himself *Palladius*, and his friend *Daiphantus*; but till I have him againe (said he) I am in deed nothing: and therefore my storie is of nothing, his entertainement (since so good a man he is) cannot be so lowe as I account my estate: and in summe, the summe of all his curtesie may be to helpe me by some meanes to seeke my frend.

14

They perceived he was not willing to open himselfe further, and therefore without further questioning brought him to the 6 house: about which they might see (with fitte consideration both of the ayre, the prospect, and the nature of the ground) all such necessarie additions to a great house, as might well shewe, *Kalander* knew that provision is the foundation of hospitalitie, and thrift the fewell of magnificence. The house it selfe was built of faire and strong stone, not affecting so much any extraordinarie kinde of finenes, as an honorable representing of a firme statelines. The lightes, doores and staires, rather directed to the use of the guest, then to the eye of the Artificer: and yet as the one cheefly heeded, so the other not neglected; each place handsome without curiositie, and homely without lothsomnes: not so daintie as not to be trode on, nor yet slubberd up with good felowshippe: all more lasting then beautifull, but that the consideration of the exceeding lasting-nesse made the eye beleeve it was exceeding beautifull. The servants not so many in number, as cleanlie in apparell, and serviceable in behaviour, testifying even in their countenaunces, that their maister tooke aswell care to be served, as of thẽ that did serve. One of them was forth-with readie to welcome the shepheards, as men, who though they were poore, their maister greatly favoured: and understanding by them, that the young man with them was to be much accounted of, for that they had seene tokens of more then common greatnes, how so ever now eclipsed with fortune: He ranne to his master, who came presentlie foorth, and pleasantly welcomming the shepheardes, but especially applying him to *Musidorus*, *Strephon* privately told him all what he knew of him, and particularly that hee found this stranger was loath to be knowen.

No said *Kalander* (speaking alowd) I am no herald to enquire 7 of mens pedegrees, it sufficeth me if I know their vertues: which (if this young mans face be not a false witnes) doe better apparell his minde, then you have done his body. While hee was speaking, there came a boy in shew like a Merchants prentice, who taking *Strephon* by the sleeve, delivered him a letter, written joyntly both to him and *Claius* from *Urania*: which they no sooner had read, but that with short leave-taking of *Kalander* (who quickly ghest and smiled at the matter) and once againe (though hastely) recommending the

yong man unto him, they went away, leaving *Musidorus* even
lothe to part with them, for the good conversation he had of
them, & obligation he accounted himselfe tied in unto them:
and therefore, they delivering his chest unto him, he opened it,
and would have presented thẽ with two very rich jewels, but
they absolutelie refused them, telling him they were more then
enough rewarded in the knowing of him, and without herken-
ing unto a replie (like men whose harts disdained all desires but
one) gate speedely away, as if the letter had brought wings to
make them flie. But by that sight *Kalander* soone judged that
his guest was of no meane calling; and therefore the more
respectfullie entertaining him, *Musidorus* found his sicknes
(which the fight, the sea, and late travell had layd upon him)
grow greatly: so that fearing some suddaine accident, he
delivered the chest to *Kalander*; which was full of most
pretious stones, gorgeously & cunningly set in diverse mãners,
desiring him he would keep those trifles, and if he died, he
would bestow so much of it as was needfull, to finde out and
redeeme a young man, naming himselfe *Daiphantus*, as then in
the handes of Laconia pirates.

8 But *Kalander* seeing him faint more and more, with carefull speede conveyed him to the most cõmodious lodging in his
house: where being possest with an extreeme burning fever, he
cõtinued some while with no great hope of life: but youth at
length got the victorie of sicknesse, so that in six weekes the
excellencie of his returned beautie was a credible embassadour
of his health; to the great joy of *Kalander*: who, as in this
time he had by certaine friendes of his that dwelt neare the
Sea in Messenia, set foorth a shippe and a galley to seeke and
succour *Daiphantus*: so at home did hee omit nothing which
he thought might eyther profite or gratifie *Palladius*.

9 For having found in him (besides his bodily giftes beyond
the degree of Admiration) by daylÿ discourses which he delighted him selfe to have with him, a mind of most excellent
composition (a pearcing witte quite voide of ostentation, high
erected thoughts seated in a harte of courtesie, an eloquence as
sweete in the uttering, as slowe to come to the uttering, a
behaviour so noble, as gave a majestie to adversitie: and all in
a man whose age could not be above one & twenty yeares,)
the good old man was even enamoured with a fatherly love

towards him; or rather became his servaunt by the bondes such vertue laid upon him; once hee acknowledged him selfe so to be, by the badge of diligent attendance.

CHAP. 3.

The [1] pictures of Kalanders dainty garden-house. His narration of the [2] Arcadian estate, [3] the King, [4] the Queene, [5] their two daughters, and [6] their gardians, with their qualities, which is the ground of all this storie.

BUt *Palladius* having gotten his health, and onely staying there to be in place, where he might heare answere of the shippes set foorth, *Kalander* one afternoone led him abroad to a wel arayed ground he had behind his house, which hee thought to shewe him before his going, as the place him selfe more then in any other delighted: the backeside of the house was neyther field, garden, nor orchard; or rather it was both fielde, garden, and orcharde: for as soone as the descending of the stayres had delivered them downe, they came into a place cunninglie set with trees of the moste tast-pleasing fruites: but scarcelie they had taken that into their consideration, but that they were suddainely stept into a delicate greene, of each side of the greene a thicket bend, behinde the thickets againe newe beddes of flowers, which being under the trees, the trees were to them a Pavilion, and they to the trees a mosaical floore: so that it seemed that arte therein would needes be delightfull by counterfaiting his enemie error, and making order in confusion.

In the middest of all the place, was a faire ponde, whose shaking christall was a perfect mirrour to all the other beauties, so that it bare shewe of two gardens; one in deede, the other in shaddowes: and in one of the thickets was a fine fountaine made thus. A naked *Venus* of white marble, wherein the graver had used such cunning, that the naturall blew veines of the marble were framed in fitte places, to set foorth the beautifull veines of her bodie. At her brest she had her babe *Æneas*, who seemed (having begun to sucke) to leave that, to looke upon her fayre eyes, which smiled at the babes follie, the meane while the breast running. Hard by was a house of pleasure builte for a Sommer retiring place, whether *Kalander* leading him, he found a square roome full of delightfull pictures, made by the most excellent workeman of Greece. There was *Diana* when *Actæon* sawe her bathing, in whose cheekes the painter had set such a colour, as was mixt betweene shame & disdaine: & one of her foolish Nymphes, who weeping, and withal lowring, one might see the workman meant to set forth teares of anger. In another table was *Atalanta*; the posture of whose lims was so livelie expressed, that if the eyes were the only judges, as they be the onely seers, one would have sworne the very picture had runne. Besides many mo, as of *Helena, Omphale, Iole :* but in none of them all beautie seemed to speake so much as in a large table, which contained a comely old man, with a lady of midle age, but of excellēt beautie; & more excellēt would have bene deemed, but that there stood betweene thē a yong maid, whose wonderfulnesse tooke away all beautie from her, but that, which it might seeme shee gave her backe againe by her very shadow. And such differēce, being knowne that it did in deed counterfeit a person living, was there betweene her and al the other, though Goddesses, that it seemd the skill of the painter bestowed on the other new beautie, but that the beautie of her bestowed new skill of the painter. Though he thought inquisitivenes an uncomely guest, he could not choose but aske who she was, that bearing shew of one being in deed, could with natural gifts go beyond the reach of inventiō. *Kalander* answered, that it was made by *Philoclea*, the yonger daughter of his prince, who also with his wife were conteined in that Table: the painter meaning to represent the present condition of the young Ladie, who stood watched by an over-curious eye of her parents: & that he would also have drawne her eldest sister, estemed her match for beautie, in her shepheardish attire; but that the rude clown her gardiā would not suffer it: nether durst he aske leave of the Prince for feare of suspitiō. *Palladius* perceaved that the matter was wrapt up in some secresie, and therefore would for modestie demaund no further: but yet his countenance could not but with dumme Eloquence desire it: Which *Kalander* perceaving, well said he, my deere guest, I know your minde, and I will satisfie it: neyther will I doo it like a niggardly answerer, going no further then the boundes of the question, but I will discover unto you, aswell that wherein my knowledge is common with others, as that which by extra-ordinarie means is delivered unto me: knowing so much in you, though not long acquainted, that I shall find your eares faithfull treasurers. So then sitting downe in two chaires, and some-times casting his eye to the picture, he thus spake.

This countrie Arcadia among all the provinces of Greece, 2 hath ever beene had in singular reputation: partly for the sweetnesse of the ayre, and other natural benefites, but princi-pally for the well tempered minds of the people, who (finding that the shining title of glorie so much affected by other nations, doth in deed helpe little to the happinesse of life) are the onely people, which as by their Justice and providence geve neither cause nor hope to their neyghbours to annoy them, so are they not sturred with false praise to trouble others quiet, thinking it a small reward for the wasting of their owne lives in ravening, that their posteritie should long after saie, they had done so. Even the Muses seeme to approve their good de-terminatiō, by chosing this countrie for their chiefe repairing place, & by bestowing their perfections so largely here, that the very shepheards have their fancies lifted to so high conceits, as the learned of other nations are content both to borrow their names, and imitate their cunning.

Here dwelleth, and raigneth this Prince (whose picture you 3 see) by name *Basilius*, a Prince of sufficient skill to governe so quiet a countrie, where the good minds of the former princes had set down good lawes, and the well bringing up of the people doth serve as a most sure bond to hold thē. But to be plaine with you, he excels in nothing so much, as in the zealous love of his people, wherein he doth not only passe al his owne fore-goers, but as I thinke al the princes living. Wherof the cause is, that though he exceed not in the vertues which get admiration; as depth of wisdome, height of courage and large-nesse of magnificence, yet is hee notable in those whiche stirre affection, as trueth of worde, meekenesse, courtesie, merciful-nesse, and liberalitie.

He being already well striken in yeares, maried a young 4 princes, named *Gynecia*, daughter to the king of Cyprus, of notable beautie, as by her picture you see: a woman of great wit, and in truth of more princely vertues, then her husband:

of most unspotted chastitie, but of so working a minde, and so vehement spirits, as a man may say, it was happie shee tooke a good course: for otherwise it would have beene terrible.

5   Of these two are brought to the worlde two daughters, so beyonde measure excellent in all the gifts allotted to reasonable creatures, that wee may thinke they were borne to shewe, that Nature is no stepmother to that sex, how much so ever some men (sharpe witted only in evill speaking) have sought to disgrace them. The elder is named *Pamela*; by many men not deemed inferiour to her sister: for my part, when I marked them both, me thought there was (if at least such perfections may receyve the worde of more) more sweetnesse in *Philoclea*, but more majestie in *Pamela*: mee thought love plaide in *Philocleas* eyes, and threatned in *Pamelas*: me thought *Philocleas* beautie onely perswaded, but so perswaded as all harts must yeelde: *Pamelas* beautie used violence, and such violence as no hart could resist: and it seemes that such proportion is betweene their mindes; *Philoclea* so bashfull as though her excellencies had stolne into her before shee was aware: so humble, that she will put all pride out of countenance: in summe, such proceeding as will stirre hope, but teach hope good mãners. *Pamela* of high thoughts, who avoides not pride with not knowing her excellencies, but by making that one of her excellencies to be voide of pride; her mothers wisdome, greatnesse, nobilitie, but (if I can ghesse aright) knit with a more constant temper. Now then, our *Basilius* being so publickly happie as to be a Prince, and so happie in that happinesse as to be a beloved Prince, and so in his private blessed as to have so excellent a wife, and so over-excellent children, hath of late taken a course which yet makes him more spoken of then all these blessings. For, having made a journey to Delphos, and safely returned, within short space hee brake up his court, and retired himselfe, his wife, and children into a certaine Forrest hereby, which hee calleth his desert, where in (besides a house appointed for stables and lodgings for certaine persons of meane calling, who do all houshold services,) hee hath builded two fine lodges. In the one of them him selfe remaines with his younger daughter *Philoclea*, which was the cause they three were matched together in this picture, without having any other creature living in that lodge with him.

Which though it bee straunge, yet not so straunge, as the 6
course he hath taken with the princesse *Pamela*, whom hee
hath placed in the other lodge: but how thinke you ac-
cõpanied? truly with none other, but one *Dametas*, the most
arrant doltish clowne, that I thinke ever was without the
priviledge of a bable, with his wife *Miso*, and daughter *Mopsa*,
in whome no witt can devise anie thing wherein they maie
pleasure her, but to exercise her patience, and to serve for a
foile of her perfections. This loutish clowne is such, that you
never saw so ill favoured a visar; his behaviour such, that he is
beyond the degree of ridiculous; and for his apparrel, even as I
would wish him: *Miso* his wife, so handsome a beldame, that
onely her face and her splayfoote have made her accused for a
witch; onley one good point she hath, that she observes *decorũ*,
having a froward mind in a wretched body. Betweene these
two personages (who never agreed in any humor, but in disagreeing) is issued forth mistresse *Mopsa*, a fitte woman to
participate of both their perfections: but because a pleasant
fellow of my acquaintance set forth her praises in verse, I will
only repeate them, and spare mine owne tongue, since she goes
for a woman. These verses are these, which I have so often
caused to be song, that I have them without booke.

What length of verse can serve brave Mopsas *good to show?*
Whose vertues strange, & beuties such, as no mã thẽ may know
Thus shrewdly burdned thẽ, how cã my Muse escape?
The gods must help, and pretious things must serve to shew her shape.
Like great god Saturn *faire, and like faire* Venus *chaste:*
As smothe as Pan, *as* Juno *milde, like goddesse* Iris *faste.*
With Cupid *she fore-sees, and goes god* Vulcans *pace:*
And for a tast of all these gifts, she steales god Momus *grace.*
Her forhead jacinth like, her cheekes of opall hue,
Her twinkling eies bedeckt with pearle, her lips as Saphir blew:
Her haire like Crapal-stone; her mouth O heavenly wyde;
Her skin like burnisht gold, her hands like silver ure untryde.
 As for her parts unknowne, which hidden sure are best:
 Happie be they which well beleeve, & never seeke the rest.

Now truely having made these descriptions unto you, me
thinkes you should imagine that I rather faine some pleasant

devise, then recount a truth, that a Prince (not banished from his own wits) could possibly make so unworthie a choise. But truely (deare guest) so it is, that Princes (whose doings have beene often soothed with good successe) thinke nothing so absurde, which they cannot make honourable. The beginning of his credite was by the Princes straying out of the way, one time he hunted, where meeting this fellow, and asking him the way; & so falling into other questiõs, he found some of his aunswers (as a dog sure if he could speake, had wit enough to describe his kennell) not unsensible, & all uttered with such rudenes, which he enterpreted plainnesse (though there be great difference betweene them) that *Basilius* conceaving a sodaine delight, tooke him to his Court, with apparant shew of his good opinion: where the flattering courtier had no sooner takē the Princes minde, but that there were straight reasons to confirme the Princes doing, & shadowes of vertues found for *Dametas*. His silence grew wit, his bluntnesse integritie, his beastly ignorance vertuous simplicitie: & the Prince (according to the nature of great persons, in love with that he had done himselfe) fancied, that his weaknesse with his presence would much be mended. And so like a creature of his owne making, he liked him more and more, and thus having first given him the office of principall heardman, lastly, since he tooke this strange determination, he hath in a manner put the life of himselfe and his children into his hands. Which authoritie (like too great a sayle for so small a boate) doth so over-sway poore *Dametas*, that if before he were a good foole in a chamber, he might be allowed it now in a comedie : So as I doubt me (I feare mee in deede) my master will in the end (with his cost) finde, that his office is not to make men, but to use men as men are; no more then a horse will be taught to hunt, or an asse to mannage. But in sooth I am afraide I have geven your eares too great a surfette, with the grosse discourses of that heavie peece of flesh. But the zealous greefe I conceve to see so great an error in my Lord, hath made me bestow more words, then I confesse so base a subject deserveth.

CHAP. 4.

The [1] *cause of* Basilius *his discourting.* [2] Philanax *his disswasive letter.* [3] Basilius *his priviledged companie.* [4] *Foure causes why old men are discoursers.* [5] *The state, the skil, and exercise of the Arcadian shepheards.*

THus much now that I have tolde you, is nothing more [1] then in effect any Arcadian knowes. But what moved him to this strange solitarines hath bin imparted (as I thinke) but to one person living. My selfe cã cõjecture, & in deed more then conjecture, by this accident that I will tell you: I have an onely sonne, by name *Clitophon,* who is now absent, preparing for his owne mariage, which I meane shortly shalbe here celebrated. This sonne of mine (while the Prince kept his Court) was of his bed-chamber; now since the breaking up thereof, returned home, and shewed me (among other things he had gathered) the coppy which he had taken of a letter: which when the prince had read, he had laid in a window, presuming no body durst looke in his writings: but my sonne not only tooke a time to read it, but to copie it. In trueth I blamed *Clitophon* for the curiositie, which made him break his duetie in such a kind, whereby kings secrets are subject to be revealed: but since it was done, I was content to take so much profite, as to know it. Now here is the letter, that I ever since for my good liking, have caried about me: which before I read unto you, I must tell you from whom it came. It is a noble-man of this countrie, named *Philanax,* appointed by the Prince, Regent in this time of his retiring, and most worthie so to be: for, there lives no man, whose excellent witte more simplie imbraseth integritie, besides his unfained love to his master, wherein never yet any could make question, saving, whether he loved *Basilius* or the Prince better: a rare temper, while most men either servile-ly yeeld to al appetites, or with an obstinate austeritie looking to that they fansie good, in effect neglect the Princes person. This then being the man, whom of all other (and most worthie) the Prince cheefly loves, it should seeme (for more then the letter I have not to ghesse by) that the Prince upon his returne from Delphos, (*Philanax* then lying sick) had written unto him his determination, rising (as evidently appeares) upon some Oracle he had there receaved: whereunto he wrote this answere.

Philanax his letter to Basilius.

2   Most redouted & beloved prince, if aswel it had pleased you at your going to Delphos as now, to have used my humble service, both I should in better season, and to better purpose have spoken: and you (if my speech had prevayled) should have beene at this time, as no way more in danger, so much more in quietnes; I would then have said, that wisdome and vertue be the only destinies appointed to mã to follow, whẽce we ought to seeke al our knowledge, since they be such guydes as cannot faile; which, besides their inward cõfort, doo lead so direct a way of proceeding, as either prosperitie must ensue; or, if the wickednes of the world should oppresse it, it can never be said, that evil hapneth to him, who falles accompanied with vertue: I would then have said, the heavenly powers to be reverenced, and not searched into; & their mercies rather by prayers to be sought, then their hidden councels by curiositie. These kind of soothsayers (since they have left us in our selves sufficient guides) to be nothing but fansie, wherein there must either be vanitie, or infalliblenes, & so, either not to be respected, or not to be prevented. But since it is weakenes too much to remember what should have beene done, and that your commandemẽt stretcheth to know what is to be done, I do (most deare Lord) with humble boldnes say, that the maner of your determination dooth in no sort better please me, then the cause of your going. These thirtie yeares you have so governed this Region, that neither your Subjectes have wanted justice in you, nor you obediẽce in them; & your neighbors have found you so hurtlesly strong, that they thought it better to rest in your friendshippe, then make newe triall of your enmitie. If this then have proceeded out of the good constitution of your state, and out of a wise providence, generally to prevent all those things, which might encõber your happines: why should you now seeke newe courses, since your owne ensample comforts you to continue, and that it is to me most certaine (though it please you not to tell me the very words of

the Oracle) that yet no destinie, nor influence whatsoever, can bring mans witte to a higher point, then wisdome and goodnes? Why should you deprive your selfe of government, for feare of loosing your government? like one that should kill himselfe for feare of death? nay rather, if this Oracle be to be accoûted of, arme up your courage the more against it: for who wil stick to him that abandones himselfe? Let your subjects have you in their eyes; let them see the benefites of your justice dayly more and more; and so must they needes rather like of present sureties, then uncertaine changes. Lastly, whether your time call you to live or die, doo both like a prince. Now for your second resolution; which is, to suffer no worthie prince to be a suiter to either of your daughters, but while you live to keep thẽ both unmaried; &, as it were, to kill the joy of posteritie, which in your time you may enjoy: moved perchance by a mis-under-stoode Oracle: what shall I say, if the affection of a father to his owne children, cannot plead sufficiëtly against such fancies? once certaine it is, the God, which is God of nature, doth never teach unnaturalnes: and even the same minde hold I touching your banishing them from companie, least, I know not what strange loves should follow. Certainly Sir, in my ladies, your daughters, nature promiseth nothing but goodnes, and their education by your fatherly care, hath beene hetherto such, as hath beene most fit to restraine all evill: geving their mindes vertuous delights, and not greeving them for want of wel-ruled libertie. Now to fall to a sodain straightning them, what can it doo but argue suspition, a thing no more unpleasant, then unsure, for the preserving of vertue? Leave womens minds, the most untamed that way of any: see whether any cage can please a bird? or whether a dogge growe not fiercer with tying? what dooth jelousie, but stirre up the mind to thinke, what it is from which they are restrayned? for they are treasures, or things of great delight, which men use to hide, for the aptnesse they have to catch mens fancies: and the thoughtes once awaked to that, harder sure it is to keepe those thoughts from accomplishment, then it had been before to have kept the minde (which being the chiefe part, by this meanes is defiled) from thinking. Lastly, for the recommending so principall a charge of the Princesse *Pamela*, (whose minde goes beyond the governing of many thousands such) to such a person as *Dametas* is (besides that the thing in it self is strange) it comes of a very evil ground, that ignorance should be the mother of faithfulnes. O no; he cannot be good, that knowes not why he is good, but stands so farre good, as his fortune may keepe him unassaied: but comming once to that, his rude simplicitie is either easily changed, or easily deceived: & so growes that to be the last excuse of his fault, which seemed to have been the first foundation of his faith. Thus farre hath your commaundement and my zeale drawn me; which I, like a man in a valley that may discern hilles, or like a poore passenger that may spie a rock, so humbly submit to your gracious consideration, beseeching you againe, to stand wholy upon your own vertue, as the surest way to maintaine you in that you are, and to avoyd any evill which may be imagined.

By the contents of this letter you may perceive, that the cause of all, hath beene the vanitie which possesseth many, who (making a perpetuall mansion of this poore baiting place of mans life) are desirous to know the certaintie of things to come; wherein there is nothing so certaine, as our continual uncertaintie. But what in particular points the oracle was, in faith I know not: nether (as you may see by one place of *Philanax* letter) he himselfe distinctly knew. But this experience shewes us, that *Basilius* judgement, corrupted with a Princes fortune, hath rather heard then followed the wise (as I take it) counsell of *Philanax*. For, having lost the sterne of his government, with much amazement to the people, among whom many strange bruits are received for currant, and with some apparance of daunger in respect of the valiant *Amphalus*, his nephew, & much envy in the ambitious number of the Nobilitie against *Philanax*, to see *Philanax* so advaunced, though (to speake simply) he deserve more thẽ as many of us as there be in Arcadia: the prince himself hath hidden his head, in such sort as I told you, not sticking plainly to cõfesse, that he means not (while he breathes) that his daughters shal have any husbãd, but keep thẽ thus solitary with him: wher he gives no other body leve to visit him at any time, but a certain priest, who being excellent in poetrie, he makes him write out such thinges as he best likes, he being no les delightful in cõversatiõ, thẽ needfull for devotiõ, & about twẽty specified shepheards, in whõ (some for exercises, & some for Eglogs) he taketh greater recreatiõ.

And now you know as much as my self: wherin if I have 4
held you over long, lay hardly the fault upon my olde age,
which in the very disposition of it is talkative: whether it be
(said he smiling) that nature loves to exercise that part most,
which is least decayed, and that is our tongue: or, that knowledge being the only thing whereof we poore old men can brag,
we cannot make it knowen but by utterance: or, that mankinde
by all meanes seeking to eternize himselfe so much the more,
as he is neere his end, dooth it not only by the children that
come of him, but by speeches and writings recommended to
the memorie of hearers and readers.   And yet thus much I wil
say for my selfe, that I have not laid these matters, either so
openly, or largely to any as your selfe: so much (if I much
fayle not) doo I see in you, which makes me both love and
trust you.   Never may he be old, answered *Palladius*, that
dooth not reverence that age, whose heavines, if it waie downe
the frayl and fleshly ballance, it as much lifts up the noble and
spirituall part: and well might you have alledged another reason,
that their wisdome makes them willing to profite others.   And
that have I received of you, never to be forgotten, but with
ungratefulnes.   But among many strange conceits you tolde
me, which have shewed effects in your Prince, truly even the
last, that he should conceive such pleasure in shepheards discourses, would not seeme the least unto me, saving that you
told me at the first, that this countrie is notable in those wits,
and that in deed my selfe having beene brought not onely to
this place, but to my life, by *Strephon* and *Claius*, in their
conference found wits as might better become such shepheards
as *Homer* speakes of, that be governors of peoples, then such
senatours who hold their councell in a shepecoate: for them
two (said *Kalander*) especially *Claius*, they are beyond the rest
by so much, as learning commonlie doth adde to nature: for,
having neglected their wealth in respect of their knowledge,
they have not so much empayred the meaner, as they bettered
the better.   Which all notwithstanding, it is a sporte to heare
howe they impute to love, whiche hath indewed their thoughts
(saie they) with suche a strength.

But certainely, all the people of this countrie from high to 5
lowe, is given to those sportes of the witte, so as you would
wonder to heare how soone even children will beginne to

versifie. Once, ordinary it is among the meanest sorte, to
make Songes and Dialogues in meeter, either love whetting
their braine, or long peace having begun it, example and emulation amending it. Not so much, but the clowne *Dametas*
will stumble sometimes upon some Songs that might become a
better brayne: but no sorte of people so excellent in that kinde
as the pastors; for their living standing but upon the looking to
their beastes, they have ease, the Nurse of Poetrie. Neither
are our shepheards such, as (I heare) they be in other countries;
but they are the verie owners of the sheepe, to which eyther
themselves looke, or their children give daylie attendaunce.
And then truely, it would delight you under some tree, or by
some rivers side (when two or three of them meet together) to
heare their rurall muse, how pretely it will deliver out, sometimes joyes, sometimes lamentations, sometimes chalengings one
of the other, sometimes under hidden formes uttering such
matters, as otherwise they durst not deale with. Then they
have most commonly one, who judgeth the price to the best
doer, of which they are no lesse gladde, then great Princes are
of triumphes: and his parte is to sette downe in writing all that
is saide, save that it may be, his pen with more leasure doth
polish the rudenesse of an unthought-on songe. Now the
choise of all (as you may well thinke) either for goodnesse of
voice, or pleasantnesse of wit, the Prince hath : among whom
also there are two or three straungers, whom inwarde melan-
cholies having made weery of the worldes eyes, have come to
spende their lives among the countrie people of *Arcadia*; &
their conversation being well approved, the prince vouchsafeth
them his presence, and not onely by looking on, but by great
courtesie and liberalitie, animates the Shepheardes the more
exquisitely to labour for his good liking. So that there is no
cause to blame the Prince for somtimes hearing them; the
blame-worthinesse is, that to heare them, he rather goes to
solitarinesse, then makes them come to companie. Neyther
doo I accuse my maister for advauncing a countriman, as
Dametas is, since God forbid, but where worthinesse is (as
truely it is among divers of that fellowship) any outward lownesse should hinder the hiest raysing, but that he would needes
make election of one, the basenesse of whose minde is such,
that it sinckes a thousand degrees lower, then the basest bodie

could carrie the most base fortune: Which although it might bee aunswered for the Prince, that it is rather a trust hee hath in his simple plainnesse, then any great advauncement, beyng but chiefe heardman: yet all honest hartes feele, that the trust of their Lord goes beyond all advauncement. But I am ever too long uppon him, when hee crosseth the waie of my speache, and by the shaddowe of yonder Tower, I see it is a fitter time, with our supper to pay the duties we owe to our stomacks, thẽ to break the aire with my idle discourses: And more witte I might have learned of *Homer* (whome even now you mentioned) who never entertayned eyther guestes or hostes with long speaches, till the mouth of hunger be throughly stopped. So withall he rose, leading *Palladius* through the gardeine againe to the parler, where they used to suppe; *Palladius* assuring him, that he had alreadie bene more fed to his liking, then hee could bee by the skilfullest trencher-men of *Media*.

CHAP. 5.

The [1] *sorow of* Kalander *for his sonne* Clitophon. *The* [2] *storie of* Argalus *and* Parthenia, *their* [3] *perfeƈtions, their* [4] *love, their* [5] *troubles, her* [6] *impoysoning,* [7] *his rare constancie,* [8] *her straunge refusall,* [9] *their pathologies, her* [10] *flight, his* [11] *revenge on his rivall the mischiefe-worker* Demagoras, *then Captaine of the rebell* Helots, *who* [12] *take him, and* [13] Clitophon *that sought to helpe him : but* [14] *both are kept alive by their new captaine.*

BUt beeing come to the supping place, one of *Kalanders* [1] servaunts rounded in his eare; at which (his collour chaungyng) hee retired him selfe into his chamber; commaunding his men diligentlie to waite and attend upon *Palladius*, and to excuse his absence with some necessarie busines he had presentlie to dispatch. Which they accordinglie did, for some fewe dayes forcing thẽselves to let no change appeare : but though they framed their countenaunces never so cunningly, *Palladius* perceaved there was some il-pleasing accident fallen out. Whereupon, being againe set alone at supper, he called to the Steward, and desired him to tell him

the matter of his suddaine alteration: who after some trifling
excuses, in the ende confessed unto him, that his maister had
received newes, that his sonne before the daie of his neere
marriage, chaunst to be at a battaile, which was to be fought
betweene the Gentlemenne of Lacedæmon and the *Helots*:
who winning the victorie, hee was there made prisoner, going
to deliver a friend of his taken prysoner by the *Helots*; that the
poore young Gentleman had offered great raunsome for his life:
but that the hate those paysaunts conceaved agaynst all Gentlemen was suche, that everie houre hee was to looke for nothing,
but some cruell death: which hether-unto had onely beene
delayed by the Captaines vehement dealing for him, who
seemed to have a hart of more manlie pittie then the rest.
Which losse had stricken the old Gentleman with such sorrowe, as if aboundance of teares did not seeme sufficiently to
witnesse it, he was alone retyred, tearing his bearde and hayre,
and cursing his old age, that had not made his grave to stoppe
his eares from such advertisements: but that his faithfull servaunts had written in his name to all his friends, followers, and
tenants (*Philanax* the governour refusing to deale in it, as a
private cause, but yet giving leave to seeke their best redresse,
so as they wronged not the state of Lacedæmon) of whom
there were now gathered upon the frontiers good forces, that
he was sure would spende their lives by any way, to redeeme
or revenge *Clitophon*. Now sir (said he) this is my maisters
nature, though his grief be such, as to live is a griefe unto him,
& that even his reason is darkened with sorrow; yet the lawes
of hospitality (long and holily observed by him) give still such a
sway to his proceeding, that he will no waie suffer the straunger
lodged under his roofe, to receyve (as it were) any infection of
his anguish, especially you, toward whom I know not whether
his love, or admiration bee greater. But *Palladius* could scarce
heare out his tale with patience: so was his hart torne in peeces
with compassion of the case, liking of *Kalanders* noble behaviour,
kindnesse for his respect to himwarde, and desire to finde some
remedie, besides the image of his deerest friend *Daiphantus*,
whom he judged to suffer eyther a like or a worse fortune:
therefore rising from the boorde, he desired the steward to tell
him particularly, the ground, and event of this accident, because
by knowledge of many circumstaunces, there might perhaps

some waie of helpe be opened. Whereunto the Steward easilie in this sorte condiscended.

My Lord (said he) when our good king *Basilius*, with better successe then expectation, tooke to wife (even in his more then decaying yeares) the faire yong princes *Gynecia*; there came with her a young Lord, cousin german to her selfe, named *Argalus*, led hether, partly with the love & honour of his noble kinswomã, partly with the humour of youth, which ever thinkes that good, whose goodnes he sees not: & in this court he received so good encrease of knowledge, that after some yeares spent, he so manifested a most vertuous mind in all his actions, that *Arcadia* gloried such a plant was transported unto them, being a Gentleman in deede most rarely accomplished, excellentlie learned, but without all vayne glory: friendly, without factiousnes: valiaunt, so as for my part I thinke the earth hath no man that hath done more heroicall actes then hee; how soever now of late the fame flies of the two princes of *Thessalia* and *Macedon*, and hath long done of our noble prince *Amphialus*: who in deede, in our partes is onely accounted likely to match him: but I say for my part, I thinke no man for valour of minde, and habilitie of bodie to bee preferred, if equalled to *Argalus*; and yet so valiant as he never durst doo any bodie injurie: in behaviour some will say ever sadde, surely sober, and somewhat given to musing, but never uncourteous; his worde ever ledde by his thought, and followed by his deede; rather liberall then magnificent, though the one wanted not, and the other had ever good choise of the receiver: in summe (for I perceive I shall easily take a great draught of his praises, whom both I and all this countrie love so well) such a man was (and I hope is) *Argalus*, as hardly the nicest eye can finde a spot in, if the over-vehement constancie of yet spotles affection, may not in harde wrested constructions be counted a spot: which in this manner began that worke in him, which hath made bothe him, and it selfe in him, over all this country famous. My maisters sonne *Clitophon* (whose losse gives the cause to this discourse, and yet gives me cause to beginne with *Argalus*, since his losse proceedes from *Argalus*) beyng a young Gentleman, as of great birth (being our kings sisters sonne) so truely of good nature, and one that can see good and love it, haunted more the companie of this worthie *Argalus*, then of any other: so as if there were not a friendship (which is so rare, as it is to bee doubted whether it bee a thing in deede, or but a worde) at least there was such a liking and friendlines, as hath brought foorth the effectes which you shall heare. About two yeares since, it so fell out, that hee brought him to a great Ladies house, sister to my maister, who had with her, her onely daughter, the faire *Parthenia*; faire in deede (fame I thinke it selfe daring not to call any fayrer, if it be not *Helena* queene of *Corinth*, and the two incomparable sisters of *Arcadia*) and that which made her fairenesse much the fayrer, was, that it was but a faire embassadour of a most faire minde, full of wit, and a wit which delighted more to judge it selfe, then to showe it selfe: her speach being as rare as pretious; her silence without sullennesse; her modestie without affectation; her shamefastnes without ignorance: in summe, one, that to praise well, one must first set downe with himselfe, what it is to be excellent: for so she is.

4   I thinke you thinke, that these perfections meeting, could not choose but find one another, and delight in that they found; for likenes of manners is likely in reason to drawe liking with affection: mens actions doo not alwaies crosse with reason: to be short, it did so in deed. They loved, although for a while the fire therof (hopes winges being cut of) were blowen by the bellowes of dispaire, upon this occasion.

5   There had beene a good while before, and so continued, a suter to this same lady, a great noble mã, though of Laconia, yet neere neighbour to *Parthenias* mother, named *Demagoras*: A man mightie in riches & power, and proude thereof, stubbornly stout, loving no bodie but him selfe, and for his owne delights sake *Parthenia*: and pursuing vehemently his desire, his riches had so guilded over all his other imperfections, that the olde Ladie (though contrarie to my Lord her brothers minde) had given her consent; and using a mothers authoritie upon her faire daughter, had made her yeeld thereunto, not because shee liked her choise, but because her obedient minde had not yet taken uppon it to make choyse; and the daie of their assurance drew neere, when my young Lord *Clitophon* brought this noble *Argalus*, perchaunce principallie to see so rare a sight, as *Parthenia* by all well judging eyes was judged.

But though fewe dayes were before the time of assurance

appointed, yet love that sawe hee had a great journey to make
in shorte time, hasted so him selfe, that before her worde could
tie her to *Demagoras*, her harte hath vowed her to *Argalus*, with
so gratefull a receipte in mutuall affection, that if shee desired
above all thinges to have *Argalus*, *Argalus* feared nothing but to
misse *Parthenia*. And now *Parthenia* had learned both liking
and misliking, loving and lothing, and out of passion began to
take the authoritie of judgement; in so much, that when the
time came that *Demagoras* (full of proude joy) thought to
receave the gifte of her selfe, shee with woordes of resolute
refusall (though with teares shewing she was sorie she must
refuse) assured her mother, she would first be bedded in her
grave, then wedded to *Demagoras*. The chaunge was no more
straunge, then unpleasant to the mother: who beyng determi-
nately (least I shoulde say of a great Lady, wilfully) bent to
marrie her to *Demagoras*, tryed all wayes which a wittie and
hard-harted mother could use, upon so humble a daughter: in
whome the onely resisting power was love. But the more shee
assaulted, the more shee taught *Parthenia* to defende: and the
more *Parthenia* defended, the more she made her mother
obstinate in the assault: who at length finding, that *Argalus*
standing betweene them, was it that most eclipsed her affection
from shining upon *Demagoras*, she sought all meanes how to
remove him, so much the more, as he manifested himself an
unremoveable suiter to her daughter: first, by imploying him
in as many dägerous enterprises, as ever the evill stepmother
Iuno recommended to the famous *Hercules*: but the more his
vertue was tried, the more pure it grew, while all the things
she did to overthrow him, did set him up upon the height of
honor; inough to have moved her harte, especially to a man
every way so worthy as *Argalus*: but she strugling against all
reason, because she would have her will, and shew her
authoritie in matching her with *Demagoras*, the more vertuous
Argalus was, the more she hated him: thinking her selfe conquered in his cöquests, and therefore still imploying him in
more and more dangerous attempts: meane while, she used all
extremities possible upon her faire daughter, to make her geve
over her selfe to her direction. But it was hard to judge,
whether he in doing, or she in suffering, shewed greater
constancie of affection: for, as to *Argalus* the world sooner

wanted occasions, then he valour to goe thorow them; so to *Parthenia*, malice sooner ceased, thẽ her unchanged patience. Lastly, by treasons, *Demagoras* and she would have made away *Argalus:* but hee with providence & courage so past over all, that the mother tooke such a spitefull grief at it, that her hart brake withall, and she died.

6   But then, *Demagoras* assuring himselfe, that now *Parthenia* was her owne, she would never be his, and receiving as much by her owne determinate answere, not more desiring his owne happines, then envying *Argalus*, whom he saw with narrow eyes, even ready to enjoy the perfeftion of his desires; strength-ning his conceite with all the mischievous counsels which dis-dayned love, and envious pride could geve unto him; the wicked wretch (taking a time that *Argalus* was gone to his countrie, to fetch some of his principall frendes to honour the mariage, which *Parthenia* had most joyfully consented unto,) the wicked *Demagoras* (I say) desiring to speake with her, with unmercifull force, (her weake armes in vaine resisting) rubd all over her face a most horrible poyson: the effeft whereof was such, that never leaper lookt more ugly thẽ she did: which done, having his men & horses ready, departed away in spite of her servãts, as redy to revenge as they could be, in such an unexpefted mischiefe. But the abhominablenes of this faft being come to my L. *Kalander*, he made such meanes, both by our kings intercession, & his own, that by the king, & Senat of Lacedæmõ, *Demagoras* was upon paine of death, banished the countrie: who hating the punishment, where he should have hated the fault, joynde himselfe, with al the powers he could make, unto the *Helots*, lately in rebellion against that state: and they (glad to have a man of such authority among thẽ) made him their general: & under him have committed divers the most outragious villanies, that a base multitude (full of desperate revenge) can imagine.

7   But within a while after this pitifull faft committed upon *Parthenia*, *Argalus* returned (poore gentleman) having her faire image in his heart, and alredy promising his eies the uttermost of his felicitie, when they (no bodie els daring to tell it him) were the first messengers to themselves of their owne misfortune. I meane not to move passions with telling you the griefe of both, when he knew her, for at first he did not, nor at first

knowledge could possibly have Vertues aide so ready, as not even weakly to lament the losse of such a jewell, so much the more, as that skilful men in that arte assured it was unrecoverable: but within a while, trueth of love (which still held the first face in his memorie) a vertuous constancie, and even a delight to be constant, faith geven, and inward worthines shining through the foulest mistes, tooke so full holde of the noble *Argalus*, that not onely in such comfort which witty arguments may bestow upon adversitie, but even with the most aboundant kindnesse that an eye-ravished lover can expresse, he laboured both to drive the extremity of sorow from her, & to hasten the celebration of their mariage: wherunto he unfainedly shewed himself no lesse cherefully earnest, then if she had never been disinherited of that goodly portion, which nature had so liberally bequeathed unto her: and for that cause deferred his intẽded revenge upon *Demagoras*, because he might continually be in her presence; shewing more hũble serviceablenes, and joy to content her, then ever before.

But as he gave this rare ensãple, not to be hoped for of any other, but of an other *Argalus:* so of the other side, she tooke as strange a course in affection: for, where she desired to enjoy him, more then to live; yet did she overthrow both her owne desire, and his, and in no sorte would yeeld to marry him; with a strange encounter of loves affects, and effects: that he by an affection sprong from excessive beautie, should delight in horrible foulnesse; and she, of a vehement desire to have him, should kindly buyld a resolution never to have him: for trueth is, that so in heart she loved him, as she could not finde in her heart he should be tied to what was unworthy of his presence.

Truely Sir, a very good Orator might have a fayre field to use eloquence in, if he did but onely repeate the lamentable, and truely affectionated speeches, while he conjured her by remembrance of her affection, & true oathes of his owne affection, not to make him so unhappy, as to think he had not only lost her face, but her hart; that her face, when it was fayrest, had been but as a marshall, to lodge the love of her in his minde; which now was so well placed, as it needed no further help of any outward harbinger: beseeching her, even with teares, to know, that his love was not so superficial, as to go no further then the skin; which yet now to him was most faire, since it was hers:

how could hee be so ungratefull, as to love her the lesse for that, which she had onely received for his sake? that he never beheld it, but therein he saw the lovelines of her love towarde him: protesting unto her, that he would never take joy of his life, if he might not enjoy her, for whom principally he was glad he had life. But (as I heard by one that overheard them) she (wringing him by the hand) made no other answere but this: my Lord (said she) God knowes I love you: if I were Princesse of the whole world, and had withal, al the blessings that ever the world brought forth, I should not make delay, to lay my selfe, & them, under your feete: or if I had continued but as I was, though (I must cõfesse) far unworthy of you, yet would I, (with too great a joy for my hart to think of) have accepted your vouchsafing me to be yours, & with faith and obedience would have supplied all other defects. But first let me be much more miserable then I am, ere I match *Argalus* to such a *Parthenia*: Live happy, deare *Argalus*, I geve you full libertie, and I beseech you take it; and I assure you I shall rejoyce (whatsoever become of me) to see you so coupled, as may be fitte, both for your honor, and satisfaction. With that she burst out in crying and weeping, not able longer to conteine her selfe from blaming her fortune, and wishing her owne death.

10 But *Argalus* with a most heavie heart still pursuing his desire, she fixt of mind to avoid further intreatie, & to flie all companie; which (even of him) grew unpleasant unto her; one night she stole away: but whether, as yet is unknowen, or in deede what is become of her.

11 *Argalus* sought her long, and in many places: at length (despairing to finde her, and the more he despaired, the more enraged) weerie of his life, but first determining to be revenged of *Demagoras*, hee went alone disguysed into the chiefe towne held by the *Helots*: where comming into his presence, garded about by many of his souldiers, he could delay his fury no lõger for a fitter time: but setting upon him, in despight of a great many that helped him, gave him divers mortall wounds, and

12 himself (no question) had been there presently murthered, but that *Demagoras* himselfe desired he might be kept alive; perchaunce with intention to feed his owne eyes with some cruell execution to bee layd upon him, but death came soner then he

lookt for; yet having had leisure to appoint his successor, a young man, not long before delivered out of the prison of the King of *Lacedæmon*, where hee should have suffered death for having slaine the kings Nephew: but him he named, who at that time was absent, making roades upon the *Lacedemonians*, but being returned, the rest of the *Helots*, for the great liking they conceived of that yong man, (especially because they had none among themselves to whom the others would yeeld) were cõtent to follow *Demagoras* appointment. And well hath it succeded with them, he having since done things beyond the hope of the yongest heads; of whom I speak the rather, because he hath hetherto preserved *Argalus* alive, under pretence to have him publiquely, and with exquisite tormentes executed, after the ende of these warres, of which they hope for a soone and prosperous issue.

And he hath likewise hetherto kept my young Lord *Clitophon* alive, who (to redeme his friend) went with certaine 13 other noble-men of *Laconia*, and forces gathered by them, to besiege this young and new successor: but he issuing out (to the wonder of all men) defeated the *Laconians*, slew many of the noble-men, & tooke *Clitophon* prisoner, whom with much a 14 doo he keepeth alive: the *Helots* being villanously cruell; but he tempereth thẽ so, sometimes by folowing their humor, some-times by striving ˙with it, that hetherto hee hath saved both their lives, but in different estates; *Argalus* being kept in a close & hard prison, *Clitophon* at some libertie. And now Sir, though (to say the truth) we can promise our selves litle of their safeties, while they are in the *Helots* hands, I have delivered all I understande touching the losse of my Lords sonne, & the cause therof: which, though it was not neces-sarie to *Clitophons* case, to be so particularly told, yet the strãgenes of it, made me think it would not be unplesant unto you.

CHAP. 6.

[1] Kalanders *expedition against the* Helots. [2] *Their estate.* [3] Palladius *his stratageme against them:* [4] *which prevayleth.* [5] *The* Helots *resistance, discomfiture, and* [6] *re-enforce by the returne of their new captaine* [7] *The combat and* [8] *enterknowledge of* Daiphantus *&* Palladius, *and by their* [9] *meanes a peace, with* [10] *the release of* Kalander *and* Clitophon.

PAlladius thanked him greatly for it, being even passionatly delighted with hearing so straunge an accidēt of a knight so famous over the world, as *Argalus*, with whome he had himselfe a long desire to meet: so had fame poured a noble emulation in him, towards him.

1 But thē (wel bethinking himself) he called for armour, desiring them to provide him of horse & guide, and armed al saving the head, he wēt up to *Kalāder*, whom he found lying upō the groūd, having ever since banished both sleepe and foode, as enemies to the mourning which passion perswaded him was reasonable. But *Palladius* raysed him up, saying unto him: No more, no more of this, my Lord *Kalander*; let us labour to finde, before wee lament the losse: you know my selfe misse one, who, though he be not my sonne, I would disdayn the favour of life after him: but while there is hope left, let not the weaknes of sorow, make the strength of it languish: take comfort, and good successe will folow. And with those wordes, comfort seemed to lighten in his eyes, and that in his face and gesture was painted victorie. Once, *Kalanders* spirits were so revived withal, that (receiving some sustenance, and taking a litle rest) he armed himselfe, and those few of his servants he had left unsent, and so himself guyded *Palladius* to the place upon the frontiers: where alredy there were assembled betwene three and four thousand men, all wel disposed (for *Kalanders* sake) to abide any perill: but like men disused with a long peace, more determinate to doo, then skilfull how to doo: lusty bodies, and brave armours: with such courage, as rather grew of despising their enimies,

38

whom they knew not, then of any confidence for any thing, which in them selves they knew; but neither cunning use of their weapons, nor arte shewed in their marching, or incamping. Which *Palladius* soone perceiving, he desired to understand (as much as could be delivered unto him) the estate of the *Helots*.

And he was answered by a man well acquainted with the 2 affaires of Laconia, that they were a kinde of people, who having been of old, freemen and possessioners, the Lacedemonians had conquered them, and layd, not onely tribute, but bondage upon them: which they had long borne; till of late the *Lacedæmonians* through greedinesse growing more heavie then they could beare, and through contempt lesse carefull how to make them beare, they had with a generall consent (rather springing by the generalnes of the cause, then of any artificiall practise) set themselves in armes, and whetting their courage with revenge, and grounding their resolutiō upon despaire, they had proceeded with unloked-for succes: having already takē divers Towns and Castels, with the slaughter of many of the gentrie; for whom no sex nor age could be accepted for an excuse. And that although at the first they had fought rather with beastly furie, then any souldierly discipline, practise had now made then comparable to the best of the *Lacedæmonians*; & more of late then ever; by reason, first of *Demagoras* a great Lord, who had made him self of their partie, and since his death, of an other Captaine they had gotten, who had brought up their ignorance, and brought downe their furie, to such a meane of good government, and withall led them so valourouslie, that (besides the time wherein *Clitophon* was taken) they had the better in some other great cōflicts: in such wise, that the estate of *Lacedæmon* had sent unto them, offering peace with most reasonable and honorable conditions. *Palladius* having gotten this generall knowledge of the partie against whom, as hee had already of the party for whom he was to fight, he went to *Kalander*, and told him plainlie, that by playne force there was small apparaunce of helping *Clitophon*: but some device was to be taken in hand, wherein no lesse discretion then valour was to be used.

Whereupon, the councel of the chiefe men was called, 3 and at last, this way *Palladius* (who by some experience, but especiallie by reading Histories, was acquainted with stratagemes) invented, and was by all the rest approved: that all the men there shoulde dresse themselves like the poorest sorte of the people in *Arcadia*, having no banners, but bloudie shirtes hanged upon long staves, with some bad bagge pipes in stead of drumme and fife, their armour they should aswell as might be, cover, or at least make them looke so rustilie, and ill-favouredly as might well become such wearers; and this the whole number should doo, saving two hundred of the best chosen Gentlemen, for courage and strength, whereof *Palladius* him selfe would be one, who should have their armes chayned, and be put in cartes like prisoners. This being performed according to the agreement, they marched on towards the towne of *Cardamila* where *Clitophon* was captive; and being come two houres before Sunneset within vewe of the walles, the *Helots* alreadie descrying their number, and beginning to sound the Allarum, they sent a cunning fellow, (so much the cunninger as that he could maske it under rudenes) who with such a kind of Rhetorike, as weeded out all flowers of Rhetorike, delivered unto the *Helots* assembled together, that they were countrie people of *Arcadia*, no lesse oppressed by their Lords, & no lesse desirous of liberty then they, & therfore had put themselves in the field, & had alreadie (besides a great number slaine) taken nine or ten skore Gentlemen prisoners, whõ they had there well & fast chained. Now because they had no strong retiring place in *Arcadia*, & were not yet of number enough to keepe the fielde against their Princes forces, they were come to them for succor; knowing, that daily more & more of their qualitie would flock unto thẽ, but that in the mean time, lest their Prince should pursue thẽ, or the *Lacedæmonian* King & Nobilitie (for the likenes of the cause) fall upon them, they desired that if there were not roome enough for them in the towne, that yet they might encampe under the walles, and for surety have their prisoners (who were such mẽ as were ever able to make their peace) kept within the towne.

4   The *Helots* made but a short consultatiõ, being glad that their contagion had spread it selfe into *Arcadia*, and making account that if the peace did not fall out betweene them and their King, that it was the best way to set fire in all the parts of *Greece*; besides their greedinesse to have so many Gentlemen in their handes, in whose raunsoms they already meant to have

a share; to which hast of concluding, two thinges wel helped;
the one, that their Captaine with the wisest of them, was at
that time absent about confirming or breaking the peace, with
the state of *Lacedæmon*: the second, that over-many good
fortunes began to breed a proude recklesnesse in them: therefore sending to view the campe, and finding that by their
speach they were *Arcadians*, with whom they had had no
warre, never suspecting a private mans credite could have
gathered such a force, and that all other tokens witnessed
them to be of the lowest calling (besides the chaines upon the
Gentlemen) they graunted not onely leave for the prisoners,
but for some others of the companie, and to all, that they might
harbour under the walles. So opened they the gates, and
received in the carts; which being done, and *Palladius* seing
fit time, he gave the signe, and shaking of their chaynes, (which
were made with such arte, that though they seemed most strong
and fast, he that ware them might easily loose them) drew their
swordes hidden in the cartes, and so setting upon the ward,
made them to flie eyther from the place, or from their bodies,
and so give entrie to all the force of the *Arcadians*, before the
Helots could make any head to resist them.

But the *Helots* being men hardened against daungers, 5
gathered as (well as they could) together in the market place,
and thence would have given a shrewd welcome to the
Arcadians, but that *Palladius* (blaming those that were slow,
hartning thẽ that were forward, but especially with his owne
ensample leading them) made such an impression into the
squadron of the *Helots*, that at first the great bodie of them
beginning to shake, and stagger; at length, every particular
bodie recommended the protection of his life to his feet. Then
Kalander cried to go to the prison, where he thought his sonne
was, but *Palladius* wisht him (first scouring the streates) to house
all the *Helots*, and make themselves maisters of the gates.

But ere that could be accomplished, the *Helots* had gotten 6
new hart, and with divers sortes of shot from corners of streats,
and house windowes, galled them; which courage was come
unto them by the returne of their Captain; who though he
brought not many with him (having disperst most of his companies to other of his holds) yet meeting a great nũber rũning
out of the gate, not yet possest by the *Arcadians*, he made them

turne face, & with banners displayed, his Trumpet give the lowdest testimonie he could of his returne, which once heard, the rest of the *Helots* which were otherwise scattered, bent thetherward, with a new life of resolution: as if their Captaine had beene a roote, out of which (as into braunches) their courage had sprong. Then began the fight to grow most sharpe, and the encounters of more cruell obstinacie. The *Arcadians* fighting to keepe that they had wonne, the *Helots* to recover what they had lost. The *Arcadians,* as in an unknowne place, having no succour but in their handes; the *Helots,* as in their own place, fighting for their livings, wives, & children. There was victory & courage against revenge and despaire: safety of both sides being no otherwise to be gotten, but by destruction.

7　　At length, the left winge of the *Arcadians* began to loose ground; which *Palladius* seeing, he streight thrust himselfe with his choise bande against the throng that oppressed thē, with such an overflowing of valour, that the Captaine of the *Helots* (whose eies soone judged of that wherwith thēselves were governed) saw that he alone was worth al the rest of the *Arcadians.* Which he so wondred at, that it was hard to say, whether he more liked his doings, or misliked the effects of his doings: but determining that upon that cast the game lay, and disdaining to fight with any other, sought onely to joine with him: which minde was no lesse in *Palladius,* having easily marked, that he was as the first mover of al the other handes. And so their thoughts ineeting in one point, they consented (though not agreed) to trie each others fortune: & so drawing themselves to be the uttermost of the one side, they began a combat, which was so much inferior to the battaile in noise and number, as it was surpassing it in bravery of fighting, & (as it were) delightful terriblenes. Their courage was guided with skill, and their skill was armed with courage; neither did their hardinesse darken their witte, nor their witte coole their hardines: both valiant, as men despising death; both confident, as unwonted to be overcome; yet doutefull by their present feeling, and respectfull by what they had already seene. Their feete stedy, their hands diligent, their eyes watchfull, & their harts resolute. The partes either not armed, or weakly armed, were well knowen, and according to the knowledge should have bene sharpely visited, but that the aunswere was as quicke as the objection. Yet some lighting; the smarte bred rage, and the rage bred smarte againe: till both sides beginning to waxe faint, and rather desirous to die accompanied, then hopeful to live victorious, the Captaine of the *Helots* with a blow, whose violence grew of furie, not of strength, or of strength proceeding of furie, strake *Palladius* upon the side of the head, that he reelde astonied: and withall the helmet fell of, he remayning bare headed: but other of the *Arcadians* were redie to shield him from any harme might rise of that nakednes.

But little needed it, for his chiefe enemie in steed of pur- 8 suing that advauntage, kneeled downe, offering to deliver the pommell of his sworde, in token of yeelding, with all speaking aloud unto him, that he thought it more libertie to be his prisoner, then any others generall. *Palladius* standing uppon him selfe, and misdoubting some craft, and the *Helots* (that were next their captaine) wavering betweene looking for some stratageme, or fearing treason, What, saide the captaine, hath *Palladius* forgotten the voice of *Daiphantus?*

By that watche worde *Palladius* knew that it was his onely 9 friende *Pyrocles*, whome he had lost upon the Sea, and therefore both most full of wonder, so to be mett, if they had not bene fuller of joye then wonder, caused the retraite to be sounded, *Daiphantus* by authoritie, and *Palladius* by persuasion; to which helped well the little advauntage that was of eyther side: and that of the *Helots* partie their Captaines behaviour had made as many amazed as sawe or heard of it: and of the *Arcadian* side the good olde *Kalander* striving more then his old age could atchieve, was newly taken prisoner. But in deede, the chiefe parter of the fraye was the night, which with her blacke armes pulled their malicious sightes one from the other. But he that tooke *Kalander*, meant nothing lesse then to save him, but onelie so long, as the Captaine might learne the enemies secrets: towardes whom he led the old Gentleman, when he caused the retreit to be sounded: looking for no other deliverie from that captivitie, but by the painfull taking away of all paine: when whome should he see nexte to the Captaine (with good tokens how valiantly he had fought that daie against the *Arcadians*) but his sonne *Clitophon?* But nowe the Captaine had caused all the principall *Helots* to be assembled, as well to deliberate what they had to do, as to receive a message from the *Arcadians*; Amõg whom *Palladius* vertue (besides the love *Kalander* bare him) having gottẽ principall authoritie, he had persuaded them to seeke rather by parley to recover the Father and the Sonne, then by the sword: since the goodnes of the Captain assured him that way to speed, and his value (wherewith he was of old acquainted) made him thinke any other way dangerous. This therfore was donne in orderly manner, giving them to understand, that as they came but to deliver *Clitophon*, so offering to leave the footing they already had in the towne, to goe away without any further hurte, so as they might have the father, & the sonne without raunsome delivered. Which conditions beyng heard and conceaved by the *Helots*, *Daiphantus* perswaded them without delay to accept them. For first (sayd he) since the strife is within our owne home, if you loose, you loose all that in this life can bee deare unto you: if you winne, it will be a blouddy victorie with no profite, but the flattering in our selves that same badde humour of revenge. Besides, it is like to stirre *Arcadia* uppon us, which nowe, by using these persons well, maie bee brought to some amitie. Lastly, but especially, least the king and nobility of *Laconia* (with whom now we have made a perfect peace) should hope, by occasion of this quarrell to joyne the *Arcadians* with them, & so breake of the profitable agreement alreadie concluded. In summe, as in al deliberations (waying the profite of the good successe with the harme of the evill successe) you shall find this way most safe and honorable.

10   The *Helots* asmuch moved by his authoritie, as perswaded by his reasons, were content therewith. Wherupon, *Palladius* tooke order that the *Arcadians* should presently march out of the towne, taking with them their prisoners, while the night with mutual diffidence might keepe them quiet, and ere day came they might be well on of their way, and so avoid those accidents which in late enemies, a looke, a word, or a particular mans quarel might engẽder. This being on both sides concluded on, *Kalander* and *Clitophon*, who now (with infinite joy did knowe each other) came to kisse the hands and feet of *Daiphantus*: *Clitophon* telling his father, how *Daiphantus* (not without danger to himselfe) had preserved him from the furious malice of the *Helots*: & even that day going to conclude the

peace (least in his absence he might receive some hurt) he had taken him in his companie, and geven him armour, upon promise he should take the parte of the *Helots*; which he had in this fight perfourmed, little knowing that it was against his father: but (said *Clitophon*) here is he, who (as a father) hath new-begotten me, and (as a God) hath saved me from many deaths, which already laid hold on me: which *Kalander* with teares of joy acknowledged (besides his owne deliverance) onely his benefite. But *Daiphantus*, who loved doing well for it selfe, and not for thanks, brake of those ceremonies, desiring to know how *Palladius* (for so he called *Musidorus*) was come into that companie, & what his present estate was: whereof receiving a brief declaration of *Kalander*, he sent him word by *Clitophon*, that he should not as now come unto him, because he held himselfe not so sure a master of the *Helots* minds, that he would adventure him in their power, who was so well knowen with an unfriendly acquaintance; but that he desired him to return with *Kalander*, whether also he within few daies (having dispatched himselfe of the *Helots*) would repaire. *Kalander* would needes kisse his hande againe for that promise, protesting, he would esteme his house more blessed thẽ a temple of the gods, if it had once received him. And then desiring pardon for *Argalus*, *Daiphantus* assured them that hee woulde die, but hee woulde bring him, (though till then kept in close prison, indeed for his safetie, the *Helots* being so animated against him as els hee could not have lived) and so taking their leave of him, *Kalander*, *Clitophon*, *Palladius* and the rest of the *Arcadians* swearing that they would no further in any sorte molest the *Helots*, they straight way marched out of the towne, carying both their dead and wounded bodies with them; and by morning were alreadie within the limits of *Arcadia*.

CHAP. 7.

[1] *The articles of peace betwene the* Lacedæmonians *&* Helots, [2] Daiphãtus *his departure frõ thé* Helots *with* Argalus *to* Kalanders *house.* [3] *The offer of a straunge Lady to* Argalus [4] *his refusal, and* [5] *who she was.*

THe *Helots* of the other side shutting their gates, gave them selves to burye their dead, to cure their woundes, and rest their weeried bodies: till (the next day bestowing the cherefull use of the light upon them) *Daiphantus* making a generall convocation spake unto them in this manner. We are first (said he) to thanke the Gods, that (further then wee had either cause to hope; or reason to imagine) have delivered us out of this gulfe of daunger, wherein we were alredie swallowed. For all being lost, (had they had not directed, my return so just as they did) it had bene too late to recover that, which being had, we could not keep. And had I not happened to know one of the principall men among them, by which meanes the truce beganne betweene us, you may easily conceive, what little reason we have to think, but that either by some supplie out of *Arcadia,* or from the Nobilitie of this Country (who would have made fruites of wisdome grow out of this occasion,) wee should have had our power turned to ruine, our pride to repentance and sorow. But now the storme, as it fell out, so it ceased: and the error committed, in retaining *Clitophon* more hardly then his age or quarrell deserved, becomes a sharply learned experience, to use in other times more moderation.

[1]   Now have I to deliver unto you the conclusion between the Kings with the Nobilitie of *Lacedæmon,* and you; which is in all points as your selves desired: aswell for that you would have graunted, as for the assurance of what is graunted. The Townes and Fortes you presently have, are still left unto you, to be kept either with or without garrison, so as you alter not the lawes of the Countrie, and pay such dueties as the rest of the *Laconians* doo. Your selves are made by publique decree, free men, and so capable both to give and receive voice in election of

Magistrates. The distinction of names betweene *Helots* and *Lacedæmonians* to bee quite taken away, and all indifferently to enjoy both names and priviledges of *Laconians*. Your children to be brought up with theirs in *Spartane* discipline : and so you (framing your selves to be good members of that estate) to bee hereafter fellowes, and no longer servaunts.

Which conditions you see, cary in themselves no more contentation then assuraunce. For this is not a peace which is made with them, but this is a peace by which you are made of them. Lastly, a forgetfulnes decreed of of all what is past, they shewing thẽselves glad to have so valiant men as you are, joyned with them : so that you are to take mindes of peace, since the cause of war is finished ; and as you hated them before like oppressours, so now to love them as brothers ; to take care of their estate because it is yours, and to labour by vertuous doing, that the posteritie may not repent your joyning. But now one Article onely they stood upon, which in the end I with your commissioners have agreed unto, that I should no more tarry here, mistaking perchaunce my humor, and thinking me as sedicious as I am young, or els it is the king *Amiclas* procuring, in respect that it was my il hap to kil his nephew *Eurileon* ; but how soever it be, I have condiscended. But so will not wee cryed almost the whole assemblie, coũcelling one an other, rather to trye the uttermost event, then to loose him by whõ they had beene victorious. But he as well with generall orations, as particular dealing with the men of most credit, made them throughly see how necessary it was to preferree such an opportunity before a vaine affection ; but yet could not prevaile, til openly he sware, that he would (if at any time the *Lacedæmonians* brake this treatie) come back againe, and be their captaine.

So then after a few dayes, setling them in perfect order, hee 2 tooke his leave of them, whose eyes bad him farwell with teares, & mouthes with kissing the places where he stept, and after making temples unto him as to a demi-God : thinking it beyond the degree of humanitie to have a witt so farre overgoing his age, and such dreadful terror proceed from so excellent beutie. But he for his sake obtayned free pardon for *Argalus*, whom also (uppon oath never to beare armes against the *Helots*) he delivered : and taking onely with him certaine principall Jewells of his owne, he would have parted alone with *Argalus*, (whose countenaunce well shewed, while *Parthenia* was lost he counted not himselfe delivered) but that the whole multitude would needs gard him into *Arcadia*. Where again leaving thẽ all to lament his departure, he by enquirie gotte to the wel-knowne house of *Kalander* : There was he received with loving joye of *Kalander*, with joyfull love of *Palladius*, with humble (though doulful) demeanor of *Argalus* (whom specially both he and *Palladius* regarded) with gratefull servisablenes of *Clitophon*, and honourable admiration of all. For being now well veiwed to have no haire of his face, to witnes him a man, who had done acts beyond the degree of a man, and to looke with a certaine almost bashefull kinde of modestie, as if hee feared the eyes of men, who was unmooved with sight of the most horrible countenaunces of death ; and as if nature had mistaken her woorke to have a *Marses* heart in a *Cupides* bodye : All that beheld him (and al that might behold him, did behold him) made their eyes quicke messengers to their minds, that there they had seene the uttermost that in mankind might be seene. The like wonder *Palladius* had before stirred, but that *Daiphantus*, as younger and newer come, had gotten now the advantage in the moyst & fickle impression of eye-sight. But while all men (saving poore *Argalus*) made the joy of their eyes speake for their harts towards *Daiphantus* : Fortune (that belike was bid to that banket, & ment then to play the good fellow) brought a pleasaũt adventure among thẽ.

3   It was that as they had newly dined, there came in to *Kalander* a messenger, that brought him word, a young noble Lady, neere kinswoman to the fair *Helen* Queene of *Corinth* ; was come thether, and desired to be lodged in his house. *Kalander* (most glad of such an occasion) went out, and all his other worthie guests with him, saving onely *Argalus*, who remained in his chamber, desirous that this company were once broken up, that he might goe in his solitarie quest after *Parthenia*. But when they met this Lady ; *Kalander* streight thought he sawe his neece *Parthenia*, and was about in such familiar sorte to have spoken unto her : But she in grave and honorable manner giving him to understand that he was mistaken, he halfe ashamed, excused himselfe with the exceeding likenes was betwene them, though indeede it seemed that his Lady was of the more pure and daintie complexion ; shee said,

it might very well be, having bene many times taken one for an other. But assoone as she was brought into the house, before she would rest her, she desired to speake with *Argalus* publickly, who she heard was in the house. *Argalus* came in hastely, and as hastelie thought as *Kalander* had done, with sodaine chaunges of joye into sorrow. But she whē she had stayd their thoughts with telling them her name, and qualitie in this sort spake unto him. My Lord *Argalus*, sayd she, being of late left in the court of Queene *Helen* of *Corinth*, as chiefe in her absence (she being upõ some occasion gone thēce) there came unto me the Lady *Parthenia*, so disguysed, as I thinke Greece hath nothing so ougly to behold. For my part, it was many dayes, before with vehement oathes, and some good proofes, she could make me thinke that she was *Parthenia*. Yet at last finding certenly it was she, and greatly pitying her misfortune, so much the more, as that all men had ever told me, (as now you doo) of the great likenes betweene us, I tooke the best care I could of her: and of her understood the whole tragicall historie of her undeserved adventure : and therewithall, of that most noble constancie in you my Lord *Argalus* : which whosoever loves not, shewes himselfe to be a hater of vertue, and unworthie to live in the societie of mankind. But no outward cherishing could salve the inward sore of her minde, but a fewe dayes since shee died : before her death earnestly desiring, and perswading me, to thinke of no husbande but of you ; as of the onely man in the world worthie to be loved ; with-all, she gave me this Ring to deliver you; desiring you, & by the authoritie of love cõ-maunding you, that the affection you bare her you should turne to me : assuring you, that nothing can please her soule more, then to see you and me matched together. Now my L. though this office be not (perchance) sutable to my estate nor sex, who shuld rather looke to be desired; yet, an extraordinarie desert requires an extraordinarie proceding : and therfore I am come (with faithfull love built upõ your worthines) to offer my self, & to beseech you to accept the offer : & if these noble gētlemē presēt will say it is great folly, let thē withal, say it is great love. And then she staid, earnestly attending *Argalus* his answere, who (first making most hartie sighes do such obsequies as he could, to *Parthenia*) thus answered her.

Madame (said he) infinitely bound am I unto you, for this, 4 no more rare, then noble courtesie ; but most bound for the goodnes I perceive you shewed to the lady *Parthenia*, (with that the teares ranne downe his eyes ; but he followed on) and as much as so unfortunat a man, fitte to be the spectacle of miserie, can doo you service ; determine you have made a purchase of a slave (while I live) never to fayle you. But this great matter you propose unto me, wherein I am not so blind, as not to see what happines it should be unto mee ; Excellent Ladie, know, that if my hart were mine to give, you before al other, should have it; but *Parthenias* it is, though dead : there I began, there I end all matter of affection : I hope I shall not long tarry after her, with whose beautie if I had onely been in love, I should be so with you, who have the same beautie : but it was *Parthenias* selfe I loved, and love ; which no likenes can make one, no cõmaundement dissolve, no foulnes defile, nor no death finish. And shall I receive (said she) such disgrace, as to be refused ? Noble Ladie (said he) let not that harde word be used; who know your exceeding worthinesse farre beyond my desert : but it is onely happinesse I refuse, since of the onely happines I could and can desire, I am refused.

5   He had scarce spoken those words, when she ranne to him, and imbrasing him, Why then *Argalus* (saide she) take thy *Parthenia*; and *Parthenia* it was in deede. But because sorow forbad him too soon to beleeve, she told him the trueth, with all circumstances; how being parted alone, meaning to die in some solitarie place, as she hapned to make her complaint, the Queen *Helen* of *Corinth* (who likewise felt her part of miseries) being then walking also alone in that lovely place, heard her, and never left, till she had knowen the whole discourse. Which the noble Queene greatly pittying, she sent her to a Phisition of hers, the most excellent man in the worlde, in hope he could helpe her : which in such sorte as they saw perfourmed, and she taking with her of the Queenes servaunts, thought yet to make this triall, whether he would quickly forget his true *Parthenia*, or no. Her speach was confirmed by the *Corinthian* Gentlemen, who before had kept her counsell, and *Argalus* easily perswaded to what more then ten thousand yeares of life he desired: and *Kalander* would needes have the mariage celebrated in his house, principallie the longer to hold his deare guestes, towardes whom he was now (besides his owne habite of

hospitalitie) carried with love and dutie : & therfore omitted no service that his wit could invent, and his power minister.

CHAP. 8.

The adventures [1] *first of* Musidorus, [2] *then of* Pyrocles *since their shipwracke, to their meeting.* [3] *The mariage of* Argalus *and* Parthenia.

BUt no waie he sawe he could so much pleasure them, as I by leaving the two friends alone, who being shruncke aside to the banqueting house where the pictures were ; there *Palladius* recounted unto him, that after they had both abādoned the burning ship (& either of them taken some thing under him the better to supporte him to the shore) he knew not how, but either with over-labouring in the fight and sodaine colde, or the too much receaving of salt water, he was past himselfe : but yet holding fast (as the nature of dying men is to doo) the chest that was under him, he was cast on the sandes, where he was taken up by a couple of Shepherds, and by them brought to life againe, and kept from drowning him selfe, when he despaired of his safetie. How after having failed to take him into the fisher boate, he had by the Shepheards persuasion come to this Gentlemans house ; where being daungerouslie sicke, he had yeelded to seeke the recovery of health, onely for that he might the sooner go seeke the deliverie of *Pyrocles* : to which purpose *Kalander* by some friends of his in *Messenia*, had alreadie set a ship or two abroad, when this accident of *Clitophons* taking had so blessedly procured their meeting. Thẽ did he set foorth unto him the noble entertainement and careful cherishing of *Kalander* towards him, & so upon occasiõ of the pictures present delivered with the franknesse of a friends tongue, as neere as he could, word by word what *Kalander* had told him touching the strange storie (with al the particularities belonging) of *Arcadia*, which did in many sortes so delight *Pyrocles* to heare ; that he would needs have much of it againe repeated, and was not contented till *Kalander* him selfe had answered him divers questions.

2   But first at *Musidorus* request, though in brief mãner, his
mind much running upõ the strange storie of *Arcadia*, he did
declare by what course of advẽtures he was come to make up
their mutuall happinesse in meeting.   When (cosin, said he) we
had stript our selves, and were both leapt into the Sea, and
swom a little toward the shoare, I found by reason of some
wounds I had, that I should not be able to get the lande, and
therefore turned backe againe to the mast of the shippe, where
you found me, assuring my selfe, that if you came alive to the
shore, you would seeke me; if you were lost, as I thought it as
good to perishe as to live, so that place as good to perish in as an
other.   There I found my sworde among some of the shrowds,
wishing (I must confesse) if I died, to be found with that in my
hand, and withall waving it about my head, that saylers by it
might have the better glimpse of me.   There you missing me,
I was taken up by Pyrates, who putting me under boorde
prisoner, presentlie sett uppon another shippe, and mainteining
a long fight, in the ende, put them all to the sworde.   Amongst
whom I might heare them greatlie prayse one younge man,
who fought most valiantlie, whom (as love is carefull, and misfortune subject to doubtfulnes) I thought certainely to be you.
And so holding you as dead, from that time till the time I sawe
you, in trueth I sought nothing more then a noble ende, which
perchance made me more hardie then otherwise I would have
bene.   Triall whereof came within two dayes after: for the
Kinges of *Lacedæmon* having sett out some Galleys, under the
charge of one of their Nephews to skowre the Sea of the
Pyrates, they met with us, where our Captaine wanting men,
was driven to arme some of his prisoners, with promise of
libertie for well fighting: among whom I was one, and being
boorded by the Admirall, it was my fortune to kil *Eurileon* the
Kings nephew: but in the end they prevailed, & we were all
takẽ prisoners: I not ˙caring much what became of me (onely
keeping the name of *Daiphantus*, according to the resolution
you know is betweene us,) but beyng laid in the jayle of
Tenaria, with speciall hate to me for the death of *Eurileon*, the
popular sort of that towne conspired with the *Helots*, and so by
night opened them the gates; where entring and killing all of
the gentle and riche faction, for honestie sake brake open all
prisons, and so delivered me; and I mooved with gratefulnesse,

and encouraged with carelesnesse of life, so behaved my selfe in some conflictes they had in fewe dayes, that they barbarouslie thinking unsensible wonders of mee, and withall so much they better trusting mee, as they heard I was hated of the Kinge of *Lacedæmon*, (their chiefe Captayne beyng slaine as you knowe by the noble *Argalus*, who helped thereunto by his perswasion) having borne a great affection unto me, and to avoyde the daungerous emulation whiche grewe among the chiefe, who should have the place, and all so affected, as rather to have a straunger then a competitour, they elected mee, (God wotte little prowde of that dignitie,) restoring unto mee such thinges of mine as being taken first by the pyrates, and then by the *Lacedæmonians*, they had gotten in the sacke of the towne. Now being in it, so good was my successe with manie victories, that I made a peace for them to their owne liking, the verie daie that you delivered *Clitophon*, whom I with much adoo had preserved. And in my peace the King *Amiclas* of *Lacedæmon* would needes have mee bannished, and deprived of the dignitie whereunto I was exalted : which (and you may see howe much you are bounde to mee) for your sake I was content to suffer, a newe hope rising in mee, that you were not dead : and so meaning to travaile over the worlde to seeke you ; and now here (my deere *Musidorus*) you have mee. And with that (embracing and kissinge each other) they called *Kalander*, of whom *Daiphantus* desired to heare the full storie, which before hee had recounted to *Palladius*, and to see the letter of *Philanax*, which hee read and well marked.

But within some daies after, the marriage betweene *Argalus* 3 and the faire *Parthenia* beyng to be celebrated, *Daiphantus* and *Palladius* selling some of their jewels, furnished themselves of very faire apparell, meaning to doo honour to their loving hoste ; who as much for their sakes, as for the marriage, set foorth each thing in most gorgeous manner. But all the cost bestowed did not so much enrich, nor all the fine deckinges so much beautifie, nor all the daintie devises so much delight, as the fairenesse of *Parthenia*, the pearle of all the maydes of *Mantinæa* : who as shee went to the Temple to bee maried, her eyes themselves seemed a temple, wherein love and beautie were married : her lippes, although they were kepte close with modest silence, yet with a pretie kinde of naturall swelling, they seemed to invite the guestes that lookt on them; her cheekes blushing, and withal when shee was spoken unto, a little smilyng, were like roses, when their leaves are with a little breath stirred : her hayre being layed at the full length downe her backe, bare shewe as if the voward fayled, yet that would conquere. *Daiphantus* marking her, O *Jupiter* (said he speaking to *Palladius*) how happens it, that Beautie is onely confined to *Arcadia* ? But *Palladius* not greatly attending his speach, some daies were continued in the solemnising the marriage, with al conceipts that might deliver delight to mens fancies.

CHAP. 9.

[1] Pyrocles *his inclination to love.* [2] *His, and* Musidorus *disputation thereabouts* [3] *broken of by* Kalander.

1   BUt such a chaunge was growen in *Daiphantus*, that (as if cheerefulnesse had bene tediousnesse, and good entertainement were turnd to discourtesie) he would ever get him selfe alone, though almost when he was in companie he was alone, so little attention he gave to any that spake unto him : even the colour and figure of his face began to receave some alteration; which he shewed little to heede : but everie morning earlie going abroad, either to the garden, or to some woods towards the desert, it seemed his only comfort was to be without a cõforter. But long it could not be hid from *Palladius*, whom true love made redy to marke, & long knowledge able to marke; & therfore being now growẽ weary of his abode in *Arcadia*, having informed himselfe fully of the strength & riches of the coũtry, of the nature of the people, and manner of their lawes: and, seing the courte could not be visited, prohibited to all men, but to certaine sheapheardish people, he greatly desired a speedy returne to his own countrie, after the many mazes of fortune he had troden. But perceaving this great alteration in his friend, he thought first to breake with him thereof, and then to hasten his returne; whereto he founde him but smally enclined : whereupon one day taking him alone with certaine graces and countenances, as if he were disputing with the trees, began in this manner to say unto him.

A mind wel trayned and long exercised in vertue (my sweete 2 and worthy cosin) doth not easily chaunge any course it once undertakes, but upon well grounded & well wayed causes. For being witnes to it selfe of his owne inward good, it findes nothing without it of so high a price, for which it should be altered. Even the very countenaunce and behaviour of such a man doth shew forth Images of the same constancy, by maintaining a right harmonie betwixt it and the inward good, in yeelding it selfe sutable to the vertuous resolution of the minde. This speech I direct to you (noble friend *Pyrocles*) the excellencie of whose minde and well chosen course in vertue, if I doo not sufficiently know, having seene such rare demonstrations of it, it is my weakenes, and not your unworthines. But as in deede I know it, and knowing it, most dearely love both it, and him that hath it ; so must I needs saye, that since our late comming into this country, I have marked in you, I will not say an alteratiõ, but a relenting truely, & a slacking of the maine career, you had so notably begon, & almost performed ; and that in such sorte, as I cannot finde sufficient reason in my great love toward you how to allow it ; for (to leave of other secreter arguments which my acquaintaunce with you makes me easily finde) this in effect to any manne may be manyfest, that whereas you were wont in all places you came, to give your selfe vehemently to the knowledge of those thinges which might better your minde ; to seeke the familiaritye of excellent men in learning and souldiery : and lastly, to put all these thinges in practise both by continuall wise proceedinge, and worthie enterprises, as occasion fell for them ; you now leave all these things undone : you let your minde fal a sleepe : beside your countenaunce troubled (which surely comes not of vertue ; for vertue like the cleare heaven, is without cloudes) and lastly you subject your selfe to solitarines, the slye enimie, that doth most separate a man from well doing. *Pyrocles* minde was all this while so fixed upon another devotion, that he no more attentively marked his friends discourse, then the childe that hath leave to playe, markes the last part of his lesson ; or the diligent Pilot in a daungerous tempest doth attend the unskilful words of a passinger : yet the very sound having imprinted the general point of his speech in his hart, pierced with any mislike of so deerely an esteemed friend, and desirous by degrees to bring him to a gentler consideration of him, with a shamefast looke (witnessing he rather could not helpe, then did not know his fault) answered him to this purpose. Excellent *Musidorus*, in the praise you gave me in the beginning of your spech, I easily acknowledge the force of your good will unto mee, for neither coulde you have thought so well of me, if extremitie of love had not made your judgement partiall, nor you could have loved me so intierlie, if you had not beene apt to make so great (though undeserved) judgements of me ; and even so must I say to those imperfections, to which though I have ever through weaknes been subject, yet you by the daily mēding of your mind have of late bin able to looke into them, which before you could not discerne ; so that the chaunge you speake of, falles not out by my impairing, but by your betring. And yet under the leave of your better judgement, I must needes say thus much, my deere cosin, that I find not my selfe wholye to be condemned, because I do not with continuall vehemēcy folow those knowledges, which you call the bettering of my minde ; for both the minde it selfe must (like other thinges) sometimes be unbent, or else it will be either weakned, or broken : And these knowledges, as they are of good use, so are they not all the minde may stretch it selfe unto : who knowes whether I feede not my minde with higher thoughts ? Trulie as I know not all the particularities, so yet I see the bounds of all these know-ledges : but the workings of the minde I finde much more infinite, then can be led unto by the eye, or imagined by any, that distract their thoughts without themselves. And in such contemplation, or as I thinke more excellent, I enjoye my solitarines ; and my solitarines perchaunce is the nurse of these contemplations. Eagles we see fly alone ; and they are but sheepe, which alwaies heard together ; cōdemne not therefore my minde somtime to enjoy it selfe ; nor blame not the taking of such times as serve most fitte for it. And alas, deere *Musi-dorus*, if I be sadde, who knowes better then you the just causes I have of sadnes ? And here *Pyrocles* sodainly stopped, like a man unsatisfied in himselfe, though his witte might wel have served to have satisfied another. And so looking with a countenaunce, as though he desired he should know his minde without hearing him speake, and yet desirous to speake, to breath out some part of his inward evill, sending againe new

blood to his face, he continued his speach in this manner. And
Lord (dere cosin, said he) doth not the pleasauntnes of this place
carry in it selfe sufficient reward for any time lost in it ? Do
you not see how all things conspire together to make this
coũtry a heavenly dwelling ? Do you not see the grasse how in
colour they excell the Emeralds, everie one striving to passe his
fellow, and yet they are all kept of an equal height ? And see
you not the rest of these beautifull flowers, each of which would
require a mans wit to know, and his life to expresse ? Do not
these stately trees seeme to maintaine their florishing olde age
with the onely happines of their seat, being clothed with a continuall spring, because no beautie here should ever fade ? Doth
not the aire breath health, which the Birds (delightfull both to
eare and eye) do dayly solemnize with the sweet cõsent of their
voyces ? Is not every *eccho* therof a perfeçt Musicke? and these
fresh and delightful brookes how slowly they slide away, as loth
to leave the company of so many things united in perfeçtion ?
and with how sweete a murmure they lament their forced
departure ? Certainelie, certainely, cosin, it must needes be
that some Goddesse enhabiteth this Region, who is the soule of
this soile: for neither is any, lesse then a Goddesse, worthie to
be shrined in such a heap of pleasures : nor any lesse thẽ a
Goddesse, could have made it so perfeçt a plotte of the celestiall
dwellings. And so ended with a deep sigh, rufully casting his
eye upon *Musidorus*, as more desirous of pittie thẽ pleading.
But *Musidorus* had all this while helde his looke fixed upon
Pyrocles countenance ; and with no lesse loving attention
marked how his words proceeded from him : but in both these
he perceived such strange diversities, that they rather increased
new doubts, then gave him ground to settle any judgement :
for, besides his eyes sometimes even great with teares, the oft
chãging of his colour, with a kind of shaking unstayednes over
all his body, he might see in his countenãce some great determi-
natiõ mixed with feare ; and might perceive in him store of
thoughts, rather stirred then digested ; his words interrupted
continually with sighes (which served as a burthen to each
sentence) and the tenor of his speech (though of his wõted
phrase) not knit together to one constãt end, but rather dissolved in it selfe, as the vehemencie of the inwarde passion
prevayled : which made *Musidorus* frame his aunswere neerest to

that humor, which should soonest put out the secret. For, having in the beginning of *Pyrocles* speech which defēded his solitarines, framed in his minde a replie against it, in the praise of honourable action, in shewing that such a kind of cōtēplatiō is but a glorious title to idlenes; that in actiō a man did not onely better himself, but benefit others; that the gods would not have delivered a soule into the body, which hath armes & legges, only instrumēts of doing, but that it wer intēded the mind should imploy thē; & that the mind should best know his own good or evill, by practise : which knowledge was the onely way to increase the one, and correct the other : besides many other argumentes, which the plentifulnesse of the matter yeelded to the sharpnes of his wit. When he found *Pyrocles* leave that, and fall into such an affected praising of the place, he left it likewise, and joyned with him therein : because he found him in that humor utter more store of passion; and even thus kindly embrasing him, he said : Your words are such (noble cousin) so sweetly and strongly handled in the praise of solitarinesse, as they would make me likewise yeeld my selfe up into it, but that the same words make me know, it is more pleasant to enjoy the companie of him that can speake such words, then by such wordes to be perswaded to follow solitari-nes. And even so doo I give you leave (sweet *Pyrocles*) ever to defend solitarines; so long, as to defende it, you ever keep com-panie. But I marvell at the excessive praises you give to this countrie; in trueth it is not unpleasant : but yet if you would returne into *Macedon*, you should see either many heavens, or find this no more then earthly. And evē *Tempe* in my *Thessalia*, (where you & I to my great happinesse were brought up together) is nothing inferiour unto it. But I think you will make me see, that the vigor of your witte can shew it selfe in any subject : or els you feede sometimes your solitarines with the conceites of the Poets, whose liberall pennes can as easilie travaile over mountaines, as molehils : and so like wel disposed men, set up every thing to the highest note ; especially, when they put such words in the mouths of one of these fantasticall mind-infected people, that children & Musitiās cal Lovers. This word, Lover, did no lesse pearce poore *Pyrocles*, then the right tune of musicke toucheth him that is sick of the *Tarantula*. There was not one part of his body, that did not feele a sodaine motion, while his hart with panting, seemed to daunce to the sounde of that word; yet after some pause (lifting up his eyes a litle from the ground, and yet not daring to place them in the eyes of *Musidorus*) armed with the verie coûtenance of the poore prisoner at the barr, whose aunswere is nothing but guiltie : with much a do he brought forth this question.   And alas, saide he, deare cosin, what if I be not so much the Poet (the freedome of whose penne canne exercise it selfe in any thing) as even that miserable subject of his conning, whereof you speake?   Now the eternall Gods forbid (mainely cryed out *Musidorus*) that ever my eare should be poysoned with so evill newes of you.   O let me never know that any base affectiõ shuld get any Lordship in your thoughts.   But as he was speaking more, *Kalander* came, and brake of their discourse, with inviting thẽ to the hunting of a goodly stagge, which beeing harbored in a wood therby, he hoped would make them good sporte, and drive away some part of *Daiphantus* melancholy.   They condiscended, & so going to their lodgings, furnished thẽ selves as liked them *Daiphantus* writing a few wordes which he left in a sealed letter against their returne.

CHAP. 10.

[1] Kalanders *hunting*.   [2] Daiphantus *his close departure*, [3] *and letter* [4] Palladius *his care, and* [5] *quest after him*, [6] *accompanied with* Clitophon.   [7] *His finding and taking on* Amphilus *his armor* [8] *Their encounter with Queene* Helens *attendants.* [9] *Her mistaking* Palladius.

THen went they together abroad, the good *Kalander* entertaining thẽ, with pleasaunt discoursing, howe well he loved the sporte of hunting when he was a young man, how much in the comparison thereof he disdained all chamber delights; that the Sunne (how great a jornie soever he had to make) could never prevent him with earlines, nor the Moone (with her sober countenance) disswade him from watching till midnight for the deeres feeding.   O, saide he, you will never live to my age, without you kepe your selves in breath with exercise, and in hart with joyfullnes: too much thinking doth consume the spirits : & oft it falles out, that while one thinkes too much of his doing, he leaves to doe the effect of his thinking. Then spared he not to remember how much *Arcadia* was chaunged since his youth : activitie & good felowship being nothing in the price it was then held in, but according to the nature of the old growing world, still worse & worse. Thẽ would he tell them stories of such gallaunts as he had knowen: and so with pleasant company beguiled the times hast, and shortned the wayes length, till they came to the side of the wood, where the houndes were in couples staying their comming, but with a whining Accent craving libertie : many of them in colour and marks so resembling, that it showed they were of one kinde. The huntsmen handsomely attired in their greene liveries, as though they were children of Sommer, with staves in their hands to beat the guiltlesse earth, when the houndes were at a fault, and with hornes about their neckes to sounde an alarum upon a sillie fugitive. The houndes were straight uncoupled, and ere long the Stagge thought it better to trust the nimblenes of his feete, then to the slender fortification of his lodging : but even his feete betrayed him ; for howsoever they went, they themselves uttered themselves to the sent of their enimies ; who one taking it of an other, and sometimes beleeving the windes advertisements, sometimes the view of (their faithfull councellors) the huntsmen, with open mouthes then denounced warre, when the warre was alreadie begun. Their crie being composed of so well sorted mouthes, that any man would perceive therein some kind of proportion, but the skilfull woodmen did finde a musick. Then delight and varietie of opinion drew the horsmen sundrie wayes ; yet cheering their houndes with voyce and horn, kept still (as it were) together. The wood seemed to conspire with them against his own citizens, dispersing their noise through all his quarters ; and even the Nimph *Echo* left to bewayle the losse of *Narcissus,* and became a hunter. But the Stagge was in the end so hotly pursued, that (leaving his flight) he was driven to make courage of despaire ; & so turning his head, made the hounds (with change of speech) to testifie that he was at bay : as if from hotte pursuite of their enemie, they were sodainly come to a parley.

But *Kalander* (by his skill of coasting the Countrey) was among the first that came in to the besiged Deere ; whom when some of the younger sort would have killed with their swordes, he woulde not suffer : but with a Crossebowe sent a death to the poore beast, who with teares shewed the unkindnesse he tooke of mans crueltie.

But by the time that the whole companie was assembled, 2 and that the Stagge had bestowed himselfe liberally among them that had killed him, *Daiphantus* was mist, for whom *Palladius* carefully enquiring, no newes could be given him, but by one that sayd, he thought he was returned home ; for that he markt him, in the chiefe of the hunting, take a by-way, which might lead to *Kalanders* house. That answer for the time satisfying, and they having perfourmed all dueties, as well for the Stagges funeral, as the hounds triumph, they returned : some talking of the fatnes of the Deeres bodie ; some of the fairenes of his head ; some of the hounds cunning ; some of their speed ; and some of their cry : til comming home (about the time that the candle begins to inherit the Suns office) they found *Daiphantus* was not to bee found. Whereat *Palladius* greatly marvailing, and a day or two passing, while neither search nor inquirie could help him to knowledge, at last he lighted upon the letter, which *Pyrocles* had written before hee went a hunting, and left in his studie among other of his writings. The letter was directed to *Palladius* himselfe, and conteyned these words.

My onely friend, violence of love leades me into such a 3 course, wherof your knowledge may much more vexe you, then help me. Therefore pardon my concealing it from you, since : if I wrong you, it is in respect I beare you. Returne into *Thessalia*, I pray you, as full of good fortune, as I am of desire : and if I live, I will in short time follow you ; if I die, love my memorie.

This was all, and this *Palladius* read twise or thrise over. 4 Ah (said he) *Pyrocles*, what meanes this alteratiõ ? what have I deserved of thee, to be thus banished of thy counsels ? Heretofore I have accused the sea, condemned the Pyrats, and hated my evill fortune, that deprived me of thee ; But now thy self is the sea, which drounes my comfort, thy selfe is the Pirat that robbes thy selfe of me : Thy owne will becomes my evill fortune. Thẽ turned he his thoughts to al forms of ghesses that might light upon the purpose and course of *Pyrocles* : for he was not so sure by his wordes, that it was love, as he was doubtful where the love was.   One time he thought, some beautie in *Laconia* had layed hold of his eyes ; an other time he feared, that it might be *Parthenias* excellencie, which had broken the bands of all former resolution.   But the more he thought, the more he knew not what to thinke, armies of objections rising against any accepted opinion.

5 Then as carefull he was what to doo himselfe : at length determined, never to leave seeking him, till his search should be either by meeting accõplished, or by death ended.   Therfore (for all the unkindnesse bearing tender respect, that his friends secrete determination should be kept from any suspition in others) he went to *Kalander*, and told him, that he had receaved a message from his friend, by which he understood he was gone backe againe into *Laconia*, about some matters greatly importing the poore men, whose protection he had undertaken, and that it was in any sorte fit for him, to follow him, but in such private wise, as not to be knowne, and that therefore he would as then bid him farewell : arming him selfe in a blacke armour, as either a badge, or prognostication of his mind : and taking onely with him good store of monie, and a fewe choise jewels, leaving the greatest number of them, & most of his apparell with *Kalander* : which he did partly to give the more cause to *Kalander* to expect their return, & so to be the lesse curiously inquisitive after thẽ : and partly to leave those honorable thankes unto him, for his charge & kindnes, which he knew he would no other way receave.   The good old man having neither reason to dissuade, nor hope to persuade, receaved the things, with mind of a keeper, not of an owner ; but before he went, desired he might have the happines, fully to know what they were : which he said, he had ever till then delaid, fearing to be any way importune : but now he could not be so much an enemie to his desires as any longer to imprison thẽ in silence.   *Palladius* tolde him that the matter was not so secrete, but that so worthie a friend deserved the knowledge, and shuld have it as soone as he might speak with his friẽd : without whose consent (because their promise bound him otherwise) he could not reveale it : but bad him hold for most assured, that if they lived but a while, he should find that they which bare the names of *Daiphãtus* and *Palladius*, would

give him & his cause to thinke his noble courtesie wel imploied. *Kalāder* would presse him no further : but desiring that he might have leave to go, or at least to sende his sonne and servaunts with him, *Palladius* brake of all ceremonies, by telling him ; his case stood so, that his greatest favour should be in making lest adoo of his parting. Wherewith *Kalander* knowing it to be more cumber then courtesie, to strive, abstained from further urging him, but not from hartie mourning the losse of so sweet a conversation.

Onely *Clitophon* by vehement importunitie obteyned to go 6 with him, to come againe to *Daiphantus*, whom he named and accoûted his Lord. And in such private guise departed *Palladius*, though having a companiõ to talke with all, yet talking much more with unkindnesse. And first they went to *Mantinæa*; whereof because *Parthenia* was, he suspected there might be some cause of his abode. But finding there no newes of him he went to *Tegæa*, *Ripa*, *Enispæ*, *Stimphalus*, and *Pheneus*, famous for the poisonous *Stygian* water, and through all the rest of *Arcadia*, making their eyes, their eares, and their tongue serve almost for nothing, but that enquirie. But they could know nothing but that in none of those places he was knowne. And so went they, making one place succeed to an other, in like uncertaintie to their search, manie times encountring strange advětures, worthy to be registred in the roulles of fame ; but this may not be omitted. As they past in a pleasant valley, (of 7 either side of which high hils lifted up their beetle-browes, as if they would over looke the pleasantnes of their under-prospect) they were by the daintines of the place, & the wearines of thěselves, invited to light frõ their horses ; & pulling of their bits, that they might something refresh their mouths upon the grasse (which plentifully grewe, brought up under the care of those wel shading trees,) they thěselves laid thě downe hard by the murmuring musicke of certain waters, which spouted out of the side of the hils, and in the bottome of the valley, made of many springs a pretie brooke, like a common-wealth of many families : but when they had a while harkened to the persuasion of sleepe, they rose, and walkt onward in that shadie place, till *Clitiphon* espied a peece of armour, & not far of an other peece : and so the sight of one peece teaching him to looke for more, he at length found all, with headpeece & shield, by the devise

whereof, which was   he streight
knew it to be the armour of his cousin, the noble *Amphialus*.
Wherupon (fearing some incõvenience hapned unto him) he
told both his doubte, and his cause of doubte to *Palladius*, who
(considering therof) thought best to make no longer stay, but
to follow on : least perchance some violēce were offered to so
worthy a Knight, whom the fame of the world seemed to set in
ballance with any Knight living.   Yet with a sodaine conceipt,
having long borne great honour to the name of *Amphialus*,
Palladius thought best to take that armour, thinking thereby to
learne by them that should know that armour, some newes of
Amphialus, & yet not hinder him in the search of *Daiphantus*
too.   So he by the help of *Clitophon* quickly put on that armour,
whereof there was no one piece wanting, though hacked in
some places, bewraying some fight not long since passed.   It
was some-thing too great, but yet served well enough.

8   And so getting on their horses, they travailed but a little
way, when in opening of the mouth of the valley into a faire
field, they met with a coach drawne with foure milke-white
horses, furnished all in blacke, with a black a more boy upõ
every horse, they al apparelled in white, the coach it self very
richly furnished in black & white.   But before they could come
so neere as to discerne what was within, there came running
upõ them above a dozen horsmen, who cried to thē to yeeld
thēselves prisoners, or els they should die.   But *Palladius* not
accustomed to grant over the possessiõ of him self upon so
unjust titles, with sword drawne gave them so rude an answer,
that divers of thē never had breath to reply again : for being
wel backt by *Clitophon*, & having an excellēt horse under him,
when he was overprest by some, he avoided them, and ere
th'other thought of it, punished in him his fellowes faults : and
so, ether with cunning or with force, or rather with a cunning
force, left none of them either living, or able to make his life
serve to others hurt.   Which being done, he approched the
coach, assuring the black boies they should have no hurt, who
were els readie to have run away, & looking into the coach,
he foũd in the one end a Lady of great beautie, & such a
beautie, as shewed forth the beames both of wisdome & good
nature, but al as much darkened, as might be, with sorow.   In
the other, two Ladies, (who by their demeanure shewed well,

they were but her servants) holding before them a picture; in which was a goodly Gẽtleman (whom he knew not) painted, having in their faces a certaine waiting sorrow, their eies being infected with their mistres weeping.

But the chiefe Ladie having not so much as once heard the noise of this cõflict (so had sorow closed up al the entries of her mind, & love tied her sẽces to that beloved picture) now the shadow of him falling upõ the picture made her cast up her eie, and seeing the armour which too wel she knew, thinking him to be *Amphialus* the Lord of her desires, (bloud cõming more freely into her cheekes, as though it would be bold, & yet there growing new againe pale for feare) with a pitiful looke (like one unjustly condẽned) My Lord *Amphialus* (said she) you have enough punished me: it is time for cruelty to leave you, & evil fortune me; if not I pray you, (& to graunt, my praier fitter time nor place you can have) accomplish the one even now, & finish the other. With that, sorrow impatient to be slowly uttered in her oftẽ staying speeches, poured it self so fast in teares, that *Palladius* could not hold her longer in errour, but pulling of his helmet, Madame (said he) I perceave you mistake me: I am a stranger in these parts, set upon (without any cause givẽ by me) by some of your servants, whom because I have in my just defence evill entreated, I came to make my excuse to you, whom seing such as I doo, I find greater cause, why I should crave pardon of you. When she saw his face, & heard his speech, she looked out of the coach, and seing her men, some slaine, some lying under their dead horses, and striving to get from under them, without making more account of the matter, Truely (said she) they are well served that durst lift up their armes against that armour. But Sir Knight, (said she) I pray you tell me, how come you by this armour? for if it be by the death of him that owed it, then have I more to say unto you. *Palladius* assured her it was not so; telling her the true manner how he found it. It is like enough (said she) for that agrees with the manner he hath lately used. But I beseech you Sir (said she) since your prowes hath bereft me of my cõpany: let it yet so farre heale the woundes it selfe hath given, as to garde me to the next towne. How great so ever my businesse be fayre Ladie (said he) it shall willingly yeeld to so noble a cause: But first even by the favour you beare to the Lorde of this noble armour, I conjure you to tell me the storie of your fortune herein, lest hereafter when the image of so excellent a Ladie in so straunge a plight come before mine eyes, I condemne my selfe of want of consideration in not having demaunded thus much.   Neither aske I it without protestation, that wherein my sworde and faith may availe you, they shall binde themselves to your service.   Your conjuration, fayre Knight (said she) is too strong for my poore spirite to disobey, and that shall make me (without any other hope, my ruine being but by one unrelieveable) to graunt your wil herein: and to say the truth, a straunge nicenesse were it in me to refraine that from the eares of a person representing so much worthinesse, which I am glad even to rockes and woods to utter.

CHAP. 11.

The story of Queene Helen [2] Philoxenus *her suiter* [3] Amphialus *an intercessor for his friende.* [4] *His praises,* [5] *birth, and* [6] *education.* [7] *Her love wonne to himselfe* [8] *His refusall and departure* [9] Philoxenus *wronge-rage against him.* [10] *Their fight.* [11] *The death of sonne and father.* [12] Amphialus *his sorrow and detestation of the Queene.* [13] *A new onset on* Palladius *for* Amphialus *his Armour:* [14] *whose griefe is amplified by meeting his dead frends dog.* [15] Palladius *his parting with* Helen *and* Clitophon.

KNow you then that my name is *Helen*, Queene by birth: and hetherto possession of the faire Citie and territorie of *Corinth*.   I can say no more of my selfe, but beloved of my people: and may justly say, beloved, since they are content to beare with my absence, and folly.   But I being left by my fathers death, and accepted by my people, in the highest degree, that countrie could receive; assoone, or rather, before that my age was ripe for it; my court quickely swarmed full of suiters; some perchaunce loving my state, others my person, but once I know all of them, howsoever my possessions were in their harts, my beauty (such as it is) was in their mouthes; many strangers of princely and noble blood, and all of mine owne country, to whom ether birth or vertue gave courage to avowe so high a desire.

Among the rest, or rather before the rest, was the Lord 2
Philoxenus, sonne and heire to the vertuous noble man *Timotheus* :
which *Timotheus* was a man both in power, riches, parentage,
and (which passed all these) goodnes, and (which followed all
these) love of the people, beyond any of the great men of my
countrie.   Now this sonne of his I must say truly, not unworthy of such a father, bending himselfe by all meanes of servise-
ablenes to mee, and setting foorth of himselfe to win my favour,
wan thus farre of mee, that in truth I lesse misliked him then
any of the rest: which in some proportion my countenaunce
delivered unto him.   Though I must protest it was a verie
false embassadour, if it delivered at all any affection, whereof my
hart was utterly void, I as then esteeming my selfe borne to rule,
& thinking foule scorne willingly to submit my selfe to be ruled.

But whiles *Philoxenus* in good sorte pursued my favour, and 3
perchaunce nourished himselfe with over much hope, because
he found I did in some sorte acknowledge his valew, one time
among the rest he brought with him a deare friend of his.
With that she loked upon the picture before her, & straight
sighed, & straight teares followed, as if the Idol of dutie ought
to be honoured with such oblations, and thẽ her speach staied
the tale, having brought her to that loke, but that looke having
quite put her out of her tale.   But *Palladius* greatly pitying so
sweete a sorrow in a Ladie, whom by fame he had already
knowen, and honoured, besought her for her promise sake, to
put silence so longe unto her moning, til she had recounted the
rest of this story.

Why said she, this is the picture of *Amphialus* : what neede 4
I say more to you ? what eare is so barbarous but hath hard of
Amphialus? who follows deeds of Armes, but every where
findes monumẽt of *Amphialus* ? who is courteous, noble, liberall,
but he that hath the example before his eyes of *Amphialus*?
where are all heroicall parts, but in *Amphialus*? O *Amphialus* I
would thou were not so excellent, or I would I thought thee
not so excellent, and yet would I not, that I would so : with
that she wept againe, til he againe solliciting the conclusion of
her story.   Then must you (said she) know the story of *Amphialus* : for his will is my life, his life my history : and indeed,
in what can I better employ my lippes, then in speaking of
Amphialus ?

5   This knight then whose figure you see, but whose mind can be painted by nothing, but by the true shape of vertue, is brothers sonne to *Basilius* King of *Arcadia*, and in his childhood esteemed his heir: till *Basilius* in his olde yeeres marrying a young and a faire Lady, had of her those two daughters, so famous for their perfection in beauty: which put by their young cosin from that expectation. Whereupon his mother (a woman of a hauty hart, being daughter to the King of *Argos*, either disdaining, or fearing, that her sonne should live under the power of *Basilius* sent him to that Lorde *Timotheus* (betwene whom and her dead husband ther had passed streight bands of mutuall hospitality to be brought up in company with his sonne *Philoxenus*?

6   A happie resolution for *Amphialus*, whose excellent nature was by this meanes trayned on with as good education, as any Princes sonne in the world could have, which otherwise it is thought his mother (farre unworthie of such a sonne) would not have given him. The good *Timotheus*) no lesse loving him then his owne sonne: well they grew in yeeres; and shortly occasions fell aptly to trie *Amphialus*, and all occasions were but steppes for him to clime fame by. Nothing was so hard, but his valour overcame: which yet still he so guided with true vertue, that although no man was in our parts spoken of but he, for his mãhood, yet, as though therein he excelled him selfe, he was cõmonly called the courteous *Amphialus*. An endlesse thing it were for me to tell, how many adventures (terrible to be spoken of) he atchieved: what monsters, what Giants, what conquest of countries: sometimes using policy, some times force, but alwaies vertue, well followed, and but followed by *Philoxenus*: betweene whom, and him, so fast a friendship by education was knit, that at last *Philoxenus* having no greater matter to employ his frindship in, then to winne me, therein desired, and had his uttermost furtheraunce: to that purpose brought he him to my court, where truly I may justly witnes with him, that what his wit could conceive (and his wit can conceave as far as the limits of reason stretch) was all directed to the setting forwarde the suite of his friend *Philoxenus*: my eares could heare nothing from him, but touching the worthines of *Philoxenus*, and of the great happines it would be unto me to have such a husband: with many arguments, which

God knowes, I cannot well remember because I did not much beleeve.

For why should I use many circũstances to come to that 7 where alredy I am, and ever while I live must continue? In fewe wordes, while he pleaded for an other, he wanne me for himselfe: if at least (with that she sighed) he would account it a winning, for his fame had so framed the way to my mind, that his presence so full of beauty, sweetnes, and noble conversation, had entred there before he vouchsafed to call for the keyes. O Lord, how did my soule hang at his lippes while he spake! O when he in feeling maner would describe the love of his frend, how well (thought I) dooth love betweene those lips! when he would with daintiest eloquence stirre pitie in me toward *Philoxenus*, why sure (said I to my selfe) *Helen*, be not afraid, this hart cannot want pitie: and when he would extol the deeds of *Philoxenus*, who indeede had but waited of him therin, alas (thought I) good *Philoxenus*, how evil doth it become thy name to be subscribed to his letter? What should I say? nay, what should I not say (noble knight) who am not ashamed, nay am delighted, thus to expresse mine owne passions?

Dayes paste; his eagernes for his friende never decreased, 8 my affection to him ever increased. At length, in way of ordinarie courtesie, I obteined of him (who suspected no such matter) this his picture, the only *Amphialus*, I feare that I shall ever enjoy: and growen bolder, or madder, or bould with madnes, I discovered my affection unto him. But, Lord, I shall never forget, how anger and courtesie, at one instant appeared in his eyes, when he heard that motion: how with his blush he taught me shame. In summe, he left nothing unassayed, which might disgrace himselfe, to grace his frēd; in sweet termes making me receive a most resolute refusal of himself. But when he found that his presence did far more perswade for himselfe, then his speeche could doo for his frend, he left my court: hoping, that forgetfulnesse (which commonly waits upon absence) woulde make roome for his friende: to whome he woulde not utter thus much (I thinke) for a kinde feare not to grieve him, or perchance (though he cares little for me) of a certaine honorable gratefulnes, nor yet to discourse so much of my secrets: but as it should seeme, meant to travell into farre countreyes, untill his friends affection either ceased, or prevayled.

9   But within a while, *Philoxenus* came to see how onward the fruites were of his friends labour, when (as in trueth I cared not much how he tooke it) he found me sitting, beholding this picture, I know not with how affectionate countenãce, but I am sure with a most affectionate mind. I straight found jelousie and disdaine tooke hold of him: and yet the froward paine of mine owne harte made me so delight to punish him, whom I esteemed the chiefest let in my way; that when he with humble gesture, and vehement speeches, sued for my favor; I told him, that I would heare him more willingly, if he would speake for *Amphialus*, as well as *Amphialus* had done for him: he never answered me, but pale and quaking, went straight away; and straight my heart misgave me some evill successe: and yet though I had authoritie inough to have stayed him (as in these fatall things it falles out, that the hie-working powers make second causes unwittingly accessarie to their determinations) I did no further but sent a foot-man of mine (whose faithfulnes to me I well knew) from place to place to follow him, and bring me word of his proceedings : which (alas) have brought foorth that which I feare I must ever rewe.

10   For he had travailed scarse a dayes jorney out of my Countrey, but that (not farre from this place) he overtooke *Amphialus*, who (by succouring a distressed Lady) had bene here stayed : and by and by called him to fight with him, protesting that one of thẽ two should die: you may easily judge how straunge it was to *Amphialus*, whose hart could accuse it selfe of no fault, but too much affection toward him, which he (refusing to fight with him) would faine have made *Philoxenus* understand, but (as my servant since tolde me) the more *Amphialus* went back, the more he followed, calling him Traytor, and coward, yet never telling the cause of this strange alteration.   Ah *Philoxenus* (saide *Amphialus*) I know I am no Traytor, and thou well knowest I am no coward: but I pray thee content thy selfe with this much, and let this satisfie thee, that I love thee, since I beare thus much of thee, but he leaving words drew his sworde, and gave *Amphialus* a great blow or two, which but for the goodnes of his armour would have slaine him: and yet so farre dıd *Amphialus* containe himselfe, stepping aside, and saying to him, Well *Philoxenus*, and thus much villany am I content to put up, not any longer for thy sake (whom I have no cause to love,

since thou dost injure me, and wilt not tell me the cause) but for thy vertuous fathers sake, to whom I am so much bound. I pray thee goe away, and conquer thy owne passions, and thou shalt make me soone yeeld to be thy servant.

But he would not attend his wordes, but still strake so fiercely at *Amphialus*, that in the end (nature prevailing above determination) he was faine to defend him selfe, and with-all to offend him, that by an unluckye blow the poore *Philoxenus* fell dead at his feete; having had time onely to speake some wordes, whereby *Amphialus* knew it was for my sake: which when *Amphialus* sawe, he forthwith gave such tokens of true felt sorrow; that as my servant said, no imagination could conceive greater woe. But that by and by, an unhappie occasion made *Amphialus* passe himselfe in sorrow: for *Philoxenus* was but newly dead, when there comes to the same place, the aged and vertuous *Timotheus*, who (having heard of his sonnes sodaine and passionate manner of parting from my Court) had followed him as speedily as he could; but alas not so speedily, but that he foũd him dead before he could over take him. Though my hart be nothing but a stage for Tragedies; yet I must confesse, it is even unable to beare the miserable representation thereof: knowing *Amphialus* and *Timotheus* as I have done. Alas what sorrow, what amasement, what shame was in *Amphialus*, when he saw his deere foster father, find him the killer of his onely sonne? In my hart I know, he wished mountaines had laine upon him, to keepe him from that meeting. As for *Timotheus*, sorow of his sonne and (I thinke principally) unkindnes of *Amphialus* so devoured his vitall spirits that able to say no more but *Amphialus, Amphialus*, have I? he sancke to the earth, and presently dyed.

But not my tongue though daily used to complaints; no nor if my hart (which is nothing but sorrow) were turned to tonges, durst it under-take to shew the unspeakeablenes of his griefe. But (because this serves to make you know my fortune,) he threw away his armour, even this which you have now upon you, which at the first sight I vainely hoped, he had put on againe; and thẽ (as ashamed of the light) he ranne into the thickest of the woods, lamẽting, & even crying out so pityfully, that my seruant, (though of a fortune not used to much tendernes) could not refraine weeping when he tolde it me. He once overtooke him, but *Amphialus* drawing his sword, which was the only part of his armes (God knowes to what purpose) he caried about him, threatned to kill him if he folowed him, and withall, bad him deliver this bitter message, that he wel inough foũd, I was the cause of al this mischiefe: & that if I were a man, he would go over the world to kill me: but bad me assure my selfe, that of all creatures in the world, he most hated me. Ah Sir knight (whose eares I think by this time are tyred with the rugged wayes of these misfortunes) now way my case, if at lest you know what love is. For this cause have I left my country, putting in hazard how my people wil in time deale by me, advẽturing what perils or dishonors might ensue, only to folow him, who proclaimeth hate against me, and to bring my neck unto him, if that may redeem my trespas & assuage his fury. And now sir (said she) you have your request, I pray you take paines to guide me to the next town, that there I may gather such of my company againe, as your valor hath left me. *Palladius* willingly cõdiscẽded: but ere they began to go, there cam *Clitophon*, who having bene something hurt by one of them, had pursued him a good way: at length overtaking him, & ready to kill him, understood they were servants to the faire Queene *Helen*, and that the cause of this enterprise was for nothing, but to make *Amphialus* prisoner, whõ they knew their mistresse sought; for she concealed her sorow, nor cause of her sorow from no body.

13 But *Clitophon* (very sorie for this accident) came back to comfort the Queene, helping such as were hurt, in the best sort that he could, & framing frẽdly cõstructiõs of this rashly undertaken enmitie, when in comes another (till that time unseene) all armed, with his bever downe, who first looking round about upon the companie, as soone as he spied *Palladius*, he drew his sword, and making no other prologue, let flie at him. But *Palladius* (sorie for so much harm as had alredy happened) sought rather to retire, and warde, thinking he might be some one that belonged to the faire Queene, whose case in his harte he pitied. Which *Clitophon* seeing, stept betweene them, asking the new come knight the cause of his quarrell; who answered him, that he woulde kill that theefe, who had stollen away his masters armour, if he did not restore it. With that *Palladius* lookt upon him, and sawe that he of the other side had *Palladius*

owne armour upon him: truely (said *Palladius*) if I have stolne
this armour, you did not buy that: but you shall not fight with
me upon such a quarrell, you shall have this armour willingly,
which I did onely put on to doo honor to the owner. But
Clitophon straight knewe by his words and voyce, that it was
Ismenus, the faithfull & diligent Page of *Amphialus*: and therefore telling him that he was *Clitophon*, and willing him to
acknowledge his error to the other, who deserved all honour,
the yong Gentleman pulled of his head-peece, and (lighting)
went to kisse *Palladius* hands; desiring him to pardon his follie,
caused by extreame griefe, which easilie might bring foorth
anger. Sweete Gentleman (saide *Palladius*) you shall onely
make me this amendes, that you shal cary this your Lords
armour from me to him, and tell him from an unknowen knight
(who admires his worthines) that he cannot cast a greater miste
over his glory, thẽ by being unkind to so excellẽt a princesse as
this Queene is. *Ismenus* promised he would, as soone as he
durst find his maister: and with that went to doo his dutie to
the Queene, whom in all these encounters astonishment made
hardy; but assoone as she saw *Ismenus* (looking to her picture)
Ismenus (said she) here is my Lord, where is yours? or come
you to bring me some sentence of death from him? if it be so,
welcome be it. I pray you speake; and speake quickly. Alas
Madame, said *Ismenus*, I haue lost my Lorde, (with that teares
came unto his eyes) for assoone as the unhappie combate was
concluded with the death both of father and sonne, my maister
casting of his armour, went his way: forbidding me upõ paine
of death to follow him.

Yet divers daies I followed his steppes; till lastly I found 14
him, having newly met with an excellent Spaniel, belonging to
his dead companion *Philoxenus*. The dog streight fawned on
my master for old knowledge: but never was there thing more
pittifull then to heare my maister blame the dog for loving his
maisters murtherer, renewing a fresh his cõplaints, with the
dumbe counceller, as if they might cõfort one another in their
miseries. But my Lord having spied me, rase up in such rage,
that in truth I feared he would kill me: yet as then he said
onely, if I would not displease him, I should not come neere him
till he sent for me: too hard a cõmaundement for me to disobey: I yeelded, leaving him onely waited on by his dog, and

as I thinke seeking out the most solitarie places, that this or any
other country can graunt him: and I returning where I had left
his armour, found an other in steed thereof, & (disdaining I must
confesse that any should beare the armour of the best Knight
living) armed my selfe therein to play the foole, as evẽ now I
did. Faire *Ismenus* (said the Queen) a fitter messenger could
hardly be to unfold my Tragedie : I see the end, I see my
ende.

15   With that (sobbing) she desired to be conducted to the next
towne, where *Palladius* left her to be waited on by *Clitophon*,
at *Palladius* earnest entreatie, who desired alone to take that
melancholy course of seeking his friend : & therefore changing
armours again with *Ismenus* (who went withal to a castle belonging to his master) he cõtinued his quest for his friend
Daiphantus.

CHAP. 12.

[1]Palladius *after long search of* Daiphantus, *lighteth on an* Amazon
Ladie. [2]*Her habite,* [3]*song,* [4]*and who she was.* [5]*Objections
of the one against women, and love of them.* [6]*The answeres
of the other for them both.* [7]*Their passionate conclusion in
relenting kindnesse.*

[1]   SO directed he his course to *Laconia*, aswell among the
   Helots, as *Spartans*. There indeed he found his fame
flourishing, his monument engraved in Marble, and yet more
durable in mens memories; but the universall lamenting his
absented presence, assured him of his present absence. Thence
into the *Elean* province, to see whether at the Olympian games
(there celebrated) he might in such concourse blesse his eyes
with so desired an encounter: but that huge and sportfull
assemblie grewe to him a tedious lonelinesse, esteeming no
bodie founde, since *Daiphantus* was lost. Afterward he passed
through *Achaia* and *Sicyonia*, to the *Corinthians*, prowde of their
two Seas, to learne whether by the streight of that *Isthmus*, it
was possible to know of his passage. But finding everie place
more dumbe then other to his demaunds, and remembring that
it was late-taken love, which had wrought this new course, he
returned againe (after two months travaile in vaine) to make
freshe searche in *Arcadia*; so much the more, as then first he

bethought him selfe of the picture of *Philoclea* (in resembling her
he had once loved) might perhaps awake againe that sleeping
passion. And hauing alreadie past over the greatest part of
Arcadia, one day comming under the side of the pleasaunt
mountaine *Mænalus*, his horse (nothing guiltie of his inquisitivenesse) with flat tiring taught him, that discrete stayes make
speedie journeis. And therefore lighting downe, and unbride-
ling his horse, he him selfe went to repose him selfe in a little
wood he sawe thereby. Where lying under the protection of a
shadie tree, with intention to make forgetting sleepe comfort a
sorrowfull memorie, he sawe a sight which perswaded, and obteyned of his eyes, that they would abide yet a while open. It
was the appearing of a Ladie, who because she walked with her
side toward him, he could not perfectly see her face; but so
much he might see of her, that was a suretie for the rest, that
all was excellent.

Well might he perceaue the hanging of her haire in fairest 2
quãtitie, in locks, some curled, & some as it were forgotten,
with such a carelesse care, & an arte so hiding arte, that she
seemed she would lay them for a paterne, whether nature
simply, or nature helped by cunning, be more excellent: the
rest whereof was drawne into a coronet of golde richly set with
pearle, and so joyned all over with gold wiers, and covered with
feathers of divers colours, that it was not unlike to an helmet,
such a glittering shew it bare, & so bravely it was held up frõ
the head. Vpon her bodie she ware a doublet of skie colour
sattin, covered with plates of gold, & as it were nailed with
pretious stones, that in it she might seeme armed; the nether
parts of her garment was so full of stuffe, & cut after such a
fashion, that though the length of it reached to the ankles, yet
in her going one might sometimes discerne the smal of her leg,
which with the foot was dressed in a short paire of crimson
velvet buskins, in some places open (as the ancient manner was)
to shew the fairenes of the skin. Over all this she ware a certaine mantell, made in such manner, that comming under the
right arme, and covering most of that side, it had no fastning of
the left side, but onely upon the top of the shoulder: where the
two endes met, and were closed together with a very riche
jewell: the devise wherof (as he after saw) was this: a *Hercules*
made in little fourme, but a distaffe set within his hand as he

once was by *Omphales* commaundement with a worde in Greeke, but thus to be interpreted, *Never more valiant*. On the same side, on her thigh shee ware a sword, which as it witnessed her to be an *Amazon*, or one following that profession, so it seemed but a needles weapon, since her other forces were without withstanding. But this Ladie walked out-right, till he might see her enter into a fine close arbour: it was of trees whose branches so lovingly interlaced one the other, that it could resist the strögest violence of eye-sight; but she went into it by a doore she opened; which moved him as warely as he could to follow her, and by and by he might heare her sing this song, with a voice no lesse beautifull to his eares, then her goodlinesse was full of harmonie to his eyes.

3   *TRansformd in shew, but more transformd in minde,*
      I cease to strive with double conquest foild:
    For (woe is me) my powers all I finde
    With outward force, and inward treason spoild.

    For from without came to mine eyes the blowe,
    Whereto mine inward thoughts did faintly yeeld;
    Both these conspird poore Reasons overthrowe;
    False in my selfe, thus have I lost the field.

    Thus are my eyes still Captive to one sight:
    Thus all my thoughts are slaves to one thought still:
    Thus Reason to his servants yeelds his right;
    Thus is my power transformed to your will.
      What marvaile then I take a womans hew,
      Since what I see, thinke, know is all but you?

4   The dittie gave him some suspition, but the voice gave him almost assurance, who the singer was. And therefore boldly thrusting open the dore, and entring into the arbour, he perceaved in deed that it was *Pyrocles* thus disguised, wherewith not receaving so much joy to have found him, as griefe so to have found him, amazedly looking upon him (as *Apollo* is painted when he saw *Daphne* sodainly turned into a Laurell) he was not able to bring forth a worde. So that *Pyrocles* (who had as much shame, as *Musidorus* had sorrow) rising to him, would have formed a substantiall excuse; but his insinua-

tion being of blushinge, and his division of sighes, his whole oration stood upon a short narration, what was the causer of this Metamorphosis? But by that time *Musidorus* had gathered his spirites together, and yet casting a gastfull countenaunce upon him (as if he would conjure some strange spirits) he thus spake unto him.

And is it possible, that this is *Pyrocles*, the onely yong Prince 5 in the world, formed by nature, and framed by education, to the true exercise of vertue? or is it indeed some *Amazon* that hath counterfeited the face of my friend, in this sort to vexe me? for likelier sure I would have thought it, that any outwarde face might have bene disguised, then that the face of so excellĕt a mind coulde have bene thus blemished. O sweete *Pyrocles*, separate your selfe a little (if it be possible) from your selfe, and let your owne minde looke upon your owne proceedings: so shall my wordes be needlesse, and you best instructed. See with your selfe, how fitt it will be for you in this your tender youth, borne so great a Prince, and of so rare, not onely expectation, but proofe, desired of your olde Father, and wanted of your native countrie, now so neere your home, to divert your thoughts from the way of goodnesse; to loose, nay to abuse your time. Lastly to overthrow all the excellent things you have done, which have filled the world with your fame; as if you should drowne your ship in the long desired haven, or like an ill player, should marre the last act of his Tragedie. Remember (for I know you know it) that if we wil be men, the reasonable parte of our soule, is to have absolute commaundement; against which if any sensuall weaknes arise, we are to yeelde all our sounde forces to the overthrowing of so unnaturall a rebellion, wherein how can we wante courage, since we are to deale against so weake an adversary, that in it selfe is nothinge but weakenesse? Nay we are to resolve, that if reason direct it, we must doo it, and if we must doo it, we will doo it; for to say I cannot, is childish, and I will not, womanish. And see how extremely every waye you endaunger your minde; for to take this womannish habit (without you frame your behaviour accordingly) is wholy vaine: your behaviour can never come kindely from you, but as the minde is proportioned unto it. So that you must resolve, if you will playe your parte to any purpose, whatsoever peevish affections are in that sexe, soften your hart to receive them, the very first downe-steppe to all wickednes: for doo not deceive your selfe, my deere cosin, there is no man sodainely excellentlie good, or extremely evill, but growes either as hee holdes himselfe up in vertue, or lets himself slide to vitiousnes. And let us see, what power is the aucthor of all these troubles: forsooth love, love, a passion, and the basest and fruitlessest of all passions: feare breedeth wit, Anger is the cradle of courage: joy openeth and enhableth the hart: sorrow, as it closeth, so it draweth it inwarde to looke to the correcting of it selfe; and so all generally have power towards some good by the direction of right Reason. But this bastarde Love (for in deede the name of Love is most unworthy-lie applied to so hatefull a humour) as it is engendered betwixt lust and idlenes; as the matter it workes upon is nothing, but a certaine base weakenes, which some gentle fooles call a gentle hart; as his adjoyned companions be unquietnes, longings, fond comforts, faint discomforts, hopes, ielousies, ungrounded rages, causlesse yeeldings; so is the hiest ende it aspires unto, a litle pleasure with much paine before, and great repentaunce after. But that end how endlesse it runs to infinite evils, were fit inough for the matter we speake of, but not for your eares, in whome indeede there is so much true disposition to vertue: yet thus much of his worthie effects in your selfe is to be seen, that (besides your breaking lawes of hospitality with *Kalander* and of friendship with me) it utterly subverts the course of nature, in making reason give place to sense, & man to woman. And truely I thinke heere-upon it first gatte the name of Love: for indeede the true love hath that excellent nature in it, that it doth transform the very essence of the lover into the thing loved, uniting, and as it were incorporating it with a secret & inward working. And herein do these kindes of love imitate the ex-cellent; for as the love of heaven makes one heavenly, the love of vertue, vertuous; so doth the love of the world make one be-come worldly, and this effeminate love of a woman, doth so womanish a man, that (if he yeeld to it) it will not onely make him an *Amazon*; but a launder, a distaff-spinner; or what so ever other vile occupation their idle heads cã imagin, & their weake hands performe. Therefore (to trouble you no longer with my tedious but loving words) if either you remember what you are, what you have bene, or what you must be: if you cõsider what it is, that moved you, or by what kinde of creature you are moved, you shall finde the cause so small, the effect so daungerous, your selfe so unworthie to runne into the one, or to be driuē by the other, that I doubt not I shall quickly have occasion rather to praise you for having conquered it, then to give you further counsell, how to doo it.

But in *Pyrocles* this speech wrought no more, but that he, 6 who before he was espied, was afraid; after, being perceived, was ashamed, now being hardly rubd upon, lefte both feare and shame, and was moved to anger. But the exceeding good will he bare to *Musidorus* striving with it, he thus, partely to satisfie him, but principally to loose the reines to his owne motions, made him answere. Cosin, whatsover good disposition nature hath bestowed upon me, or howsoever that disposition hath bene by bringing up cōfirmed, this must I confesse, that I am not yet come to that degree of wisdome, to thinke light of the sexe, of whom I have my life; since if I be any thing (which your friendship rather finds, thē I acknowledge) I was to come to it, born of a womā, & nursed of a womā. And certēly (for this point of your speach doth neerest touch me) it is strāge to see the unman-like cruelty of mākind; who not cōtent with their tyrānous ābition, to have brought the others vertuous patience under them (like to childish maisters) thinke their masterhood nothing, without doing injury to them, who (if we will argue by reason) are framed of nature with the same parts of the minde for the exercise of vertue, as we are. And for example, even this estate of *Amazons*, (which I now for my greatest honor do seek to counterfaite) doth well witnes, that if generally the swetnes of their dispositiōs did not make them see the vainnesse of these thinges, which we accōpt glorious, they nether want valor of mind, nor yet doth their fairnes take away their force. And truely we men, and praisers of men, should remember, that if we have such excellēcies, it is reason to thinke them excellent creatures, of whom we are: since a Kite never brought forth a good flying Hauke. But to tel you true, as I thinke it superfluous to use any wordes of such a subject, which is so praised in it selfe, as it needes no praises; so withall I feare lest my conceate (not able to reach unto them) bring forth wordes, which for their unworthines may be a disgrace unto thē I so inwardly honor. Let this suffice, that they are capable of vertue: &

vertue (ye your selves say) is to be loved, & I too truly: but this I willingly cōfesse, that it likes me much better, when I finde vertue in a faire lodging, then when I am bound to seeke it in an ill favoured creature, like a pearle in a dounghill. As for my fault of being an uncivill guest to *Kalander*, if you could feele what an inward guest my selfe am host unto: ye would thinke it very excuseable, in that I rather performe the dueties of an host, then the ceremonies of a guest. And for my breaking the lawes of friendshippe with you, (which I would rather dye, then effectually doo) truely, I could finde in my hart to aske you pardon for it, but that your handling of me gives me reason to my former dealing. And here *Pyrocles* stayed, as to breath himselfe, having bene transported with a litle vehemency, because it seemed him *Musidorus* had over-bitterly glaunsed against the reputation of woman-kinde: but then quieting his countenance (aswell as out of an unquiet mind it might be) he thus proceeded on: And poore Love (said he) deare cosin, is little beholding unto you, since you are not contented to spoile it of the honor of the highest power of the mind, which notable mē have attributed unto it; but ye deject it below all other passions, in trueth somewhat strangely; since, if love receive any disgrace, it is by the company of these passions you preferre before it. For those kinds of bitter objections (as, that lust, idlenes, and a weak harte, shoulde be, as it were, the matter and forme of love) rather touch me, deare *Musidorus*, then love: But I am good witnesse of mine own imperfections, & therefore will not defende my selfe: but herein I must say, you deale contrary to your self: for if I be so weak, then can you not with reason stir me up as ye did, by remēbrance of my own vertue: or if indeed I be vertuous, thē must ye cōfesse, that love hath his working in a vertuous hart: & so no dout hath it, whatsoever I be: for if we love vertue, in whom shal we love it but in a vertuous creature? without your meaning be, I should love this word *vertue*, where I see it written in a book. Those troblesome effects you say it breedes, be not the faults of love, but of him that loves; as an unable vessel to beare such a licour: like evill eyes, not able to look on the Sun; or like an ill braine, soonest overthrowē with best wine. Even that heavenly love you speake of, is accōpanied in some harts with hopes, griefs, longings, & dispaires. And in that heavēly love, since ther are

two parts, the one the love it self, th'other the excellency of
the thing loved; I, not able at the first leap to frame both
in me, do now (like a diligent workman) make ready the chiefe
instrument, and first part of that great worke, which is love it
self; which whẽ I have a while practised in this sort, then you
shall see me turn it to greater matters. And thus gently you
may (if it please you) think of me. Neither doubt ye, because
I weare a womans apparell, I will be the more womannish, since,
I assure you (for all my apparrel) there is nothing I desire more,
then fully to prove my selfe a man in this enterprise. Much
might be said in my defence, much more for love, and most
of all for that divine creature, which hath joyned me and love
together. But these disputations are fitter for quiet schooles, then
my troubled braines, which are bent rather in deeds to performe,
then in wordes to defende the noble desire which possesseth me.
O Lord (saide *Musidorus*) how sharp-witted you are to hurt
your selfe? No (answered he) but it is the hurt you speake of,
which makes me so sharp-witted. Even so (said *Musidorus*)
as every base occupation makes one sharp in that practise,
and foolish in all the rest. Nay rather (answered *Pyrocles*) as
each excellent thing once well learned, serves for a measure of all
other knowledges. And is that become (said *Musidorus*) a
measure for other things, which never received measure in
it selfe? It is counted without measure (answered *Pyrocles*,)
because the workings of it are without measure: but otherwise,
in nature it hath measure, since it hath an end allotted unto it.
The beginning being so excellent, I would gladly know the end.
Enjoying, answered *Pyrocles*, with a great sigh. O (said *Musidorus*) now set ye foorth the basenes of it: since if it ende in
enjoying, it shewes all the rest was nothing. Ye mistake me
(answered *Pyrocles*) I spake of the end to which it is directed;
which end ends not, no sooner then the life. Alas, let your
owne braine dis-enchaunt you (said *Musidorus*.) My hart is too
farre possessed (said *Pyrocles*.) But the head gives you direction.
And the hart gives me life; aunswered *Pyrocles*.

But *Musidorus* was so greeved to see his welbeloved friend 7
obstinat, as he thought, to his owne destruction, that it forced
him with more then accustomed vehemency, to speake these
words; Well, well, (saide he) you list to abuse your selfe; it
was a very white and red vertue, which you could pick out of a

painterly glosse of a visage : Confesse the truth; and ye shall finde, the utmost was but beautie; a thing, which though it be in as great excellencye in your selfe as may be in any, yet I am sure you make no further reckning of it, then of an outward fading benefite Nature bestowed upon you. And yet such is your want of a true grounded vertue, which must be like it selfe in all points, that what you wisely account a trifle in your selfe, you fondly become a slave unto in another. For my part I now protest, I have left nothing unsaid, which my wit could make me know, or my most entier friendship to you requires of me; I do now besech you even for the love betwixt us (if this other love have left any in you towards me) and for the remembraunce of your olde careful father (if you can remẽber him that forget your self) lastly for *Pyrocles* owne sake (who is now upon the point of falling or rising) to purge your selfe of this vile infeƈtion; other wise give me leave, to leave of this name of friendsh[i]p, as an idle title of a thing which cannot be, where vertue is abolished. The length of these speaches before had not so much cloied *Pyrocles*, though he were very unpatient of long deliberations, as the last farewel of him he loved as his owne life, did wound his soule, thinking him selfe afflicted, he was the apter to conceive unkindnesse deepely: insomuch, that shaking his head, and delivering some shewe of teares, he thus uttered his griefes. Alas (said he) prince *Musidorus*, how cruelly you deale with me; if you seeke the viƈtory, take it; and if ye liste, triumph. Have you all the reason of the world, and with me remaine all the imperfeƈtions; yet such as I can no more lay from me, then the Crow can be perswaded by the Swanne to cast of all his black fethers. But truely you deale with me like a Phisition, that seeing his patient in a pestilent fever, should chide him, in steede of ministring helpe, and bid him be sick no more; or rather like such a friend, that visiting his friend condemned to perpetuall prison; and loaden with greevous fetters, should will him to shake of his fetters, or he wuld leave him. I am sicke, & sicke to the death; I am a prisoner, neither is any redresse, but by her to whom I am slave. Now if you list to leave him that loves you in the hiest degree: But remember ever to cary this with you, that you abandon your friend in his greatest extremity.

And herewith the deepe wound of his love being rubbed

afresh with this new unkindnes, begã (as it were) to bleed
again, in such sort that he was not hable to beare it any
longer, but gushing out aboundance of teares, and crossing
his armes over his woefull hart, as if his teares had beene
out-flowing blood, his armes an over-pressing burthen, he
suncke downe to the ground, which sodaine traunce went so
to the hart of *Musidorus*, that falling down by him & kissing
the weping eyes of his friend, he besought him not to make
account of his speach; which if it had bene over vehement, yet
was it to be borne withall, because it came out of a love much
more vehement; that he had not thought fancie could have received so deep a wound: but now finding in him the force of
it, hee woulde no further contrary it; but imploy all his service
to medicine it, in such sort, as the nature of it required. But
even this kindnes made *Pyrocles* the more melte in the former
unkindnes, which his manlike teares well shewed, with a silent
look upõ *Musidorus*, as who should say, And is it possible that
Musidorus should threaten to leave me? And this strooke
Musidorus minde and senses so dumbe too, that for griefe being
not able to say any thing, they rested, with their eyes placed
one upon another, in such sort, as might well paint out the true
passion of unkindnes to be never aright, but betwixt them that
most dearely love.

And thus remayned they a time; till at length, *Musidorus*
embrasing him, said, And will you thus shake of your friend?
It is you that shake me of (saide *Pyrocles*) being for my unper-
fectnes unworthie of your friendshippe. But this (said *Musidorus*) shewes you more unperfect, to be cruell to him, that
submits himselfe unto you; but since you are unperfect (said he
smiling) it is reason you be governed by us wise and perfect men.
And that authoritie will I beginne to take upon me, with three
absolute cõmandements: The first, that you increase not your
evill with further griefes: the second, that you love her with all
the powers of your mind: & the last cõmandemẽt shalbe, ye
cõmand me to do what service I can, towards the attaining of
your desires. *Pyrocles* hart was not so oppressed with the
mighty passiõs of love and unkindnes, but that it yeelded to
some mirth at this commaundement of *Musidorus*, that he should
love: so that something cleering his face from his former shewes
of griefe; Wel (said he) deare cousin, I see by the well choosing

of your commandementes, that you are fitter to be a Prince, then a Counseller: and therfore I am resolved to imploy all my endevour to obey you; with this condition, that the comandementes ye commaund me to lay upon you, shall onely be, that you continue to love me, and looke upon my imperfe&ions, with more affe&tion then judgemẽt. Love you? (said he) alas, how can my hart be seperated from the true imbrasing of it, without it burst, by being too full of it? But (said he) let us leave of these flowers of newe begun frendship: and now I pray you againe tel me; but tell it me fully, omitting no circumstance, the storie of your affe&tions both beginning, and proceeding: assuring your selfe, that there is nothing so great, which I will feare to doo for you: nor nothing so small, which I will disdaine to doo for you. Let me therfore receive a cleere understãding, which many times we misse, while those things we account small, as a speech, or a look are omitted, like as a whole sentence may faile of his congruitie, by wanting one particle. Therefore betweene frends, all must be layd open, nothing being superfluous, nor tedious. You shalbe obeyed (said *Pyrocles*) and here are we in as fitte a place for it as may be; for this arbor no body offers to come into but my selfe; I using it as my melancholy retiring place, and therefore that respe&t is born unto it; yet if by chãce any should come, say that you are a servant sent from the Q. of the *Amazons* to seeke me, and then let me alone for the rest. So sate they downe, and *Pyrocles* thus said.

CHAP. 13.

[1] *How* Pyrocles *fell in love with* Philoclea. [2] *His counsell and course therein.* [3] *His disguising into* Zelmane. [4] *Her meeting with* Damætas, [5] Basilius, [6] *the Queene and her daughters, &* *their speaches.* [7] *Her abode there over entreated;* [8] *and the place thereof described.*

[1] COusin (saide hee) then began the fatall overthrowe of all my libertie, when walking among the pi&tures in *Kalanders* house, you your selfe delivered unto mee what you had understood of *Philoclea*, who muche resembling (though I must say much surpassing) the Ladie *Zelmane*, whom too well I loved:

there were mine eyes infefted, & at your mouth did I drinke my
poison.   Yet alas so sweete was it unto me, that I could not be
contented, til *Kalander* had made it more and more strong with
his declaratiõ.   Which the more I questioned, the more pittie I
conceaved of her unworthie fortune : and when with pittie once
my harte was made tender, according to the aptnesse of the
humour, it receaved quickly a cruell impression of that wonderful passiõ which to be definde is impossible, because no wordes
reach to the strange nature of it: they onely know it, which
inwardly feele it, it is called love.   Yet did I not (poore wretch)
at first know my disease, thinking it onely such a woonted kind
of desire, to see rare sights; & my pitie to be no other, but the
fruits of a gentle nature.   But evẽ this arguing with my selfe
came of further thoughts; & the more I argued, the more my
thoughts encreased.   Desirous I was to see the place where she
remained, as though the *Architefture* of the lodges would have
bene much for my learning; but more desirous to see her selfe,
to be judge, forsooth, of the painters cũning.   For thus at the
first did I flatter my selfe, as though my wound had bene no
deeper : but when within short time I came to the degree of
uncertaine wishes, and that the wishes grew to unquiet longings,
when I could fix my thoughts upõ nothing, but that within little
varying, they should end with *Philoclea*: when each thing I saw,
seemed to figure out some parts of my passions; whẽ even
Parthenias faire face became a lefture to me of *Philocleas*
imagined beautie; when I heard no word spoken, but that me
thought it caried the sum of *Philocleas* name: then indeed,
then I did yeeld to the burthen, finding my selfe prisoner,
before I had leasure to arme my selfe; & that I might well, like
the spaniel, gnaw upon the chaine that ties him, but I should
sooner marre my teeth, then procure liberty.

   Yet I take to witnesse the eternall spring of vertue, that I
had never read, heard, nor seene any thing; I had never any
tast of Philosophy, nor inward feeling in my selfe, which for a
while I did not call for my succour.   But (alas) what resistance
was there, when ere long my very reason was (you will say corrupted) I must needs confesse, conquered; and that me thought
even reason did assure me, that all eies did degenerate from their
creation, which did not honour such beautie ?   Nothing in
trueth could holde any plea with it, but the reverent friend-

ship I bare unto you. For as it went against my harte to breake
any way from you, so did I feare more then anie assault to breake
it to you: finding (as it is indeed) that to a hart fully resolute,
counsaile is tedious, but reprehension is lothsome: & that there
is nothing more terrible to a guilty hart, then the eie of a respected fried. This made me determine with my self, (thinking
it a lesse fault in friedship to do a thing without your knowledge,
then against your wil) to take this secret course: Which conceit was most builded up in me, the last day of my parting and
speaking with you; whe upõ your speach with me, & my but
naming love, (when els perchaũce I would have gone further) I
saw your voice & coũtenance so chaunge, as it assured me, my
revealing it should but purchase your griefe with my cumber:
& therfore (deere *Musidorus*) evẽ ran away frõ thy wel knowne
chiding: for having writtẽ a letter, which I know not whether
you found or no, & taking my chiefe jewels with me, while you
were in the middest of your sport, I got a time (as I think) unmarked, to steale away, I cared not whether so I might scape
you: & so came I to *Ithonia* in the province of *Messenia*; wher
lying secret I put this in practise which before I had devised.
For remẽbring by *Philanax* his letter, & *Kalãders* speech, how
3 obstinately *Basilius* was determined not to mary his daughters,
& therfore fearing, lest any publike dealing should rather increase her captivitie, then further my love; Love (the refiner
of inventiõ) had put in my head thus to disguise my self, that
under that maske I might (if it were possible,) get accesse, and
what accesse could bring forth, commit to fortune & industry:
determining to beare the countenance of an *Amazon*. Therfore
in the closest maner I could, naming my selfe *Zelmane*, for that
deere Ladies sake, to whose memorie I am so much bound, I
caused this apparell to be made, and bringing it neere the lodges,
which are harde at hand, by night, thus dressed my selfe, resting
till occasion might make me found by them, whom I sought:
which the next morning hapned as well, as my owne plot could
have laide it. For after I had runne over the whole petigree of
my thoughts, I gave my selfe to sing a little, which as you know
I ever delighted in, so now especially, whether it be the nature
of this clime to stir up Poeticall fancies, or rather as I thinke, of
love; whose scope being pleasure, will not so much as utter his
griefes, but in some forme of pleasure.

But I had song very little, when (as I thinke displeased with 4 my bad musike) comes master *Dametas* with a hedging bill in his hand, chafing, and swearing by the pãtable of *Pallas*, & such other othes as his rusticall bravery could imagine; & whẽ he saw me, I assure you my beauty was no more beholding to him thẽ my harmony; for leaning his hands upon his bil, & his chin vpon his hãds, with the voice of one that plaieth *Hercules* in a play, but never had his fancie in his head, the first word he spake to me, was, am not I *Dametas?* why, am not I *Dametas?* he needed not name him selfe: for *Kalanders* description had set such a note upõ him, as made him very notable unto me, and therefore the height of my thoughts would not discend so much as to make him any answer, but continued on my inward discourses: which (he perchaunce witnes of his owne unworthines, & therefore the apter to thinke him selfe contẽned) tooke in so hainous manner, that standing upõ his tip-toes, and staring as though he would have a mote pulled out of his eie, Why (said he) thou womã, or boy, or both, what soever thou be, I tell thee here is no place for thee, get thee gone, I tell thee it is the Princes pleasure, I tell thee it is *Dametas* pleasure. I could not choose, but smile at him, seeing him looke so like an Ape that had newly taken a purgation; yet taking my selfe with the maner, spake these wordes to my selfe: O spirite (saide I) of mine, how canst thou receave anie mirth in the midst of thine agonies, and thou mirth how darest thou enter into a minde so growne of late thy professed enemie? Thy spirite (saide *Dametas*) doost thou thinke me a spirite? I tell thee I am *Basilius* officer, and have charge of him, and his daughters. O onely pearle (said I sobbing) that so vile an oyster should keepe thee? By the combecase of *Diana* (sware *Dametas*) this woman is mad: oysters, and pearles? doost thou thinke I will buie oysters? I tell thee once againe get thee packing, and with that lifted up his bill to hit me with the blunt ende of it: but indeede that put me quite out of my lesson, so that I forgat al *Zelmanes-ship*, and drawing out my sworde, the basenesse of the villaine yet made me stay my hande, and he (who, as *Kalander* tolde me, from his childehood ever feared the blade of a sworde) ran backe, backward (with his hands above his head) at lest twentie paces, gaping and staring, with the verie grace (I thinke) of the clownes, that by *Latonas* prayers were turned into Frogs. At length staying, finding

himselfe without the compasse of blowes, he fell to a fresh
scolding, in such mannerlie manner, as might well shewe he had
passed through the discipline of a Taverne. But seeing me
walke up and downe, without marking what he saide, he went
his way (as I perceived after) to *Basilius*: for within a while he
came unto mee, bearing in deed shewes in his countenaunce of
an honest and well-minded gentleman, and with as much
courtesie, as *Dametas* with rudenesse saluting me, Faire Lady
(saide he) it is nothing strange, that such a solitary place as this
should receive solitary persons; but much do I marvaile, how
such a beauty as yours is, should be suffered to be thus alone. I
(that now knew it was my part to play) looking with a grave
majestie upon him, as if I found in my selfe cause to be reverenced. They are never alone (saide I) that are accompanied
with noble thoughts. But those thoughts (replied *Basilius*)
cãnot in this your lonelines neither warrant you from suspition
in others, nor defend you from melancholy in your selfe. I then
shewing a mislike that he pressed me so farre, I seeke no better
warraunt (saide I) then my owne conscience, nor no greater
pleasures, then mine owne contentation. Yet vertue seekes to
satisfie others, (saide *Basilius*.) Those that be good (saide I,)
and they wil be satisfied as long as they see no evill. Yet will
the best in this country, (said *Basilius*) suspect so excellent a
beauty being so weakely garded. Then are the best but starke
nought, (aunswered I) for open suspecting others, comes of
secrete condemning themselves; But in my countrie (whose
manners I am in all places to maintaine and reverence) the
generall goodnes (which is nourished in our harts) makes
every one thinke the strength of vertue in an other, whereof
they finde the assured foundation in themselves. Excellent
Ladie (said he) you praise so greatly, (and yet so wisely) your
coũtry, that I must needes desire to know what the nest is, out
of which such Byrds doo flye. You must first deserve it (said I)
before you may obtaine it. And by what meanes (saide
Basilius) shall I deserve to know your estate? By letting me
first knowe yours (aunswered I.) To obey you (said he) I will
doe it, although it were so much more reason, yours should be
knowen first, as you doo deserve in all points to be preferd.
Know you (faire Lady) that my name is *Basilius*, unworthily
Lord of this coũtry: the rest, either fame hath brought to your

eares, or (if it please you to make this place happie by your
presence) at more leasure you shall understand of me. I that
from the beginning assured my selfe it was he, but would not
seeme I did so, to keepe my gravitie the better, making a peece of
reverēce unto him, Mighty Prince (said I) let my not knowing
you serve for the excuse of my boldnes, and the little reverence
I doe you, impute it to the manner of my coūtry, wh[i]ch is
the invincible Lande of the *Amazons*; My selfe neece to *Senicia*,
Queene thereof, lineally descended of the famous *Penthesilea*,
slaine by the bloody hand of *Pyrrhus*. I having in this my
youth determined to make the worlde see the *Amazons* excellencies, aswell in private, as in publicke vertue, have passed
some daungerous adventures in divers coūtries: till the unmercifull Sea deprived me of my company: so that shipwrack casting
me not far hence, uncertaine wandring brough₊ me to this place.
But *Basilius* (who now began to tast that, which since he hath
swallowed up, as I will tell you) fell to more cunning intreating
my aboad, then any greedy host would use to well paying
passingers. I thought nothing could shoot righter at the mark
of my desires; yet had I learned alredy so much, that it was
aganst my womanhoode to be forward in my owne wishes.
And therefore he (to prove whither intercessions in fitter
mouthes might better prevaile) commaunded *Dametas* to bring
forth-with his wife and daughters thether; three Ladies,
although of divers, yet all of excellent beauty.

His wife in grave Matronlike attire, with countenaunce and 6
gesture sutable, and of such fairnes (being in the strengh of her
age) as if her daughters had not bene by, might with just price
have purchased admiration; but they being there, it was enough
that the most dainty eye would thinke her a worthy mother of
such children. The faire *Pamela*, whose noble hart I finde doth
greatly disdaine, that the trust of her vertue is reposed in such a
louts hands as *Dametas*, had yet to shew an obedience, taken on
a shepeardish apparell, which was but of Russet cloth cut after
their fashion, with a straight body, open brested, the nether parte
ful of pleights, with long and wide sleeves: but beleeve me she
did apparell her apparell, and with the pretiousnes of her body
made it most sumptuous. Her haire at the full length, wound
about with gold lace, onely by the comparison to see how farre
her haire doth excell in colour: betwixt her breasts (which

sweetly rase up like two faire Mountainets in the pleasaunt valley of *Tempe*) there honge a very riche *Diamond* set but in a blacke horne, the worde I have since read is this; *yet still my selfe*. And thus particularly have I described them, because you may know that mine eyes are not so partiall, but that I marked them too. But when the ornament of the Earth, the modell of heaven, the Triumphe of Nature, the light of beauty, Queene of Love, yoũg *Philoclea* appeared in her Nimphe-like apparell, so neare nakednes, as one might well discerne part of her perfeƈtions; & yet so apparelled, as did shew she kept best store of her beuty to her self : her haire (alas too poore a word, why should I not rather call thẽ her beames) drawẽ up into a net, able to take *Jupiter* when he was in the forme of an Eagle; her body (O sweet body) covered with a light taffeta garment, so cut, as the wrought smocke came through it in many places, inough to have made your restraind imaginatiõ have thought what was under it : with the cast of her blacke eyes; blacke indeed, whether nature so made them, that we might be the more able to behold & bear their wõderfull shining, or that she, (goddesse like) would work this miracle in her selfe, in giving blacknes the price above all beauty. Then (I say) indeede me thought the Lillies grew pale for envie, the roses me thought blushed to see sweeter roses in her cheekes, & the apples me thought, fell downe frõ the trees, to do homage to the apples of her breast; Then the cloudes gave place, that the heavẽs might more freshly smile upõ her; at the lest the cloudes of my thoughts quite vanished : and my sight (then more cleere and forcible then ever) was so fixed there, that (I imagine) I stood like a well wrought image, with some life in shew, but none in praƈtise. And so had I beene like inough to have stayed long time, but that *Gynecia* stepping betweene my sight and the onely *Philoclea*, the chaunge of objeƈt made mee recover my senses : so that I coulde with reasonable good manner receive the salutation of her, and of the Princesse *Pamela*, doing thẽ yet no further reverẽce then one Prince useth to another. But when I came to the never-inough praised *Philoclea*, I could not but fall downe on my knees, and taking by force her hand, and kissing it (I must confesse) with more then womanly ardency, Divine Lady, (saide I) let not the worlde, nor these great princes marvaile, to se me (contrary to my manner) do this especiall honor unto you, since all both men and women, do owe this to the perfection of your beauty. But she blushing (like a faire morning in Maye) at this my singularity, and causing me to rise, Noble Lady, (saide she) it is no marvaile to see your judgement mistaken in my beauty, since you beginne with so great an errour, as to do more honour unto me then to them, whom I my selfe owe all service. Rather (answered I with a bowed downe countenaunce) that shewes the power of your beauty, which forced me to do such an errour, if it were an errour. You are so well acquainted (saide she sweetely, most sweetely smiling,) with your owne beautie, that it makes you easilie fall into the discourse of beauty. Beauty in me? (said I truely sighing) alas if there be any, it is in my eyes, which your blessed presence hath imparted unto them.

But then (as I thinke) *Basilius* willing her so do, Well 7 (saide she) I must needs confesse I have heard that it is a great happines to be praised of them that are most praise worthie; And well I finde that you are an invincible *Amazon*, since you will overcome, though in a wrong matter. But if my beauty be any thing, then let it obtaine thus much of you, that you will remaine some while in this cõpanie, to ease your owne travail, and our solitarines. First let me dye (said I) before any word spoken by such a mouth, should come in vaine.

And thus with some other wordes of entertaining, was my staying concluded, and I led among them to the lodge; truely a place for pleasantnes, not unfitte to flatter solitarinesse; for it being set upon such an unsensible rising of the ground, as you are come to a prety height before almost you perceive that you ascend, it gives the eye lordship over a good large circuit, which according to the nature of the coũtry, being diversified betwene hills and dales, woods and playnes, one place more cleere, and the other more darksome, it seemes a pleasant picture of nature, with lovely lightsomnes and artificiall shadowes. The Lodge is of a yellow stone, built in the forme of a starre; having round about a garden framed into like points: and beyond the gardein, ridings cut out, each aunswering the Angles of the Lodge: at the end of one of them is the other smaller Lodge, but of like fashion; where the gratious *Pamela* liveth: so that the Lodge seemeth not unlike a faire *Comete*, whose taile stretcheth it selfe to a starre of lesse greatnes.

CHAP. 14.

[1] *The devises of the first banket to* Zelmane. [2] *Her crosses in love,*
[3] *by the love of* Basilius [4] *and* Gynecia [5] *The conclusion between*
Musidorus *and* Zelmane.

1 SO *Gynecia* her selfe bringing me to my Lodging, anone after
I was invited and brought downe to suppe with them in
the gardein, a place not fairer in naturall ornaments, then artificiall inventions: wherein is a banquetting house among certaine
pleasant trees, whose heads seemed curled with the wrappings
about of Vine branches. The table was set neere to an excellent
water-worke; for by the casting of the water in most cunning maner, it makes (with the shining of the Sunne upon it) a
perfect rainbow, not more pleasant to the eye then to the mind,
so sensibly to see the proof of the heavenly *Iris*. There were
birds also made so finely, that they did not onely deceive the
sight with their figure, but the hearing with their songs; which
the watrie instruments did make their gorge deliver. The table
at which we sate, was round, which being fast to the floore
whereon we sate, and that devided from the rest of the buildings
(with turning a vice, which *Basilius* at first did to make me
sport) the table, and we about the table, did all turne rounde, by
meanes of water which ranne under, and carried it about as a
Mille. But alas, what pleasure did it to mee, to make divers
times the full circle round about, since *Philoclea* (being also set)
was carried still in equall distance from me, and that onely my
eyes did overtake her; which when the table was stayed, and
wee beganne to feede, dranke much more eagerlie of her beautie,
then my mouth did of any other licour. And so was my common sense deceived (being chiefly bent to her) that as I dranke
the wine, and withall stale a looke on her, me seemed I tasted
her deliciousnesse. But alas, the one thirste was much more
inflamed, then the other quenched. Sometimes my eyes would
lay themselves open to receive all the dartes she did throwe,
somtimes cloze up with admiration, as if with a contrary fancie,
they woulde preserve the riches of that sight they had gotten,
or cast my lidde as curtaines over the image of beautie, her

presence had painted in them. True it is, that my Reason (now growen a servant to passion) did yet often tel his master, that he should more moderatly use his delight. But he, that of a rebell was become a Prince, disdayned almost to allow him the place of a Counseller: so that my senses delights being too strŏg for any other resolution, I did even loose the raines unto them : hoping, that (going for a woman) my lookes would passe, either unmarked, or unsuspected.

Now thus I had (as me thought) well playd my first acte, 2 assuring my selfe, that under that disguisment, I should find opportunitie to reveal my self to the owner of my harte. But who would thinke it possible (though I feele it true) that in almost eight weekes space, I have lived here (having no more companie but her parents, and I being familiar, as being a woman, and watchfull, as being a lover) yet could never finde opportunitie to have one minutes leasure of privie conference : the cause whereof is as strange, as the effects are to me miserable. And (alas) this it is.

At the first sight that *Basilius* had of me (I think *Cupid* 3 having headed his arrows with my misfortune) he was striken (taking me to be such as I professe) with great affectiŏ towards me, which since is growen to such a doting love, that (till I was faine to gette this place, sometimes to retire unto freely) I was even choaked with his tediousnes. You never saw fourscore yeares daunce up and downe more lively in a young Lover: now, as fine in his apparrell, as if he would make me in love with a cloake ; and verse for verse with the sharpest-witted Lover in *Arcadia*. Doo you not think that this is a sallet of woormwood, while mine eyes feede upon the *Ambrosia* of *Philocleas* beauty.

But this is not all ; no this is not the worst ; for he (good man) were easy enough to be dealt with: but (as I thinke) Love and mischeefe having made a wager, which should have most power in me, have set *Gynecia* also on such a fire towardes me, as will never (I feare) be quenched but with my destruction. For she (being a woman of excellent witte, and of strong working thoughts) whether she suspected me by my over-vehement showes of affection to *Philoclea* (which love forced me unwisely to utter, while hope of my maske foolishly incouraged me) or that she hath takĕ some other marke of me, that I am not a woman:

or what devil it is hath revealed it unto her, I know not; but so it is, that al her countenances, words and gestures, are miserable portraitures of a desperate affection. Whereby a man may learne, that these avoydings of companie, doo but make the passions more violent, when they meete with fitte subjects. Truely it were a notable dumb shew of *Cupids* kingdome, to see my eyes (languishing with over-vehement longing) direct themselves to *Philoclea:* & *Basilius* as busie about me as a Bee, & indeed as cumbersome; making such suits to me, who nether could if I would; nor would if I could, helpe him: while the terrible witte of *Gynecia*, carried with the beere of violent love, runnes thorow us all. And so jelious is she of my love to her daughter, that I could never yet beginne to open my mouth to the unevitable *Philoclea*, but that her unwished presence gave my tale a cōclusion, before it had a beginning.

And surely if I be not deceived, I see such shewes of liking, and (if I bee acquainted with passions) of almost a passionate liking in the heavenly *Philoclea*, towardes me, that I may hope her eares would not abhorre my discourse. And for good *Basilius*, he thought it best to have lodged us together, but that the eternall hatefulnes of my destinie, made *Gynecias* jelousie stoppe that, and all other my blessings. Yet must I confesse, that one way her love doth me pleasure: for since it was my foolish fortune, or unfortunate follie, to be knowen by her, that keepes her from bewraying me to *Basilius*. And thus (my *Musidorus*) you have my Tragedie played unto you by my selfe, which I pray the gods may not in deede proove a Tragedie. And there he ended, making a full point of a hartie sigh.

5   *Musidorus* recōmended to his best discourse, all which *Pyrocles* had told him. But therein he found such intricatenes, that he could see no way to lead him out of the maze; yet perceiving his affection so groūded, that striving against it, did rather anger then heale the wound, and rather call his friend-shippe in question, then give place to any friendly counsell. Well (said he) deare cosin, since it hath pleased the gods to mingle your other excellencies with this humor of love, yet happie it is, that your love is imployed upon so rare a woman: for certainly, a noble cause dooth ease much a grievous case. But as it stands now, nothing vexeth me, as that I cānot see wherein I can be servisable unto you. I desire no greater

service of you (āswered *Pyrocles*) thē that you remayn secretly in this country, & some-times come to this place; either late in the night, or early in the morning, where you shal have my key to ēter, bicause as my fortune, eyther amendes or empaires. I may declare it unto you, and have your counsell and further-aunce: & hereby I will of purpose lead her, that is the prayse, and yet the staine of all womankinde, that you may have so good a view, as to allowe my judgement: and as I can get the most convenient time, I wil come unto you; for though by reason of yonder wood you cannot see the Lodge; it is harde at hande. But now, (said she) it is time for me to leave you, and towardes evening wee will walke out of purpose hether-ward, therefore keepe your selfe close in that time. But *Musidorus* bethinking him selfe that his horse might happen to bewray them, thought it best to returne for that day, to a village not farre of, and dispatching his horse in some sorte, the next day early to come a foote thither, and so to keepe that course afterward, which *Pyrocles* very well liked of. Now fare-well deere cousin (said he) from me, no more *Pyrocles*, nor *Daiphantus* now, but *Zelmane* : *Zelmane* is my name, *Zelmane* is my title, *Zelmane* is the onely hope of my advauncement. And with that word going out, and seeing that the coast was cleare, *Zelmane* dismissed *Musidorus*, who departed as full of care to helpe his friend, as before he was to disswade him.

CHAP. 15.

1 *The Labyrinth of* Zelmanes *love.* 2 *The Ladies exercises.* 3 *The challenge of* Phalantus *in paragon of* Artexias *beautie.* 4 *The description of their persons and affections :* 5 *and occasion of this challenge.* 6 *The successe thereof abroad.*

Zelmane returned to the Lodge, where (inflamed by *Philoclea*, 1 watched by *Gynecia*, and tired by *Basilius*) she was like a horse, desirous to runne, and miserablie spurred, but so short rainde, as he cannot stirre forward : *Zelmane* sought occasion to speake with *Philoclea* ; *Basilius* with *Zelmane* ; and *Gynecia* hindered them all. If *Philoclea* hapned to sigh (and sigh she did often) as if that sigh were to be wayted on, *Zelmane* sighed also; whereto *Basilius* and *Gynecia* soone made up foure parts of sorow. Their affection increased their conversation; and their conversation increased their affection. The respect borne bredde due ceremonies; but the affection shined so through them, that the ceremonies seemed not ceremonious. *Zelmanes* eyes were (like children afore sweet meate) eager, but fearefull of their ill-pleasing governors. Time in one instant, seeming both short, and long unto them: short, in the pleasingnes of such presence: long, in the stay of their desires.

2   But *Zelmane* fayled not to intice them all many times abroad, because she was desirous her friend *Musidorus* (neere whom of purpose she ledde them) might have full sight of them. Some-times angling to a little River neere hand, which for the moisture it bestowed upon rootes of some flourishing Trees, was rewarded with their shadowe. There would they sitte downe, & pretie wagers be made betweene *Pamela* and *Philoclea*, which could soonest beguile silly fishes; while *Zelmane* protested, that the fitte pray for them was hartes of Princes. She also had an angle in her hand; but the taker was so taken, that she had forgotten taking. *Basilius* in the meane time would be the cooke him selfe of what was so caught, & *Gynecia* sit stil, but with no stil pensifnesse. Now she brought them to see a seeled Dove, who the blinder she was, the higher she strave. Another time a Kite, which having a gut cunningly pulled out of her, and so let flie, called all the Kites in that quarter, who (as often-times the worlde is deceaved) thinking her prosperous when indeed she was wounded, made the poore Kite find, that opinion of riches may wel be dangerous.

3   But these recreations were interrupted by a delight of more gallant shew; for one evening as *Basilius* returned from having forced his thoughts to please themselves in such small conquests, there came a shepheard, who brought him word that a Gentle-mã desired leave to do a message from his Lord unto him. *Basilius* granted; wherupon the Gentleman came, and after the dutifull ceremonies observed, in his maisters name tolde him, that he was sent from *Phalãtus* of *Corinth*, to crave licence, that as he had done in many other courts, so he might in his presence defie all *Arcadian* Knights in the behalfe of his mistres beautie, who would besides, her selfe in person be pre-

sent, to give evident proofe what his launce should affirme. The conditions of his chalenge were, that the defendant should bring his mistresse picture, which being set by the image of *Artesia* (so was the mistresse of *Phalantus* named) who in six courses should have better of the other, in the judgement of *Basilius*, with him both the honors and the pictures should remaine. *Basilius* (though he had retired him selfe into that solitarie dwelling, with intention to avoid, rather then to accept any matters of drawing company; yet because he would entertaine *Zelmane*, (that she might not think the time so gainefull to him, losse to her) graunted him to pitch his tent for three dayes, not farre from the lodge, and to proclayme his chalenge, that what *Arcadian* Knight (for none els but upon his perill was licensed to come) woulde defende what he honored against *Phalantus*, should have the like freedome of accesse and returne.

This obteyned and published, *Zelmane* being desirous to 4 learne what this *Phalantus* was, having never knowne him further then by report of his owne good, in somuch as he was commonly called, The faire man of armes, *Basilius* told her that he had had occasion by one very inward with him, to knowe in parte the discourse of his life, which was, that he was bastard-brother to the faire *Helen* Queene of *Corinth*, and deerly esteemed of her for his exceeding good parts, being honorablie courteous, and wronglesly valiaunt, considerately pleasant in conversation, & an excellent courtier without unfaithfulnes; who (finding his sisters unperswadeable melancholy, thorow the love of *Amphialus*) had for a time left her court, and gone into *Laconia*: where in the warre against the *Helots*, he had gottẽ the reputatiõ of one, that both durst & knew. But as it was rather choise thẽ nature, that led him to matters of armes, so as soon as the spur of honor ceased, he willingly rested in peaceable delightes, being beloved in all cõpanies for his lovely qualities, & (as a mã may terme it) cunning cherefulnes, wherby to the Prince & Court of *Laconia*, none was more agreable thẽ *Phalantus*: and he not given greatly to struggle with his owne disposition, followed the gentle currant of it, having a fortune sufficient to content, & he content with a sufficient fortune. But in that court he sawe, and was acquainted with this *Artesia*, whose beautie he now defendes, became her servant, said him selfe, and perchaunce thought

97

him selfe her lover. But certainly, (said *Basilius*) many times it falles out, that these young companiös make themselves beleeve they love at the first liking of a likely beautie ; loving, because they will love for want of other businesse, not because they feele indeed that divine power, which makes the heart finde a reason in passion : and so (God knowes) as inconstantly leane upon the next chaunce that beautie castes before them. So therefore taking love uppon him like a fashion, he courted this Ladie *Artesia*, who was as fit to paie him in his owne monie as might be. For she thinking she did wrong to her beautie if she were not prowde of it, called her disdaine of him chastitie, and placed her honour in little setting by his honouring her : determining never to marrie, but him, whome she thought worthie of her : and that was one, in whome all worthinesse were harboured. And to this conceipt not onely nature had bent her, but the bringing up she receaved at my sister in lawe *Cecropia*, had confirmed her : who having in her widowhood taken this young *Artesia* into her charge ; because her Father had bene a deare friend of her dead husbandes, and taught her to thinke that there is no wisdome but in including heaven & earth in ones self: and that love, courtesie, gratefulnesse, friendship, and all other vertues are rather to be taken on, then taken in ones selfe : And so good discipline she found of her, that liking the fruits of her owne planting, she was cötent (if so her sonne could have liked of it) to have wished her in marriage to my Nephew *Amphialus*. But I thinke that desire hath lost some of his heate, since she hath knowne, that such a Queene as *Helen* is, doth offer so great a price as a kingdome, to buie his favour ; for if I be not deceaved in my good sister *Cecropia*, shee thinks no face so beautifull, as that which lookes under a crowne. But *Artesia* indeede liked well of my Nephew *Amphialus* ; for I cã never deeme that love, which in hauty harts proceeds of a desire onely to please, and as it were, peacock themselves ; but yet she hath shewed vehemencie of desire that way, I thinke, because all her desires be vehemët, in so much that she hath both placed her onely brother (a fine youth called *Ismenus*) to be his squire, and her selfe is content to waite upon my sister, till she may see the uttermost what she may worke in *Amphialus* : who being of a melancholie (though I must needes saye courteous and noble) mind, seems to love nothing lesse then

Love : & of late having through some adventure, or inwarde miscontentment, withdrawne him selfe frō any bodies knowledge, where he is : *Artesia* the easier condiscended to goe to the court of *Laconia*, whether she was sent for by the Kinges wife, to whome she is somewhat allied.

And there after the war of the *Helots*, this Knight *Phalantus*, (at least for tongue-delight) made him selfe her servaunt, and she so little caring, as not to showe mislike thereof, was content onely to be noted to have a notable servaunt. For truely one in my court neerely acquainted with him, within these few dayes made me a pleasaunt description of their love, while he with cheerefull lookes would speake sorowfull words, using the phrase of his affection in so high a stile, that *Mercurie* would not have wooed *Venus* with more magnificent Eloquence : but els neyther in behaviour, nor action, accusing in him selfe anie great trouble in minde, whether he sped or no. And she of the other side, well finding howe little it was, and not caring for more, yet taught him, that often it falleth out but a foolishe wittinesse, to speake more then one thinkes.

For she made earnest benefite of his jest, forcing him in respect of his promise, to doo her suche service, as were both cumbersome and costly unto him, while he stil thought he went beyond her, because his harte did not commit the idolatrie. So that lastlie, she (I thinke) having in minde to make the fame of her beautie an oratour for her to *Amphialus*, (perswading her selfe perhaps, that it might fall out in him, as it dothe in some that have delightfull meate before them, and have no stomacke to it, before other folkes prayse it) she tooke the advauntage one daye uppon *Phalantus* unconscionable praysinges of her, and certaine cast-awaie vowes, howe much he would doo for her sake, to arrest his woord assoone as it was out of his mouth, and by the vertue thereof to charge him to goe with her thorow all the courts of *Greece*, & with the chalenge now made, to give her beauty the principality over all other. *Phalantus* was entrapped, and saw round about him, but could not get out. Exceedinglie perplexed he was (as he confest to him that tolde mee the tale) not for doubt hee had of him selfe (for indeede he had litle cause, being accounted, with his Launce especially (whereupon the challenge is to be tryed) as perfect as any that *Greece* knoweth ; but because he feared to offend his sister

Helen, and with all (as he said) he could not so much beleeve his love, but that he might thinke in his hart (whatsoever his mouth affirmed) that both she, my daughters, and the faire *Parthenia* (wife to a most noble Gentleman, my wives neere kinsman) might far better put in their clayme for that prerogative. But his promise had bound him prentice, and therfore it was now better with willingnes to purchase thankes, then with a discontented doing to have the paine, and not the reward : and therefore went on, as his faith, rather then love, did lead him.

6   And now hath he already passed the courts of *Laconia*, *Elis*, *Argos* and *Corinth* : and (as many times it happēs) that a good pleader makes a bad cause to prevaile ; so hath his Lawnce brought captives to the triumph of *Artesias* beauty, such, as though *Artesia* be among the fairest, yet in that company were to have the preheminence : for in those courts many knights (that had bene in other far countries) defēded such as they had seene, and liked in their travaile : but their defence had bene such ; as they had forfayted the picture of their Ladies, to give a forced false testimonie to *Artesias* excellencie. And now lastly is he come hether, where he hath leave to trye his fortune. But I assure you, if I thought it not in dew & true cōsideratiō an injurious service & churlish curtesie, to put the danger of so noble a title in the deciding of such a dāgerles cōbat, I would make yong master *Phalantus* know, that your eyes can sharpē a blūt Launce, and that age, which my graye haires (onely gotten by the loving care of others) make seeme more then it is, hath not diminished in me the power to protect an undeniable verity. With that he bustled up himselfe, as though his harte would faine have walked abroad. *Zelmane* with an inwarde smiling gave him outward thanks, desiring him to reserve his force for worthier causes.

CHAP. 16.

[1] Phalantus *and* Artesias *pompous entraunce.* [2] *The painted muster of an eleven conquered beauties.*

S O passing their time according to their woont, they wayted
for the cŏming of *Phalantus,* who the next morning
having alredy caused his tents to be pitched, neere to a faire
tree hard by the Lodge, had uppon the tree made a shield to bee
hanged up, which the defendant should strike, that woulde call
him to the mainteyning his challendge. The *Impresa* in the
shield ; was a heaven full of starres, with a speech signifying,
that it was *the beauty which gave it the praise.*

Himselfe came in next after a triumphant chariot, made of
Carnatiŏ velvet inriched with purle & pearle, wherein *Artesia*
sat, drawne by foure winged horses with artificiall flaming
mouths, and fiery winges, as if she had newly borrowed them
of *Phœbus.* Before her marched, two after two, certaine foote-
mẽ pleasantly attired, who betweene them held one picture after
another of them that by *Phalantus* well running had lost the
prize in the race of beauty, and at every pace they stayed, turning the pictures to each side, so leasurely, that with perfect
judgement they might be discerned.

The first that came in (folowing the order of the time [1]
wherein they had bene wonne) was the picture of *Andromana,*
Queene of *Iberia* ; whom a *Laconian* Knight having sometime
(and with speciall favour) served, (though some yeares since
retourned home) with more gratefulnes then good fortune
defended. But therein *Fortune* had borrowed witte ; for indeede she was not cŏparable to *Artesia* ; not because she was
a good deale elder (for time had not yet beene able to impoverish
her store thereof) but an exceeding red haire with small eyes,
did (like ill companions) disgrace the other assembly of most
commendable beauties.

Next after her was borne the counterfaite of the princesse [2]
of *Elis,* a Lady that taught the beholders no other point of
beauty, but this, that as lyking is, not alwaies the child of

beauty, so whatsoever liketh; is beautyfull; for in that visage there was nether Majestie, grace, favour, nor fairenesse; yet she wanted not a servaunt that woulde have made her fairer then the faire *Artesia*. But he wrote her praises with his helmet in the dust, and left her picture to be as true a witnes of his overthrow, as his running was of her beauty.

3   After her was the goodly *Artaxia*, great Q. of *Armenia*, a Lady upon whom nature bestowed, & wel placed her delightful colours; & withal, had proportioned her without any fault, quickly to be discovered by the senses, yet altogether seemed not to make up that harmony, that *Cupid* delights in; the reasõ wherof might seem a mannish countenance, which overthrew that lovely sweetnes, the noblest power of womankinde, farre fitter to prevaile by parley, then by battell.

4   Of a farre contrary consideratiõ was the representation of her that next followed, which was *Erona* Queene of *Licia*, who though of so browne a haire, as no man should have injuried it to have called it blacke, and that in the mixture of her cheeks the white did so much overcome the redde (though what was, was very pure) that it came neare to palenes, and that her face was a thought longer then the exacte *Symmetrians* perhaps would allow; yet love plaid his part so well, in everie part, that it caught holde of the judgement, before it could judge, making it first love, & after acknowledge it faire, for there was a certaine delicacie, which in yeelding, conquered; & with a pitiful looke made one find cause to crave helpe himselfe.

5   After her came two Ladies, of noble, but not of royall birth: the former was named *Baccha*, who though very faire, and of a fatness rather to allure, then to mislike, yet her brests over-familiarly laide open, with a mad countenaunce about her mouth, betweene simpring & smyling, her head bowed somwhat down, seemed to lãguish with over-much idlenes, with an inviting look cast upward, disswading with too much perswading, while hope might seem to overcome desire.

6   The other (whose name was written *Leucippe*) was of a fine daintines of beauty, her face carying in it a sober simplicitie; like one that could do much good, & ment no hurt, her eyes having in them such a cheerefulnes, as nature seemed to smile in them: though her mouth and cheekes obeyed that pretty demurenes which the more one markes, the more one woulde

judge the poore soule apt to beleve; & therfore the more pitie to deceive her.

Next came the Queene of *Laconia*, one that seemed borne 7 in the confines of beauties kingdome : for all her lineamĕts were neither perfect possessions thereof, nor absent strangers thereto : but she was a Queene, and therefore beautyfull.

But she that followed, conquered indeed with being 8 conquered; & might well have made all the beholders waite upõ her triumph, while her selfe were led captive. It was the excellĕtly-faire Queene *Helen*, whose Iacinth haire curled by nature, & intercurled by arte (like a fine brooke through goldĕ sãds) had a rope of faire pearles, which now hiding, now hidden by the haire, did as it were play at fast or loose, each with other, mutually giving & receiving riches. In her face so much beautie & favour expressed, as if *Helen* had not bene knowĕ, some would rather have judged it the painters exercise, to shew what he could do, thĕ coũterfaiting of any living patterne : for no fault the most fault finding wit could have foũd, if it were not, that to the rest of the body the face was somewhat too little : but that little was such a sparke of beauty, as was able to enflame a world of love. For every thing was full of a choyce finenes, that if it wãted any thing in majestie, it supplied it with increase of pleasure; & if at the first it strake not admiration, it ravished with delight. And no in-differĕt soule there was, which if it could resist frõ subjecting it self to make it his princesse, that would not lõg to have such a playfelow. As for her attire, it was costly and curious, though the look (fixt with more sadnes thĕ it seemed nature had bestowed to any that knew her fortune) bewraied, that as she used those ornamĕts, not for her self, but to prevaile with another, so she feared, that all would not serve.

Of a farre differing (though esteemed equall) beautie, was 9 the faire *Parthenia*, who next wayted on *Artesias* triumph, though farre better she might have sitte in the throne. For in her every thing was goodly, and stately; yet so, that it might seeme that great-mindednes was but the auncient-bearer to humblenes. For her great graie eye, which might seem full of her owne beauties, a large, and exceedingly faire forhead, with all the rest of her face and body, cast in the mould of Noblenes; was yet so attired, as might shew, the mistres thought it either not to deserve, or not to need any exquisite decking, having no adorning but cleanlines; and so farre from all arte, that it was full of carelesnesse: unlesse that carelesnesse it selfe (in spite of it selfe) grew artificiall. But *Basilius* could not abstaine from praising *Parthenia*, as the perfect picture of a womanly vertue, and wively faithfulnes: telling withall *Zelmane*, how he had understoode, that when in the court of *Laconia*, her picture (maintained by a certaine *Sycionian* Knight) was lost, thorow want, rather of valour, then justice: her husband (the famous *Argalus*) would in a chafe have gone and redeemed it · with a new triall. But she (more sporting then sorrowing for her undeserved champion) tolde her husbande, she desired to be beautifull in no bodies eye but his; and that she would rather marre her face as evill as ever it was, then that it should be a cause to make *Argalus* put on armour. Then would *Basilius* have tolde *Zelmane*, that which she alredie knew, of the rare triall of their coupled affection: but the next picture made the mouth give place to their eyes.

10   It was of a young mayd, which sate pulling out a thorne out of a Lambs foote, with her looke so attentive uppon it, as if that little foote coulde have bene the circle of her thoughts; her apparell so poore, as it had nothing but the inside to adorne it; a shephooke lying by her with a bottle upon it. But with al that povertie, beauty plaid the prince, and commanded as many harts as the greatest Queene there did. Her beautie and her estate made her quicklie to be knowne to be the faire shepheardesse, *Urania*, whom a rich knight called *Lacemon*, farre in love with her, had unluckely defended.

11   The last of all in place, because last in the time of her being captive, was *Zelmane*, daughter to the King *Plexirtus*: who at the first sight seemed to have some resembling of *Philoclea*, but with more marking (cōparing it to the present *Philoclea*, who indeed had no paragon but her sister) they might see, it was but such a likenesse, as an unperfect glasse doth give; aunswerable enough in some feitures, & colors, but erring in others. But *Zelmane* sighing, turning to *Basilius*, Alas sir (said she) here be some pictures which might better become the tōbes of their Mistresses, then the triumphe of *Artesia*. It is true sweetest Lady (saide *Basilius*) some of them be dead, and some other captive: But that hath happened so late, as it may

be the Knightes that defended their beauty, knew not so much: without we will say (as in some harts I know it would fall out) that death it selfe could not blot out the image which love hath engravẽ in thẽ. But divers besides these (said *Basilius*) hath *Phalantus* woon, but he leaves the rest, carying onely such, who either for greatnes of estate, or of beauty, may justly glorifie the glory of *Artesias* triumph.

CHAP. 17.

¹ *The overthrow of five* Arcadian *knights.* ² *The young shepheards prettie challenge.* ³ *What passions the sixth knights foyle bredde in* Zelmane. ⁴ Clitophon *hardly overmatched by* Phalantus. ⁵ *The ill arayed, & the black knights contention for prioritie against* Phalantus. ⁶ *The halting knights complaint against the black knight.* ⁷ Phalantus *fall by the ill furnisht knight.* ⁸ *The crosse-parting of* Phalantus *with* Artesia, ⁹ *and who the victor was.*

THus talked *Basilius* with *Zelmane*, glad to make any matter 1 subject to speake of, with his mistresse, while *Phalantus* in this pompous manner, brought *Artesia* with her gẽtlewomẽ, into one Tent, by which he had another: where they both wayted who would first strike upon the shielde, while *Basilius* the Judge appointed sticklers, and trumpets, to whom the other should obey. But non that day appeared, nor the next, till already it had consumed halfe his allowance of light; but then there came in a knight, protesting himselfe as contrarie to him in minde, as he was in apparrell. For *Phalantus* was all in white, having in his bases, and caparison imbroidered a waving water: at each side whereof he had nettings cast over, in which were divers fishes naturally made, & so pretily, that as the horse stirred, the fishes seemed to strive, and leape in the nette.

But the other knight, by name *Nestor*, by birth an *Arcadian*, & in affection vowed to the faire Shepherdesse, was all in black, with fire burning both upõ his armour, and horse. His *impresa* in his shield, was a fire made of Juniper, with this word, *More easie, and more sweete.* But this hote knight was cooled with a fall, which at the third course he received of *Phalantus*, leaving his picture to keepe companie with the other of the same stampe; he going away remedilesly chafing at his rebuke. The next was *Polycetes*, greatly esteemed in *Arcadia*, for deedes he had done in armes : and much spoken of for the honourable love he had long borne to *Gynecia*; which *Basilius* himselfe was content, not onely to suffer, but to be delighted with; he carried it in so honorable and open plainnes, setting to his love no other marke, then to do her faithfull service. But neither her faire picture, nor his faire running, could warrant him from overthrow, and her from becomming as then the last of *Artesias* victories: a thing *Gynecias* vertues would little have recked at another time, nor then, if *Zelmane* had not seene it. But her champion went away asmuch discomforted, as discomfited. Then *Telamon* for *Polixena*, & *Eurimelo* for *Elpine*, and *Leon* for *Zoana*; all brave Knights, all faire Ladies, with their going down, lifted up the ballance of his praise for activitie, and hers for fairenes.

2   Upon whose losse as the beholders were talking, there comes into the place where they ranne, a shepheard stripling (for his height made him more then a boy, & his face would not allow him a mã) brown of cõplexiõ (whether by nature, or by the Suns familiaritie) but very lovely withall; for the rest so perfectly proportioned, that Nature shewed, she dooth not like men who slubber up matters of meane account. And well might his proportion be judged; for he had nothing upon him but a paire of sloppes, and upon his bodie a Gote-skinne, which he cast over his shoulder, doing all things with so pretie grace, that it seemed ignorance could not make him do amisse, because he had a hart to do well, holding in his right hand a long staffe, & so cõming with a looke ful of amiable fiercenes, as in whom choller could not take away the sweetnes, he came towards the king, and making a reverence (which in him was comely because it was kindly) My liege Lord (said he) I pray you heare a few words; for my hart wil break if I say not my minde to you. I see here the picture of *Urania*, which (I cannot tell how, nor why) these men when they fall downe, they say is not so faire as yonder gay woman. But pray God, I may never see my olde mother alive, if I think she be any more match to

Urania, then a Goate is to a fine Lambe; or then the Dog that keepes our flock at home, is like your white Greihounde, that pulled down the Stagge last day.

And therefore I pray you let me be drest as they be, and my hart gives me, I shall tumble him on the earth: for indeede he might aswell say, that a Couslip is as white as a Lillie: or els I care not let him come with his great staffe, and I with this in my hand, and you shall see what I can doo to him. *Basilius* sawe it was the fine shepheard *Lalus*, whom once he had afore him in Pastorall sportes, and had greatly delighted in his wit full of prety simplicitie, and therefore laughing at his earnestnesse, he bad him be content, since he sawe the pictures of so great Queenes, were faine to follow their champions fortune. But *Lalus* (even weeping ripe) went among the rest, longing to see some bodie that would revenge *Uranias* wronge; and praying hartely for every bodie that ran against *Phalantus*, then began to feele poverty, that he could not set him selfe to that triall. But by and by, even when the Sunne (like a noble harte) began to shew his greatest countenaunce in his lowest estate, there came in a Knight, called *Phebilus*, a Gentleman of that coũtry, for whom hatefull fortune had borrowed the dart of Love, to make him miserable by the sight of *Philoclea*. For he had even from her infancie loved her, and was striken by her, before she was able to knowe what quiver of arrowes her eyes caried; but he loved and dispaired; and the more he dispaired, the more he loved. He sawe his owne unworthines, and thereby made her excellencie have more terrible aspect upon him: he was so secrete therein, as not daring to be open, that to no creature he ever spake of it, but his hart made such silent complaints within it selfe, that while all his senses were attentive thereto, cunning judges might perceave his minde: so that he was knowne to love though he denied, or rather was the better knowne, because he denied it. His armour and his attire was of a Sea couler, his *Impresa*, the fishe called *Sepia*, which being in the nette castes a blacke inke about it selfe, that in the darkenesse thereof it may escape: his worde was, *Not so*. *Philocleas* picture with almost an idolatrous magnificence was borne in by him. But streight jelousie was a harbinger for disdaine in *Zelmanes* harte, when she sawe any (but her selfe) should be avowed a champion for *Philoclea*: in somuch that she wisht his shame, till she sawe him shamed: for at the second course he was striken quite from out of the saddle, so full of grief, and rage withall, that he would faine with the sworde have revenged it: but that being contrary to the order set downe, *Basilius* would not suffer; so that wishing him selfe in the bottome of the earth, he went his way, leaving *Zelmane* no lesse angry with his los, thē she would have beene with his victory. For if she thought before a rivals prayse woulde have angred her, her Ladies disgrace did make her much more forget what she then thought, while that passion raigned so much the more, as she saw a pretie blush in *Philocleas* cheekes bewray a modest discontentment. But the night commaunded truce for those sportes, & *Phalantus* (though intreated) would not leave *Artesia*, who in no case would come into the house, having (as it were) suckte of *Cecropias* breath a mortall mislike against *Basilius*.

4   But the night measured by the short ell of sleepe, was soone past over, and the next morning had given the watchful stars leave to take their rest, when a trumpet summoned *Basilius* to play his judges parte: which he did, taking his wife & daughters with him; *Zelmane* having lockt her doore, so as they would not trouble her for that time: for already there was a Knight in the fielde, readie to prove *Helen* of *Corinth* had receaved great injury, both by the erring judgement of the challenger, and the unlucky weakenesse of her former defender. The new Knight was quickly knowne to be *Clitophon* (*Kalāders* sonne of *Basilius*-his sister) by his armour, which al guilt, was so well hādled, that it shewed like a glittering sande and gravell, interlaced with silver rivers: his device he had put in the picture of *Helen* which hee defended. It was the *Ermion*, with a speach that signified, *Rather dead then spotted*. But in that armour since he had parted frō *Helen* (who would no longer his companie, finding him to enter into termes of affection,) he had performed so honourable actiōs, (stil seeking for his two friends by the names of *Palladius* and *Daiphātus*,) that though his face were covered, his being was discovered, which yet *Basilius* (which had brought him up in his court) would not seeme to do; but glad to see triall of him, of whom he had heard very well, he commaunded the trumpets to sound; to which the two brave Knights obeying, they performed their

courses, breaking their six staves, with so good, both skill in the hitting, & grace in the maner, that it bred some difficulty in the judgement. But *Basilius* in the ende gave sentence against *Clitophon*, because *Phalantus* had broken more staves upõ the head, & that once *Clitophon* had received such a blowe, that he had lost the raines of his horse, with his head well nie touching the crooper of the horse. But *Clitophon* was so angry with the judgemẽt, (wherin he thought he had received wrõg) that he omitted his duty to his Prince, & uncle; and sodainly went his way, still in the quest of them, whom as then he had left by seeking: & so yeelded the field to the next commer.

Who comming in about two houres after, was no lesse 5 marked then al the rest before, because he had nothing worth the marking. For he had neither picture, nor device, his armour of as old a fashion (besides the rustie poorenesse,) that it might better seeme a monument of his graundfathe[r]s courage: about his middle he had in steede of bases, a long cloake of silke, which as unhandsomely, as it needes must, became the wearer: so that all that lookt on, measured his length on the earth alreadie, since he had to meete one who had bene victorious of so many gallants. But he went on towardes the shielde, and with a sober grace strake it; but as he let his sworde fall upon it, another Knight, all in blacke came rustling in, who strake the shield almost assoone as he, and so strongly, that he brake the shield in two: the ill appointed Knight (for so the beholders called him) angrie with that, (as he accounted,) insolent injurie to himselfe, hit him such a sound blowe, that they that looked on saide, it well became a rude arme. The other aunswered him againe in the same case, so that Launces were put to silence, the swordes were so busie.

But *Phalantus* angry of this defacing his shield, came upon the blacke Knight, and with the pommell of his sworde set fire to his eyes, which presently was revenged, not onely by the Blacke, but the ill apparelled Knight, who disdained another should enter into his quarrell, so as, who ever sawe a matachin daunce to imitate fighting, this was a fight that did imitate the matachin: for they being but three that fought, everie one had adversaries, striking him, who strooke the third, and revenging perhaps that of him, which he had receaved of the other. But *Basilius* rising himselfe to parte them, the sticklers authoritie scarslie able to perswade cholerike hearers; and parte them he did.

6   But before he could determine, comes in a fourth, halting on foote, who complained to *Basilius*, demaunding justice on the blacke Knight, for having by force taken away the picture of *Pamela* from him, whiche in little forme he ware in a Tablet, and covered with silke had fastened it to his Helmet, purposing for want of a bigger, to paragon the little one with *Artesias* length, not doubting but in that little quantitie, the excellencie of that would shine thorow the weakenesse of the other: as the smallest starre dothe thorow the whole Element of fire.   And by the way he had met with this blacke Knight, who had (as he said) robbed him of it.   The injurie seemed grievous, but when it came fully to be examined, it was found, that the halting Knight meeting the other, asking the cause of his going thetherward, and finding it was to defend *Pamelas* divine beautie against *Artesias*, with a prowde jollitie commaunded him to leave that quarrell onely for him, who was onely worthy to enter into it.   But the blacke Knight obeying no such cõmandements, they fell to such a bickering, that he gat a halting, & lost his picture.   This understood by *Basilius*, he told him he was now fitter to looke to his owne bodie, then an others picture: & so (uncomforted therein) sent him away to learn of *Æsculapius* that he was not fit for *Venus*.

5   But then the question arising who should be the former against *Phalantus*, of the blacke, or the ill apparelled Knight (who now had gotten the reputation of some sturdy loute, he had so well defended himselfe) of the one side, was alleged the having a picture which the other wanted: of the other side, the first striking the shield; but the conclusion was, that the ill apparelled Knight should have the precedence, if he delivered the figure of his mistresse to *Phalantus*; who asking him for it, Certainely (said he) her liveliest picture, (if you could see it) is in my hart, & the best cõparison I could make of her, is of the Sunne & of all other the heavenly beauties.   But because perhappes all eyes cannot taste the Divinitie of her beautie, and would rather be dazeled, then taught by the light, if it bee not clowded by some meaner thing; know you then, that I defend that same Ladie, whose image *Phebilus* so feebly lost yesternight, and in steede of an other (if you overcome mee) you

shall have me your slave to carrie that image in your mistresse triumphe. *Phalantus* easilie agreed to the bargaine, which alreadie he made his owne.

But when it came to the triall, the ill apparelled Knight 7 choosing out the greatest staves in all the store, at the first course gave his head such a remembraunce, that he lost almost his remembraunce, he him selfe receyving the incounter of *Phalantus* without any extraordinarie motion. And at the seconde gave him such a counterbuffe, that because *Phalantus* was so perfite a horseman, as not to be driven from the saddle, the saddle with broken girthes was driven from the horse: *Phalantus* remaining angrie and amazed, because now being come almost to the last of his promised enterprise, that disgrace befell him, which he had never before knowne.

But the victorie being by the judges given, and the trumpets 8 witnessed to the ill apparelled Knight; *Phalantus* disgrace was ingrieved in lieu of comforte by *Artesia*; who telling him she never lookt for other, bad him seeke some other mistresse. He excusing himselfe, and turning over the fault to Fortune, Then let that be your ill Fortune too (saide she) that you have lost me.

Nay truely Madame (saide *Phalantus*) it shall not be so: for I thinke the losse of such a Mistresse will proove a great gaine: and so concluded; to the sporte of *Basilius*, to see young folkes love, that came in maskt with so great pompe, goe out with so little constancie. But *Phalantus* first professing great service to *Basilius* for his curteous intermitting his solitary course for his sake, would yet conduct *Artesia* to the castle of *Cecropia*, whether she desired to goe: vowing in himselfe, that neither hart, nor mouth-love, should ever any more intangle him. And with that resolution he left the company.

Whence all being dismissed (among whom the black knight 9 wēt away repyning at his luck, that had kept him frō winning the honor, as he knew he shuld have don, to the picture of *Pamela*) the ill apparelled knight (who was only desired to stay, because *Basilius* meant to shew him to *Zelmane*) puld of his Helmet, & then was knowē himselfe to be *Zelmane*: who that morning (as she told) while the others were busie, had stolne out to the Princes stable, which was a mile of frō the Lodge, had gotten a horse (they knowing it was *Basilius* pleasure she

should be obeyed) & borrowing that homely armour for want
of a better, had come upon the spur to redeem *Philocleas*
picture, which she said, she could not beare, (being one of that
little wildernesse-company) should be in captivitie, if the
cunning she had learned in her coũtrye of the noble *Amazons*,
could withstãd it: & under that pretext faine she would have
givẽ a secret pasport to her affection. But this act painted at
one instant rednesse in *Philocleas* face, and palenesse in *Gynecias*,
but broght forth no other coũtenãces but of admiratiõ, no
speches but of cõmẽdatiõs: al these few (besides love) thinking
they honoured them selves, in honouring so accomplished a
person as *Zelmane*: whom dayly they sought with some or
other sports to delight, for which purpose *Basilius* had in a
house not farre of, servaunts, who though they came not
uncalled, yet at call were redye.

CHAP. 18.

[1] Musidorus *disguised.*   [2] *His song.*   [3] *His love,* [4] *the cause thereof.*
   [5] *His course therein.*

A Nd so many daies were spent, and many waies used, while
Zelmane was like one that stoode in a tree waiting a
good occasiõ to shoot, & *Gynecia* a blauncher, which kept the
dearest deere from her. But the day being come, which
according to an apointed course, the sheapheards were to
assẽble, & make their pastorall sports afore *Basilius*: *Zelmane*
(fearing, lest many eyes, and comming divers waies, might hap
to spy *Musidorus*) went out to warne him thereof.

1   But before she could come to the Arbour, she sawe walking
from her-ward, a man in sheapperdish apparrel who being in
the sight of the Lodge it might seeme he was allowed there.
A lõg cloke he had on, but that cast under his right arme,
wherein he held a shephooke, so finely wrought, that it
gave a bravery to poverty; & his rayments, though they were
meane, yet received they hansomnes by the grace of the wearer;
though he himselfe went but a kinde of languishing pace, with
his eies somewhat cast up to heaven, as though his fancyes
strave to mount higher; sometimes throwne downe to the

ground, as if the earth could not beare the burthens of his sorrowes; at length, with a lamētable tune, he songe these fewe verses.

> Come shepheards weedes, become your masters minde: 2
> Yeld outward shew, what inward chance he tryes:
> Nor be abasht, since such a guest you finde,
> Whose strongest hope in your weake comfort lyes.
>
> Come shepheards weedes, attend my woefull cryes:
> Disuse your selves from sweete Menalcas voice:
> For other be those tunes which sorrow tyes,
> From those cleere notes which freely may rejoyce.
>   Then power out plaint, and in one word say this:
>   Helples his plaint, who spoyles himselfe of blisse.

And having ended, he strake himselfe on the brest; saying, O miserable wretch, whether do thy destenies guide thee? The voice made *Zelmane* hasten her pace to overtake him: which having done, she plainly perceaved that it was her deare friend *Musidorus*, whereat marvailing not a little, she demaunded of him, whether the Goddesse of those woods had such a powre to trāsforme every body, or whether, as in all enterprises else he had done, he meant thus to match her in this newe alteration.

Alas, (said *Musidorus*) what shall I say, who am loth to say, 3 and yet faine would have said? I find indeed, that all is but lip-wisdome, which wants experience. I now (woe is me) do try what love can doo. O *Zelmane*, who will resist it, must either have no witte, or put out his eyes? can any man resist his creation? certainly by love we are made, and to love we are made. Beasts onely cannot discerne beauty, and let them be in the role of Beasts that doo not honor it. The perfect friendship *Zelmane* bare him, and the great pitie she (by good triall) had of such cases, coulde not keepe her from smiling at him, remembring how vehemently he had cryed out against the folly of lovers. And therefore a litle to punish him, Why how now deere cousin (said she) you that were last day so hie in Pulpit against lovers, are you now become so meane an auditor? Remember that love is a passion; and that a woorthie mans reason must ever have the masterhood. I recant, I recant (cryed *Musidorus*,) and withall falling downe prostrate, O thou celestial, or infernal spirit of Love, or what other heavẽly or hellish title thou list to have (for effeᶜts of both I finde in my selfe) have compassion of me, and let thy glory be as great in pardoning them that be submitted to thee, as in conquering those that were rebellious. No, no saide *Zelmane*, I see you well enough: you make but an enterlude of my mishaps, and doo but counterfaite thus, to make me see the deformitie of my passions: but take heede, that this jest do not one day turne to earnest. Now I beseech thee (saide *Musidorus* taking her fast by the hand) even for the truth of our friend-ship, of which (if I be not altogether an unhappy man) thou hast some rememberaunce, & by those sacred flames which (I know) have likewise neerely touched thee; make no jest of that, which hath so ernestly pearced me thorow, nor let that be light to thee, which is to me so burdenous, that I am not able to beare it. *Musidorus* both in words & behaviour, did so lively deliver out his inward grief, that *Zelmane* found indeede, he was thorowly woũded: but there rose a new jelousy in her minde, lest it might be with *Philoclea*, by whom, as *Zelmane* thought, in right all hartes and eyes should be inherited. And therefore desirous to be cleered of that doubt, *Musidorus* shortly (as in hast and full of passionate perplexednes,) thus recounted his case unto her.

4   The day (said he) I parted from you, I being in mind to returne to a towne, from whence I came hether, my horse being before tired, would scarce beare me a mile hence: where being benighted, the light of a candle (I saw a good way of) guided me to a young shepheards house, by name *Menalcas*, who seing me to be a straying sträger, with the right honest hospitality which seemes to be harboured in the *Arcadian* brests, & though not with curious costlines, yet with cleanly sufficiencie, entertained me: and having by talke with him, found the manner of the countrie, something more in particular, then I had by *Kalanders* report, I agreed to sojourne with him in secret, which he faithfully promised to observe. And so hether to your arbour divers times repaired: & here by your meanes had the sight (O that it had never bene so, nay, O that it might ever be so) of a Goddesse, who in a definite compasse

can set forth infinite beauty. All this while *Zelmane* was racked with jealousie. But he went on, For (saide he) I lying close, and in truth thinking of you, and saying thus to my selfe, O sweet *Pyrocles*, how art thou bewitched? where is thy vertue? where is the use of thy reason? how much am I inferior to thee in the state of the mind? And yet know I, that all the heavens cannot bring me to such thraldome. Scarcely, thinke I, had I spoken this word, when the Ladies came foorth; at which sight, I thinke the very words returned back again to strike my soule; at least, an unmeasurable sting I felt in my selfe, that I had spoken such words. At which sight? said *Zelmane*, not able to beare him any longer. O (sayd *Musidorus*) I know your suspition; No, no, banish all such feare, it was, it is, and must be *Pamela*. Then all is safe (sayd *Zelmane*) proceede, deare *Musidorus*. I will not (said he) impute it to my late solitarie life (which yet is prone to affections) nor, to the much thinking of you (though that cald the consideratiõ of love into my mind, which before I ever neglected) nor to the exaltation of *Venus*; nor revenge of *Cupid*; but even to her, who is the Planet, nay, the Goddesse, against which, the onely shielde must be my Sepulchre. When I first saw her, I was presently striken, and I (like a foolish child, that when any thing hits him, wil strike himselfe again upon it) would needs looke againe; as though I would perswade mine eyes, that they were deceived. But alas, well have I found, that Love to a yeelding hart is a king; but to a resisting, is a tyrant. The more with arguments I shaked the stake, which he had planted in the grounde of my harte, the deeper still it sanke into it. But what meane I to speake of the causes of my love, which is as impossible to describe, as to measure the backside of heaven? Let this word suffice, I love.

And that you may know I doo so, it was I that came in black armour to defende her picture, where I was both prevented, and beaten by you. And so, I that waited here to do you service, have now my self most need of succor. But wherupon got you your self this aparrel? said *Zelmane*. I had forgotten to tel you (said *Musidorus*) though that were one principall matter of my speech; so much am I now master of my owne minde. But thus it happened: being returned to *Menalcas* house, full of tormenting desire, after a while faynting under the weight, my courage stird up my wit to seeke for some releefe, before I yeelded to perish. At last this came into my head, that very evening, that I had to no purpose last used my horse and armour. I tolde *Menalcas*, that I was a *Thessalian* Gentle-man, who by mischaunce having killed a great favorit of the Prince of that coũtry, was pursued so cruelly, that in no place, but either by favour, or corruption, they would obtaine my destruction; and that therefore I was determined (till the fury of my persecutions might be asswaged) to disguise my selfe among the shephards of *Arcadia*, & (if it were possible) to be one of them that were allowed the Princes presence; Because if the woorst should fall, that I were discovered, yet having gotten the acquaintance of the Prince, it might happen to move his hart to protect me. *Menalcas* (being of an honest dispositiõ) pittied my case, which my face through my inward torment made credible; and so (I giving him largely for it) let me have this rayment, instructing me in all the particularities, touching himselfe, or my selfe, which I desired to know: yet not trusting so much to his constancie, as that I would lay my life, and life of my life, upon it, I hired him to goe into *Thessalia* to a friend of mine, & to deliver him a letter frõ me; conjuring him to bring me as speedy an answeere as he could, because it imported me greatly to know, whether certaine of my friendes did yet possesse any favour, whose intercessiõs I might use for my restitution. He willingly tooke my letter, which being well sealed, indeed conteyned other matter. For I wrote to my trustie servant *Calodoulus* (whom you know) that assoone as he had delivered the letter, he should keep him prisoner in his house, not suffering him to have conference with any body, till he knewe my further pleasure: in all other respects that he should use him as my brother. And thus is *Menalcas* gone, and I here a poore shepheard; more proud of this estate, thẽ of any kingdom: so manifest it is, that the highest point outward things can bring one unto, is the contentmẽt of the mind: with which, no estate; without which, all estates be miserable. Now have I chosen this day, because (as *Menalcas* tolde me) the other shepheards are called to make their sports, and hope that you wil with your credite, finde meanes to get me allowed among them. You neede not doubt (answered *Zelmane*) but that I will be your good mistresse:

marrie the best way of dealing must be by *Dametas*, who since his blunt braine hath perceived some favour the Prince dooth beare unto me (as without doubt the most servile flatterie is lodged most easilie in the grossest capacitie; for their ordinarie conceite draweth a yeelding to their greaters, and then have they not witte to learne the right degrees of duetie) is much more serviceable unto me, then I can finde any cause to wish him. And therefore dispaire not to winne him: for every present occasion will catch his senses, and his senses are masters of his sillie mind; onely reverence him, and reward him, and with that bridle and saddle you shall well ride him. O heaven and earth (said *Musidorus*) to what a passe are our mindes brought, that from the right line of vertue, are wryed to these crooked shifts? But ô Love, it is thou that doost it: thou changest name upõ name; thou disguisest our bodies, and disfigurest our mindes. But in deed thou hast reason, for though the wayes be foule, the journeys end is most faire and honourable.

CHAP. 19.

[1] *The meanes of* Musidorus *his apprentisage unto* Dametas. [2] *The preparation and place of the Pastorals.* [3] *The Lyons assault on* Philoclea, *and death by* Zelmane. [4] *The shee beares on* Pamela, *and death by* Dorus. [5] *The* Io Pæan *of* Dametas, [6] *and his scape from the beare.* [7] *The victors praises.* [8] *Whence those beasts were sent.*

NO more sweete *Musidorus* (said *Zelmane*) of these philo- 1 sophies; for here comes the very person of *Dametas*. And so he did in deed, with a sword by his side, a forrest-bill on his neck, and a chopping-knife under his girdle: in which provided sorte he had ever gone, since the feare *Zelmane* had put him in. But he no sooner sawe her, but with head and armes he laid his reverence afore her; inough to have made any man forsweare all courtesie. And then in *Basilius* name, he did invite her to walke downe to the place, where that day they were to have the Pastoralles.

But when he spied *Musidorus* to be none of the shepheards allowed in that place, he would faine have perswaded himselfe to utter some anger, but that he durste not; yet muttering, and champing, as though his cudde troubled him; he gave occasion to *Musidorus* to come neare him, and feine this tale of his owne life: That he was a younger brother of the shepheard *Menalcas*, by name *Dorus*, sent by his father in his tender age to *Athens*, there to learne some cunning more then ordinarie, that he might be the better liked of the Prince: and that after his fathers death, his brother *Menalcas* (latelie gone thether to fetch him home) was also deceased: where (upon his death) he had charged him to seek the service of *Dametas*, and to be wholy, and ever guyded by him; as one in whose judgement and integritie, the Prince had singular confidence. For token whereof, he gave to *Dametas* a good summe of golde in redy coine, which *Menalcas* had bequeathed unto him, upon condition he should receive this poore *Dorus* into his service, that his mind and manner might grow the better by his dayly example. *Dametas*, that of all manners of stile could best conceive of golden eloquence, being withall tickled by *Musidorus* prayses, had his brayne so turned, that he became slave to that, which he, that shewed to be his servant, offered to give him: yet for countenance sake, he seemed very squeimish, in respect of the charge he had of the Princesse *Pamela*. But such was the secrete operation of the golde, helped with the perswasion of the Amazon *Zelmane*, (who sayde it was pittie so handsome a young man should be any where els, then with so good a master) that in the ende he agreed (if that day he behaved himselfe so to the lyking of *Basilius*, as he might be cõtented) that then he would receive him into his service.

2 And thus went they to the Lodge, where they foũd *Gynecia* and her daughters ready to go to the field, to delight themselves there a while, untill the shepheards comming: whether also taking *Zelmane* with them, as they went, *Dametas* told them of *Dorus*, and desired he might be accepted there that day, in steed of his brother *Menalcas*. As for *Basilius*, he staied behind to bring the shepherds, with whom he meant to cõfer, to breed the better *Zelmanes* liking (which he onely regarded) while the other beautifull band came to the faire field, appointed for the shepherdish pastimes. It was indeed a place of delight;

for thorow the middest of it, there ran a sweete brooke, which
did both hold the eye open with her azure streams, & yet seeke
to close the eie with the purling noise it made upon the pibble
stones it ran over: the field it self being set in some places with
roses, & in al the rest constantly preserving a florishing greene;
the Roses added such a ruddy shew unto it, as though the field
were bashfull at his owne beautie: about it (as if it had bene to
inclose a *Theater*) grew such a sort of trees, as eyther excellency
of fruit, statelines of grouth, continuall greennes, or poeticall
fancies have made at any time famous. In most part of which
there had bene framed by art such pleasant arbors, that (one
tree to tree, answering another) they became a gallery aloft
from almost round about, which below gave a perfect shadow,
a pleasant refuge then from the cholericke looke of *Phœbus*.

In this place while *Gynecia* walked hard by them, carying 3
many unquiet cõtentions about her, the Ladies sate them
downe, inquiring many questiõs of the shepheard *Dorus*; who
(keeping his eie still upon *Pamela*) answered with such a
trembling voice, & abashed coûtenance, & oftentimes so far
from the matter, that it was some sport to the young Ladies,
thinking it want of education, which made him so discounten-
aunced with unwoonted presence. But *Zelmane* that saw in
him the glasse of her owne miserie, taking the hande of *Philoclea*, and with burning kisses setting it close to her lips (as if it
should stande there like a hand in the margine of a Booke, to
note some saying worthy to be marked) began to speake these
wordes. O Love, since thou art so changeable in mens estates,
how art thou so constãt in their torments? when sodainly there
came out of a wood a monstrous Lion, with a she Beare not far
from him, of litle lesse fiercenes, which (as they ghest) having
bene hûted in Forests far of, were by chaûce come thether,
where before such beastes had never bene seene. Then care,
not feare; or feare, not for themselves, altered some thing the
coûtenances of the two Lovers, but so, as any man might
perceive, was rather an assembling of powers, then dismaiednes
of courage. *Philoclea* no sooner espied the Liõ, but that obeying the cõmandement of feare, she lept up, & ran to the lodge-
ward, as fast as her delicate legs could carrie her, while *Dorus*
drew *Pamela* behind a tree, where she stood quaking like the
Partridge, on which the Hawke is evẽ ready to seaze. But

the Lion (seing *Philoclea* run away) bent his race to her-ward, & was ready to seaze him selfe on the pray, when *Zelmane* (to whome daunger then was a cause of dreadlesnes, all the cōpositions of her elemēts being nothing but fierie) with swiftnesse of desire crost him, and with force of affection strake him such a blow upon his chine, that she opened al his body: wherwith the valiant beast turning upō her with open jawes, she gave him such a thrust thorow his brest, that al the Liō could do, was with his paw to teare of the mantle and sleeve of *Zelmane*, with a little scratch, rather then a wound; his death-blow having takē away the effect of his force. But there withall he fell downe, & gave *Zelmane* leasure to take of his head, to carrie it for a present to her Ladie *Philoclea*: who all this while (not knowing what was done behind her) kept on her course, like *Arethusa* when she ran from *Alpheus*; her light apparell being carried up with the winde, that much of those beauties she would at another time have willingly hidden, was present to the sight of the twise wounded *Zelmane*. Which made *Zelmane* not folow her over hastily, lest she should too soone deprive her selfe of that pleasure: But carying the Lions head in her hand, did not fully overtake her, till they came to the presence of *Basilius*. Nether were they lōg there, but that *Gynecia* came thether also: who had bene in such a traunce of musing, that *Zelmane* was fighting with the Lion, before she knew of any Lions cōming: but then affection resisting, and the soone ending of the fight preventing all extremitie of feare, she marked *Zelmanes* fighting. And when the Lions head was of, as *Zelmane* ran after *Philoclea*, so she could not find in her hart but run after *Zelmane*: so that it was a new sight, Fortune had prepared to those woods, to see these great personages thus runne one after the other: each carried forward with an inwarde violence: *Philoclea* with such feare, that she thought she was still in the Lions mouth: *Zelmane* with an eager and impatient delight, *Gynecia* with wings of Love, flying they neither knew, nor cared to know whether. But now, being all come before *Basilius* amazed with this sight, and feare having such possessiō in the faire *Philoclea*, that her bloud durst not yet to come to her face, to take away the name of palenesse from her most pure whitenes, *Zelmane* kneeled down, and presented the Lions head unto her. Only Ladie (said she) here see you the punishment of that unnatural beast, which cõtrary to her owne kind wold have wronged Princes bloud, guided with such traiterous eies, as durst rebell against your beauty. Happy am I, and my beautie both (answered the sweete *Philoclea* then blushing, for feare had bequeathed his roome to his kinsman bashfulnes) that you excellent *Amazon*, were there to teach him good manners. And even thankes to that beautie (answered *Zelmane*) which can give an edge to the bluntest swordes? There *Philoclea* told her father, how it had hapned: but as she had turned her eyes in her tale to *Zelmane*, she perceived some bloud upõ *Zelmanes* shoulder, so that starting with the lovely grace of pitty, she shewed it to her Father and mother: who, as the nurse sometimes with over-much kissing may forget to give the babe sucke, so had they with too much delighting, in beholding and praysing *Zelmane*, left of to marke whether she needed succour. But then they ran both unto her, like a father and mother to an onely childe, and (though *Zelmane* assured them, it was nothing) would needes see it; *Gynecia* having skill in surgery, an arte in those daies much esteemed, because it served to vertuous courage, which evẽ Ladies would (evẽ with the contẽpt of courage) seeme to cherish. But looking upon it (which gave more inward bleeding woũds to *Zelmane*, for she might sometimes feele *Philocleas* touch, whiles she helped her mother) she found it was indeed of no great importance: yet applied she a pretious baulme unto it, of power to heale a greater griefe.

But even then, & not before, they remẽbred *Pamela*, & therefore *Zelmane* (thinking of her friend *Dorus*) was running back to be satisfied, whẽ they might all see *Pamela* cõming between *Dorus* & *Dametas*, having in her hãd the paw of a Beare, which the shepheard *Dorus* had newly presented unto her, desiring her to accept it, as of such a beast, which though she deserved death for her presumption, yet was her will to be esteemed, since she could make so sweet a choice. *Dametas* for his part came piping and dauncing, the meriest man in a parish. But whẽ he came so neere, as he might be heard of *Basilius*, he would needs breake thorow his eares with this joyfull song of their good successe.

5

Now thanked be the great *God* Pan,
     which thus preserves my loved life:
Thanked be I that keepe a man,
     who ended hath this fearefull strife:
For if my man must praises have,
     what then must I that keepe the knave?

For as the *Moone* the eies doth please,
     with gentle beames not hurting sight:
Yet hath sir *Sunne* the greatest praise,
     because from him doth come her light:
So if my man must praises have,
     what then must I that keepe the knave?

4   Being al now come together, & all desirous to know each
others advētures, *Pamelas* noble hart would needs gratefully
make knowne the valiāt mean of her safety: which (directing
her speach to her mother) she did in this māner. As soone
(said she) as ye were all run away, and that I hoped to be in
safetie, there came out of the same woods a foule horrible
Beare, which (fearing belike to deale while the Lion was
present, as soone as he was gone) came furiously towardes the
place where I was, and this young shepheard left alone by me;
I truly (not guilty of any wisedome, which since they lay to
my charge, because they say, it is the best refuge against that
beast, but evē pure feare bringing forth that effect of wisedome)
fell downe flat of my face, needing not coūterfait being dead,
for indeed I was litle better. But this shepheard having no
other weapon, but that knife you see, standing before the place
where I lay, so behaved him selfe, that the first sight I had
(when I thought my selfe nearer *Charons* ferry,) was the shepheard shewing me his bloudy knife in token of victory. I pray
you (saide *Zelmane*, speaking to *Dorus*, whose valour she was
carefull to have manifested) in what sorte, so ill weaponed,
could you atchive this enterprise? Noble Ladie (saide *Dorus*)
the manner of these beastes fighting with any man, is to stande
up upon their hinder feete: and so this did, & being ready to
give me a shrewd imbracement, I thinke, the God *Pan*, (ever
carefull of the chiefe blessings of *Arcadia*) guided my hand so
just to the hart of the beast, that neither she could once touch

me, nor (which is the only matter in this worthy remēbrāce) breed any dāger to the Princesse. For my part, I am rather (withall subjeċted humblenes) to thanke her excellencies, since the duety thereunto gave me harte to save my selfe, then to receive thankes for a deede, which was her onely inspiring. And this *Dorus* spake, keeping affeċtion as much as he could, backe from cōming into his eyes and gestures. But *Zelmane* (that had the same Charaċter in her heart) could easily discerne it, and therefore to keepe him the longer in speach, desired to understand the conclusion of the matter; and how the honest *Dametas* was escaped.

Nay (said *Pamela*) none shall take that office from my selfe, 6 being so much bound to him as I am, for my education. And with that word (scorne borrowing the countenance of myrth) somewhat she smiled, and thus spake on? When (said she) *Dorus* made me assuredly perceive, that all cause of feare was passed (the truth is) I was ashamed to finde my selfe alone with this shepheard: and therefore looking about me, if I could see any bodie; at length we both perceived the gentle *Dametas*, lying with his breast and head as farre as he could thrust him-selfe into a bush: drawing up his legges as close unto him as hee coulde: for, like a man of a very kind nature, soone to take pittie of himselfe, he was full resolved not to see his owne death. And when this shepheard pushed him, bidding him to be of good cheere; it was a good while, ere we could perswade him, that *Dorus* was not the beare: so that he was faine to pull him out by the heeles, & shew him the beast, as deade as he could wish it: which you may beleeve me, was a very joyful sight unto him. But then he forgate al curtesie, for he fel upon the beast, giving it many a manfull wound: swearing by much, it was not wel such beasts shuld be suffered in a cōmō welth. And then my governour, as full of joy, as before of feare, came dauncing and singing before us as even now you saw him. Well wel (said *Basilius*) I have not chosen *Dametas* for his fighting, nor for his discoursing, but for his plainenesse and honestie, and therein I know he will not deceave me.

But then he told *Pamela* (not so much because she should 7 know it, as because he would tell it) the wonderfull aċt *Zelmane* had perfourmed, which *Gynecia* likewise spake off, both in such extremitie of praising, as was easie to be seene, the construċtions of their speach might best be made by the Grammer rules of affection. *Basilius* told with what a gallant grace shee ranne with the *Lyons* head in her hand, like another *Pallas* with the spoiles of *Gorgon*. *Gynecia* sware, shee sawe the face of the young *Hercules* killing the *Nemean* Lion, & all with a gratefull assent confirmed the same praises: onely poore *Dorus* (though of equall desert, yet not proceeding of equall estate) should have bene left forgotten, had not *Zelmane* againe with great admiration, begun to speake of him; asking, whether it were the fashion or no, in *Arcadia*, that sheepherds should performe such valorous enterprises. This *Basilius* (having the quicke sense of a lover) tooke, as though his Mistres had given a secret reprehension, that he had not shewed more gratefulnesse to *Dorus*; and therefore (as nymblie as he could) enquired of his estate, adding promise of great rewards: among the rest, offering to him, if he would exercise his courage in souldierie, he would commit some charge unto him under his Lieutenant *Philanax*. But *Dorus* (whose ambition clymed by another stayre) having first answered touching his estate, that he was brother to the shepheard *Menalcas*; who among other, was wont to resort to the Princes presence, & excused his going to souldierie, by the unaptnesse he found in himselfe that way: he told *Basilius*, that his brother in his last testament had willed him to serve *Dametas*; and therefore (for due obedience thereunto) he would thinke his service greatly rewarded, if he might obtaine by that meane to live in the sight of his Prince, and yet practise his owne chosen vocation. *Basilius* (liking well his goodly shape and handsome manner) charged *Dametas* to receive him like a sonne into his house: saying, that his valour, and *Dametas* truth would be good bulwarkes against such mischiefes, as (he sticked not to say) were threatned to his daughter *Pamela*.

2   *Dametas*, no whit out of countenance with all that had bene said (because he had no worse to fal into then his owne) accepted *Dorus*: and with all, telling *Basilius*, that some of the shepheards were come; demaunded in what place he would see their sports: who first curious to know whether it were not more requisite for *Zelmanes* hurt to rest, then sit up at those pastimes; and she (that felt no wound but one) earnestly desiring to have Pastorals, *Basilius* commanded it should be at

the gate of the lodge: where the throne of the Prince being
(according to the auncient manner) he made *Zelmane* sit
betweene him & his wife therin, who thought her selfe
betweene drowning and burning: and the two young Ladies of
either side the throne, and so prepared their eyes and eares to
bee delighted by the shepheards.

But before al of them were assembled to begin their sports, 8
there came a fellow, who being out of breath (or seeming so to
be for haste) with humble hastines told *Basilius*, that his
Mistres, the Lady *Cecropia*, had sent him to excuse the mischance of her beastes ranging in that dãgerous sort, being
happened by the folly of the keeper; who thinking himself
able to rule them, had caried them abroad, & so was deceived:
whom yet (if *Basilius* would punish for it) she was readie to
deliver. *Basilius* made no other answere, but that his Mistres
if shee had any more such beastes, should cause them to be
killed: and then he told his wife & *Zelmane* of it, because they
should not feare those woods; as though they harbored such
beasts, where the like had never bene seene. But *Gynecia*
tooke a further conceit of it, mistrusting *Cecropia*, because shee
had heard much of the divellish wickednesse of her heart, and
that particularly she did her best to bring up her sonne
Amphialus (being brothers sonne to *Basilius*) to aspire to the
crowne, as next heire male after *Basilius*; and therefore saw no
reason, but that she might conjecture, it proceeded rather of
some mischievous practise, than of misfortune. Yet did she
onely utter her doubt to her daughters, thinking, since the
worst was past, shee would attend a further occasion, least over
much haste might seeme to proceede of the ordinarie mislike
betweene sisters in Lawe: onely they marvelled, that *Basilius*
looked no further into it; who (good man) thought so much of
his late conceived common wealth, that all other matters were
but digressions unto him. But the shepheards were ready, and
with wel handling themselves, called their senses to attend
their pastimes.

The first Eclogues.

BASILIUS, because *Zelmane* so would have it, used the artificiall day of torches, to lighten the sports their invẽtions could minister. And yet because many more shepheards were newly come, then at the first; he did in a gentle manner chastise the cowardise of the fugitive shepheards: with making them (for that night) the Torch-bearers, and the others later come, he willed with all freedome of speech and behaviour, to keepe their accustomed method. Which while they prepared to do, *Dametas*, who much disdained (since his late authority) all his old companions, brought his servant *Dorus* in good acquaintance and allowance of thẽ ; & himselfe stood like a directer over thẽ, with nodding, gaping, winking, or stamping shewing how he did like, or mislike those things he did not understand. The first sports the shepheards shewed, were full of such leapes & gambols, as being accorded to the Pipe (which they bare in their mouthes, even as they daunced) made a right picture of their chiefe god *Pan*, and his companions the *Satyres*. Then would they cast away their Pipes ; and holding hand in hand, daunce as it were in a braule, by the onely cadence of their voices, which they would use in singing some short coplets, whereto the one halfe beginning, the other halfe should answere. As the one halfe saying,

We love, and have our loves rewarded.

The others would aunswere.

We love, and are no whit regarded.

The first againe.

We finde most sweete affections snare,

With like tune it should be as in quire sent back againe.

That sweete, but sower despairefull care.

A third time likewise thus:

Who can despaire, whom hope doth beare ?

The aunswere.

And who can hope, that feeles despaire ?

Then all joyning their voyces, and dauncing a faster measure, they would conclude with some such words:

> *As without breath, no pipe doth move,*
> *No musike kindly without love.*

Having thus varied both their songs and daunces into divers sorts of inventions; their last sport was one of them to provoke another to a more large expressing of his passions: which *Lalus* (accounted one of the best singers amongst them) having marked in *Dorus* dauncing, no lesse good grace & hansome behaviour, then extreame tokens of a travelled minde; began first with his Pipe, and then with his voice, thus to chalenge *Dorus*, and was by him answered in the underwritten sort.

Lalus and Dorus.

COme Dorus, come, let songs thy sorowes signifie :   Lalus.
   And if for want of use thy minde ashamed is,
That verie shame with Loves high title dignifie.
  No stile is held for base, where Love well named is :
Ech eare suckes up the words, a true love scattereth,
And plaine speach oft, then quaint phrase, better framed is.

Nightingales seldome sing, the Pie still chattereth: Dorus.
The wood cries most, before it throughly kindled be,
Deadly wounds inward bleed, ech sleight sore mattereth.
  Hardly they heard, which by good hunters singled be.
Shallow brookes murmure most, deep silent slide away;
Nor true love loves those loves with others mingled be.

If thou wilt not be seene, thy face goe hide away,   Lalus.
Be none of us, or els maintaine our fashion :
Who frownes at others feastes, dooth better bide away.
  But if thou hast a Love, in that Loves passion,
I challenge thee by shew of her perfection,
Which of us two deserveth most compassion.

Thy challenge great, but greater my protection :   Dorus.
Sing then, and see (for now thou hast inflamed me)
Thy health too meane a match for my infection.

No, though the heav'ns for high attempts have blamed me,
Yet high is my attempt, O Muse historifie
Her praise, whose praise to learne your skill hath framed me.

Lalus. *Muse hold your peace: but thou, my God Pan, glorifie*
My Kalas giftes: who with all good gifts filled is.
Thy pipe, ô Pan, shall helpe, though I sing sorilie.
    A heape of sweetes she is, where nothing spilled is;
Who though she be no Bee, yet full of honie is:
A Lillie field, with plowe of Rose which tilled is.
    Milde as a Lambe, more daintie then a Conie is;
Her eyes my eyesight is, her conversation
More gladde to me, then to a miser monie is.
    What coye account she makes of estimation?
How nice to touch, how all her speeches peized be?
A Nimph thus turnde, but mended in translation.

Dorus. *Such Kala is: but ah, my fancies raysed be*
In one, whose name to name were high presumption,
Since vertues all, to make her title, pleased be.
    O happie Gods, which by inward assumption
Enjoy her soule, in bodies faire possession,
And keep it joynde, fearing your seates consumption.
    How oft with raine of teares skies make confession,
Their dwellers rapt with sight of her perfeEtion
From heav'nly throne to her heav'n use digression?
    Of best things then what world can yeeld confeEtion
To liken her? Decke yours with your comparison:
She is her selfe, of best things the colleEtion.

Lalus. *How oft my dolefull Sire cried to me, tarrie sonne*
When first he spied my love? how oft he said to me,
Thou art no souldier fitte for Cupids garrison?
    My sonne, keepe this, that my long toyle hath laide to me:
Love well thine owne: me thinkes, woolles whitenes passeth all:
I never found long love such wealth hath paide to me.
    This winde he spent: but when my Kala glasseth all
My sight in her faire limmes, I then assure my selfe,
Not rotten sheepe, but high crownes she surpasseth all.
    Can I be poore, that her golde haire procure my selfe?
Want I white wooll, whose eyes her white skinne garnished?
Till I get her, shall I to keepe enure my selfe?

How oft, when reason saw, love of her harnised   Dorus
With armour of my hart, he cried, O vanitie,
To set a pearle in steele so meanely varnished?

   Looke to thy selfe; reach not beyond humanitie:
Her minde, beames, state farre from thy weake wings banished:
And Love, which lover hurts is inhumanitie.

   Thus Reason said: but she came, Reason vanished;
Her eyes so maistering me, that such objection
Seemde but to spoyle the foode of thoughts long famished.

   Her peereles height my minde to high erection
Drawes up; and if hope-fayling ende lives pleasure,
Of fayrer death how can I make election?

   Once my well-waiting eyes espied my treasure,   Lalus.
With sleeves turnde up, loose haire, and brest enlarged,
Her fathers corne (moving her faire limmes) measure.

   O cried I, of so meane worke be discharged:
Measure my case, how by thy beauties filling
With seede of woes my hart brimme-full is charged.

   Thy father bids thee save, and chides for spilling.
Save then my soule, spill not my thoughts well heaped,
No lovely praise was ever got by killing.

   These bolde words she did heare, this fruite I reaped,
That she, whose looke alone might make me blessed,
Did smile on me, and then away she leaped.

   Once, ô sweete once, I saw with dread oppressed   Dorus.
Her whom I dread; so that with prostrate lying
Her length the earth in Loves chiefe clothing dressed.

   I saw that riches fall, and fell a crying;
Let not dead earth enjoy so deare a cover,
But deck therewith my soule for your sake dying.

   Lay all your feare upon your fearefull lover:
Shine eyes on me, that both our lives be guarded;
So I your sight, you shall your selves recover.

   I cried, and was with open rayes rewarded:
But straight they fledde, summond by cruell honor,
Honor, the cause, desart is not regarded.

   This mayde, thus made for joyes, ô Pan bemone her,   Lalus.
That without love she spends her yeares of love:
So faire a fielde would well become an owner.

> And if enchantment can a harde hart move,
> Teach me what circle may acquaint her sprite,
> Affections charmes in my behalfe to prove.
>   The circle is my (round about her) sight:
> The power I will invoke dwelles in her eyes:
> My charme should be, she haunt me day and night.

Dorus.
> Farre other care, ô Muse, my sorrow tries,
> Bent to such one, in whom, my selfe must say,
> Nothing can mend that point that in her lies.
>   What circle then in so rare force beares swaye?
> Whose sprite all sprites can spoile, raise, damne, or save:
> No charme holdes her, but well possesse she may;
>   Possesse she doth, and makes my soule her slave:
> My eyes the bandes, my thoughts the fatall knot.
> No thralles like them that inward bondage have.

Lalus.
> Kala at length conclude my lingring lotte:
> Disdaine me not, although I be not faire.
> Who is an heire of many hundred sheep
> Doth beauties keep, which never Sunne can burne,
> Nor stormes doo turne: fairenes serves oft to wealth.
> Yet all my health I place in your good-will.
> Which if you will (ô doo) bestow on me,
> Such as you see, such still you shall me finde.
> Constant and kind: my sheep your foode shall breed,
> Their wooll your weede, I will you Musique yeeld
> In flowrie fielde; and as the day begins
> With twenty ginnes we will the small birds take,
> And pastimes make, as Nature things hath made.
> But when in shade we meet of mirtle bowes,
> Then Love allowes, our pleasures to enrich,
> The thought of which doth passe all worldly pelfe.

Dorus.
> Lady your selfe, whom nether name I dare,
> And titles are but spots to such a worthe,
> Heare plaints come forth from dungeon of my minde.
> „The noblest kinde rejects not others woes.
> I have no shewes of wealth: my wealth is you,
> My beauties hewe your beames, my health your deeds;
> My minde for weeds your vertues liverie weares.

My foode is teares; my tunes waymenting yeeld :
Despaire my fielde ; the flowers spirits warrs :
My day newe cares ; my ginnes my daily sight,
In which do light small birds of thoughts orethrowne :
My pastimes none : time passeth on my fall :
Nature made all, but me of dolours made :
I finde no shade, but where my Sunne doth burne :
No place to turne; without, within it fryes :
Nor helpe by life or death who living dyes.

   But if my Kala this my suite denies,   Lalus.
Which so much reason beares,
Let crowes picke out mine eyes, which saw too much :
If still her minde be such,
My earthy moulde will melte in watrie teares.

My earthy moulde doth melte in watrie teares,   Dorus.
And they againe resolve
To aire of sighes, sighes to the hartes fire turne,
Which doth to ashes burne :
So doth my life within it selfe dissolve,

   So doth my life within it selfe dissolve,   Lalus.
That I am like a flower
New plucked from the place where it did breed,
Life showing, dead indeed :
Such force hath Love above poore Natures power.

   Such force hath Love above poore Natures power,   Dorus.
That I growe like a shade,
Which being nought seems somewhat to the eyen,
While that one body shine.
Oh he is mard that is for others made.

   Oh he is mard that is for others made.   Lalus.
Which thought doth marre my piping declaration,
Thinking how it hath mard my shepheards trade.
   Now my hoarse voice doth faile this occupation,
And others long to tell their loves condition :
Of singing take to thee the reputation.

Dorus. *Of singing take to thee the reputation*
New friend of mine; I yeeld to thy habilitie:
My soule doth seeke another estimation.
    But ah my Muse *I would thou hadst agilitie,*
To worke my Goddesse so by thy invention,
On me to cast those eyes, where shine nobilitie.
    Seen, and unknowne; heard, but without attention.

THis Eclogue betwixt *Lalus & Dorus*, of every one of the beholders received great commendations. When *Basilius* called to a yong shepheard, who nether had daunced nor song with thẽ, but layne al this while upõ the ground at the foot of a cypresse tree, in so deep a melancholy, as though his mind were banished from the place he loved, to be in prison in his body : & desired him he would begin some Eclogue, with some other of the shepheards, according to the accustomed guise : or els declare the discourse of his owne fortune, unknowne to him; as being a straunger in that coũtry. But he praied the King to pardon him, the time being far too joyful to suffer the rehersall of his miseries. Yet, to satisfy *Basilius* some way, he sange this songe, he had learned before he had subjected his thoughts to acknowledge no maister, but a mistresse.

AS I my little flocke on Ister banke
    (A little flocke; but well my pipe they couthe)
Did piping leade, the Sunne already sanke
Beyond our worlde, and ere I got my boothe
Each thing with mantle black the night doth scothe;
    Saving the glowe worme, which would curteous be
    Of that small light oft watching shepheards see.

The welkin had full niggardly enclosed
In cofer of dimme clowdes his silver groates,
Icleped starres; each thing to rest disposed:
The caves were full, the mountaines voide of goates:
The birds eyes closde closed their chirping notes.
    As for the Nightingale woodmusiques King,
    It August *was, he daynde not then to sing.*

Amid my sheepe, though I sawe nought to feare
Yet (for I nothing sawe) I feared sore ;
Then fonde I which thing is a charge to beare
As for my sheepe I dradded mickle more
Then ever for my selfe since I was bore :
 I sate me downe : for see to goe ne could,
 And sange unto my sheepe lest stray they should.

The songe I sange old Lanquet *had me taught,*
Lanquet, *the shepheard best swift* Ister *knewe,*
For clerkly reed, and hating what is naught,
For faithfull hart, cleane hands, and mouth as true :
With his sweet skill my skillesse youth he drewe,
 To have a feeling tast of him that sitts
 Beyond the heaven, far more beyond your witts.

He said, the Musique best thilke powers pleasd
Was jumpe concorde betweene our wit and will :
Where highest notes to godlines are raisd,
And lowest sinke not downe to jote of ill :
With old true tales he woont mine eares to fill,
 How sheepheards did of yore, how now they thrive,
 Spoiling their flock, or while twixt thē they strive.

He liked me, but pitied lustfull youth :
His good strong staffe my slippry yeares upbore :
He still hop'd well, because he loved truth ;
Till forste to parte, with harte and eyes even sore,
To worthy Coriden *he gave me ore.*
 But thus in okes true shade recounted he
 Which now in nights deepe shade sheep heard of me.

Such maner time there was (what time I n'ot)
When all this Earth, this damme or mould of ours
Was onely won'd with such as beastes begot :
Unknowne as then were they that builded towers :
The cattell wild, or tame, in natures bowers
 Might freely rome, or rest, as seemed them :
 Man was not man their dwellings in to hem.

The beastes had sure some beastly pollicie:
For nothing can endure where order n'is.
For once the Lion by the Lambe did lie;
The fearefull Hinde the Leopard did kisse:
Hurtles was Tygers pawe and Serpents hisse.
*   This thinke I well, the beasts with courage clad*
*   Like Senators a harmeles empire had.*

At which whether the others did repine,
(For envie harbreth most in feeblest hartes)
Or that they all to chaunging did encline,
(As even in beasts their dāmes leave chaunging parts)
The multitude to Jove a suite empartes,
*   With neighing, blaying, braying, and barking,*
*   Roring, and howling for to have a King.*

A King, in language theirs they said they would:
(For then their language was a perfect speech)
The birdes likewise with chirpes, and puing could
Cackling, and chattring, that of Jove beseech.
Onely the owle still warnde them not to seech
*   So hastily that which they would repent:*
*   But sawe they would, and he to deserts went.*

Jove wisely said (for wisedome wisely sayes)
O beasts, take heed what you of me desire.
Rulers will thinke all things made them to please,
And soone forget the swincke due to their hire.
But since you will, part of my heav'nly fire
*   I will you lende; the rest your selves must give,*
*   That it both seene. and felte may with you live.*

Full glad they were and tooke the naked sprite,
Which streight the Earth yclothed in his claye:
The Lion, harte; the Ounce gave active might;
The Horse, good shape; the Sparrow, lust to playe;
Nightingale, voice, entising songes to saye.
*   Elephant gave a perfect memorie:*
*   And Parot, ready tongue, that to applie.*

The Foxe gave crafte; the Dog gave flatterie;
Asse, pacience; the Mole, a working thought;
Eagle, high looke; Wolfe secrete crueltie :
Monkie, sweet breath; the Cow, her faire eyes brought;
The Ermion, whitest skinne, spotted with nought;
The sheep, mild-seeming face; climing, the Beare;
The Stagge did give the harme eschewing feare.

The Hare, her sleights; the Cat, his melancholie;
Ante, industrie; and Connie, skill to builde;
Cranes, order; Storkes, to be appearing holie;
Camœleon, ease to chaunge; Ducke, ease to yelde;
Crocodile, teares, which might be falsely spilde :
Ape great thing gave, though he did mowing stand,
The instrument of instruments, the hand.

Ech other beast likewise his present brings :
And (but they drad their Prince they ought should want)
They all consented were to give him wings :
And aye more awe towards him for to plant,
To their owne worke this priviledge they graunt,
That from thenceforth to all eternitie,
No beast should freely speake, but onely he.

Thus Man was made; thus Man their Lord became :
Who at the first, wanting, or hiding pride,
He did to beastes best use his cunning frame;
With water drinke, herbes meate, and naked hide,
And fellow-like let his dominion slide;
Not in his sayings saying I, but we :
As if he meant his lordship common be.

But when his seate so rooted he had found,
That they now skilld not, how from him to wend;
Then gan in guiltlesse earth full many a wound,
Iron to seeke, which gainst it selfe should bend,
To teare the bowels, that good corne should send.
But yet the common Damme none did bemone;
Because (though hurt) they never heard her grone.

Then gan the factions in the beastes to breed;
Where helping weaker sort, the nobler beastes,
(As Tygers, leopards, beares, and Lions seed)
Disdaind with this, in deserts sought their restes;
Where famine ravine taught their hungrie chestes,
  That craftily he forst them to do ill,
  Which being done he afterwards would kill.

For murthers done, which never erst was seene,
By those great beastes, as for the weakers good,
He chose themselves his guarders for to bene,
Gainst those of might, of whom in feare they stood,
As horse and dogge, not great, but gentle blood:
  Blith were the commons cattell of the fielde,
  Tho when they saw their foen of greatnes kilde.

But they or spent, or made of slender might,
Then quickly did the meaner cattell finde,
The great beames gone, the house on shoulders light:
For by and by the horse faire bitts did binde:
The dogge was in a coller taught his kinde.
  As for the gentle birds like case might rewe
  When falcon they, and gossehauke saw in mewe.

Worst fell to smallest birds, and meanest heard,
Whom now his owne, full like his owne he used.
Yet first but wooll, or fethers off he teard:
And when they were well us'de to be abused,
For hungrie teeth their flesh with teeth he brused:
  At length for glutton taste he did them kill:
  At last for sport their sillie lives did spill.

But yet ô man, rage not beyond thy neede:
Deeme it no gloire to swell in tyrannie.
Thou art of blood; joy not to see things bleede:
Thou fearest death; thinke they are loth to die.
A plaint of guiltlesse hurt doth pierce the skie.
  And you poore beastes, in patience bide your hell,
  Or know your strengths, and then you shall do well.

Thus did I sing, and pipe eight sullen houres
To sheepe, whom love, not knowledge, made to heare,
Now fancies fits, now fortunes balefull stowers :
But then I homewards call'd my lambkins deare :
For to my dimmed eyes beganne t'appeare
  The night growne old, her blacke head waxen gray,
  Sure shepherds signe, that morne should soone fetch day.

ACcording to the nature of diverse eares, diverse judgements streight followed : some praising his voice, others his words fit to frame a pastorall stile, others the strangenes of the tale, and scanning what he shuld meane by it. But old *Geron* (who had borne him a grudge ever since in one of their Eclogues he had taken him up over-bitterly) tooke hold of this occasion to make his revenge, and said, He never saw thing worse proportioned, then to bring in a tale of he knew not what beastes at such a sport-meeting, when rather some song of love, or matter for joyfull melody was to be brought forth. But, said he, This is the right conceipt of young men, who thinke, then they speake wiseliest, when they cannot understand themselves. But little did the melancholike shepherd regard either his dispraises, or the others praises, who had set the foundation of his honour there ; where he was most despised. And therefore he returning againe to the traine of his desolate pensivenesse, *Geron* invited *Histor* to answere him in Eclogue-wise ; who indeed having bene long in love with the faire *Kala*, and now by *Lalus* overgone ; was growne into a detestation of marriage. But thus it was.

Geron. Histor.

IN *faith, good* Histor, *long is your delay,*
  From holy marriage sweete and surest meane :
Our foolish lust in honest rules to stay.
  I pray thee doo to Lalus *sample leane :*
Thou seest, how friske, and jolly now he is,
That last day seem'd, he could not chew a beane.
  Beleeve me man, there is no greater blisse,
Then is the quiet joy of loving wife ;
Which who so wants, halfe of himselfe doth misse.

Geron.

THE COUNTESSE OF PEMBROKES

Friend without change, playfellow without strife,
Foode without fulnes, counsaile without pride,
Is this sweet doubling of our single life.

Histor.　*No doubt to whom so good chance did betide,*
As for to finde a pasture strawed with golde,
He were a foole, if there he did not bide.
　Who would not have a Phœnix if he could?
The humming Waspe, if it had not a stinge,
Before all flies the Waspe accept I would.
　But this bad world, few golden fieldes doth bring,
Phœnix but one, of Crowes we millions have:
The Waspe seemes gay, but is a combrous thing.
　If many Kalaes *our* Arcadia *gave,*
Lalus *example I would soone ensue,*
And thinke, I did my selfe from sorrow save.
　But of such wives we finde a slender crew;
Shrewdnes so stirres, pride so puffes up the hart,
They seldome ponder what to them is due.
　With meager lookes, as if they still did smart;
Puiling, and whimpring, or else scolding flat,
Make home more paine then following of the cart.
　Ether dull silence, or eternall chat;
Still contrarie to what her husband sayes;
If he do praise the dog, she likes the cat.
　Austere she is, when he would honest playes;
And gamesome then, when he thinkes on his sheepe;
She bids him goe, and yet from jorney stayes.
　She warre doth ever with his kinsfolke keepe,
And makes them fremb'd, who frinds by nature are,
Envying shallow toyes with malice deepe.
　And if forsooth there come some new found ware,
The little coine his sweating browes have got,
Must goe for that, if for her lowres he care:
　Or els; Nay faith, mine is the lucklest lot,
That ever fell to honest woman yet:
No wife but I hath such a man, God wot.
　Such is their speech, who be of sober wit;
But who doo let their tongues shew well their rage,
Lord, what bywords they speake, what spite they spit?

The house is made a very lothsome cage,
Wherein the birde doth never sing but cry ;
With such a will as nothing can asswage.

Dearely the servants doo their wages buy,
Revil'd for ech small fault, sometimes for none :
They better live that in a gaile doo lie.

Let other fowler spots away be blowne ;
For I seeke not their shame, but still me thinkes,
A better life it is to lye alone.

Who for ech fickle feare from vertue shrinkes, Geron.
Shall in his life embrace no worthy thing :
No mortall man the cuppe of suretie drinkes.

The heav'ns doo not good haps in handfuls bring,
But let us pike our good from out much bad :
That still our little world may know his king.

But certainly so long we may be glad,
While that we doo what nature doth require,
And for th'event we never ought be sad.

Man oft is plag'de with aire, is burnt with fire,
In water dround, in earth his buriall is ;
And shall we not therefore their use desire ?

Nature above all things requireth this,
That we our kind doo labour to maintaine ;
Which drawne-out line doth hold all humane blisse.

Thy father justly may of thee complaine,
If thou doo not repay his deeds for thee,
In granting unto him a grandsires gaine.

Thy common-wealth may rightly grieved be,
Which must by this immortall be preserved,
If thus thou murther thy posteritie.

His very being he hath not deserved,
Who for a selfe-conceipt will that forbeare,
Whereby that being aye must be conserved.

And God forbid, women such cattell were,
As you paint them : but well in you I finde,
No man doth speake aright, who speakes in feare.

Who onely sees the ill is worse then blind.
These fiftie winters maried have I beene ;
And yet finde no such faults in womankind.

I have a wife worthie to be a Queene,
So well she can command, and yet obay;
In ruling of a house so well shee's seene.

And yet in all this time, betwixt us tway,
We beare our double yoke with such consent,
That never past foule word, I dare well say.

But these be your love-toyes, which still are spent
In lawlesse games, and love not as you should,
But with much studie learne late to repent.

How well last day before our Prince you could
Blinde Cupids workes with wonder testifie?
Yet now the roote of him abase you would.

Goe to, goe to, and Cupid now applie
To that where thou thy Cupid maist avowe,
And thou shalt finde, in women vertues lie.

Sweete supple mindes which soone to wisdome bowe
Where they by wisdomes rule directed are,
And are not forst fonde thraldome to allow.

As we to get are fram'd, so they to spare:
We made for paine, our paines they made to cherish:
We care abroad, and they of home have care.

O Histor, seeke within thy selfe to flourish:
Thy house by thee must live, or els be gone:
And then who shall the name of Histor nourish?

Riches of children passe a Princes throne;
Which touch the fathers hart with secret joy,
When without shame he saith, these be mine owne.

Marrie therefore; for marriage will destroy
Those passions which to youthfull head doo clime
Mothers and Nurses of all vaine annoy.

ALl the assemblie laught at the lustines of the old fellowe, and easilie perceived in *Histor*, he liked *Lalus* fortune better, then he loved his person.   But *Basilius* to entermixe with these light notes of libertie, some sadder tune, set to the key of his own passion, not seeing there *Strephon* or *Klaius*, (who called thence by *Uranias* letter, were both gone to continue their suite, like two true runners, both employing their best speed, but not one hindring the other) he called to one *Lamō* of their acquaintance, and willed him to sing some one of their songs; which he redily performed in this doble Sestine.

Strephon. Klaius.

YOu Gote-heard Gods, that love the grassie mountaines,   Strephon.
  You Nimphes that haunt the springs in pleasant vallies,
You Satyrs joyde with free and quiet forrests,
Vouchsafe your silent eares to playning musique,
Which to my woes gives still an early morning :
And drawes the dolor on till wery evening.

O Mercurie, foregoer to the evening,   Klaius.
  O heavenlie huntresse of the savage mountaines,
  O lovelie starre, entitled of the morning,
  While that my voice doth fill these wofull vallies,
  Vouchsafe your silent eares to plaining musique,
  Which oft hath Echo tir'd in secrete forrests.

I that was once free-burges of the forrests,   Strephon.
  Where shade from Sunne, and sports I sought at evening,
  I that was once esteem'd for pleasant musique,
  Am banisht now among the monstrous mountaines
  Of huge despaire, and foule afflictions vallies,
  Am growne a shrich-owle to my selfe each morning.

I that was once delighted every morning,   Klaius.
  Hunting the wilde inhabiters of forrests,
  I that was once the musique of these vallies,
  So darkened am, that all my day is evening,
  Hart-broken so, that molehilles seeme high mountaines,
  And fill the vales with cries in steed of musique.

Long since alas, my deadly Swannish musique   Strephon
  Hath made it selfe a crier of the morning,
  And hath with wailing strēgth clim'd highest mountaines :
  Long since my thoughts more desert be then forrests :
  Long since I see my joyes come to their evening,
  And state throwen downe to over-troden vallies.

THE COUNTESSE OF PEMBROKES

Klaius.   *Long since the happie dwellers of these vallies,*
        Have praide me leave my strange exclaiming musique,
        Which troubles their dayes worke, and joyes of evening :
        Long since I hate the night, more hate the morning :
        Long since my thoughts chase me like beasts in forrests,
        And make me wish my selfe layd under mountaines.

Strephon.   *Me seemes I see the high and stately mountaines,*
        Transforme themselves to lowe dejeſted vallies :
        Me seemes I heare in these ill-changed forrests,
        The Nightingales doo learne of Owles their musique :
        Me seemes I feele the comfort of the morning
        Turnde to the mortall serene of an evening.

Klaius.   *Me seemes I see a filthie clowdie evening,*
        As soon as Sunne begins to clime the mountaines :
        Me seemes I feele a noysome sent, the morning
        When I doo smell the flowers of these vallies :
        Me seemes I heare, when I doo heare sweete musique,
        The dreadfull cries of murdred men in forrests.

Strephon.   *I wish to fire the trees of all these forrests ;*
        I give the Sunne a last farewell each evening ;
        I curse the fidling finders out of Musicke :
        With envie I doo hate the loftie mountaines ;
        And with despite despise the humble vallies :
        I doo detest night, evening, day, and morning.

Klaius.   *Curse to my selfe my prayer is, the morning :*
        My fire is more, then can be made with forrests ;
        My state more base, then are the basest vallies :
        I wish no evenings more to see, each evening ;
        Shamed I have my selfe in sight of mountaines,
        And stoppe mine eares, lest I growe mad with Musicke.

Strephon.   *For she, whose parts maintainde a perfeſt musique,*
        Whose beautie shin'de more then the blushing morning,
        Who much did passe in state the stately mountaines,
        In straightnes past the Cedars of the forrests,
        Hath cast me wretch into eternall evening,
        By taking her two Sunnes from these darke vallies.

For she, to whom compar'd, the Alpes are vallies, Klaius.
  She, whose lest word brings from the spheares their musique,
At whose approach the Sunne rose in the evening,
Who, where she went, bare in her forhead morning,
Is gone, is gone from these our spoyled forrests,
Turning to desarts our best pastur'de mountaines.

These mountaines witnesse shall, so shall these vallies, Strephon.
These forrests eke, made wretched by our musique, Klaius.
Our morning hymne is this, and song at evening.

ZElmane seing no body offer to fill the stage, as if her long restrained conceits had new burst out of prison, she thus desiring her voice should be accorded to nothing but *Philocleas* eares, laying fast holde on her face with her eyes, she sange these Sapphiques, speaking as it were to her owne Hope.

IF *mine eyes can speake to doo harty errande,*
  Or mine eyes language she doo hap to judge of,
So that eyes message be of her receaved,
      Hope we do live yet.

But if eyes faile then, when I most doo need them,
Or if eyes language be not unto her knowne,
So that eyes message doo returne rejected,
      Hope we doo both dye.

Yet dying, and dead, doo we sing her honour;
So become our tombes monuments of her praise;
So becomes our losse the triumph of her gayne;
      Hers be the glory.

If the spheares senselesse doo yet hold a musique,
If the Swannes sweet voice be not heard, but at death,
If the mute timber when it hath the life lost,
      Yeldeth a lutes tune.

Are then humane mindes priviledg'd so meanly,
As that hatefull death can abridge them of powre,
With the vowe of truth to recorde to all worldes,
      That we be her spoiles?

Thus not ending, endes the due praise of her praise;
Fleshly vaile consumes; but a soule hath his life,
Which is helde in love, love it is, that hath joynde
Life to this our soule.

But if eyes can speake to doo harty errande,
Or mine eyes language she doo hap to judge of,
So that eyes message be of her receaved,
Hope we doo live yet.

WHat exclaiming praises *Basilius* gave to *Zelmanes* songe, any man may ghesse, that knowes love is better then a paire of spectacles to make every thing seeme greater, which is seene through it: and then is it never tongue-tied, where fit commendation (whereof womankind is so licorous) is offered unto it. Yea, he fel prostrate on the ground, and thanked the Gods, they had preserved his life so long, as to heare the very musique they themselves used, in an earthly body. But the wasting of the torches served as a watch unto them, to make them see the time waste; and therefore the King (though unwilling) rose from the seate, which he thought excellently setled on the one side: and considering *Zelmanes* late hurte, perswaded her to take that farre-spent nights rest. And so of all sides they went to recommend themselves to the elder brother of death.

The end of the first Booke.

THE SECOND BOOKE

OF THE COUNTESSE OF
PEMBROKES ARCADIA.

CHAP. I.

The love-complaintes [1]*of* Gynecia, [2]Zelmane, [3]*and* Basilius. [4]*Her,* [5]*and his wooing of* Zelmane, *and her shifting of both,* [6]*to bemone her selfe.*

IN *these pastorall* pastimes a great number of dayes were sent to follow their flying predecessours, while the cup of poison (which was deeply tasted of this nöble companie) had left no sinewe of theirs without mortally searching into it; yet never manifesting his venomous worke, till once, that the night (parting away angerly, that she could distill no more sleepe into the eies of lovers) had no sooner given place to the breaking out of the morning light, and the Sunne bestowed his beames upon the tops of the mountaines, but that the wofull *Gynecia* (to whom rest was no ease) had left her loathed lodging, and gotten her selfe into the solitary places those deserts were full of, going up and downe with such unquiet motions, as a grieved & hopeles mind is wont to bring forth. There appeered unto the eies of her judgement the evils she was like to run into, with ougly infamie waiting upon them: she felt the terrou[r]s of her owne conscience: she was guilty of a long exercised vertue, which made this vice the fuller of deformitie. The uttermost of the good she could aspire unto, was a mortall wound to her vexed spirits: and lastly no small part of her evils was, that she was wise to see her evils. In so much, that having a great while throwne her coũtenaunce ghastly about her (as if she had called all the powers of the worlde to witnesse of her wretched estate) at length casting up her watrie eyes to heaven, O Sunne (said she) whose unspotted light directs the steps of mortall mankind, art thou not ashamed to impart the clearnesse of thy presence to such a dust-creeping worme as I am? O you heavens (which continually keepe the course allotted unto you) can none of your influences prevaile so much upon the miserable *Gynecia*, as to make her preserve a course so lõg embraced by her? O deserts, deserts, how fit a guest am I for you, since my hart can people you with wild ravenous beastes, which in you are wanting? O Vertue, where doost thou hide thy selfe? or what hideous thing is this which doth eclips thee? or is it true that thou weart never but a vaine name, and no essentiall thing, which hast thus left thy professed servant, when she had most need of thy lovely presence? O imperfeĉt proportiõ of reason, which cã too much forsee, & too little prevent. Alas, alas (said she) if there were but one hope for all my paines, or but one excuse for all my faultinesse. But wretch that I am, my torment is beyond all succour, & my evill deserving doth exceed my evill fortune. For nothing els did my husband take this straunge resolutiõ to live so solitarily: for nothing els have the winds delivered this straunge guest to my country: for nothing els have the destinies reserved my life to this time, but that only I (most wretched I) should become a plague to my selfe, and a shame to womankind. Yet if my desire (how unjust so ever it be) might take effeĉt, though a thousand deaths folowed it, and every death were followed with a thousand shames; yet should not my sepulcher receive me without some contentment. But alas, though sure I am, that *Zelmane* is such as can answere my love; yet as sure I am, that this disguising must needs come for some foretakẽ cõceipt. And then, wretched *Gynecia*, where cãst thou find any smal groũd-plot for hope to dwel upon? No, no, it is *Philoclea* his hart is set upon: it is my daughter I have borne to supplant me. But if it be so, the life I have given thee (ungratefull *Philoclea*) I will sooner with these handes bereave thee of, then my birth shall glory, she hath " bereaved me of my desires. In shame there is no cõfort, but to be beyond all bounds of shame.

2   Having spokẽ thus, she began to make a piteous war with hir faire haire, when she might heare (not far frõ her) an extremely dolefull voice, but so suppressed with a kind of whispering note, that she could not conceave the wordes distinĉtly. But " (as a lamentable tune is the sweetest musicke to a wofull mind) she drewe thether neere-away, in hope to find some cõpaniõ of her misery. And as she passed on, she was stopped with a nũber of trees, so thickly placed together, that she was afraid

she should (with rushing thorow) stop the speach of the lamentable partie, which she was so desirous to understand. And therefore setting her downe as softly as she could (for she was now in distaunce to heare) she might first perceave a Lute excellently well played upon, and then the same dolefull voice accompanying it with these verses.

I N vaine, mine Eyes, you labour to amende
   With flowing teares your fault of hasty sight :
Since to my hart her shape you so did sende;
   That her I see, though you did lose your light.

In vaine, my Hart, now you with sight are burnd,
   With sighes you seeke to coole your hotte desire :
Since sighes (into mine inward fornace turnd)
   For bellowes serve to kindle more the fire.

Reason, in vaine (now you have lost my hart)
   My head you seeke, as to your strongest forte :
Since there mine eyes have played so false a parte,
   That to your strength your foes have sure resorte.
   Then since in vaine I find were all my strife,
   To this strange death I vainely yeeld my life.

The ending of the song served but for a beginning of new plaints, as if the mind (oppressed with too heavy a burthẽ of cares) was faine to discharge it self of al sides, & as it were, paint out the hideousnes of the paine in al sortes of coulours. For the wofull person (as if the lute had evill joined with the voice) threw it to the ground with such like words: Alas, poore Lute, how much art thou deceiv'd to think, that in my miseries thou couldst ease my woes, as in my careles times thou was wont to please my fancies? The time is changed, my Lute, the time is changed; and no more did my joyfull minde then receive every thing to a joyful consideration, then my carefull mind now makes ech thing tast like the bitter juyce of care. The evill is inward, my Lute, the evill is inward; which all thou doost doth serve but to make me thinke more freely off, and the more I thinke, the more cause I finde of thinking, but lesse of hoping. And alas, what is then thy harmony, but the sweete meats of sorrow? The discord of my thoughts, my Lute, doth ill agree to the concord of thy strings; therefore be not ashamed to leave thy master, since he is not afraide to forsake himselfe.

4   And thus much spokē (in steed of a conclusion) was closed up with so harty a groning, that *Gynecia* could not refraine to shew her selfe, thinking such griefes could serve fitly for nothing, but her owne fortune. But as she came into the little Arbour of this sorrowfull musicke, her eyes met with the eyes of *Zelmane*, which was the party that thus had indited her selfe of miserie: so that either of them remained confused with a sodaine astonishment. *Zelmane* fearing, least shee had heard some part of those complaints, which shee had risen up that morning of purpose, to breath out in secret to her selfe. But *Gynecia* a great while stoode still, with a kind of dull amasement, looking stedfastly upon her: at length returning to some use of her selfe, shee began to aske *Zelmane*, what cause carried her so early abroad? But as if the opening of her mouth to *Zelmane*, had opened some great flood-gate of sorrow (wherof her heart could not abide the violēt issue) she sanke to the ground, with her hands over her face, crying vehemently, *Zelmane* helpe me, O *Zelmane* have pittie on me. *Zelmane* ranne to her, marvelling what sodaine sicknesse had thus possessed her: and beginning to aske her the cause of her paine, and offring her service to be imployed by her: *Gynecia* opening her eyes wildly upon her, pricked with the flames of love, and the torments of her owne conscience: O *Zelmane*, *Zelmane*, (said she) doost thou offer me phisicke, which art my onely poyson? Or wilt thou doo me service, which hast alredie brought me into eternall slaverie? *Zelmane* then knowing well at what marke she shot, yet loth to enter into it; Most excellent Ladie (said she) you were best retire your selfe into your lodging, that you the better may passe this sodaine fitte. Retire my selfe? (said *Gynecia*) If I had retyred my selfe into my selfe, when thou to me (unfortunate guest) camest to draw me from my selfe; blessed had I beene, and no neede had I had of this counsaile. But now alas, I am forced to flie to thee for succour, whom I accuse of all my hurt; and make thee judge of my cause, who art the onely author of my mischiefe. *Zelmane* the more astonished, the more she understood her, Madam (said she) whereof do you accuse me, that I will not cleere my selfe? Or wherein may I steed you, that you may not command me? Alas, answered *Gynecia*, what

shall I say more? Take pitty of me, O *Zelmane*, but not as *Zelmane*, and disguise not with me in words, as I know thou doost in apparell.

Zelmane was much troubled with that word, finding her selfe 3 brought to this streight. But as shee was thinking what to answere her; they might see olde *Basilius* passe harde by them, without ever seeing them: complayning likewise of love verie freshly; and ending his complaint with this song, Love having renewed both his invention, and voyce.

*L*Et not old age disgrace my high desire,
  O heavenly soule, in humaine shape conteind :
Old wood inflam'de, doth yeeld the bravest fire,
  When yonger dooth in smoke his vertue spend.

Ne let white haires, which on my face doo grow,
  Seeme to your eyes of a disgracefull hewe :
Since whitenesse doth present the sweetest show,
  Which makes all eyes doo honour unto you.

Old age is wise and full of constant truth;
  Old age well stayed from raunging humor lives :
Old age hath knowne what ever was in youth :
  Old age orecome, the greater honour gives.
    And to old age since you your selfe aspire,
    Let not old age disgrace my high desire.

Which being done, he looked verie curiously upon himselfe, sometimes fetching a little skippe, as if he had said, his strength had not yet forsaken him. But *Zelmane* having in this time gotten leasure to thinke for an answere; looking upon *Gynecia*, as if she thought she did her some wrong: Madam (said she) I am not acquainted with those words of disguising, neither is it the profession of an *Amazon*, neither are you a partie with whom it is to be used. If my service may please you, imploy it, so long as you do me no wrong in misjudgeing of me. Alas *Zelmane* (said *Gynecia*) I perceive you know ful little, how percing the eyes are of a true lover. There is no one beame of those thoughts you have planted in me, but is able discerne a greater cloud then you doo goe in. Seeke not to conceale your selfe further from me, nor force not the passion of love into violent extremities. Nowe was *Zelmane* brought to an exigent, when the king, turning his eyes that way thorow the trees, perceived his wife and mistres togither: so that framing the most lovely countenance he could, he came straightway towards them; and at the first word (thanking his wife for having entertained *Zelmane*,) desired her she would now returne into the lodge, because hee had certaine matters of estate to impart to the Ladie *Zelmane*. The Queene (being nothing troubled with jelousie in that point) obeyed the kings commaundement; full of raging agonies, and determinatly bent, that as she would seeke all loving meanes to winne *Zelmane*, so she would stirre up terrible tragedies, rather then faile of her entent. And so went she from them to the lodge-ward, with such a battaile in her thoughts, and so deadly an overthrow given to her best resolutions, that even her bodie (where the fielde was fought) was oppressed withall: making a languishing sicknesse waite upon the triumph of passion; which the more it prevailed in her, the more it made her jelousie watchfull, both over her daughter, and *Zelmane*; having ever one of them entrusted to her owne eyes.

But as soone as *Basilius* was ridde of his wives presence, falling downe on his knees, O Lady (said he) which hast onely had the power to stirre up againe those flames which had so long layn deade in me; see in me the power of your beautie; which can make old age come to aske counsaile of youth; and a Prince uncõquered, to become a slave to a stranger. And whẽ you see that power of yours, love that at lest in me, since it is yours, although of me you see nothing to be loved. Worthy Prince (answered *Zelmane*, taking him up from his kneeling) both your manner, and your speech are so straunge unto me, as I know not how to answere it better then with silence. If silence please you (said the king) it shal never displease me, since my heart is wholly pledged to obey you: otherwise if you would vouchsafe mine eares such happinesse, as to heare you, they shall convay your words to such a mind, which is with the humblest degree of reverẽce to receive them. I disdaine not to speake to you (mightie Prince said *Zelmane*,) but I disdaine to speake to any matter which may bring my honor into question. And therewith, with a brave counterfeited scorne she departed from the king; leaving him not so sorie for his short answere, as proud in himself that he had broken the matter. And thus did the king (feeding his minde with those thoughts) passe great time in writing verses, & making more of himselfe, then he was wont to doo: that with a little helpe, he would have growne into a prettie kind of dotage.

But *Zelmane* being ridde of this loving, but little-loved company, Alas (said she) poore *Pyrocles*, was there ever one, but I, that had received wrong, and could blame no body? that having more then I desire, am still in want of that I woulde? Truly Love, I must needes say thus much on thy behalfe; thou hast imployed my love there, where all love is deserved; and for recompence hast sent me more love then ever I desired. But what wilt thou doo *Pyrocles*? which way canst thou finde to ridde thee of thy intricate troubles? To her whom I would be knowne to, I live in darkenesse: and to her am revealed, from whom I would be most secreat. What shift shall I finde against the diligent love of *Basilius*? what shield against the violent passions of *Gynecia*? And if that be done, yet how am I the neerer to quench the fire that consumes me? Wel, well, sweete *Philoclea*, my whole confidence must be builded in thy divine spirit, which cannot be ignorant of the cruell wound I have received by you.

CHAP. 2.

[1]Dametas-*his enstructing of* Dorus. [2]Zelmanes *discourse to* Dorus *of her difficulties*; [3]*& his to her of his successe in love.* [4]*His love-suits made to* Mopsa, *meant to* Pamela: *with their answeres.*

BUt as sicke folkes, when they are alone, thinke companie would relieve them, & yet having company do find it noysome; changing willingly outward objects, when indeed the evill is inward: So poore *Zelmane* was no more weery of *Basilius*, then she was of her selfe, when *Basilius* was gone: and ever the more, the more she turned her eyes to become her owne judges. Tyred wherewith, she longed to meete her friende *Dorus*; that upon the shoulders of friendship she might lay the burthen of sorrow: and therefore went toward the other lodge: where among certaine Beeches she found *Dorus*, apparelled in flanen, with a goats skin cast upon him, & a garland of Laurell mixt with Cypres leaves on his head, wayting on his master *Dametas*, who at that time was teching him how with his sheephooke to catch a wanton Lambe, & with the same to cast a litle ,clod at any one that strayed out of cõpanie. And while *Dorus* was practising, one might see *Dametas* hold his hand under his girdle behind him, nodding from the wast upwards, & swearing he never knew man go more aukewardly to worke: & that they might talke of booke-learning what they would; but for his part, he never saw more unfeatlie fellowes, then great clearks were.

2 But *Zelmanes* comming saved *Dorus* from further chiding. And so she beginning to speake with him of the number of his masters sheepe, and which Province of *Arcadia* bare the finest wooll, drewe him on to follow her in such countrie discourses, till (being out of *Dametas* hearing) with such vehemencie of passion, as though her harte would clime into her mouth, to take her tongues office, she declared unto him, upon what briers the roses of her affections grew: how time still seemed to forget her, bestowing no one houre of comfort upon her; she remaining stil in one plight of ill fortune, saving so much worse, as continuance of evill dooth in it selfe increase evill. Alas my *Dorus* (said she) thou seest how long and languishingly the weekes are paste over us since our laste talking. And yet am I the same, miserable I, that I was: onely stronger in longing, and weaker in hoping. Then fell she to so pitifull a declaration of the insupportablenes of her desires, that *Dorus* eares (not able to shew what woundes that discourse gave unto them) procured his eyes with teares to give testimonie, how much they suffered for her suffering: till passion (a most cumbersome guest to it selfe) made *Zelmane* (the sooner to shake it of) earnestly intreate *Dorus*, that he also (with like freedome of discourse) would bestow a Mappe of his little worlde, upon her; that she might see, whether it were troubled with such unhabitable climes of colde despaires, and hotte rages, as hers was. And so walking under a fewe Palme trees, (which being loving in their own nature, seemed to give their shadow the willinglier, because they held discourse of love) *Dorus* thus entred to the description of his fortune.

Alas (said he) deare Cosin, that it hath pleased the high 3 powers to throwe us to such an estate, as the onely entercourse of our true friendshippe, must be a bartring of miseries. For my parte, I must confesse indeede, that from a huge darkenes of sorrowes, I am crept (I cannot say to a lightsomnes, but) to a certain dawning, or rather, peeping out of some possibilitie of comfort: But woe is me, so farre from the marke of my desires, that I rather thinke it such a light, as comes through a small hole to a dungeon, that the miserable caitife may the better remember the light, of which he is deprived: or like a scholler, who is onely come to that degree of knowledge, to finde him selfe utterly ignorant.

But thus stands it with me: After that by your meanes I was exalted to serve in yonder blessed lodge, for a while I had, in the furnace of my agonies, this refreshing; that (because of the service I had done in killing of the Beare) it pleased the Princesse (in whom indeede statelines shines through courtesie) to let fall some gratious looke upon me. Sometimes to see my exercises, sometimes to heare my songes. For my parte, my harte woulde not suffer me to omitte any occasion, whereby I might make the incomparable *Pamela*, see how much extraordinarie devotion I bare to her service: and withall, strave to appeare more worthy in her sight; that small desert, joyned to so great affection, might prevaile something in the wisest Ladie. But too well (alas) I founde, that a shepheards service was but considered of as from a shepheard, and the acceptation limitted to no further proportion, then of a good servant. And when my countenance had once given notice, that there lay affection under it, I sawe straight, Majesty (sitting in the throne of Beautie) draw foorth such a sworde of just disdaine, that I remayned as a man thunder-striken; not daring, no not able, to beholde that power. Now, to make my estate knowen, seemed againe impossible, by reason of the suspitiousnes of *Dametas*, *Miso*, and my young Mistresse, *Mopsa*. For, *Dametas* (according to the constitution of a dull head) thinkes no better way to shewe him selfe wise, then by suspecting every thing in his way. Which suspition *Miso* (for the hoggish shrewdnesse of her braine) and *Mopsa* (for a very unlikely envie she hath stumbled upon, against the Princesses unspeakeable beautie) were very gladde to execute. So that I (finding my service by this meanes lightlie

regarded, my affection despised, and my selfe unknowen) remayned no fuller of desire, then voyde of comfort how to come
to my desire. Which (alas) if these trees could speak, they
might well witnesse. For, many times have I stoode here, bewailing my selfe unto them: many times have I, leaning to
yonder Palme, admired the blessednes of it, that coulde beare
Love without sence of paine. Many times, when my masters
cattle came hether to chewe their cudde, in this fresh place, I
might see the young Bull testifie his love. But how? with
proud lookes, and joyfulnes. O wretched mankind (said I then
to my selfe) in whom witte (which should be the governer of
his welfare) becomes the traitor to his blessednes. These beasts,
like children to nature, inherite her blessings quietly; we, like
bastards, are layd abroad, even as foundlinges to be trayned up by
griefe and sorrow. Their mindes grudge not their bodies comfort, nor their sences are letted from enjoying their objects: we
have the impediments of honor, and the torments of conscience.
Truely in such cogitatiõs have I somtimes so long stood, that
me thought my feete began to grow into the ground, with such
a darkenes and heavines of minde, that I might easilie have bene
perswaded to have resigned over my very essence. But Love,
(which one time layeth burthens, another time giveth wings)
when I was at the lowest of my downward thoughts, pulled up
my harte to remẽber, that nothing is atchieved before it be
throughlie attempted; and that lying still doth never goe forward: and that therefore it was time, now or never, to sharpen
my invention, to pearce thorow the hardnes of this enterprise;
never ceasing to assemble al my conceites, one after the other;
how to manifest both my minde and estate. Till at last, I
lighted and resolved on this way, which yet perchaunce you will
think was a way rather to hide it.

4   I began to counterfeite the extremest love towards *Mopsa*,
that might be: and as for the love, so lively it was indeed
within me, (although to another subject) that litle I needed to
counterfait any notable demonstrations of it: and so making a
contrariety the place of my memory, in her fowlnes I beheld
Pamelas fayrenesse, still looking on *Mopsa*, but thinking on
Pamela; as if I saw my Sunne shine in a puddled water: I
cryed out of nothing but *Mopsa*: to *Mopsa* my attendance was
directed: to *Mopsa* the best fruites I coulde gather were

brought: to *Mopsa* it seemed still that mine eye conveyed my tongue. So that *Mopsa* was my saying; *Mopsa* was my singing; *Mopsa*, (that is onely suteable in laying a foule complexion upon a filthy favour, setting foorth both in sluttishnesse) she was the load-starre of my life, she the blessing of mine eyes, she the overthrowe of my desires, and yet the recompence of my overthrowe; she the sweetnesse of my harte, even sweetning the death, which her sweetnesse drew upon me. In summe, what soever I thought of *Pamela*, that I saide of *Mopsa*; whereby as I gatte my maisters good-will, who before spited me, fearing lest I should winne the Princesse favour from him, so did the same make the Princesse be better content to allow me her presence: whether indeede it were, that a certaine sparke of noble indignation did rise in her, not to suffer such a baggage to winne away any thing of hers, how meanely soever she reputed of it; or rather (as I thinke) my words being so passionate; and shooting so quite contrarie from the markes of *Mopsaes* worthinesse, she perceived well enough, whither they were directed: and therefore being so masked, she was contented, as a sporte of witte to attend them. Whereupon one day determining to find some means to tel (as of a third person) the tale of mine owne love, and estate, finding *Mopsa* (like a Cuckoo by a Nightingale) alone with *Pamela*, I came in unto them, and with a face (I am sure) full of clowdy fancies, tooke a harpe, and songe this songe.

S Ince so mine eyes are subject to your sight,
That in your sight they fixed have my braine;
Since so my harte is filled with that light,
That onely light doth all my life maintaine;

Since in sweete you all goods so richly raigne,
That where you are no wished good can want;
Since so your living image lives in me,
That in my selfe your selfe true love doth plant;
How can you him unworthy then decree,
In whose chiefe parte your worthes implanted be?

The song being ended, which I had often broken of in the middest with grievous sighes, which overtooke every verse I sange, I let fall my harpe frō me; & casting my eie sometime upon *Mopsa*, but setting my sight principally upon *Pamela*, And is it the onely fortune most bewtiful *Mopsa* (said I) of wretched *Dorus*, that fortune should be measure of his mind? Am I onely he that because I am in miserie, more miserie must be laid upon me? must that which should be cause of compassion, become an argument of cruelty against me? Alas excellent *Mopsa*, consider, that a vertuous Prince requires the life of his meanest subject, and the heavenly Sunne disdaines not to give light to the smallest worme. O *Mopsa*, *Mopsa*, if my hart could be as manifest to you, as it is uncomfortable to me, I doubt not the height of my thoughts should well countervaile the lownesse of my qualitie. Who hath not heard of the greatnes of your estate? who seeth not, that your estate is much excelled with that sweet uniting of al beauties, which remaineth & dwelleth with you? who knowes not, that al these are but ornamĕts of that divine sparke within you, which being descĕded from heaven could not els-where picke out so sweete a mansion? But if you will knowe what is the bande that ought to knit all these excellencies together, it is a kinde of mercyfulnesse to such a one, as is in his soule devoted to those perfections. *Mopsa* (who already had had a certaine smackring towardes me) stood all this while with her hand sometimes before her face, but most cŏmonly with a certaine speciall grace of her owne, wagging her lips, and grinning in steede of smiling: but all the wordes I could get of her, was, wringing her waste, and thrusting out her chinne, In faith you jest with me: you are a merry man indeede. But the ever-pleasing *Pamela* (that well found the Comedie would be marred, if she did not helpe *Mopsa* to her parte) was cŏtent to urge a little further of me. Maister *Dorus* (said the faire *Pamela*) me thinks you blame your fortune very wrongfully, since the fault is not in Fortune, but in you that cannot frame your selfe to your fortune: and as wrongfully do require *Mopsa* to so great a disparagement as to her Fathers servaunt; since she is not worthy to be loved, that hath not some feeling of her owne worthines. I staied a good while after her words, in hope she would have continued her speech (so great a delight I receaved in hearing her) but seeing her say no further, (with a quaking all over my body) I thus answered her. Ladie, most worthie of all dutie, how falles it out that you in whom all vertue shines, will take the patronage of fortune, the onely rebellious handmaide against vertue? Especially, since before your eyes, you have a pittifull spectacle of her wickednesse, a forlorne creature, which must remaine not such as I am, but such as she makes me, since she must be the ballance of worthinesse or disparagement. Yet alas, if the condemned man (even at his death) have leave to speake, let my mortall wound purchase thus much consideration; since the perfections are such in the partie I love, as the feeling of them cannot come into any unnoble hart; shall that harte, which doth not onely feele them, but hath all the working of his life placed in them, shall that hart I saie, lifted up to such a height, be counted base? O let not an excellent spirit doo it selfe such wrong, as to thinke, where it is placed, imbraced, and loved; there can be any unworthinesse, since the weakest mist is not easilier driven away by the Sunne, then that is chased away with so high thoughts. I will not denie (answered the gratious *Pamela*) but that the love you beare to *Mopsa*, hath brought you to the consideration of her vertues, and that consideration may have made you the more vertuous, and so the more worthie: But even that then (you must confesse) you have received of her, and so are rather gratefully to thanke her, then to presse any further, till you bring something of your owne wherby to claime it. And truely *Dorus*, I must in *Mopsaes* behalfe say thus much to you, that if her beauties have so overtaken you, it becomes a true Love to have your harte more set upon her good then your owne, and to beare a tenderer respect to her honour, then your satisfaction. Now by my hallidame, Madame (said *Mopsa*, throwing a great number of sheeps eyes upon me) you have even touched mine owne minde to the quicke, forsooth. I (finding that the pollicie that I had used, had at lest wise procured thus much happinesse unto me, as that I might even in my Ladies presence, discover the sore which had deepely festered within me, and that she could better conceave my reasons applied to *Mopsa*, then she would have vouchsafed them, whilest her selfe was a partie) thought good to pursue on my good beginning, using this fit occasion of *Pameleas* wit, and *Mopsaes* ignorance. Therfore with an humble pearcing eye, looking upon *Pamela*, as if I had rather bene cõdemned by her mouth, then highly exalted by the other, turning my selfe to *Mopsa*, but keeping mine eye where it was, faire *Mopsa* (said I) well doo I finde by the wise knitting together of your answere, that any disputatiõ I can use is asmuch too weake, as I unworthy. I find my love shalbe proved no love, without I leve to love, being too unfit a vessell in whõ so high thoughts should be engraved. Yet since the Love I beare you, hath so joyned it self to the best part of my life, as the one cãnot depart, but that th'other will follow, before I seeke to obey you in making my last passage, let me know which is my unworthines, either of mind, estate, or both? *Mopsa* was about to say, in neither; for her hart I thinke tûbled with over much kindnesse, when *Pamela* with a more favourable countenance thẽ before (finding how apt I was to fall into dispaire) told me, I might therein have answered my selfe; for besides that it was graunted me, that the inward feeling of *Mopsaes* perfeẽtiõs had greatly beautified my minde, there was none could denie, but that my minde and bodie deserved great allowance. But *Dorus* (sayd she) you must be so farre maister of your love, as to consider, that since the judgement of the world stands upon matter of fortune, and that the sexe of womankind of all other is most bound to have regardfull eie to mens judgements, it is not for us to play the philosophers, in seeking out your hidden vertues: since that, which in a wise prince would be coûted wisdome, in us wil be taken for a light-grounded affeẽtiõ: so is not one thing, one, done by divers persons. There is no man in a burning fever feeles so great contentmẽt in cold water greedily received (which assoone as the drinke ceaseth, the rage reneweth) as poore I found my soule refreshed with her sweetly pronoûced words; & newly, & more violẽtly againe enflamed, assoone as she had closed up her delightfull speach, with no lesse wel graced silence. But remẽbring in my self that aswell the Souldier dieth which standeth still, as he that gives the bravest onset: & seeing that to the making up of my fortune, there wanted nothing so much as the making knowne of mine estate, with a face wel witnessing how deeply my soule was possessed, & with the most submissive behavior, that a thralled hart could expresse, evẽ as my words had bene too thicke for my mouth, at lẽgth spake to this purpose. Alas, most worthy Princesse (said I) & do not then your owne sweet words sufficiẽtly testifie, that there was never mã could have a juster aẽtiõ against filthy fortune, thẽ I, since all other things being granted me, her blindnesse is my onely let?

O heavẽly God, I would either she had such eyes as were able
to discerne my deserts, or I were blind not to see the daily cause
of my misfortune. But yet (said I) most honoured Lady, if my
miserable speeches have not already cloied you, & that the verie
presence of such a wretch become not hatefull in your eyes; let
me reply thus much further against my mortall sentence, by
telling you a storie, which happened in this same country long
since (for woes make the shortest time seeme long) whereby you ”
shall see that my estate is not so contemptible, but that a Prince
hath bene content to take the like upon him, and by that onely
hath aspired to enjoy a mightie Princesse. *Pamela* gratiously
harkened, and I told my tale in this sort.

CHAP. 3.

Dorus–*his tale of his owne* ¹*education,* ²*travaile,* ³*enamoring,* ⁴*meta-
morphosing,* ⁵*saving from sea,* ⁶*and being* Musidorus. ⁷*His
octave.* ⁸*Pamelas and Mopsas answere to his suit.* ⁹*His
present to them;* ¹⁰*and perplexitie in himselfe.*

IN the countrie of *Thessalia,* (alas why name I that accursed
country, which brings forth nothing, but matters for tragedies?
but name it I must) in *Thessalia* (I say) there was (well may I
say, there was) a Prince (no, no Prince, whõ bondage wholly
possessed; but yet accounted a Prince, and) named *Musidorus.*
O *Musidorus, Musidorus;* but to what serve exclamations, where
there are no eares to receive the sounde? This *Musidorus,* being
yet in the tendrest age, his worthy father paied to nature (with
a violent death) her last dueties, leaving his childe to the faith of
his friends, and the proofe of time: death gave him not such
pangs as the foresight-full care hee had of his silly successour.
And yet if in his foresight he could have seene so much, happie
was that good Prince in his timely departure, which barred him
from the knowledge of his sonnes miseries, which his knowledge
could neither have prevented, nor relieved. The young
Musidorus (being thus, as for the first pledge of the destinies
good will, deprived of his principall stay) was yet for some
yeares after (as if the starres would breath themselves for a

greater mischiefe) lulled up in as much good luck, as the heed-full love of his dolefull mother, and the florishing estate of his country could breed unto him.

2   But when the time now came, that miserie seemed to be ripe for him, because he had age to know misery, I thinke there was a conspiracy in all heavenly & earthly things, to frame fit occasion to leade him unto it. His people (to whom all forraine matters in foretime were odious) beganne to wish in their be-loved Prince, experience by travaile: his deare mother (whose eyes were held open, onely with the joy of looking upon him) did now dispense with the comfort of her widowhead life, desiring the same her subjectes did, for the increase of her sonnes worthinesse. And here-to did *Musidorus* owne vertue (see how vertue can be a minister to mischiefe) sufficiently provoke him: for indeed thus much I must say for him, although the likenesse of our mishaps makes me presume to patterne my selfe unto him) that well-doing was at that time his scope, from which no faint pleasure could with-hold him. But the present occasion which did knit all this togither, was his uncle the king of *Macedon*; who having lately before gottẽ such victories, as were beyond expectation, did at this time send both for the Prince his sonne (brought up togither, to avoid the warres, with *Musidorus*) and for *Musidorus* himselfe, that his joy might be the more full, having such partakers of it. But alas, to what a sea of miseries my plaintfull toong doth lead me; and thus out of breath, rather with that I thought, then that I said, I stayed my speech, till *Pamela* shewing by countenance that such was her pleasure, I thus continued it. These two young Princes to satisfie the king, tooke their way by sea, towards *Thrace*, whether they would needs go with a Navie to succour him: he being at that time before *Bizantium* with a mighty Army beseeging it; where at that time his court was. But when the conspired heavens had gotten this Subject of their wrath upon so fit a place as the sea was, they streight began to breath out in boystrous windes some part of their malice against him; so that with the losse of all his Navie, he onely with the Prince his cosin, were cast a land, farre off from the place whether their desires would have guided them. O cruell winds in your unconsiderate rages, why either beganne you this furie, or why did you not end it in his end? But your cruelty was such, as you would spare his life

for many deathfull torments. To tel you what pittiful mishaps fell to the young Prince of *Macedon* his cosen, I should too much fill your eares with strange horrors; neither will I stay upon those laborsome advẽtures, nor loathsome misadventures, to which, & through which his fortune and courage conducted him; My speach hastneth it self to come to the ful-point of *Musidorus* his infortunes. For as we finde the most pestilẽt diseases do gather into themselves al the infirmitie, with which the body before was annoyed; so did his last misery embrace in the extremitie of it self all his former mischiefes.

Arcadia, Arcadia was the place prepared to be the stage of 3 his endlesse overthrow. *Arcadia* was, (alas well might I say it is) the charmed circle, where all his spirits for ever should be enchaunted. For here (and no where els) did his infected eyes make his minde know, what power heavenly beauty hath to throw it downe to hellish agonies. Here, here did he see the *Arcadian* Kings eldest daughter, in whom he forthwith placed so all his hopes of joy, and joyfull parts of his heart, that he left in himselfe nothing, but a maze of longing, and a dungeon of sorrow. But alas what can saying make them beleeve, whom seeing cannot perswade? Those paines must be felt before they cã be understood; no outward utterance can command a conceipt. Such was as then the state of the King, as it was no time by direct meanes to seeke her. And such was the state of his captived wil, as he could delay no time of seeking her.

In this intangled case, he cloathed himselfe in a shepheards 4 weede, that under the basenesse of that forme, he might at lest have free accesse to feed his eyes with that, which should at length eate up his hart. In which doing, thus much without doubt he hath manifested, that this estate is not alwayes to be rejected, since under that vaile there may be hidden things to be esteemed. And if he might with taking on a shepherds look cast up his eyes to the fairest Princesse Nature in that time created; the like, nay the same desire of mine need no more to be disdained, or held for disgracefull. But now alas mine eyes waxe dimme, my toong beginnes to falter, and my hart to want force to help, either with the feeling remembrance I have, in what heape of miseries the caitife Prince lay at this time buried. Pardon therfore, most excellent Princesse, if I cut off the course of my dolorous tale, since if I be understood, I have said enough, for the defence of my basenesse; and for that which after might befall to that patterne of ill fortune, (the matters are monstrous for my capacitie) his hatefull destinies must best declare their owne workemanship.

5   Thus having delivered my tale in this perplexed manner, to the end the Princesse might judge that he ment himselfe, who spake so feelingly; her aunswere was both strange, and in some respect comfortable. For would you thinke it? she hath heard heretofore of us both, by meanes of the valiant prince *Plangus*, and particularly of our casting away: which she (following my owne stile) thus delicately brought foorth. You have told (said she) *Dorus*, a prettie tale; but you are much deceived in the latter end of it. For the prince *Musidorus* with his cosen *Pyrocles* did both perish upon the coast of *Laconia*; as a noble gentleman, called *Plangus* (who was well acquainted with the historie) did assure my father. O how that speach of hers did poure joyes in my hart? ô blessed name (thought I) of mine, since thou hast bene in that toong, and passed through those lips, though I can never hope to approch them. As for *Pyrocles* (said I) I will not denie it, but that he is perished: (which I said, least sooner suspition might arise of your being, then your selfe would have it) and yet affirmed no lye unto her, since I onely said, I would not deny it. But for *Musidorus* (said I) I perceive indeed you have neither heard or read the story of that unhappy Prince; for this was the verie objection, which that peerelesse Princesse did make unto him, whē he sought to appeare such as he was before her wisdome: and thus as I have read it faire written in the certaintie of my knowledge he might answere her, that indeed the ship wherein he came, by a treason was perished, and therfore that *Plangus* might easily be deceaved: but that he himselfe was cast upon the coast of *Laconia*, where he was taken up by a couple of shepheards, who lived in those dayes famous; for that both loving one faire maide, they yet remained constant friends; one of whose songs not long since was song before you by the shepheard *Lamon*, and brought by them to a noble-mans house, neere *Mantinea*, whose sonne had a little before his mariage, bene taken prisoner, and by the helpe of this Prince, *Musidorus* (though naming himselfe by another name) was delivered. Now these circumlocutions I did use, because of the one side I

knewe the Princesse would knowe well the parties I ment;
and of the other, if I should have named *Strephon*, *Claius*,
Kalander, and *Clitophon*, perhappes it would have rubd some
conjecture into the heavie heade of Mistresse *Mopsa*.

And therfore (said I) most divine Lady, he justly was to 6
argue against such suspitions; that the Prince might easily by
those parties be satisfied, that upon that wrack such a one was
taken up: and therefore that *Plangus* might well erre, who
knew not of anies taking up againe: that he that was so preserved, brought good tokens to be one of the two, chiefe of
that wracked companie: which two since *Plangus* knew to be
Musidorus and *Pyrocles*, he must needes be one of them,
although (as I said) upon a foretaken vowe, he was otherwise at
that time called. Besides, the Princesse must needes judge,
that no lesse then a Prince durst undertake such an enterprise,
which (though he might gette the favour of the Princesse) he
could never defend with lesse thẽ a Princes power, against the
force of *Arcadia*. Lastly, (said he) for a certaine demonstration,
he presumed to shew unto the Princesse a marke he had on his
face, as I might (said I) shew this of my neck to the rare
Mopsa: and withall, shewed my necke to them both, where
(as you know) there is a redde spotte, bearing figure (as they
tell me) of a Lyons pawe, that she may ascertaine her selfe,
that I am *Menalcas* brother. And so did he, beseeching her to
send some one she might trust, into *Thessalia*, secretely to be
advertised, whether the age, the complexion, and particularly
that notable signe, did not fully agree with this Prince *Musidorus*. Doo you not know further (saide she, with a setled
countenance, not accusing any kind of inwarde motion) of that
storie. Alas no, (said I) for even here the Historiographer
stopped, saying, The rest belonged to Astrologie. And therewith, thinking her silent imaginations began to worke upon
somewhat, to mollifie them (as the nature of Musick is to do)
and withal, to shew what kind of shepheard I was, I took up
my Harpe, and sang these few verses.

M
Y sheepe are thoughts, which I both guide and serve: 7.
    Their pasture is faire hilles of fruitlesse Love:
On barren sweetes they feede, and feeding sterve:
I waile their lotte, but will not other prove.

My sheepehooke is wanne hope, which all upholdes:
My weedes, Desire, cut out in endlesse foldes.
What wooll my sheepe shall beare, whiles thus they live,
In you it is, you must the judgement give.

And then, partly to bring *Mopsa* againe to the matter (lest she should too much take heed to our discourses) but principally, if it were possible, to gather some comfort out of her answeares, I kneeled downe to the Princesse, and humblie besought her to move *Mopsa* in my behalfe, that she would unarme her hart of that steely resistãce against the sweet blowes of Love: that since all her parts were decked with some particular ornamẽt; her face with beautie, her head with wisdome, her eyes with majestie, her countenance with gracefulnes, her lippes with lovelines, her tongue with victorie; that she woulde make her hart the throne of pitie, being the most excellent rayment of the most excellent part.

8   *Pamela*, without shew either of favour or disdaine, either of heeding or neglecting what I had said, turned her speech to *Mopsa*, and with such a voice and action, as might shewe she spake of a matter which little did concerne her, Take heede to your selfe (saide she) *Mopsa*, for your shepheard can speake well: but truely, if he doo fully proove himselfe such as he saith, I mean, the honest shepheard *Menalchas* his brother, and heire, I know no reason why you shoulde thinke scorne of him. *Mopsa* though (in my conscience) she were even then farre spent towards me, yet she answered her, that for all my queint speeches, she would keepe her honestie close inough: And that as for the highe way of matrimony, she would steppe never a foote further, till my maister her father had spoken the whole word him selfe, no she would not.   But ever and anon turning her muzzell toward me, she threwe such a prospect upon me, as might well have given a surfet to any weake lovers stomacke. But Lord what a foole am I, to mingle that drivels speeches among my noble thoughts? but because she was an Actor in this Tragedie, to geve you a ful knowledge, and to leave nothing (that I can remember) unrepeated.

9   Now the Princesse being about to withdrawe her selfe from us, I tooke a Jewell, made in the figure of a Crab-fish, which, because it lookes one way and goes another, I thought it did

fitly patterne out my looking to *Mopsa*, but bending to *Pamela*: The word about it was, *By force, not choice*; and still kneeling, besought the Princesse that she would vouchsafe to give it *Mopsa*, and with the blessednes of her hande to make acceptable unto her that toye which I had founde, followinge of late an acquaintaunce of mine at the plowe. For (sayd I) as the earth was turned up, the plow-share lighted upon a great stone: we puld that up, & so found both that, and some other pretty thinges which we had devided betwixt us.

Mopsa was benummed with joy when the Princesse gave it 10 her: but in the Princesse I could finde no apprehension of what I either said or did, but with a calme carelesnesse letting each thing slide, justly as we doo by their speeches, who neither in matter nor person doo any way belong unto us) which kind of colde temper, mixt with that lightning of her naturall majestie, is of all others most terrible unto me: for yet if I found she contemned me, I would desperatly labour both in fortune and vertue to overcome it; if she onely misdoubted me, I were in heaven; for quickly I woulde bring sufficient assurance: lastly, if she hated me, yet I should know what passion to deale with; and either with infinitenes of desert I would take away the fewell from that fire; or if nothing would serve, then I would give her my hart-bloud to quench it. But this cruell quietnes, neither retiring to mislike, nor proceeding to favour; gratious, but gratious still after one maner; all her courtesies having this engraven in them, that what is done, is for vertues sake, not for the parties; ever keeping her course like the Sun, who neither for our prayses, nor curses, will spare or stoppe his horses. This (I say) heavenlines of hers, (for how so ever my miserie is I cannot but so entitle it) is so impossible to reach unto, that I almost begin to submitte my selfe to the tyrannie of despaire, not knowing any way of perswasiõ, where wisdome seemies to be unsensible. I have appeared to her eyes, like my selfe, by a device I used with my master, perswading him, that we two might put on a certaine rich apparrel I had provided, and so practise some thing on horsback before *Pamela*, telling him, it was apparell I had gotten for playing well the part of a King in a Tragedie at *Athens*: my horse indeed was it I had left at *Menalcas* house, and *Dametas* got one by friendship out of the Princes stable. But how soever I show, I am no base bodie, all I doo is but to beate a rocke and get fome.

CHAP. 4.

[1] Basilius *his hauking.* [2] Gynecias *hurte by* Dametas *overturning her coache.* [3] *Her jelousie over* Zelmane. Philocleas [4] *love-passions,* [5] *vowe of chastitie,* [6] *revocation,* [7] *lamentation.*

[1] BUt as *Dorus* was about to tell further, *Dametas* (who came whistling, & counting upon his fingers, how many loade of hay his seventeen fat oxen eat up in a yeare) desired *Zelmane* from the King that she would come into the lodge, where they stayed for her. Alas (said *Dorus,* taking his leave) the sum is this, that you may wel find you have beatẽ your sorrow against such a wall, which with the force of rebound may wel make your sorrow strõger. But *Zelmane* turning her speach to *Dametas,* I shall grow (said she) skilfull in country matters, if I have often conference with your servaunt. In sooth (answered *Dametas* with a gracelesse skorne) the Lad may prove wel enough, if he oversoone thinke not too well of himselfe, and will beare away that he heareth of his elders. And therewith as they walked to the other lodge, to make *Zelmane* find she might have spẽt her time better with him, he began with a wilde Methode to runne over all the art of husbandrie: especially imploying his tongue about well dunging of a fielde: while poore *Zelmane* yeelded her eares to those tedious strokes, not warding them so much as with any one answere, till they came to *Basilius,* and *Gynecia,* who attẽded for her in a coach to carrie her abroad to see some sportes prepared for her. *Basilius* and *Gynecia* sitting in the one ende, placed her at the other, with her left side to *Philoclea. Zelmane* was moved in her minde, to have kissed their feete for the favour of so blessed a seate : for the narrownesse of the coach made them joine from the foote to the shoulders very close together ; the truer touch wherof though it were barred by their envious apparell, yet as a perfect Magnes, though put in an ivorie boxe, will

thorow the boxe send forth his imbraced vertue to a beloved needle; so this imparadised neighbourhood made *Zelmanes* soule cleave unto her, both thorow the ivory case of her body, and the apparell which did over-clowd it. All the bloud of *Zelmanes* body stirring in her, as wine will do when suger is hastely put into it, seeking to sucke the sweetnes of the beloved guest; her hart, like a lion new imprisoned, seeing him that restraines his libertie, before the grate; not panting, but striving violently (if it had bene possible) to have leapt into the lappe of *Philoclea*. But *Dametas*, even then proceeding from being maister of a carte, to be doctor of a coach, not a little prowd in himselfe, that his whippe at that time guided the rule of *Arcadia*, drave the coach (the cover whereof was made with such joints, that as they might (to avoid the weather) pull it up close when they listed, so when they would they might put each ende downe, and remaine as discovered & open sighted as on horsebacke) till upon the side of the forrest they had both greyhounds, spaniels, and hounds: whereof the first might seeme the Lords, the second the Gentlemen, and the last the Yeomen of dogges; a cast of Merlins there was besides, which flying of a gallant height over certaine bushes, would beate the birdes (that rose) downe unto the bushes, as Faulcons will doo wilde-foule over a river. But the sporte which for that daie *Basilius* would principallie shewe to *Zelmane*, was the mountie at a Hearne, which getting up on his wagling winges with paine, till he was come to some height, (as though the aire next to the earth were not fit for his great bodie to flie thorow) was now growen to diminish the sight of himself, & to give example to great persons, that the higher they be, the lesse they should show: whē a Jerfaulcon was cast of after her, who streight spying where the pray was, fixing her eie with desire, & guiding her wing by her eie, used no more strēgth then industry. For as a good builder to a hie tower will not make his stayre upright, but winding almost the ful cōpasse about, that the steepnes be the more unsensible: so she, seing the towring of her pursued chase, went circkling, & cōpassing about, rising so with the lesse sence of rising; & yet finding that way scantly serve the greedines of her hast, as an ambitious body wil go far out of the direct way, to win to a point of height which he desires; so would she (as it were) turne taile to the Heron, & flie quite out another way, but all was to returne in a higher pitche; which once gotten, she would either beate with cruell assaults the Heron, who now was driven to the best defence of force, since flight would not serve; or els clasping with him, come downe together, to be parted by the overpartiall beholders.

2   Divers of which flights *Basilius* shewing to *Zelmane*, thus was the richesse of the time spent, and the day deceassed before it was thought of, till night like a degenerating successour made his departure the better remembred.   And therefore (so constrained) they willed *Dametas* to drive homeward, who (halfe sleeping, halfe musing about the mending of a vine-presse) guided the horses so ill, that the wheele comming over a great stub of a tree, it overturned the coach.   Which though it fell violently upon the side where *Zelmane* & *Gynecia* sat, yet for *Zelmanes* part, she would have bene glad of the fall, which made her beare the sweete burthen of *Philoclea*, but that she feared she might receave some hurt.   But indeede neither she did, nor any of the rest, by reason they kept their armes and legs within the coach, saving *Gynecia*, who with the onely bruze of the fall had her shoulder put out of joinct; which though by one of the Faulkeners cunning, it was set well againe, yet with much paine was she brought to the lodge; and paine (fetching his ordinary companion, a fever with him) drave her to entertaine them both in her bedde.

3   But neither was the fever of such impatient heate, as the inwarde plague-sore of her affection, nor the paine halfe so noysome, as the jealousie she conceaved of her daughter *Philoclea*, lest this time of her sicknesse might give apt occasion to *Zelmane*, whom she misdoubted.   Therefore she called *Philoclea* to her, and though it were late in the night, commaunded her in her eare to go to the other lodge, and send *Miso* to her, with whom she would speake, and she lie with her sister *Pamela*. The meane while *Gynecia* kepte *Zelmane* with her, because she would be sure, she should be out of the lodge, before she licenced *Zelmane*.   *Philoclea* not skild in any thing better then obedience, went quietly downe; and the Moone then full (not thinking skorne to be a torche-bearer to such beautie) guided her steppes, whose motions bare a minde, which bare in it selfe farre more stirring motions.   And alas (sweete *Philoclea*) how hath my penne till now forgot thy passions, since to thy

memorie principally all this long matter is intended? pardon
the slacknes to come to those woes, which having caused in
others, thou didst feele in thy selfe.

The sweete minded *Philoclea* was in their degree of well
doing, to whom the not knowing of evill serveth for a ground
of vertue, and hold their inward powers in better forme with
an unspotted simplicitie, then many, who rather cūningly seeke
to know what goodnes is, then willingly take into themselves
the following of it. But as that sweet & simple breath of
heavenly goodnesse, is the easier to be altered, because it hath
not passed through the worldlie wickednesse, nor feelingly found
the evill, that evill caries with it; so now the Ladie *Philoclea*
(whose eyes and senses had receaved nothing, but according as
the naturall course of each thing required; which frō the
tender youth had obediently lived under her parents behests,
without framing out of her own wil the fore-chosing of any
thing) whē now she came to appoint, wherin her judgemēt was
to be practized, in knowing faultines by his first tokēs, she was
like a yong faune, who cōming in the wind of the hunters,
doth not know whether it be a thing or no to be eschewed;
whereof at this time she began to get a costly experience. For
after that *Zelmane* had a while lived in the lodge with her, and
that her onely being a noble straunger had bred a kind of heed-
full attention; her cōming to that lonely place (where she had
no body but her parents) a willingnes of conversatiō; her wit
& behaviour, a liking & silent admiration; at length the
excellency of her natural gifts, joined with the extreme shewes
she made of most devout honouring *Philoclea*, (carying thus in
one person the only two bāds of good will, lovelines &
lovingnes) brought forth in her hart a yeelding to a most friēdly
affectiō; which when it had gotten so ful possession of the
keies of her mind, that it would receave no message frō her
senses, without that affection were the interpreter; thē streight
grew an exceeding delight stil to be with her, with an unmeasurable liking of al that *Zelmane* did: maters being so
turned in her, that where at first, liking her manners did breed
good-wil, now good-wil became the chiefe cause of liking her
manners: so that within a while *Zelmane* was not prized for
her demeanure, but the demeanure was prized because it was
Zelmanes. Thē followed that most natural effect of cōforming

ones self to that, which she did like, and not onely wishing to
be her selfe such an other in all thinges, but to ground an
imitation upon so much an esteemed authoritie: so that the
next degree was to marke all *Zelmanes* dooings, speeches, and
fashions, and to take them into herselfe, as a patterne of worthy
proceeding. Which when once it was enacted, not onely by
the comminaltie of Passions, but agreed unto by her most noble
Thoughts, and that by Reason it self (not yet experienced in
the issues of such matters) had granted his royall assent; then
Friendship (a diligent officer) tooke care to see the statute
thorowly observed. Then grew on that not onely she did
imitate the sobernes of her countenance, the gracefulnesse of
her speech, but even their particular gestures: so that as
Zelmane did often eye her, she would often eye *Zelmane*; & as
Zelmanes eyes would deliver a submissive, but vehement desire
in their looke, she, though as yet she had not the desire in her,
yet should her eyes answere in like pearcing kindnesse of a
looke. *Zelmane* as much as *Gynecias* jealousie would suffer,
desired to be neere *Philoclea*; *Philoclea*, as much as *Gynecias*
jealousie would suffer, desired to be neere *Zelmane*. If *Zelmane*
tooke her hand, and softly strained it, she also (thinking the
knots of friendship ought to bee mutuall) would (with a sweete
fastnes) shew she was loth to part from it. And if *Zelmane*
sighed, she would sigh also; whē *Zelmane* was sad, she deemed
it wisdome, and therefore she would be sad too. *Zelmanes*
lāguishing coūtenāce with crost armes, and sometimes cast-up
eyes, she thought to havc an excellent grace: and therefore she
also willingly put on the same countenāce: til at the last (poore
soule, ere she were aware) she accepted not onely the band, but
the service; not only the signe, but the passion signified. For
whether it were, that her wit in cōtinuāce did finde, that
Zelmanes friendship was full of impatient desire, having more thē
ordinarie limits, & therfore shee was content to second *Zelmane*,
though her selfe knew not the limits; or that in truth, true-
love (well considered) have an infective power. At last she fell
in acquaintance with loves harbinger, wishing. First she would
wish, that they two might live all their lives togither, like two
of *Dianas* Nimphes. But that wish, she thought not sufficient,
because she knew, there would be more Nimphes besides them,
who also would have their part in *Zelmane*. Thē would she

wish, that she were her sister, that such a natural band might make her more speciall to her. But against that, she considered, that though being her sister, if she happened to be married, she should be robbed of her. Then growne bolder, she would wish either her selfe, or *Zelmane* a man, that there might succeed a blessed marriage betwixt them. But when that wish had once displaied his ensigne in her minde, then followed whole squadrons of longings, that so it might be, with a maine battaile of mislikings, and repynings against their creation, that so it was not. Then dreames by night beganne to bring more unto her, then she durst wish by day, whereout making did make her know her selfe the better by the image of those fancies. But as some diseases when they are easie to be cured, they are hard to be knowne, but when they grow easie to be knowne, they are almost impossible to be cured: so the sweete *Philoclea*, while she might prevent it, she did not feele it, now she felt it, when it was past preventing; like a river, no rampiers being built against it, till alreadie it have over-flowed. For now indeed, Love puld of his maske, and shewed his face unto her, and told her plainly, that shee was his prisoner. Then needed she no more paint her face with passions; for passions shone thorow her face; Then her rosie coulor was often encreased with extraordinarie blushing: and so another time, perfect whitenesse ascended to a degree of palenesse; now hot, then cold, desiring she knew not what, nor how, if she knew what. Then her minde (though too late) by the smart was brought to thinke of the disease, and her owne proofe taught her to know her mothers minde; which (as no error gives so strong assault, as that which comes armed in the authoritie of a parent, so) greatly fortified her desires, to see, that her mother had the like desires. And the more jealous her mother was, the more she thought the Jewell precious, which was with so many lookes garded. But that prevailing so far, as to keepe the two lovers from private conference, then began she to feele the sweetnesse of a lovers solitarinesse, when freely with words and gestures, as if *Zelmane* were present, shee might give passage to her thoughts, and so as it were utter out some smoke of those flames, wherewith else she was not only burned, but smothered. As this night, that going from the one lodge to the other by her mothers commandement, with dolefull gestures and uncertaine paces, shee did willingly accept the times offer, to be a while alone: so that going a little aside into the wood; where manie times before she had delighted to walke, her eyes were saluted with a tuft of trees, so close set togither, as with the shade the moone gave thorow it, it might breede a fearefull kinde of devotion to looke upon it. But true thoughts of love banish all vaine fancie of superstition. Full well she did both remember and like the place; for there had she often with their shade beguiled *Phœbus* of looking upon her: There had she enjoyed her selfe often, while she was mistresse of her selfe, and had no other thoughts, but such as might arise out of quiet senses.

5 But the principall cause that invited her remembrance, was a goodly white marble stone, that should seeme had bene dedicated in ancient time to the *Silvan* gods: which she finding there a fewe dayes before *Zelmanes* comming, had written these words upon it, as a testimonie of her mind, against the suspition her captivitie made her thinke she lived in. The writing was this.

> Y*Ou living powres enclosed in stately shrine*
>   *Of growing trees; you rurall Gods that wield*
> *Your scepters here, if to your eares divine*
> *A voice may come, which troubled soule doth yeld:*
>   *This vowe receave, this vowe ô Gods maintaine;*
>   *My virgin life no spotted thought shall staine.*

> *Thou purest stone, whose purenesse doth present*
> *My purest minde; whose temper hard doth showe*
> *My tempred hart; by thee my promise sent*
> *Unto my selfe let after-livers know.*
>   *No fancy mine, nor others wronge suspect*
>   *Make me, ô. vertuous Shame, thy lawes neglect.*

> *O Chastitie, the chiefe of heavenly lightes,*
> *Which makst us most immortall shape to weare,*
> *Holde thou my hart, establish thou my sprights:*
> *To onely thee my constant course I beare.*
>   *Till spotlesse soule unto thy bosome flye,*
>   *Such life to leade, such death I vow to dye.*

But now that her memorie served as an accuser of her 6 change, and that her own hand-writing was there, to beare testimony against her fall; she went in among those few trees, so closed in the toppes togither, as they might seeme a little chappell: and there might she by the help of the moone-light perceive the goodly stone, which served as an altar in that wooddie devotion. But neither the light was enough to reade the words, and the inke was alreadie foreworne, and in many places blotted: which as she perceaved, Alas (said she) faire Marble, which never receivedst spot but by my writing, well do these blots become a blotted writer. But pardon her which did not dissemble then, although she have chaunged since. Enjoy, enjoy the glorie of thy nature, which can so constantly beare the markes of my inconstancie. And herewith hiding her eyes with her soft hand, there came into her head certaine verses, which if she had had present commoditie, she would have adjoyned as a retractation to the other. They were to this effect.

> My words, in hope to blaze my stedfast minde,
>   This marble chose, as of like temper knowne:
> But loe, my words defaste, my fancies blinde,
> Blots to the stone, shame to my selfe I finde:
>   And witnesse am, how ill agree in one,
>   A womans hand with constant marble stone.
>
> My words full weake, the marble full of might;
> My words in store, the marble all alone;
> My words blacke inke, the marble kindly white;
> My words unseene, the marble still in sight,
>   May witnesse beare, how ill agree in one,
>   A womans hand, with constant marble stone.

But seeing she could not see meanes to joyne as thē this 7 recantation to the former vow, (laying all her faire length under one of the trees) for a while she did nothing but turne up and downe, as if she had hoped to turne away the fancie that mastred her, and hid her face, as if she could have hidden her selfe from her owne fancies. At length with a whispring note to her selfe; O me unfortunate wretch (said she) what poysonous heates be these, which thus torment me? How hath the sight of this strange guest invaded my soule? Alas, what entrance found this desire, or what strength had it thus to conquer me? Then, a cloud passing betweene her sight and the moone, O *Diana* (said she) I would either the cloud that now hides the light of my vertue would as easily passe away, as you will quickly overcome this let; or els that you were for ever thus darkned, to serve for an excuse of my outragious folly. Then looking to the starres, which had perfitly as then beautified the cleere skie: My parēts (said she) have told me, that in these faire heavenly bodies, there are great hiddē deities, which have their working in the ebbing & flowing of our estates. If it be so, then (O you Stars) judge rightly of me, & if I have with wicked intēt made my selfe a pray to fancie, or if by any idle lustes I framed my harte fit for such an impression, then let this plague dayly encrease in me, till my name bee made odious to womankind. But if extreame and unresistable violence have oppressed me, who will ever do any of you sacrifice (ô you Starres) if you do not succour me. No, no, you will not help me. No, no, you cannot helpe me: Sinne must be the mother, and shame the daughter of my affeċtion. And yet are these but childish objeċtions (simple *Philoclea*) it is the impossibilitie that dooth torment me: for, unlawfull desires are punished after the effeċt of enjoying; but unpossible desires are punished in the desire it selfe. O then, ô tenne times unhappie that I am, since where in all other hope kindleth love; in me despaire should be the bellowes of my affeċtion: and of all despaires the most miserable, which is drawen from impossibilitie. The most covetous man longs not to get riches out of a groūd which never can beare any thing; Why? because it is impossible. The most ambitious wight vexeth not his wittes to clime into heaven; Why? because it is impossible. Alas then, ô Love, why doost thou in thy beautifull sampler sette such a worke for my Desire to take out, which is as much impossible? And yet alas, why doo I thus condemne my Fortune, before I heare what she can say for her selfe? What doo I, sillie wench, knowe what Love hath prepared for me? Doo I not see my mother, as well, at lest as furiouslie as my selfe, love *Zelmane?* And should I be wiser then my mother? Either she sees a possibilitie in that which I think impossible, or els impossible loves neede not misbecome me. And doo I not see *Zelmane* (who doth not thinke a thought which is not first wayed by wisdome and vertue) doth not she vouchsafe to love me with like ardour? I see it, her eyes depose it to be true; what then? and if she can love poore me, shall I thinke scorne to love such a woman as *Zelmane?* Away then all vaine examinations of why and how. Thou lovest me, excellent *Zelmane*, and I love thee: and with that, embrasing the very grounde whereon she lay, she said to her selfe (for even to her selfe she was ashamed to speake it out in words) O my *Zelmane*, governe and direct me: for I am wholy given over unto thee.

CHAP. 5.

[1] *The bedfellow communication of* Philoclea *and* Pamela. [2] Pamelas *narration of her shepheardes making love,* [3] *of* Dorus *and* Dametas *horsemanshippe,* [4] *of his hote pursuite, and her colde acceptance.* [5] *His letter.* [6] *Her relenting,* [7] *and* Philocleas *sole complaint.*

IN this depth of muzes, and divers sorts of discourses, would she have ravingly remained, but that *Dametas* and *Miso* (who were rounde about to seeke her, understanding she was to come to their lodge that night) came hard by her; *Dametas* saying, That he would not deale in other bodies matters; but for his parte, he did not like that maides should once stirre out of their fathers houses, but if it were to milke a cow, or save a chicken from a kites foote, or some such other matter of importance. And *Miso* swearing that if it were her daughter *Mopsa*, she woulde give her a lesson for walking so late, that should make her keepe within dores for one fortnight. But their jangling made *Philoclea* rise, and pretending as though she had done it but to sport with them, went with them (after she had willed *Miso* to waite upon her mother) to the lodge; where (being now accustomed by her parents discipline, as well as her sister, to serve her selfe) she went alone up to *Pamelas* chamber: where meaning to delight her eies, and joy her thoughts with the sweet conversation of her beloved sister, she found her (though it were in the time that the wings of night doth blow sleep most willingly into mortall creatures) sitting in a chaire, lying backward, with her head almost over the back of it, & looking upon a wax-cãdle which burnt before her; in one hand holding a letter, in the other her hand-kerchiefe, which had lately dronk up the teares of her eyes, leaving in steed of them, crimsen circles, like redde flakes in the element, when the weather is hottest. Which *Philoclea* finding (for her eyes had learned to know the badges of sorowes) she earnestlie intreated to knowe the cause thereof, that either she might comforte, or accompanie her dolefull humor. But *Pamela*, rather seeming sorie that she had perceived so much, then willing to open any further, O my *Pamela* (said *Philoclea*) who are to me a sister in nature, a mother in counsell, a Princesse by the law of our coũtrey, and which name (me thinke) of all other is the dearest, a friend by my choice and your favour, what meanes this banishing me from your counsels? Do you love your sorrowe so well, as to grudge me part of it? Or doo you thinke I shall not love a sadde *Pamela*, so well as a joyfull? Or be my eares unwoorthie, or my tongue suspeɕted? What is it (my sister) that you should conceale from your sister, yea and servant *Philoclea?* These wordes wanne no further of *Pamela*, but that telling her they might talke better as they lay together, they impoverished their cloathes to inriche their bed, which for that night might well scorne the shrine of *Venus* : and there cherishing one another with deare, though chaste embracements; with sweet, though cold kisses; it might seeme that Love was come to play him there without darte; or that weerie of his owne fires, he was there to refreshe himselfe betweene their sweete-breathing lippes. But *Philoclea* earnestly againe intreated *Pamela* to open her griefe; who (drawing the curtain, that the candle might not complaine of her blushing) was ready to speake : but the breath almost formed into words, was againe stopt by her, and turned into sighes. But at last, I pray you (said she) sweete *Philoclea*, let us talke of some other thing : & tell me whether you did ever see any thing so amẽded as our Pastoral sports be, since that *Dorus* came hether? O Love, how farre thou seest with blind eyes? *Philoclea* had straight found her, and therefore to draw out more, In deed (said she) I have often wondred to my selfe how such excellẽcies could be in so meane a person; but belike Fortune was afraide to lay her treasures, where they should be staind with so many perfections: onely I marvaile how he can frame himselfe to hide so rare giftes under such a block as *Dametas*. Ah (said *Pamela*) if you knew the cause: but no more doo I neither; and to say the trueth: but Lord, how are we falne to talke of this fellow? and yet indeed if you were sometimes with me to marke him, while *Dametas* reades his rusticke lecture unto him (how to feede his beastes before noone, where to shade them in the extreame heate, how to make the manger hansome for his oxen, when to use the goade, & when the voice: giving him rules of a heardmã, though he pretēded to make him a shep-heard) to see all the while with what a grace (which seemes to set a crowne upon his base estate) he can descend to those poore matters, certainly you would: but to what serves this? no doubt we were better sleepe then talke of these idle matters. Ah my *Pamela* (said *Philoclea*) I have caught you, the constant-nes of your wit was not wont to bring forth such disjointed speeches: you love, dissemble no further. It is true (said *Pamela*) now you have it; and with lesse adoo should, if my hart could have thoght those words suteable for my mouth. But indeed (my *Philoclea*) take heed: for I thinke Vertue it self is no armour of proofe against affection. Therfore learne by my example. Alas thought *Philoclea* to her selfe, your sheeres come to late to clip the birds wings that already is flowne away.

But then *Pamela* being once set in the streame of her Love, 2 went away a maine withall, telling her how his noble qualities had drawne her liking towardes him; but yet ever waying his meanenes, & so held continually in due limits; till seeking many meanes to speake with her, & ever kept from it (as wel because she shund it, seing and disdaining his mind, as because of her jealous jaylours) he had at length used the finest pollicie that might be in counterfaiting love to *Mopsa*, & saying to *Mopsa* what soever he would have her know: and in how passionate manner he had told his owne tale in a third person, making poore *Mopsa* beleve, that it was a matter fallen out many ages before. And in the end, because you shal know my teares come not, neither of repētance nor misery, who thinke you, is my *Dorus* fallen out to be? even the Prince *Musidorus*, famous over all *Asia*, for his heroical enterprises, of whom you remember how much good the straunger *Plangus* told my father; he not being drowned (as *Plangus* thought) though his cousin *Pyrocles* indeed perished. Ah my sister, if you had heard his words, or seene his gestures, when he made me know what, and to whom his love was, you would have matched in your selfe (those two rarely matched together) pittie and delight. Tell me deare sister (for the gods are my witnesses I desire to doo vertuously) can I without the detestable staine of ungratefulnesse abstaine from loving him, who (far exceeding the beautifulnesse of his shape with the beautifulnesse of his minde, and the greatnesse of his estate with the greatnesse of his actes) is content so to abase him selfe, as to become *Dametas* servaunt for my sake? you will say, but how know I him to be *Musidorus*, since the handmaid of wisdome is slow belief? That cõsideratiõ did not want in me, for the nature of desire it selfe is no easier to receive beliefe, then it is hard to ground belief. For as desire is glad to embrace the first shew of comfort, so is desire desirous of perfect assuraunce: and that have I had of him, not onely by necessary arguments to any of cõmon sense, but by sufficient demonstrations. Lastly he would have me send to *Thessalia:* but truly I am not as now in mind to do my honorable Love so much wrong, as so far to suspect him: yet poor soule knowes he no other, but that I doo both suspect, neglect, yea & detest him. For every day he finds one way or other to set forth him selfe unto me, but all are rewarded with like coldnesse of acceptation.

3   A few daies since, he & *Dametas* had furnished thẽselves very richly to run at the ring before me. O how mad a sight it was to see *Dametas*, like rich Tissew furd with lambe skins? But ô how well it did with *Dorus*, to see with what a grace he presented him selfe before me on horseback, making majestie wait upon humblenes? how at the first, standing stil with his eies bent upõ me, as though his motiõs were chained to my looke, he so staide till I caused *Mopsa* bid him doo something upon his horse: which no sooner said, but (with a kinde rather of quick gesture, then shew of violẽce) you might see him come towards me, beating the groũd in so due time, as no daunce can observe better measure. If you remember the ship we saw once, whẽ the Sea went hie upon the coast of *Argos*; so went the beast: But he (as if Cẽtaurlike he had bene one peece with the horse) was no more moved, then one is with the going of

his owne legges: and in effect so did he command him, as his owne limmes, for though he had both spurres and wande, they seemed rather markes of soveraintie, then instruments of punishment; his hand and legge (with most pleasing grace) commãding without threatning, & rather remẽbring then chastising, at lest if sometimes he did, it was so stolen, as neyther our eyes could discerne it, nor the horse with any chaunce did cõplaine of it, he ever going so just with the horse, either foorth right, or turning, that it seemed as he borrowed the horses body, so he lent the horse his minde: in the turning one might perceive the bridle-hand somthing gently stir, but indeed so gently, as it did rather distill vertue, then use violence. Him self (which me thinkes is straunge) shewing at one instant both steadines & nimblenes; somtimes making him turne close to the groũd, like a cat, when scratchingly she wheeles about after a mouse: sometimes with a little more rising before, now like a Raven leaping from ridge to ridge, then like one of *Dametas* kiddes bound over the hillocks: and all so done, as neither the lustie kinde shewed any roughnesse, nor the easier any idlenesse : but still like a well obeyed maister, whose becke is enough for a discipline, ever concluding ech thing he did with his face to me-wards, as if thence came not onely the beginning, but ending of his motions. The sporte was to see *Dametas*, how he was tost from the sadle to the mane of the horse, and thence to the ground, giving his gay apparell almost as foule an outside, as it had an inside. But as before he had ever said, he wanted but horse & apparell to be as brave a courtier as the best, so now brused with proofe, he proclaimed it a folly for a man of wisedome, to put himselfe under the tuition of a beast; so as *Dorus* was fayne alone to take the Ringe. Wherein truely at lest my womanish eyes could not discerne, but that taking his staffe from his thigh, the descending it a little downe, the getting of it up into the rest, the letting of the point fall, and taking the ring was but all one motion, at lest (if they were divers motions) they did so stealingly slippe one into another, as the latter parte was ever in hande, before the eye could discerne the former was ended. Indeed *Dametas* found fault that he shewed no more strength in shaking of his staffe: but to my conceite the fine cleernes of bearing it was exceeding delightfull.

4   But how delightfull soever it was, my delight might well
be in my soule, but it never went to looke out of the window
to doo him any comfort.   But how much more I found reason
to like him, the more I set all the strength of mind to suppresse
it, or at lest to conceale it.   Indeed I must confesse, as some
Physitions have tolde me, that when one is cold outwardly,
he is not inwardly; so truly the colde ashes layed upon my
fire, did not take the nature of fire from it.   Full often hath
my brest swollen with keeping my sighes imprisoned; full
often have the teares, I drave backe from mine eyes, turned
backe to drowne my harte.   But alas what did that helpe poore
Dorus? whose eyes (being his diligent intelligencers) coulde
carrie unto him no other newes, but discomfortable.   I thinke
no day past, but by some one invention he would appeare unto
me to testifie his love.   One time he daunced the Matachine
daunce in armour (O with what a gracefull dexteritie?) I thinke
to make me see, that he had bene brought up in such exercises:
an other time he perswaded his maister (to make my time
seeme shorter) in manner of a Dialogue, to play *Priamus* while
he plaide *Paris*.   Thinke (sweet *Philoclea*) what a *Priamus* we
had: but truely, my *Paris* was a *Paris*, and more then a *Paris*:
who while in a savage apparell, with naked necke, armes, and
legges, he made love to *Oenone*, you might wel see by his
chaunged countenance, and true teares, that he felte the parte
he playde.   Tell me (sweet *Philoclea*) did you ever see such a
shepheard? tell me, did you ever heare of such a Prince?   And
then tell me, if a small or unworthy assaulte have conquered
me.   Truely I would hate my life, if I thought vanitie led me.
But since my parents deale so cruelly with me, it is time for
me to trust something to my owne judgement.   Yet hetherto
have my lookes bene as I told you, which continuing after
many of these his fruitles trials, have wrought such change in
him, as I tell you true (with that worde she laid her hand upon
her quaking side) I doo not a little feare him.   See what a
letter this is (then drewe she the curtaine and tooke the letter
from under the pillowe) which to daie (with an afflicted
humblenesse) he delivered me, pretending before *Mopsa*, that I
should read it unto her, to mollifie (forsooth) her iron stomacke;
with that she read the letter containing thus much.

MOst blessed paper, which shalt kisse that hãd, where to 5
al blessednes is in nature a servãt, do not yet disdain
to cary with thee the woful words of a miser now despairing:
neither be afraid to appeare before her, bearing the base title of
the sender.   For no sooner shal that divine hande touch thee,
but that thy basenesse shall be turned to most hie preferment.
Therefore mourne boldly my Inke; for while she lookes upõ
you, your blacknes wil shine: crie out boldly my Lamẽtatiõ;
for while she reads you, your cries wil be musicke.   Say then
(O happy messenger of a most unhappy message) that the too
soone borne, too late dying creature, which dares not speake,
no not looke, no not scarcely thinke (as from his miserable selfe,
unto her heavenly highnesse) onely presumes to desire thee (in
the time that her eyes and voice doo exalt thee) to say, and in
this manner to say, not from him, O no, that were not fit, but
of him.   Thus much unto her sacred judgement: O you, the
onely, the onely honour to women, to men the onely admiration, you that being armed by Love, defie him that armed you,
in this high estate wherein you have placed me, yet let me
remember him to whom I am bound for bringing me to your
presence; and let me remember him, who (since he is yours,
how meane so ever it be) it is reasõ you have an account of
him.   The wretch (yet your wretch) though with languishing
steppes runnes fast to his grave, and will you suffer a temple (how
poorely-built soever, but yet a temple of your deitie) to be
rased?   But he dyeth: it is most true, he dyeth; and he in
whom you live, to obey you, dieth.   Whereof though he
plaine, he doth not complaine: for it is a harme, but no wrong,
which he hath received.   He dyes, because in wofull language
all his senses tell him, that such is your pleasure: for since you
will not that he live, alas, alas, what followeth, what followeth
of the most ruined *Dorus*, but his ende?   Ende then, evill
destinyed *Dorus*, ende; and ende thou wofull letter, end; for it
suffiseth her wisedome to know, that her heavenly will shalbe
accomplished.

O my *Philoclea*, is hee a person to write these words? and 6
are these words lightly to be regarded?   But if you had seene,
when with trembling hand he had delivered it, how hee went
away, as if he had beene but the coffin that carried himselfe to
his sepulcher.   Two times I must confesse I was about to take

curtesie into mine eyes; but both times the former resolution stopt the entrie of it: so that he departed without obtaining any further kindnesse. But he was no sooner out of the doore, but that I looked to the doore kindly; and truely the feare of him ever since hath put me into such perplexitie, as now you found me. Ah my *Pamela* (said *Philoclea*) leave sorrow. The river of your teares will soone loose his fountaine; it is in your hand as well to stitch up his life againe, as it was before to rent it. And so (though with self-grieved mind) she comforted her sister, till sleepe came to bath himselfe in *Pamelaes* faire weeping eyes.

5 Which when *Philoclea* found, wringing her hands, O me (said she) indeed the onely subject of the destinies displeasure, whose greatest fortunatenes is more unfortunate, then my sisters greatest unfortunatenesse. Alas shee weepes because she would be no sooner happy; I weepe because I can never be happie; her teares flow from pittie; mine from being too farre lower then the reach of pittie. Yet doo I not envie thee, deare *Pamela*, I do not envy thee: onely I could wish that being thy sister in nature, I were not so farre off a kin in fortune.

CHAP. 6.

[1] *The Ladies uprising,* [2] *and interrogatories to* Dorus *concerning* Pyrocles *and* Euarchus. [3] *His historiologie of* Euarchus *kingly excellencies,* [4] *his entry on a most corrupt estate,* [5] *and reformation thereof by royall arts and actions.* [6] *His, and* Dorilaus *crosse-mariage to ech others sister, having by ech a sonne; their mutuall defence, with* Dorilaus *death.*

BUt the darkenesse of sorrow overshadowing her mind, as the night did her eyes, they were both content to hide themselves under the wings of sleepe, till the next morning had almost lost his name, before the two sweet sleeping sisters awaked frõ dreames, which flattered them with more comfort, then their waking could, or would consent unto. For then they were called up by *Miso*; who having bene with *Gynecia*, had received commaundement to be continually with her daughters, and particularly not to let *Zelmane* and *Philoclea* have any private cõferēce, but that she should be present to heare what passed. But *Miso* having now her authoritie encreased, came with skowling eyes to deliver a slavering good morrow to the two Ladies, telling them, it was a shame for them to marre their complexions, yea and conditions to, with long lying a bedde: & that, when she was of their age, she trowed, she would have made a handkerchiefe by that time of the day. The two sweete Princes with a smiling silence answered her entertainement, and obeying her direction, covered their daintie beauties with the glad clothes. But as soone as *Pamela* was readie (& sooner she was then her sister) the agony of *Dorus* giving a fit to her selfe, which the words of his letter (lively imprinted in her minde) still remembred her of, she called to *Mopsa*, and willed her to fetch *Dorus* to speake with her: because (she said) she would take further judgement of him, before she would move *Dametas* to graunt her in mariage unto him. *Mopsa* (as glad as of sweete-meate to goe of such an arrant) quickly returned with *Dorus* to *Pamela*, who entended both by speaking with him to give some comfort to his passionate harte, and withall to heare some part of his life past; which although fame had alreadie delivered unto her, yet she desired in more particular certainties to have it from so beloved an historian. Yet the sweetnesse of vertues disposition jealous, even over it selfe, suffred her not to enter abruptlie into questions of *Musidorus* (whom she was halfe ashamed she did love so well, and more then halfe sorie she could love no better) but thought best first to make her talke arise of *Pyrocles*, and his vertuous father: which thus she did.

Dorus (said she) you told me the last day, that *Plangus* was deceaved in that he affirmed the Prince *Musidorus* was drowned: but withall, you confessed his cosen *Pyrocles* perished; of whom certainly in that age there was a great losse, since (as I have heard) he was a young Prince, of whõ al mē expected as much, as mans power could bring forth, & yet vertue promised for him, their expectation should not be deceaved. Most excellent Ladie (said *Dorus*) no expectatiõ in others, nor hope in himself could aspire to a higher mark, thē to be thought worthy to be praised by your judgement, & made worthy to be praised by your mouth. But most sure it is, that as his fame could by no meanes get so sweete & noble an aire to flie in, as in your breath, so could not you (leaving your selfe aside) finde in the world a fitter subject of commendation; as noble, as a long succession of royall ancestors, famous, and famous of victories could make him: of shape most lovely, and yet of mind more lovely; valiant, curteous, wise, what should I say more? sweete *Pyrocles*, excellent *Pyrocles*, what can my words but wrong thy perfections, which I would to God in some small measure thou hadst bequethed to him that ever must have thy vertues in admiration; that masked at least in them, I might have found some more gratious acceptation? with that he imprisoned his looke for a while upon *Mopsa*, who thereupon fell into a verie wide smiling. Truely (said *Pamela*) *Dorus* I like well your minde, that can raise it selfe out of so base a fortune, as yours is, to thinke of the imitating so excellent a Prince, as *Pyrocles* was. Who shootes at the mid-day Sunne, though he be sure he shall never hit the marke; yet as sure he is, he shall shoote higher, then who aymes but at a bush. But I pray you *Dorus* (said she) tell me (since I perceave you are well acquainted with that storie) what Prince was that *Euarchus* father to *Pyrocles*, of whom so much fame goes, for his rightly royall vertues, or by what wayes he got that opinion. And then so descend to the causes of his sending first away from him, and then to him for that excellent sonne of his, with the discourse of his life and losse: and therein you may (if you list) say something of that same *Musidorus* his cosen, because, they going togither, the story of *Pyrocles* (which I onely desire) may be the better understood.

3   Incomparable Lady (said he) your commandement doth not onely give me the wil, but the power to obey you, such influence hath your excellencie. And first, for that famous King *Euarchus*, he was (at this time you speake off) King of *Macedon*, a kingdome, which in elder time had such a soveraintie over all the provinces of *Greece*, that evẽ the particular kings therin did acknowledge (with more or lesse degrees of homage) some kind of fealty thereunto: as among the rest, even this now most noble (and by you ennobled) kingdome of *Arcadia*. But he, whẽ he came to his crowne, finding by his later ancestors either negligẽce, or misfortune, that in some ages many of those duties had bin intermitted, would never stirre up old

titles (how apparant soever) whereby the publike peace (with the losse of manie not guiltie soules) should be broken; but contenting himselfe to guide that shippe, wherein the heavens had placed him, shewed no lesse magnanimitie in daungerlesse despising, then others in daungerous affecting the multiplying of kingdomes: for the earth hath since borne enow bleeding witnesses, that it was no want of true courage. Who as he was most wise to see what was best, and most just in the perfourming what he saw, & temperate in abstaining from any thing any way contrary: so thinke I, no thought can imagine a greater harte to see and contemne daunger, where daunger would offer to make any wrongfull threatning upon him. A Prince, that indeed especially measured his greatnesse by his goodnesse: and if for any thing he loved greatnesse, it was, because therein he might exercise his goodnes. A Prince of a goodly aspect, and the more goodly by a grave majestie, wherewith his mind did decke his outward graces; strong of body, and so much the stronger, as he by a well disciplined exercise taught it both to do, and suffer. Of age, so as he was about fiftie yeares when his *Nephew Musidorus* tooke on such shepherdish apparell for the love of the worlds paragon, as I now weare.

This King left Orphan both of father and mother, (whose father & grandfather likewise had dyed yong) he found his estate, when he came to age (which allowed his authoritie) so disjoynted even in the noblest & strongest lims of governmẽt, that the name of a King was growne evẽ odious to the people, his autority having bin abused by those great Lords, & litle kings: who in those betweene-times of raigning (by unjust favouring those that were partially theirs, & oppressing them that woulde defende their libertie against them had brought in (by a more felt then seene maner of proceeding) the worst kind of *Oligarchie*; that is, whẽ men are governed in deede by a fewe, and yet are not taught to know what those fewe be, to whom they should obey. For they having the power of kinges, but not the nature of kings, used the authority as men do their farms, of which they see within a yeere they shal goe out: making the Kinges sworde strike whom they hated, the Kings purse reward whom they loved: and (which is worst of all) making the Royall countenance serve to undermine the Royall soveraintie. For the Subjectes could taste no sweeter fruites of having a King, then grievous taxations to serve vaine purposes; Lawes made rather to finde faults, then to prevent faultes: the Court of a Prince rather deemed as a priviledged place of unbrideled licentiousnes, then as a biding of him, who as a father, should give a fatherly example unto his people. Hence grew a very dissolution of all estates, while the great men (by the nature of ambition never satisfied) grew factious among themselves: and the underlings, glad indeede to be underlings to them they hated lest, to preserve them from such they hated most. Men of vertue suppressed, lest their shining should discover the others filthines; and at length vertue it selfe almost forgotten, when it had no hopefull end whereunto to be directed; olde men long nusled in corruption, scorning them that would seeke reformation; yong men very fault-finding, but very faultie: and so to new-fanglenes both of manners, apparrell, and each thing els, by the custome of selfe-guiltie evill, glad to change though oft for a worse; marchandise abused, and so townes decayed for want of just and naturall libertie; offices, even of judging soules, solde; publique defences neglected; and in summe, (lest too long I trouble you) all awrie, and (which wried it to the most wrie course of all) witte abused, rather to faine reason why it should be amisse, then how it should be amended.

5   In this, and a much worse plight then it is fitte to trouble your excellent eares withal, did the King *Euarchus* finde his estate, when he tooke upon him the regiment: which by reason of the long streame of abuse, he was forced to establish by some even extreme severitie, not so much for the very faultes themselves, (which he rather sought to prevent then to punish) as for the faultie ones; who strong, even in their faultes, scorned his youth, and coulde not learne to disgest, that the man which they so long had used to maske their owne appetites, should now be the reducer of them into order. But so soone as some fewe (but in deede notable) examples, had thundred a duetie into the subjects hartes, he soone shewed, no basenes of suspition, nor the basest basenes of envie, could any whit rule such a Ruler. But then shined foorth indeede all love among them, when an awfull feare, ingendred by justice, did make that love most lovely: his first & principall care being to appeare unto his people, such as he would have them be, & to be such as he appeared; making his life the example of his lawes, as it were, his actions arising

out of his deedes. So that within small time, he wanne a singular love in his people, and engraffed singular confidence. For how could they chuse but love him, whom they found so truely to love thē? He even in reason disdayning, that they that have charge of beastes, should love their charge, and care for them; and that he that was to governe the most excellent creature, should not love so noble a charge. And therefore, where most Princes (seduced by flatterie to builde upon false grounds of government) make themselves (as it were) another thing from the people; and so count it gaine what they can get from them: and (as if it were two counter-ballances, that their estate goes hiest when the people goes lowest) by a fallacie of argument thinking themselves most Kinges, when the subject is most basely subjected: he contrariwise, vertuouslie and wisely acknowledging, that he with his people made all but one politike bodie, whereof himselfe was the head; even so cared for them, as he woulde for his owne limmes: never restrayning their liberty, without it stretched to licenciousnes, nor pulling from them their goods, which they found were not imployed to the purchase of a greater good: but in all his actions shewing a delight to their welfare, broght that to passe, that while by force he tooke nothing, by their love he had all. In summe (peerelesse Princesse) I might as easily sette downe the whole Arte of governement, as to lay before your eyes the picture of his proceedings. But in such sorte he flourished in the sweete comforte of dooing much good, when by an action of leaving his Countrie, he was forced to bring foorth his vertue of magnanimitie, as before he had done of justice.

He had onely one sister, a Ladie (lest I should too easilie 6 fall to partiall prayses of her) of whom it may be justly said, that she was no unfit brāch to the noble stock wherof she came. Her he had given in mariage to *Dorilaus*, Prince of *Thessalia*, not so much to make a frēdship, as to cōfirm the frēdship betwixt their posteritie, which betwene them, by the likenes of vertue, had been long before made: for certainly, *Dorilaus* could neede no amplifiers mouth for the highest point of praise. Who hath not heard (said *Pamela*) of the valiāt, wise, and just *Dorilaus*, whose unripe death doth yet (so many yeares since) draw teares frō vertuous eyes? And indeede, my father is wont to speak of nothing with greater admiration, then of the notable friendshippe (a rare thing in Princes, more rare betwene Princes) that so holily was observed to the last, of those two excellent men. But (said she) goe on I pray you. *Dorilaus* (said he) having maried his sister, had his mariage in short time blest (for so are folke woont to say, how unhappie soever the children after grow) with a sonne, whom they named *Musidorus*: of whom I must needes first speake before I come to *Pyrocles*; because as he was borne first, so upon his occasion grew (as I may say accidentally) the others birth. For scarcely was *Musidorus* made partaker of this oft-blinding light, when there were found numbers of Southsayers, who affirmed strange & incredible things should be performed by that childe; whether the heavens at that time listed to play with ignorant mankind, or that flatterie be so presumptuous, as even at times to borow the face of Divinitie. But certainly, so did the boldnes of their affirmation accompanie the greatnes of what they did affirme (even descending to particularities, what kingdomes he should overcome) that the King of *Phrygia* (who over-superstitiously thought him selfe touched in the matter) sought by force to destroy the infant, to prevent his after-expectations: because a skilful man (having compared his nativity with the child) so told him. Foolish mã, either vainly fearing what was not to be feared, or not considering, that if it were a worke of the superiour powers, the heavens at length are never children. But so he did, & by the aid of the Kings of *Lydia* and *Crete* (joining together their armies) invaded *Thessalia*, & brought *Dorilaus* to some behind-hand of fortune, when his faithfull friend & brother *Euarchus* came so mightily to his succour, that with some enterchanging changes of fortune, they begat of a just war, the best child, peace. In which time *Euarchus* made a crosse mariage also with *Dorilaus* his sister, & shortly left her with child of the famous *Pyrocles*, driven to returne to the defence of his owne countrie, which in his absence (helped with some of the ill contented nobilitie) the mighty King of *Thrace*, & his brother, King of *Pannonia*, had invaded. The successe of those warres was too notable to be unknowne to your eares, to which it seemes all worthy fame hath glory to come unto. But there was *Dorilaus* (valiantly requiting his friẽds helpe) in a great battaile deprived of his life, his obsequies being no more solẽnised by the teares of his par-

takers, thẽ the bloud of his enimies; with so pearcing a sorrow
to the constant hart of *Euarchus*, that the newes of his sons birth
could lighten his countenance with no shew of comfort, although
al the comfort that might be in a child, truth it selfe in him
forthwith delivered. For what fortune onely southsayers fore-
told of *Musidorus*, that all men might see prognosticated in
Pyrocles; both Heavens & Earth giving tokẽs of the comming
forth of an Heroicall vertue. The senate house of the planets
was at no time to set, for the decreeing of perfeċtiõ in a man,
as at that time all folkes skilful therin did acknowledge : onely
love was threatned, and promised to him, and so to his cousin,
as both the tempest and haven of their best yeares. But as death
may have prevented *Pyrocles*, so unworthinesse must be the death
to *Musidorus*.

CHAP. 7.

[1]*The education of* Pyrocles & Musidorus. [2]*Their friendship,*
[3]*navigation,* [4]*and first shipwracke.* [5]*The straunge gratitude
of two brothers to them, upon their liberalitie to those two
brothers.*

BUt the mother of *Pyrocles* (shortly after her childe-birth) 1
dying, was cause that *Euarchus* recommended the care of
his only son to his sister; doing it the rather because the warre
continued in cruell heat, betwixt him & those evil neighbours
of his. In which meane time those young Princes (the only
comforters of that vertuous widow) grewe on so, that *Pyrocles*
taught admiration to the hardest conceates: *Musidorus* (perchaunce because among his subjeċtes) exceedingly beloved:
and by the good order of *Euarchus* (well perfourmed by his
sister) they were so brought up, that all the sparkes of vertue,
which nature had kindled in thẽ, were so blowne to give forth
their uttermost heate that justly it may be affirmed, they enflamed the affeċtions of all that knew thẽ. For almost before
they could perfeċtly speake, they began to receave cõceits not
unworthy of the best speakers: excellent devises being used, to
make even their sports profitable; images of battailes, & fortifi-

catiõs being then delivered to their memory, which after, their stronger judgemẽts might dispens, the delight of tales being cõverted to the knowledge of al the stories of worthy Princes, both to move them to do nobly, & teach them how to do nobly; the beautie of vertue still being set before their eyes, & that taught them with far more diligent care, then Grãmatical rules, their bodies exercised in all abilities, both of doing and suffring, & their mindes acquainted by degrees with daungers; & in sum, all bent to the making up of princely mindes: no servile feare used towardes them, nor any other violent restraint, but stil as to Princes: so that a habite of commaunding was naturalized in them, and therefore the farther from Tyrannie: Nature having done so much for them in nothing, as that it made them Lords of truth, whereon all the other goods were builded.

2   Among which I nothing so much delight to recount, as the memorable friendship that grewe betwixt the two Princes, such as made them more like then the likenesse of all other vertues, and made them more neer one to the other, then the neerenes of their bloud could aspire unto; which I think grew the faster, and the faster was tied betweene them, by reason that *Musidorus* being elder by three or foure yeares, it was neither so great a difference in age as did take away the delight in societie, and yet by the difference there was taken away the occasion of childish contentions; till they had both past over the humour of such contentions.   For *Pyrocles* bare reverẽce ful of love to *Musidorus*, & *Musidorus* had a delight full of love in *Pyrocles*. *Musidorus*, what he had learned either for body or minde, would teach it to *Pyrocles*; and *Pyrocles* was so glad to learne of none, as of *Musidorus*: till *Pyrocles*, being come to sixtene yeares of age, he seemed so to overrun his age in growth, strength, and al things following it, that not *Musidorus*, no nor any man living (I thinke) could performe any action, either on horse, or foote, more strongly, or deliver that strength more nimbly, or become the delivery more gracefully, or employ al more vertuously. Which may well seeme wonderfull: but wonders are no wonders in a wonderfull subject.

3   At which time understanding that the King *Euarchus*, after so many yeares warre, and the conquest of all *Pannonia*, and almost *Thrace*, had now brought the cõclusion of al to the siege of *Bizantium* (to the raising of which siege great forces were

made) they would needs fall to the practise of those vertues, which they before learned. And therefore the mother of *Musidorus* nobly yeelding over her owne affects to her childrens good (for a mother she was in effect to thẽ both) the rather that they might helpe her beloved brother, they brake of all delayes; which *Musidorus* for his parte thought already had devoured too much of his good time, but that he had once graunted a boone (before he knew what it was) to his deere friend *Pyrocles*; that he would never seeke the adventures of armes, until he might go with him: which having fast boũd his hart (a true slave to faith) he had bid a tedious delay of following his owne humour for his friends sake, till now finding him able every way to go thorow with that kinde of life, he was as desirous for his sake, as for his owne, to enter into it. So therefore preparing a navie, that they might go like themselves, and not onely bring the comfort of their presence, but of their power to their deere parent *Euarchus,* they recommended themselves to the Sea, leaving the shore of *Thessalia* full of teares and vowes; and were received thereon with so smooth and smiling a face, as if *Neptune* had as then learned falsely to fawne on Princes. The winde was like a servaunt, wayting behind them so just, that they might fill the sailes as they listed; and the best saylers shewing themselves lesse covetous of his liberalitie, so tempered it, that they all kept together like a beautifull flocke, which so well could obey their maisters pipe: without sometimes, to delight the Princes eies, some two or three of them would strive, who could (either by the cunning of well spending the windes breath, or by the advantageous building of their mooving houses) leave their fellowes behind them in the honour of speed: while the two Princes had leasure to see the practise of that, which before they had learned by bookes: to consider the arte of catching the winde prisoner, to no other ende, but to runne away with it; to see how beautie, and use can so well agree together, that of all the trinckets, where with they are attired, there is not one but serves to some necessary purpose. And (ô Lord) to see the admirable power & noble effects of Love, whereby the seeming insensible Loadstone, with a secret beauty (holding the spirit of iron in it) can draw that hard-harted thing unto it, and (like a vertuous mistresse) not onely make it bow it selfe, but with it make it aspire to so high a Love, as of the heavenly Poles; and thereby to bring foorth the noblest deeds, that the children of the Earth can boast of. And so the Princes delighting their cŏceats with cŏfirming their knowledge, seing wherein the Sea-discipline differed from Land-service, they had for a day & almost a whole night, as pleasing entertainement, as the falsest hart could give to him he meanes worst to.

4   But by that the next morning began a little to make a guilden shewe of a good meaning, there arose even with the Sun, a vaile of darke cloudes before his face, which shortly (like inck powred into water) had blacked over all the face of heaven; preparing (as it were) a mournefull stage for a Tragedie to be plaied on. For forthwith the windes began to speake lowder, and as in a tumultuous kingdome, to thinke themselves fittest instruments of commaundement; and blowing whole stormes of hayle and raine upon them, they were sooner in daunger, then they coulde almost bethinke themselves of chaunge. For then the traiterous Sea began to swell in pride against the afflicted Navie, under which (while the heaven favoured them) it had layne so calmely, making mountaines of it selfe, over which the tossed and tottring ship shoulde clime, to be streight carried downe againe to a pit of hellish darkenesse; with such cruell blowes against the sides of the shippe (that which way soever it went, was still in his malice) that there was left neither power to stay, nor way to escape. And shortly had it so dissevered the loving companie, which the daie before had tarried together, that most of them never met againe, but were swallowed up in his never-satisfied mouth. Some indeed (as since was knowne) after long wandring returned into *Thessalia*; other recovered *Bizantium*, and served *Euarchus* in his warre. But in the ship wherein the Princes were (now left as much alone as proud Lords be when fortune fails them) though they employed all industrie to save themselves, yet what they did was rather for dutie to nature, then hope to escape. So ougly a darkenesse, as if it would prevent the nights comming, usurped the dayes right: which (accompanied sometimes with thunders, alwayes with horrible noyses of the chafing winds) made the masters and pilots so astonished, that they knew not how to direct, and if they knew they could scarcely (when they directed) heare their owne whistle. For the sea strave with the winds which should be lowder, & the shrouds of the ship with a ghastful noise to

them that were in it, witnessed, that their ruine was the wager
of the others contention, and the heaven roaring out thunders
the more amazed them, as having those powers for enimies.
Certainely there is no daunger carries with it more horror, then
that which growes in those flowing kingdomes. For that
dwelling place is unnaturall to mankind, and then the terrible-
nesse of the continuall motion, the dissolutiö of the fare being
from comfort, the eye and the eare having ougly images ever
before it, doth still vex the minde, even when it is best armed
against it. But thus the day past (if that might be called a day)
while the cunningest mariners were so conquered by the storme,
as they thought it best with striking sailes to yeelde to be
governed by it: the valiantest feeling inward dismayednesse,
and yet the fearefullest ashamed fully to shew it, seeing that
the Princes (who were to parte from the greatest fortunes) did
in their countenances accuse no point of feare, but encouraging
them to doo what might be done (putting their handes to everie
most painefull office) taught them at one instant to promise
themselves the best, and yet not to despise the worst. But so
were they carryed by the tyrannie of the winde, and the treason
of the sea, all that night, which the elder it was, the more way-
ward it shewed it selfe towards them: till the next morning
(knowne to be a morning better by the houre-glasse, then by
the day cleerenesse) having runne fortune as blindly, as it selfe
ever was painted, lest the conclusion should not aunswere to the
rest of the play, they were driven upon a rocke: which hidden
with those outragious waves, did, as it were, closely dissemble
his cruel mind, till with an unbeleeved violence (but to them
that have tried it) the shippe ranne upon it; and seeming
willinger to perish then to have her course stayed, redoubled
her blowes, till she had broken her selfe in peeces; and as it
were tearing out her owne bowels to feede the seas greedinesse,
left nothing within it but despaire of safetie, and expectation of
a loathsome end. There was to be seene the diverse manner of
minds in distresse: some sate upon the toppe of the poupe
weeping and wailing, till the sea swallowed them; some one
more able to abide death, then feare of death, cut his owne
throate to prevent drowning; some prayed, and there wanted
not of them which cursed, as if the heavens could not be more
angrie then they were. But a monstrous crie begotten of manie

roaring vowes, was able to infect with feare a minde that had not prevented it with the power of reason.

5   But the Princes using the passions of fearing evill, and desiring to escape, onely to serve the rule of vertue, not to abandon ones selfe, lept to a ribbe of the shippe, which broken from his fellowes, floted with more likelyhood to doo service, then any other limme of that ruinous bodie; upon which there had gotten alreadie two brethren, well knowne servants of theirs; and streight they foure were carryed out of sight, in that huge rising of the sea, from the rest of the shippe. But the peece they were on sinking by little and little under them, not able to support the weight of so manie, the brethren (the elder whereof was *Leucippus*, the younger *Nelsus*) shewed themselves right faithfull and gratefull servants unto them; gratefull (I say) for this cause: Those two gentlemen had bene taken prisoners in the great warre the king of *Phrygia* made upon *Thessalia*, in the time of *Musidorus* his infancie; and having beene solde into another countrie (though peace fell after betweene these Realmes) could not be delivered, because of their valor knowne, but for a farre greater summe, then either all their friends were able, or the Dowager willing to make, in respect of the great expences her selfe and people had bene put to in those warres; and so had they remained in prison about thirteene yeares, when the two young Princes (hearing speaches of their good deserts) found meanes both by selling all the Jewels they had of great price, and by giving under their hands great estates when they should come to be Kings (which promises their vertue promised for them should be kept) to get so much treasure as redeemed them from captivitie. This remembred, and kindly remembred by these two brothers, perchance helped by a naturall duetie to their Princes blood, they willingly left holde of the boord, committing themselves to the seas rage, & even when they went to dye, themselves praying for the Princes lives. It is true, that neither the paine nor daunger, so moved the Princes hartes as the tendernesse of that loving part, farre from glorie, having so few lookers on; farre from hope of reward, since themselves were sure to perish.

CHAP. 8.

[1]Pyrocles *cast on the shore of Phrygia* [2]*led prisoner to the King.* [3]*That suspicious tyrant naturalized.* [4]*His intent to kill* Pyrocles. [5]Musidorus-*his escape from sea, and offer to dye for his friend.* [6]*Their contention for death.* [7]*Preparation for* Musidorus *execution.* [8]*His straunge deliverie by* Pyrocles, [9]*and a sodaine mutinie.* [10]*Their killing the bad King,* [11]*and creating a better.*

BUt now of all the royal Navie they had left but one peece of one ship, whereon they kept themselves in all trueth, having enterchaunged their cares, while either cared for other, ech comforting and councelling how to labour for the better, and to abide the worse. But so fell it out, that as they were carryed by the tide (which there seconded by the storme ran exceedingly swiftly) *Musidorus* seeing (as he thought) *Pyrocles* not well upon the boord, as he would with his right hand have helped him on better, he had no sooner unfastned his hold, but that a wave forcibly spoiled his weaker hand of hold; and so for a time parted those friends, each crying to the other, but the noise of the sea drowned their farewell. But *Pyrocles* (then carelesse of death, if it had come by any meanes, but his owne) was shortly brought out of the seas furie to the lands comfort; when (in my conscience I know) that comfort was but bitter unto him. And bitter indeed it fell out even in it selfe to be unto him.

For being cast on land much brused & beaten both with the 2 seas hard farewell, and the shores rude welcome; and even almost deadly tired with the length of his uncomfortable labour, as he was walking up to discover some bodie, to whom he might goe for reliefe, there came streight running unto him certaine, who (as it was after knowne) by appointment watched (with manie others) in diverse places along the coast: who laide handes of him, and without either questioning with him, or shewing will to heare him, (like men fearefull to appeare curious) or which was worse having no regard to the hard plight he was in (being so wette and weake) they carried him some miles thence, to a house of a principall officer of that countrie. Who with no more civilitie (though with much more busines then those under-fellowes had shewed) beganne in captious manner to put interrogatories unto him. To which he (unused to such enter-tainment) did shortlie and plainely aunswere, what he was, and how he came thither.

But that no sooner knowne, with numbers of armed men to garde him (for mischiefe, not from mischiefe) he was sent to the Kings court, which as then was not above a dayes journey off, with letters from that officer, containing his owne serviceable diligence in discovering so great a personage; adding with all more then was true of his conjectures, because he would endeare his owne service.

3   This country whereon he fell was *Phrygia*, and it was to the King thereof to whom he was sent, a Prince of a melancholy constitution both of bodie and mind; wickedly sad, ever musing of horrible matters; suspecting, or rather condemning all men of evill, because his minde had no eye to espie goodnesse: and therefore accusing *Sycophantes*, of all men did best sort to his nature; but therefore not seeming *Sycophantes*, because of no evill they said, they could bring any new or doubtfull thing unto him, but such as alreadie he had bene apt to determine; so as they came but as proofes of his wisedome: fearefull and never secure; while the feare he had figured in his minde had any possibilitie of event. A tode-like retyrednesse, and closenesse of minde; nature teaching the odiousnesse of poyson, and the daunger of odiousnesse. Yet while youth lasted in him, the exercises of that age, and his humour (not yet fullie discovered) made him something the more frequentable, and lesse daungerous. But after that yeares beganne to come on with some, though more seldome shewes of a bloudie nature, and that the prophecie of *Musidorus* destinie came to his eares (delivered unto him, and received of him with the hardest interpretation, as though his subjectes did delight in the hearing thereof.) Then gave he himselfe indeede to the full currant of his disposition, espetially after the warre of *Thessalia*, wherein (though in trueth wrongly) he deemed, his unsuccessings proceeded of their unwillingnes to have him prosper: and then thinking him selfe contemned, (knowing no countermine against contempt, but terror) began to let nothing passe which might beare the colour of a fault,

without sharpe punishment: & when he wanted faults, excellencie grew a fault; and it was sufficient to make one guiltie, that he had power to be guiltie.   And as there is no honor, to which impudent povertie cannot make it selfe serviceable, so were there en w of those desperate ambitious, who would builde their houses upon others ruines, which after shoulde fall by like practises.   So as servitude came mainly upon that poore people, whose deedes were not onely punished, but words corrected, and even thoughts by some meane or other puld out of thē: while suspitiõ bred the mind of crueltie, and the effectes of crueltie stirred a new cause of suspition.   And in this plight (ful of watchfull fearefulnes) did the storme deliver sweete *Pyrocles* to the stormie minde of that Tyrant, all men that did such wrong to so rare a stranger (whose countenaunce deserved both pitie and admiration) condemning thēselves as much in their hearts, as they did brag in their forces.

But when this bloudy King knew what he was, and in what 4 order he and his cosin *Musidorus* (so much of him feared) were come out of *Thessalia*, assuredly thinking (because ever thinking the worst) that those forces were provided against him; glad of the perishing (as he thought) of *Musidorus*, determined in publique sort to put *Pyrocles* to death.   For having quite loste the way of noblenes, he strave to clime to the height of terriblenes; and thinking to make all men adread, to make such one an enemie, who would not spare, nor feare to kill so great a Prince; and lastly, having nothing in him why to make him his friend, thought, he woulde make him away, for being his enemie.   The day was appointed, and all things appointed for that cruell blow, in so solemne an order, as if they would set foorth tyrãny in most gorgeous decking.   The Princely youth of invincible valour, yet so unjustly subjected to such outragious wrong, carrying himselfe in all his demeanure so constãtly, abiding extremitie, that one might see it was the cutting away of the greatest hope of the world, and destroying vertue in his sweetest grouth.

But so it fell out that his death was prevented by a rare ex- 5 ample of friendshippe in *Musidorus*: who being almost drowned, had bene taken up by a Fisherman belonging to the kingdome of *Pontus*; and being there, and understanding the full discourse (as Fame was very prodigall of so notable an accident) in what case

Pyrocles was; learning withall, that his hate was farre more to him then to *Pyrocles*, he founde meanes to acquaint him selfe with a noble-man of that Countrie, to whom largely discovering what he was, he found him a most fitte instrument to effectuate his desire. For this noble-man had bene one, who in many warres had served *Euarchus*, and had bene so mind-striken by the beautie of vertue in that noble King, that (though not borne his Subject) he even profeste himselfe his servaunt. His desire therefore to him was, to keepe *Musidorus* in a strong Castle of his, and then to make the King of *Phrygia* understande, that if he would deliver *Pyrocles*, *Musidorus* woulde willingly put him selfe into his handes: knowing well, that how thirstie so ever he was of *Pyrocles* bloud, he woulde rather drinke that of *Musidorus*.

The Nobleman was loath to preserve one by the losse of another, but time urging resolution: the importunitie of *Musidorus* (who shewed a minde not to over-live *Pyrocles*) with the affection he bare to *Euarchus*, so prevayled, that he carried this strange offer of *Musidorus*, which by that Tyrant was greedelie accepted.

6 And so upon securitie of both sides, they were enterchanged. Where I may not omitte that worke of friendshippe in *Pyrocles*, who both in speache and coũtenance to *Musidorus*, well shewed, that he thought himselfe injured, and not releeved by him: asking him, what he had ever seene in him, why he could not beare the extremities of mortall accidentes as well as any man? and why he shoulde envie him the glorie of suffering death for his friendes cause, and (as it were) robbe him of his owne possession? But in this notable contention, (where the conquest must be the conquerers destruction, and safetie the punishment of the conquered) *Musidorus* prevayled: because he was a more welcome prize to the unjuste King, that wisht none well, to them worse then others, and to him worste of all: and as chearefully going towardes, as *Pyrocles* went frowardly fromwarde his death, he was delivered to the King, who could not be inough sure of him, without he fed his owne eies upon one, whom he had begon to feare, as soone as the other began to be.

7 Yet because he would in one acte, both make ostentation of his owne felicitie (into whose hands his most feared enemie was fallen) and withal cut of such hopes from his suspected subjects (when they should knowe certainly he was dead) with much

more skilful cruelty, and horrible solemnitie he caused each
thing to be prepared for his triumph of tyrannie. And so the
day being come, he was led foorth by many armed men (who
often had beene the fortifiers of wickednes) to the place of
execution: where comming with a mind comforted in that he
had done such service to *Pyrocles*, this strange encounter he had.

The excelling *Pyrocles* was no sooner delivered by the kings 8
servants to a place of liberty, then he bent his witte and courage,
(and what would not they bring to passe?) how ether to deliver
Musidorus, or to perish with him. And (finding he could get
in that countrie no forces sufficient by force to rescue him) to
bring himselfe to die with him, (little hoping of better event)
he put himselfe in poore rayment, and by the helpe of some few
crownes he tooke of that noble-man, (who full of sorrow, though
not knowing the secrete of his intent, suffered him to goe in
such order from him) he (even he, born to the greatest expectation,
and of the greatest bloud that any Prince might be) submitted himselfe to be servant to the executioner that should put
to death *Musidorus*: a farre notabler proofe of his friendship,
considering the height of his minde, then any death could be.
That bad officer not suspecting him, being araied fit for such an
estate, & having his beautie hidden by many foule spots he
artificially put upon his face, gave him leave not onely to weare
a sworde himselfe, but to beare his sworde prepared for the
justified murther. And so *Pyrocles* taking his time, when *Musidorus* was upon the scaffold (separated somewhat from the rest,
as allowed to say something) he stept unto him, & putting the
sworde into his hande not bound (a point of civility the officers
used towards him, because they doubted no such enterprise)
Musidorus (said he) die nobly. In truth, never mã betweene
joy before knowledge what to be glad of, and feare after cõsider-
ing his case, had such a confusion of thoughts, as I had, when
I saw *Pyrocles*, so neare me. But with that *Dorus* blushed, and
Pamela smiled: and *Dorus* the more blushed at her smiling, and
she the more smiled at his blushing; because he had (with the
remembraunce of that plight he was in) forgotten in speaking
of him selfe to use the third person. But *Musidorus* turned againe
her thoughts from his cheekes to his tongue in this sorte: But
(said he) when they were with swordes in handes, not turning
backs one to the other (for there they knew was no place

of defence) but making that a preservation in not hoping to be preserved, and now acknowledging themselves subject to death, meaning onely to do honour to their princely birth, they flew amongst thẽ all (for all were enimies) & had quickly either with flight or death, left none upon the scaffolde to annoy them. Wherein *Pyrocles* (the excellent *Pyrocles*) did such wonders beyond beliefe, as was hable to leade *Musidorus* to courage, though he had bene borne a coward. But indeed, just rage & desperate vertue did such effects, that the popular sorte of the beholders began to be almost superstitiously amazed, as at effectes beyond mortall power. But the King with angry threatnings from-out a window (where he was not ashamed, the worlde should behold him a beholder) cõmaunded his garde, and the rest of his souldiers to hasten their death. But many of them lost their bodies to loose their soules, when the Princes grew almost so weary, as they were ready to be conquered with conquering.

9 But as they were stil fighting with weake armes, and strong harts, it happened, that one of the souldiers (cõmaũded to go up after his fellowes against the Princes) having received a light hurt, more woũded in his hart, went backe with as much diligence, as he came up with modestie: which another of his fellowes seeing, to pike a thanke of the King, strake him upon the face, reviling him, that so accompanied, he would runne away from so fewe. But he (as many times it falls out) onely valiant, when he was angrie, in revenge thrust him through: which with his death was streight revenged by a brother of his: and that againe requited by a fellow of the others. There began to be a great tumult amongst the souldiers; which seene, and not understood by the people (used to feares but not used to be bolde in them) some began to crie treason; and that voice streight multiplying it selfe, the King (O the cowardise of a guiltie conscience) before any man set upon him, fled away. Where-with a bruit (either by arte of some well meaning men, or by such chaunce as such thinges often fall out by) ran from one to the other, that the King was slaine; wherwith certaine yong men of the bravest minds, cried with lowde voice, Libertie; and encouraging the other Citizens to follow them, set upon the garde, and souldiers as chiefe instruments of Tyrannie: and quickly, aided by the Princes, they had left none

of them alive, nor any other in the cittie, who they thought had in any sorte set his hand to the worke of their servitude, and (God knowes) by the blindnesse of rage, killing many guiltles persons, either for affinity to the Tyrant, or enmitie to the tyrant-killers. But some of the wisest (seeing that a popular licence is indeede the many-headed tyranny) prevailed with the rest to make *Musidorus* their chiefe: choosing one of them (because Princes) to defende them, and him because elder and most hated of the Tyrant, and by him to be ruled: whom foorthwith they lifted up, Fortune (I thinke) smiling at her worke therein, that a scaffold of execution should grow a scaffold of coronation.

But by and by there came newes of more certaine truth, 10 that the King was not dead, but fled to a strong castle of his, neere hãd, where he was gathering forces in all speed possible to suppresse this mutinie. But now they had run themselves too farre out of breath, to go backe againe the same career; and too well they knew the sharpnesse of his memorie to forget such an injury; therefore learning vertue of necessitie, they continued resolute to obey *Musidorus*. Who seing what forces were in the citie, with them issued against the Tyrant, while they were in this heat; before practises might be used to dissever them: & with them met the King, who likewise hoping little to prevaile by time, (knowing and finding his peoples hate) met him with little delay in the field: where him selfe was slaine by *Musidorus*, after he had seene his onely sonne (a Prince of great courage & beautie, but fostred in bloud by his naughty Father) slaine by the hand of *Pyrocles*. This victory obteined, with great, and truly not undeserved honour to the two Princes, the whole estates of the country with one consent, gave the crowne and all other markes of soveraigntie to *Musidorus*; desiring nothing more, then to live under such a government, as they promised thẽselves of him.

But he thinking it a greater greatnes to give a kingdome, 11 then get a kingdome; understanding that there was left of the bloud Roiall, & next to the successiõ, an aged Gentleman of approved goodnes (who had gotten nothing by his cousins power, but danger frõ him, and odiousnes for him) having past his time in modest secrecy, & asmuch from entermedling in matters of government, as the greatnesse of his bloud would suffer him,

did (after having received the full power to his owne hands)
resigne all to the noble-mã: but with such conditions, & cautions
of the conditions, as might assure the people (with asmuch
assurãce as worldly matters beare) that not onely that governour, of whom indeed they looked for al good, but the nature
of the government, should be no way apt to decline to Tyrãny.

CHAP. 9.

[1] *The two brothers escape to the shore of* Pontus. [2] *Incõstancy,* [3] *and
envie purtraied in the King & his Counsellor.* [4] *The advancement & overthrow by them of those two brothers.* [5] *The
revenge thereof by the two Princes.* [6] *The cruelties of two
revengefull Gyants, and their death by the Princes.* [7] *Their
honours, and their honourable mindes.*

1 THis dooing set foorth no lesse his magnificẽce, then the
other aĉt did his magnanimitie: so that greatly praysed
of al, and justly beloved of the newe King, who in all both
wordes and behaviour protested him selfe their Tenaunt, or
Liegeman, they were drawne thence to revenge those two
servãts of theirs, of whose memorable faith, I told you (most
excellẽt Princesse) in willingly giving themselves to be drowned
for their sakes : but drowned indeed they were not, but gat
with painefull swimming upon a rocke: frõ whence (after being
come as neere famishing, as before drowning) the weather
breaking up, they were brought to the maine lande of *Pontus*;
the same coũtry upon which *Musidorus* also was fallen, but not
in so luckie a place.

2 For they were brought to the King of that country, a
Tyrant also, not thorow suspition, greedines, or unrevẽgeful-
nes, as he of *Phrygia*, but (as I may terme it) of a wanton
crueltie: inconstant of his choise of friends, or rather never
having a friẽd, but a playfellow ; of whom when he was
wearie, he could not otherwise rid himself, thẽ by killing thẽ:
giving somtimes prodigally, not because he loved them to whom
he gave, but because he lusted to give: punishing, not so much
for hate or anger, as because he felt not the smart of punishment: delighted to be flattered, at first for those vertues which

were not in him, at length making his vices vertues worthy the
flattering : with like judgement glorying, when he had happened
to do a thing well, as when he had performed some notable
mischiefe.

He chaŭced at that time (for indeed long time none lasted 3
with him) to have next in use about him, a mã of the most
envious dispositiŏ, that (I think) ever infeĉted the aire with his
breath : whose eies could not looke right upon any happie mã,
nor eares beare the burthen of any bodies praise : cõtrary to the
natures of al other plagues, plagued with others well being;
making happines the ground of his unhappinesse, & good newes
the argumẽt of his sorrow : in sum, a man whose favour no
man could winne, but by being miserable.

And so, because these two faithfull servants of theirs came 4
in miserable sorte to that Courte, he was apte inough at first to
favour them ; and the King understanding of their adventure,
(wherein they had shewed so constant a faith unto their Lordes)
suddainly falles to take a pride in making much of them, extolling them with infinite prayses, and praysing him selfe in his
harte, in that he praysed them. And by and by were they
made great courtiers, and in the way of minions, when advauncement (the most mortall offence to envy) stirred up their
former friend, to overthrow his owne worke in them; taking
occasion upon the knowledge (newly come to the court) of the
late King of *Phrygia* destroied by their two Lordes, who having
bene a neere kinsman to this Prince of *Pontus*, by this envious
Coŭcellour, partly with suspition of praĉtise, partly with glory
of in-part revẽging his cousins death, the King was suddainly
turned, (and every turne with him was a downe-fall) to locke
them up in prison, as servaunts to his enimies, whom before he
had never knowne, nor (til that time one of his own subjeĉts
had entertained and dealt for them) did ever take heed of. But
now earnest in every present humour, and making himselfe
brave in his liking, he was content to give them just cause
of offence, when they had power to make just revenge. Yet
did the Princes send unto him before they entred into war,
desiring their servants liberty. But he swelling in thier hŭble-
nes, (like a bubble swollen up with a small breath, broken with
a great) forgetting, or never knowing humanitie, caused their
heads to be striken off, by the advice of his envious Councellor

(who now hated them so much the more, as he foresaw the happines in having such, and so fortunate masters) and sent them with unroyall reproches to *Musidorus* and *Pyrocles*, as if they had done traiterously, and not heroically in killing his tyrannicall Cosen.

5   But that injurie went beyond al degree of reconcilement; so that they making forces in *Phrygia* (a kingdome wholy at their commandement, by the love of the people, and gratefulnesse of the King) they entred his country; and wholy conquering it (with such deeds as at lest Fame said were excellent) tooke the King; and by *Musidorus* commaundement (*Pyrocles* hart more enclined to pitie) he was slaine upon the tombe of their two true Servants; which they caused to be made for them with royall expences, and notable workmanship to preserve their deade lives.   For his wicked Servant he should have felt the like, or worse, but that his harte brake even to death with the beholding the honour done to the deade carcasses?   There might *Pyrocles* quietly have enjoyed that crowne, by all the desire of that people, most of whom had revolted unto him: but he, finding a sister of the late Kings (a faire and well esteemed Ladie) looking for nothing more, then to be oppressed with her brothers ruines, gave her in marriage to the noble man his fathers old friend, and endowed them with the crowne of that kingdome.   And not content with those publike actions, of princely, and (as it were) governing vertue, they did (in that kingdome and some other neere about) divers acts of particular trials, more famous, because more perilous.   For in that time those regions were full both of cruell monsters, & monstrous men : all which in short time by private combats they delivered the countries of.

6   Among the rest, two brothers of huge both greatnesse & force, therefore commonly called giants, who kept thẽselves in a castle seated upon the top of a rocke, impregnable, because there was no comming unto it, but by one narrow path, where one mans force was able to keepe downe an armie.   These brothers had a while served the King of *Pontus*, and in all his affaires (especially of war, wherunto they were onely apt) they had shewed, as uncõquered courage, so a rude faithfulnes: being men indeed by nature apter to the faults of rage, then of deceipt ; not greatly ambitious, more then to be well and

uprightly dealt with; rather impatient of injury, then delighted with more then ordinary curtesies; and in injuries more sensible of smart or losse, then of reproch or disgrace. These men being of this nature (and certainely Jewels to a wise man, considering what indeed wonders they were able to performe) yet were discarded by that unworthy Prince, after many notable deserts, as not worthy the holding. Which was the more evident to them; because it sodainly fell from an excesse of favor, which (many examples having taught them) never stopt his race till it came to an headlong overthrow: they full of rage, retyred themselves unto this castle. Where thinking nothing juster thẽ revenge, nor more noble then the effects of anger, that (according to the nature) ful of inward bravery and fiercenes, scarcely in the glasse of Reason, thinking it self faire, but when it is terrible, they immediately gave themselves to make all the countrie about them (subject to that King) to smart for their Lords folly: not caring how innocent they were, but rather thinking the more innocent they were, the more it testified their spite, which they desired to manifest. And with use of evill, growing more and more evill, they tooke delight in slaughter, and pleasing themselves in making others wracke the effect of their power: so that where in the time that they obeyed a master, their anger was a serviceable power of the minde to doo publike good; so now unbridled, and blinde judge of it selfe, it made wickednesse violent, and praised it selfe in excellencie of mischiefe; almost to the ruine of the countrie, not greatly regarded by their carelesse and loveless king. Till now these Princes finding them so fleshed in crueltie, as not to be reclaimed, secreatly undertooke the matter alone: for accompanied they would not have suffered them to have mounted; and so those great fellowes scornefully receiving them, as foolish birds falne into their net, it pleased the eternall justice to make thẽ suffer death by their hands: So as they were manifoldly acknowledged the savers of that countrie.

It were the part of a verie idle Orator to set forth the 7 numbers of wel-devised honors done unto them: But as high honor is not onely gotten and borne by paine, and daunger, but must be nurst by the like, or els vanisheth as soone as it appeares to the world: so the naturall hunger thereof (which was in *Pyrocles*) suffered him not to account a resting seate of that, which ever either riseth, or falleth, but still to make one action beget another ; whereby his doings might send his praise to others mouthes to rebound againe true contentment to his spirite. And therefore having well established those kingdomes, under good governours, and rid them by their valure of such giants and monsters, as before time armies were not able to subdue, they determined in unknowne order to see more of the world, & to imploy those gifts esteemed rare in them, to the good of mankinde ; and therefore would themselves (understanding that the King *Euarchus* was passed all the cumber of his warres) goe privately to seeke exercises of their vertue ; thinking it not so worthy, to be brought to heroycall effects by fortune, or necessitie (like *Ulysses* and *Aeneas*) as by ones owne choice, and working. And so went they away from verie unwilling people to leave them, making time haste it selfe to be a circumstance of their honour, and one place witnesse to another of the truth of their doings. For scarcely were they out of the cōfines of *Pontus*, but that as they ridde alone armed, (for alone they went, one serving the other) they mette an adventure ; which though not so notable for any great effect they perfourmed, yet worthy to be remembred for the un-used examples therein, as well of true natural goodnes, as of wretched ungratefulnesse.

CHAP. 10.

[1] *The pitifull state, and storie of the* Paphalgonian *unkinde King, and his kind sonne,* [2] *first related by the son,* [3] *then by the blind father.* [4] *The three Princes assaulted by* Plexirtus *and his traine:* [5] *assisted by their King of* Pontus *and his troupes.* [6] Plexirtus *succoured and saved by two brothers, that vertuously loved a most vicious man.* [7] *Beseeged by the new King,* [8] *he submitteth, & is pardoned.* [9] *The two Princes depart to aide the Queene of* Lycia.

1   I T was in the kingdome of *Galacia*, the season being (as in the depth of winter) very cold, and as then sodainely growne to so extreame and foule a storme, that never any

winter (I thinke) brought foorth a fowler child: so that the
Princes were even compelled by the haile, that the pride of the
winde blew into their faces, to seeke some shrowding place
within a certaine hollow rocke offering it unto them, they
made it their shield against the tempests furie. And so staying
there, till the violence thereof was passed, they heard the speach
of a couple, who not perceiving them (being hidde within that
rude canapy) helde a straunge and pitifull disputation which
made them steppe out; yet in such sort, as they might see
unseene. There they perceaved an aged man, and a young,
scarcely come to the age of a man, both poorely arayed,
extreamely weather-beaten; the olde man blinde, the young
man leading him: and yet through all those miseries, in both
these seemed to appeare a kind of noblenesse, not sutable to
that affliction. But the first words they heard, were these of
the old man. Well *Leonatus* (said he) since I cannot perswade
thee to lead me to that which should end my griefe, & thy
trouble, let me now entreat thee to leave me: feare not, my
miserie cannot be greater then it is, & nothing doth become
me but miserie; feare not the danger of my blind steps, I
cannot fall worse then I am. And doo not I pray thee, doo
not obstinately continue to infect thee with my wretchednes.
But flie, flie from this region, onely worthy of me. Deare
father (answered he) doo not take away from me the onely
remnant of my happinesse: while I have power to doo you service, I am not wholly miserable. Ah my sonne (said he, and
with that he groned, as if sorrow strave to breake his harte,)
how evill fits it me to have such a sonne, and how much doth
thy kindnesse upbraide my wickednesse? These dolefull
speeches, and some others to like purpose (well shewing they
had not bene borne to the fortune they were in,) moved the
Princes to goe out unto them, and aske the younger what they
were? Sirs (answered he, with a good grace, and made the
more agreable by a certaine noble kinde of pitiousnes) I see well
you are straungers, that know not our miserie so well here
knowne, that no man dare know, but that we must be miserable. In deede our state is such, as though nothing is so
needfull unto us as pittie, yet nothing is more daungerous unto
us, then to make our selves so knowne as may stirre pittie.
But your presence promiseth, that cruelty shall not over-runne

hate. And if it did, in truth our state is soncke below the degree of feare.

2   This old man (whom I leade) was lately rightfull Prince of this countrie of *Paphlagonia*, by the hard-harted ungratefulnes of a sonne of his, deprived, not onely of his kingdome (whereof no forraine forces were ever able to spoyle him) but of his sight, the riches which Nature graūts to the poorest creatures. Whereby, & by other his unnaturall dealings, he hath bin driven to such griefe, as even now he would have had me to have led him to the toppe of this rocke, thēce to cast himselfe headlong to death: and so would have made me (who received my life of him) to be the worker of his destruction. But noble Gentlemen (said he) if either of you have a father, and feele what duetifull affection is engraffed in a sonnes hart, let me intreate you to convey this afflicted Prince to some place of rest & securitie. Amongst your worthie actes it shall be none of the least, that a King, of such might and fame, and so unjustly oppressed, is in any sort by you relieved.

3   But before they could make him answere, his father began to speake, Ah my sonne (said he) how evill an Historian are you, that leave out the chiefe knotte of all the discourse? my wickednes, my wickednes. And if thou doest it to spare my eares, (the onely sense nowe left me proper for knowledge) assure thy selfe thou dost mistake me. And I take witnesse of that Sunne which you see (with that he cast up his blinde eyes, as if he would hunt for light,) and wish my selfe in worse case then I do wish my selfe, which is as evill as may be, if I speake untruely; that nothing is so welcome to my thoughts, as the publishing of my shame. Therefore know you Gentlemen (to whom from my harte I wish that it may not prove ominous foretokē of misfortune to have mette with such a miser as I am) that whatsoever my sonne (ô God, that trueth binds me to reproch him with the name of my sonne) hath said, is true. But besides those truthes, this also is true, that having had in lawful mariage, of a mother fitte to beare royall children, this sonne (such one as partly you see, and better shall knowe by my shorte declaration) and so enjoyed the expectations in the world of him, till he was growē to justifie their expectations (so as I needed envie no father for the chiefe comfort of mortalitie, to leave an other ones-selfe after me) I was caried by a bastarde

sonne of mine (if at least I be bounde to beleeve the words
of that base woman my concubine, his mother) first to mislike,
then to hate, lastly to destroy, to doo my best to destroy, this
sonne (I thinke you thinke) undeserving destruction. What
waies he used to bring me to it, if I should tell you, I should
tediously trouble you with as much poysonous hypocrisie,
desperate fraude, smoothe malice, hidden ambition, & smiling
envie, as in any living person could be harbored. But I list it
not, no remembrance, (no, of naughtines) delights me, but mine
own; & me thinks, the accusing his traines might in some
manner excuse my fault, which certainly I loth to doo. But
the conclusion is, that I gave order to some servants of mine,
whom I thought as apte for such charities as my selfe, to leade
him out into a forrest, & there to kill him.

But those theeves (better natured to my sonne then my
selfe) spared his life, letting him goe, to learne to live poorely:
which he did, giving himselfe to be a private souldier, in a
countrie here by. But as he was redy to be greatly advaunced
for some noble peeces of service which he did, he hearde newes
of me: who (dronke in my affection to that unlawfull and unnaturall sonne of mine) suffered my self so to be governed by
him, that all favors and punishments passed by him, all offices,
and places of importance, distributed to his favourites; so that
ere I was aware, I had left my self nothing but the name of a
King: which he shortly wearie of too, with many indignities
(if any thing may be called an indignity, which was laid upon
me) threw me out of my seat, and put out my eies; and then
(proud in his tyrannie) let me goe, nether imprisoning, nor
killing me: but rather delighting to make me feele my miserie;
miserie indeed, if ever there were any; full of wretchednes,
fuller of disgrace, and fullest of guiltines. And as he came to
the crowne by so unjust meanes, as unjustlie he kept it, by
force of stranger souldiers in *Cittadels*, the nestes of tyranny,
& murderers of libertie; disarming all his own countrimen,
that no man durst shew himself a wel-willer of mine: to say
the trueth (I think) few of thẽ being so (considering my cruell
follie to my good sonne, and foolish kindnes to my unkinde
bastard:) but if there were any who fell to pitie of so great a
fall, and had yet any sparkes of unstained duety lefte in them
towardes me, yet durst they not shewe it, scarcely with giving

me almes at their doores; which yet was the onelie sustenaunce
of my distressed life, no bodie daring to shewe so much charitie,
as to lende me a hande to guide my darke steppes: Till this
sonne of mine (God knowes, woorthie of a more vertuous, and
more fortunate father) forgetting my abhominable wrongs, not
recking danger, & neglecting the present good way he was in
doing himselfe good, came hether to doo this kind office you
see him performe towards me, to my unspeakable griefe; not
onely because his kindnes is a glasse evẽ to my blind eyes, of
my naughtines, but that above all griefes, it greeves me he
should desperatly adventure the losse of his soul-deserving life
for mine, that yet owe more to fortune for my deserts, as if he
would cary mudde in a chest of christall. For well I know, he
that now raigneth, how much soever (and with good reason)
he despiseth me, of all men despised; yet he will not let
slippe any advantage to make away him, whose just title (ennobled by courage and goodnes) may one day shake the seate of
a never secure tyrannie. And for this cause I craved of him
to leade me to the toppe of this rocke, indeede I must confesse,
with meaning to free him from so Serpentine a companion as I
am. But he finding what I purposed, onely therein since he
was borne, shewed himselfe disobedient unto me. And now
Gentlemen, you have the true storie, which I pray you publish
to the world, that my mischievous proceedinges may be the
glorie of his filiall pietie, the onely reward now left for so great
a merite. And if it may be, let me obtaine that of you, which
my sonne denies me: for never was there more pity in saving
any, then in ending me; both because therein my agonies shall
ende, and so shall you preserve this excellent young man, who
els wilfully folowes his owne ruine.

4   The matter in it self lamentable, lamentably expressed by
the old Prince (which needed not take to himselfe the gestures
of pitie, since his face could not put of the markes thereof)
greatly moved the two Princes to compassion, which could not
stay in such harts as theirs without seeking remedie. But by
and by the occasion was presented: for *Plexirtus* (so was the
bastard called) came thether with fortie horse, onely of purpose
to murder this brother; of whose comming he had soone
advertisement, and thought no eyes of sufficient credite in such
a matter, but his owne; and therefore came him selfe to be

actor, and spectator.   And as soone as he came, not regarding
the weake (as he thought) garde of but two men, commaunded
some of his followers to set their handes to his, in the killing of
Leonatus.   But the young Prince (though not otherwise armed
but with a sworde) how falsely soever he was dealt with by
others, would not betray him selfe: but bravely drawing it out,
made the death of the first that assaulted him, warne his
fellowes to come more warily after him.   But then *Pyrocles*
and *Musidorus* were quickly become parties (so just a defence
deserving as much as old friendship) and so did behave them
among that cõpanie (more injurious, then valiant) that many of
them lost their lives for their wicked maister.

Yet perhaps had the number of them at last prevailed, if 5
the King of *Pontus* (lately by them made so) had not come
unlooked for to their succour.   Who (having had a dreame
which had fixt his imagination vehemently upon some great
daunger, presently to follow those two Princes whom he most
deerely loved) was come in all hast, following as well as he
could their tracke with a hundreth horses in that countrie,
which he thought (considering who then raigned) a fit place
inough to make the stage of any Tragedie.

But then the match had ben so ill made for *Plexirtus,* that 6
his ill-led life, & worse gotten honour should have tumbled
together to destructiõ; had there not come in *Tydeus* & *Telenor,*
with fortie or fiftie in their suit, to the defence of *Plexirtus.*
These two were brothers, of the noblest house of that country,
brought up frõ their infancie with *Plexirtus:* men of such
prowesse, as not to know feare in themselves, and yet to teach
it others that should deale with them: for they had often made
their lives triumph over most terrible daungers; never dis-
mayed, and ever fortunate; and truely no more setled in their
valure, then disposed to goodnesse and justice, if either they
had lighted on a better friend, or could have learned to make
friendship a child, and not the father of Vertue.   But bringing
up (rather then choise) having first knit their minds unto him,
(indeed craftie inough, eyther to hide his faultes, or never to
shew them, but when they might pay home) they willingly
held out the course, rather to satisfie him, then al the world;
and rather to be good friendes, then good men: so as though
they did not like the evill he did, yet they liked him that did

the evill; and though not councellors of the offence, yet protectors of the offender.   Now they having heard of this sodaine going out, with so small a company, in a country full of evil-wishing minds toward him (though they knew not the cause) followed him; till they found him in such case as they were to venture their lives, or else he to loose his: which they did with such force of minde and bodie, that truly I may justly say, *Pyrocles* & *Musidorus* had never till then found any, that could make them so well repeate their hardest lesson in the feates of armes.   And briefly so they did, that if they overcame not; yet were they not overcome, but caried away that ungratefull maister of theirs to a place of securitie; howsoever the Princes laboured to the cõtrary.   But this matter being thus far begun, it became not the constãcie of the Princes so to leave it; but in all hast making forces both in *Pontus* and *Phrygia*, they had in fewe dayes, lefte him but only that one strong place where he was.   For feare having bene the onely knot that had fastned his people unto him, that once untied by a greater force, they all scattered from him; like so many birdes, whose cage had bene broken.

7   In which season the blind King (having in the chief cittie of his Realme, set the crowne upõ his sonne *Leonatus* head) with many teares (both of joy and sorrow) setting forth to the whole people, his owne fault & his sonnes vertue, after he had kist him, and forst his sonne to accept honour of him (as of his newe-become subject) evẽ in a moment died, as it should seeme: his hart broken with unkindnes & affliction, stretched so farre beyond his limits with this excesse of cõfort, as it was able no longer to keep safe his roial spirits.   But the new King (having no lesse lovingly performed all duties to him dead, then alive) pursued on the siege of his unnatural brother, asmuch for the revenge of his father, as for the establishing of his owne quiet.   In which siege truly I cannot but acknowledge the prowesse of those two brothers, then whom the Princes never found in all their travell two men of greater habilitie to performe, nor of habler skill for conduct.

8   But *Plexirtus* finding, that if nothing els, famin would at last bring him to destructiõ, thought better by hũblenes to creepe, where by pride he could not march.   For certainely so had nature formed him, & the exercise of craft conformed him

to all turnings of sleights, that though no mã had lesse goodnes in his soule then he, no man could better find the places whence argumĕts might grow of goodnesse to another: though no man felt lesse pitie; no man could tel better how to stir pitie: no mã more impudĕt to deny, where proofes were not manifest; no man more ready to confesse with a repenting mãner of aggravating his owne evil, where denial would but make the fault fowler. Now he tooke this way, that having gotten a pasport for one (that pretended he would put *Plexirtus* alive into his hãds) to speak with the King his brother, he him selfe (though much against the minds of the valiant brothers, who rather wished to die in brave defence) with a rope about his necke, barefooted, came to offer himselfe to the discretion of *Leonatus*. Where what submission he used, how cunningly in making greater the faulte he made the faultines the lesse, how artificially he could set out the torments of his owne cõscience, with the burdensome comber he had found of his ambitious desires, how finely seeming to desire nothing but death, as ashamed to live, he begd life, in the refusing it, I am not cunning inough to be able to expresse: but so fell out of it, that though at first sight *Leonatus* saw him with no other eie, then as the murderer of his father; & anger already began to paint revenge in many colours, ere long he had not only gotten pitie, but pardon, and if not an excuse of the fault past, yet an opinion of a future amẽdment: while the poore villaines (chiefe ministers of his wickednes, now betraied by the author therof,) were delivered to many cruell sorts of death; he so handling it, that it rather seemed, he had rather come into the defence of an unremediable mischiefe already cõmitted, then that they had done it at first by his consent.

In such sort the Princes left these recõciled brothers 9 (*Plexirtus* in all his behaviour carying him in far lower degree of service, then the ever-noble nature of *Leonatus* would suffer him) & taking likewise their leaves of their good friend the King of *Pontus* (who returned to enjoy their benefite, both of his wife and kingdome) they privately went thence, having onely with them the two valiant brothers, who would needs accõpanie them, through divers places; they foure dooing actes more daungerous, though lesse famous, because they were but privat chivalries: till hearing of the faire and vertuous Queene

Erona of *Lycia*, besieged by the puissant King of *Armenia*, they
bent ₍hemselves to her succour, both because the weaker
(& weaker as being a Ladie,) & partly because they heard the
King of *Armenia* had in his company three of the most famous
men living, for matters of armes, that were knowne to be in the
worlde. Whereof one was the Prince *Plangus*, (whose name
was sweetened by your breath, peerlesse Ladie, when the last
daie it pleased you to mention him unto me) the other two
were two great Princes (though holding of him) *Barzanes* and
Euardes, men of Giant-like both hugenes and force: in which
two especially, the trust the King had of victorie, was reposed.
And of them, those two brothers *Tydeus* and *Telenor* (sufficient
judges in warlike matters) spake so high commendations, that
the two yong Princes had even a youthfull longing to have
some triall of their vertue. And therefore as soone as they
were entred into *Lycia* they joyned thēselves with them that
faithfully served the poore Queene, at that time besieged: and
ere long animated in such sort their almost overthrowne harts,
that they went by force to relieve the towne, though they were
deprived of a great part of their strength by the parting of the
two brothers, who were sent for in all hast to returne to their
old friend and maister, *Plexirtus*: who (willingly hood-
winking themselves from seeing his faultes, and binding themselves to beleeve what he said) often abused the vertue of
courage to defend his fowle vice of injustice. But now they
were sent for to advaunce a conquest he was about; while
Pyrocles and *Musidorus* pursued the deliverie of the Queene
Erona.

CHAP. 11.

[1] Dorus *his suite to* Pamela *interrupted by* Mopsas *waking.* [2] *The
sisters going with* Zelmane *to wash themselves.* [3] *The
pleasantnes of the river.* [4] *The pleasure* Zelmane *had in
seeing them, uttered* [5] *in speach,* [6] *and song.* [7] *She led by a
spaniel, to know, and hurte her noble rivall.* [8] *The parting
of that fraye.*

I Have heard (said *Pamela*) that parte of the story of *Plangus*
whē he passed through this country: therfore you may
(if you list) passe over that warre of *Eronaes* quarrell, lest if you

214

speake too much of warre matters, you should wake *Mopsa*, which might happily breed a great broile. He looked, and saw 1 that *Mopsa* indeed sat swallowing of sleepe with opē mouth, making such a noise withal, as no bodie could lay the stealing of a nappe to her charge. Whereupon, willing to use that occasion, he kneeled downe, and with humble-hartednesse, & harty earnestnes printed in his graces, Alas (said he) divine Lady, who have wrought such miracles in me, as to make a Prince (none of the basest) to thinke all principalities base, in respect of the sheephooke, which may hold him up in your sight; vouchsafe now at last to heare in direct words my humble sute, while this dragō sleepes, that keepes the golden fruite. If in my desire I wish, or in my hopes aspire, or in my imagination faine to my selfe any thing which may be the lest spot to that heavenly vertue, which shines in all your doings; I pray the eternal powers, that the words I speak may be deadly poysons, while they are in my mouth, and that all my hopes, all my desires, all my imaginations, may onely worke their owne confusion. But if love, love of you, love of your vertues, seeke onely that favour of you, which becommeth that gratefulnes, which cānot misbecome your excellencie, O doo not: He would have said further, but *Pamela* calling aloud *Mopsa*, she sodainly start up, staggering, and rubbing her eies, ran first out of the doore, and then backe to them, before she knew how she went out, or why she came in againe: till at length, being fully come to her little selfe, she asked *Pamela*, why she had called her. For nothing (said *Pamela*) but that you might heare some tales of your servants telling: and therefore now (said she) *Dorus* go on.

But as he (who found no so good sacrifice, as obedience) 2 was returning to the story of himselfe, *Philoclea* came in, & by and by after her, *Miso*; so as for that time they were faine to let *Dorus* depart. But *Pamela* (delighted evē to preserve in her memory, the words of so wel a beloved speaker) repeated the whole substance to her sister, till their sober dinner being come and gone, to recreate themselves something, (even tyred with the noysomnes of *Misos* conversation) they determyned to goe (while the heate of the day lasted) to bath themselves (such being the maner of the *Arcadian* nymphes often to doo) in the river of *Ladon*, and take with them a Lute, meaning to delight

them under some shadow. But they could not stir, but that
Miso with her daughter *Mopsa* was after them: and as it lay
in their way to passe by the other lodge, *Zelmane* out of her
window espied them, and so stale downe after them: which
she might the better doo because that *Gynecia* was sicke, and
Basilius (that day being his birth-day) according to his maner,
was busie about his devotions; and therefore she went after,
hoping to finde some time to speake with *Philoclea*: but not a
word could she beginne, but that *Miso* would be one of the
audience; so that she was driven to recommend thinking,
speaking, and all, to her eyes, who diligently perfourmed her
trust, till they came to the rivers side; which of all the rivers
3 of *Greece* had the price for excellent purenesse and sweetenesse,
in so much as the verie bathing in it, was accoũted exceeding
healthfull.   It ranne upon so fine and delicate a ground, as one
could not easely judge, whether the River did more wash the
gravell, or the gravel did purifie the River; the River not
running forth right, but almost continually winding, as if the
lower streames would returne to their spring, or that the River
had a delight to play with it selfe.   The banckes of either side
seeming armes of the loving earth, that faine would embrace
it; and the River a wanton nymph which still would stirre
from it: either side of the bancke being fringed with most
beautifull trees, which resisted the sunnes dartes from over-
much pearcing the naturall coldnes of the River.   There was
the

But among
the rest a goodly *Cypres*, who bowing her faire head over the
water, it seemed she looked into it, and dressed her greene
lockes, by that running River. There the Princesses determining to bath themselves, though it was so priviledged a place,
upon paine of death, as no bodie durst presume to come thither,
yet for the more surety, they looked round about, and could see
nothing but a water spaniell, who came downe the river, shewing that he hunted for a duck, & with a snuffling grace,
disdaining that his smelling force coulde not as well prevaile
thorow the water, as thorow the aire; & therefore wayting
with his eye, to see whether he could espie the duckes getting
up againe: but then a little below them failing of his purpose,
he got out of the river, & shaking off the water (as great men

do their friends, now he had no further cause to use it) in-weeded himselfe so, as the Ladies lost the further marking his sportfulnesse: and inviting *Zelmane* also to wash her selfe with them, and she excusing her selfe with having taken a late cold, they began by peece-meale to take away the eclipsing of their apparell.

Zelmane would have put to her helping hand, but she was 4 taken with such a quivering, that she thought it more wise-dome to leane her selfe to a tree and looke on, while *Miso* and *Mopsa* (like a couple of foreswat melters) were getting the pure silver of their bodies out of the ure of their garments. But as the rayments went of to receave kisses of the ground, *Zelmane* envied the happinesse of all, but of the smocke was even jealous, and when that was taken away too, and that *Philoclea* remained (for her *Zelmane* onely marked) like a *Dyamond* taken from out the rocke, or rather like the Sun getting from under a cloud, and shewing his naked beames to the full vew, then was the beautie too much for a patient sight, the delight too strong for a stayed conceipt: so that *Zelmane* could not choose but runne, to touch, embrace, and kisse her; But conscience made her come to her selfe, & leave *Philoclea*, who blushing, and withall smiling, making shamefast-nesse pleasant, and pleasure shamefast, tenderly moved her feete, unwonted to feele the naked ground, till the touch of the cold water made a prettie kinde of shrugging come over her bodie, like the twinckling of the fairest among the fixed stars. But the River it selfe gave way unto her, so that she was streight brest high; which was the deepest that there-about she could be: and when cold *Ladon* had once fully imbraced them, him-selfe was no more so cold to those Ladies, but as if his cold complexion had bene heated with love, so seemed he to play about every part he could touch.

Ah sweete, now sweetest *Ladon* (said *Zelmane*) why dost 5 thou not stay thy course to have more full tast of thy happines? But the reason is manifest, the upper streames make such haste to have their part of embracing, that the nether (though lothly) must needs give place unto them. O happie *Ladon*, within whom she is, upon whom her beautie fals, thorow whom her eye perceth. O happie *Ladon*, which art now an unperfect mirror of al perfection, canst thou ever forget

the blessednes of this impression? if thou do, then let thy bed
be turned from fine gravel, to weeds & mudde; if thou doo,
let some unjust niggards make weres to spoile thy beauty; if
thou do, let some greater river fal into thee, to take away the
name of *Ladon*. Oh *Ladon*, happie *Ladon*, rather slide then
run by her, lest thou shouldest make her legs slippe from her;
and then, O happy *Ladon*, who would then cal thee, but the
most cursed *Ladon*? But as the Ladies plaid them in the water,
somtimes striking it with their hands, the water (making lines
in his face) seemed to smile at such beating, and with twentie
bubbles, not to be content to have the picture of their face in
large upon him, but he would in ech of those bubbles set forth
the miniature of them.

6   But *Zelmane*, whose sight was gaine-said by nothing but the
transparent vaile of *Ladon*, (like a chamber where a great fire is
kept, though the fire be at one stay, yet with the continuance
continually hath his heate encreased) had the coales of her
affection so kindled with wonder, and blowne with delight, that
nowe all her parts grudged, that her eyes should doo more homage, then they, to the Princesse of them. In somuch that
taking up the Lute, her wit began to be with a divine furie
inspired; her voice would in so beloved an occasion second her
wit; her hands accorded the Lutes musicke to the voice; her
panting hart daunced to the musicke; while I thinke her feete
did beate the time; while her bodie was the roome where it
should be celebrated; her soule the Queene which shoulde be
delighted. And so togither went the utterance and the invention, that one might judge, it was *Philocleas* beautie which did
speedily write it in her eyes; or the sense thereof, which did
word by word endite it in her minde, whereto she (but as an
organ) did onely lend utterance. The song was to this purpose.

> WHat toong can her perfections tell
>   In whose each part all pens may dwell?
> Her haire fine threeds of finest gould
> In curled knots mans thought to hold:
> But that her fore-head sayes in me
> A whiter beautie you may see.
> Whiter indeed; more white then snow,
> Which on cold winters face doth grow.

That doth present those even browes,
Whose equall line their angles bowes,
Like to the Moone when after chaunge
Her horned head abroad doth raunge:
And arches be to heavenly lids,
Whose winke ech bold attempt forbids.
For the blacke starres those Spheares containe,
The matchlesse paire, even praise doth staine.
No lampe, whose light by Art is got,
No Sunne, which shines, and seeth not,
Can liken them without all peere,
Save one as much as other cleere:
Which onely thus unhappie be,
Because themselves they cannot see.
    Her cheekes with kindly claret spred.
Aurora like new out of bed,
Or like the fresh Queene-apples side,
Blushing at sight of Phœbus pride.
    Her nose, her chinne pure ivorie weares:
No purer then the pretie eares.
So that therein appeares some blood,
Like wine and milke that mingled stood
In whose Incirclets if ye gaze,
Your eyes may tread a Lovers maze.
But with such turnes the voice to stray,
No talke untaught can finde the way.
The tippe no jewell needes to weare:
The tippe is jewell of the eare.
    But who those ruddie lippes can misse?
Which blessed still themselves doo kisse.
Rubies, Cherries, and Roses new,
In worth, in taste, in perfitte hewe:
Which never part but that they showe
Of pretious pearle the double rowe,
The second sweetly-fenced warde,
Her heav'nly-dewed tongue to garde.
Whence never word in vaine did flowe.
    Faire under these doth stately growe,
The handle of this pretious worke,
The neck, in which strange graces lurke.

THE COUNTESSE OF PEMBROKES

Such be I thinke the sumptuous towers
Which skill dooth make in Princes bowers.
So good a say invites the eye,
A little downward to espie,
The livelie clusters of her brests,
Of Venus *babe the wanton nests:*
Like pomels round of Marble cleere:
Where azurde veines well mixt appeere.
With dearest tops of porphyrie.

   Betwixt these two a way doth lie,
A way more worthie beauties fame,
Then that which beares the Milkie *name.*
This leades into the joyous field,
Which onely still doth Lillies yeeld:
But Lillies such whose native smell
The Indian odours doth excell.
Waste it is calde, for it doth waste
Mens lives, untill it be imbraste.

   There may one see, and yet not see
Her ribbes in white all armed be.
More white then Neptunes *fomie face,*
When strugling rocks he would imbrace.

   In those delights the wandring thought
Might of each side astray be brought,
But that her navel doth unite,
In curious circle, busie sight:
A daintie seale of virgin-waxe,
Where nothing but impression lackes.

   Her bellie then gladde sight doth fill,
Justly entitled Cupids *hill.*
A hill most fitte for such a master,
A spotlesse mine of Alablaster.
Like Alablaster faire and sleeke,
But soft and supple satten like.
In that sweete seate the Boy doth sport:
Loath, I must leave his chiefe resort.
„ For such a use the world hath gotten,
„ The best things still must be forgotten.

   Yet never shall my song omitte
Thighes, for Ovids *song more fitte;*

Which flanked with two sugred flankes,
Lift up their stately swelling bankes;
That Albion *clives in whitenes passe:*
With hanches smooth as looking glasse.

 But bow all knees, now of her knees
My tongue doth tell what fancie sees.
The knottes of joy, the gemmes of love,
Whose motion makes all graces move.
Whose bought incav'd doth yeeld such sight,
Like cunning Painter shadowing white.
The gartring place with child-like signe,
Shewes easie print in mettall fine.
But then againe the flesh doth rise
In her brave calves, like christall skies.
Whose Atlas *is a smallest small,*
More white then whitest bone of all.

 Thereout steales out that round cleane foote
This noble Cedars pretious roote:
In shewe and sent pale violets,
Whose steppe on earth all beautie sets.

 But back unto her back, my Muse,
Where Ledas *swanne his feathers mewes,*
Along whose ridge such bones are met,
Like comfits round in marchpane set.

 Her shoulders be like two white Doves,
Pearching within square royall rooves,
Which leaded are with silver skinne,
Passing the hate-sport Ermelin.
And thence those armes derived are;
The Phœnix *wings are not so rare*
For faultlesse length, and stainelesse hewe,

 Ah woe is me, my woes renewe;
Now course doth leade me to her hand,
Of my first love the fatall band.
Where whitenes dooth for ever sitte:
Nature *her selfe enameld it.*
For there with strange compact dooth lie
Warme snow, moyst pearle, softe ivorie.
There fall those Saphir-coloured brookes,
Which conduit-like with curious crookes,

Sweete Ilands make in that sweete land.
As for the fingers of the hand,
The bloudy shaftes of Cupids *warre,*
With amatists they headed are.

   Thus hath each part his beauties part,
But how the Graces doo impart
To all her limmes a speciall grace,
Becomming every time and place.
Which doth even beautie beautifie,
And most bewitch the wretched eye.
How all this is but a faire Inne
Of fairer guestes, which dwell within.
Of whose high praise, and praisefull blisse,
Goodnes the penne, heaven paper is.
The inke immortall fame dooth lende :
As I began, so must I ende.

   No tongue can her perfeƈtions tell,
In whose each part all tongues may dwell.

But as *Zelmane* was cõming to the latter end of her song,
she might see the same water-spaniell which before had hũted,
come and fetch away one of *Philocleas* gloves ; whose fine proportion, shewed well what a daintie guest was wont there
to be lodged. It was a delight to *Zelmane*, to see that the
dogge was therewith delighted, and so let him goe a little way
withall, who quickly caried it out of sight among certaine trees
and bushes, which were very close together. But by & by he
came againe, & amongst the raiments (*Miso* and *Mopsa* being
preparing sheets against their comming out) the dog lighted
upon a little booke of foure or five leaves of paper, & was
bearing that away to. But then *Zelmane* (not knowing what
importãce it might be of) ran after the dog, who going streight
to those bushes, she might see the dog deliver it to a Gentleman
who secretly lay there. But she hastily cõming in, the Gẽtleman rose up, & with a courteous (though sad) countenance
presented himselfe unto her. *Zelmanes* eies streight willed her
mind to marke him : for she thought, in her life she had never
seene a mã of a more goodly presence, in whom strong making
tooke not away delicacie, nor beautie fiercenesse : being indeed
such a right manlike man, as Nature often erring, yet shewes

she would faine make. But when she had a while (not without admiration) vewed him, she desired him to deliver backe the glove & paper, because they were the Ladie *Philocleas*; telling him withall, that she would not willingly let thẽ know of his close lying in that prohibited place, while they were bathing thẽselues; because she knew they would be mortally offended withall. Faire Ladie (answered he) the worst of the complaint is already passed, since I feele of my fault in my self the punish-mẽt. But for these things I assure you, it was my dogs wanton boldnesse, not my presumption. With that he gave her backe the paper: But for the glove (said he) since it is my Ladie *Philocleas*, give me leave to keepe it, since my hart cãnot per-suade it selfe to part from it. And I pray you tell the Lady (Lady indeed of all my desires) that owes it, that I will direct my life to honour this glove with serving her. O villain (cried out *Zelmane*, madded with finding an unlooked-for Rivall, and that he would make her a messenger) dispatch (said she) and deliver it, or by the life of her that owes it, I wil make thy soul (though too base a price) pay for it. And with that drewe out her sworde, which (*Amazon*-like) she ever ware about her. The Gentlemã retired himself into an open place frõ among the bushes; & thẽ drawing out his too, he offred to deliver it unto her, saying withall, God forbid I should use my sworde against you, since (if I be not deceived) you are the same famous *Amazon*, that both defended my Ladies just title of beautie against the valiant *Phalantus*, & saved her life in killing the Lion: therfore I am rather to kisse your hands, with ac-knowledging my selfe boũd to obey you. But this courtesie was worse then a bastonado to *Zelmane*: so that againe with ragefull eyes she bad him defend himselfe, for no lesse then his life should answere it. A hard case (said he) to teach my sworde that lesson, which hath ever used to turne it self to a shield in a Ladies presence. But *Zelmane* harkening to no more wordes, began with such wittie furie to pursue him with blowes & thrusts, that Nature & Vertue commanded the Gentleman to looke to his safetie. Yet stil courtesie, that seemed incorpo-rate in his hart, would not be perswaded by daunger to offer any offence, but only to stand upon the best defensive gard he could; somtimes going backe, being content in that respect to take on the figure of cowardise; sometime with strong and well-met wards; sometime cunning avoidings of his body; and some-times faining some blowes, which himself puld backe before they needed to be withstood. And so with play did he a good while fight against the fight of *Zelmane*, who (more spited with that curtesie, that one that did nothing should be able to resist her) burned away with choller any motions, which might grow out of her owne sweet dispositiõ, determining to kill him if he fought no better; & so redoubling her blowes, drave the stranger to no other shift, then to warde, and go backe; at that time seeming the image of innocencie against violence. But at length he found, that both in publike and private respectes, who standes onely upon defence, stands upon no defence: For *Zelmane* seeming to strike at his head, and he going to warde it, withall stept backe as he was accustomed, she stopt her blow in the aire, and suddenly turning the point, ranne full at his breast; so as he was driven with the pommell of his sworde (having no other weapon of defence) to beate it downe: but the thrust was so strong, that he could not so wholy beate it awaie, but that it met with his thigh, thorow which it ranne. But *Zelmane* retiring her sworde, and seeing his bloud, victorious anger was conquered by the before-conquered pittie; and hartily sorie, and even ashamed with her selfe she was, considering how little he had done, who well she found could have done more. In so much that she said, truly I am sorie for your hurt, but your selfe gave the cause, both in refusing to deliver the glove, and yet not fighting as I knowe you could have done. But (saide shee) because I perceave you disdayne to fight with a woman, it may be before a yeare come about, you shall meete with a neere kinsman of mine, *Pyrocles* Prince of *Macedon*, and I give you my worde, he for me shall maintaine this quarell against you. I would (answered *Amphialus*) I had many more such hurtes to meete and know that worthy Prince, whose vertue I love & admire, though my good destiny hath not bene to see his person.

8   But as they were so speaking, the yong Ladies came, to whõ *Mopsa* (curious in any thing, but her own good behaviour) having followed & seene *Zelmane* fighting, had cried, what she had seene, while they were drying themselves, & the water (with some drops) seemed to weepe, that it should parte from such bodies. But they carefull of *Zelmane* (assuring themselves

that any *Arcadian* would beare reverence to them) *Pamela* with
a noble mind, and *Philoclea* with a loving (hastily hiding the
beauties, whereof Nature was prowde, and they ashamed) they
made quicke worke to come to save *Zelmane*. But already they
found them in talke, & *Zelmane* careful of his wound. But
whẽ they saw him they knew it was their cousin germain, the
famous *Amphialus*; whom yet with a sweete-graced bitternes
they blamed for breaking their fathers commaundement, especially while themselves were in such sort retired. But he
craved pardon, protesting unto them that he had onely bene to
seeke solitary places, by an extreme melancholy that had a good
while possest him, and guided to that place by his spaniell, where
while the dog hunted in the river, he had withdrawne himselfe
to pacifie with sleepe his over-watched eyes : till a dreame
waked him, and made him see that whereof he had dreamed, &
withall not obscurely signified that he felt the smart of his owne
doings. But *Philoclea* (that was even jealous of her self for
Zelmane) would needs have her glove, and not without so mighty
a loure as that face could yeeld. As for *Zelmane* when she
knew, it was *Amphialus*, Lord *Amphialus* (said she) I have lõg
desired to know you, heretofore I must confesse with more good
will, but still with honoring your vertue, though I love not your
person : & at this time I pray you let us take care of your
wound, upon cõdition you shal hereafter promise, that a more
knightly combat shalbe performed betweene us. *Amphialus*
answered in honorable sort, but with such excusing himselfe,
that more and more accused his love to *Philoclea*, & provoked
more hate in *Zelmane*. But *Mopsa* had already called certaine
shepheards not far of (who knew & wel observed their limits)
to come and helpe to carrie away *Amphialus*, whose wound
suffered him not without daunger to straine it : and so he
leaving himselfe with them, departed from them, faster bleeding
in his hart, then at his wound : which bound up by the sheetes,
wherwith *Philoclea* had bene wrapped, made him thanke the
wound, and blesse the sword for that favour.

CHAP. 12.

[1]*How* Basilius *found* Plangus: [2]*his lamētation.* [3]Philoclea
entreated by Zelmane *to relate the storie of* Erona.

[1] HE being gone, the Ladies (with mery anger talking, ın
what naked simplicitie their cousin had seene thē)
returned to the lodge-warde : yet thinking it too early (as long
as they had any day) to breake of so pleasing a company, with
going to performe a cūbersome obediēnce, *Zelmane* invited them
to the little arbour, only reserved for her, which they willingly
did: and there sitting, *Pamela* having a while made the lute in
his lāguage, shew how glad it was to be touched by her fingers,
Zelmane delivered up the paper, which *Amphialus* had at first
yeelded unto her: and seeing written upon the backside of it,
the complaint of *Plangus*, remembring what *Dorus* had told her,
and desiring to know how much *Philoclea* knew of her estate,
she tooke occasion in the presenting of it, to aske whether it
were any secret, or no. No truely (answered *Philoclea*) it is but
even an exercise of my fathers writing, upon this occasion : He
was one day (somwhile before your comming hether) walking
abroade, having us two with him, almost a mile hence; and
crossing a hie way, which comes from the cittie of *Megalopolis*,
he saw this Gentleman, whose name is there written, one of the
proprest and best-graced men that ever I sawe, being of middle
age, and of a meane stature. He lay as then under a tree,
while his servaunts were getting fresh post-horses for him. It
might seeme he was tired with the extreme travaile he had
taken, and yet not so tyred, that he forced to take any rest ; so
hasty he was upon his journey: and withall so sorrowfull, that
the very face thereof was painted in his face ; which with pitifull
motions, even groanes, teares, and passionate talking to him selfe,
moved my Father to fall in talke with him: who at first not
knowing him, answered him in such a desperate phrase of griefe,
that my Father afterward tooke a delight to set it downe in such
forme as you see: which if you read, what you doubt of, my
sister and I are hable to declare unto you. *Zelmane* willingly
opened the leaves, and read it, being written Dialogue-wise in
this manner.

Plangus.   Basilius.

ALas how long this pilgrimage doth last?
   What greater ills have now the heavens in store,
  To couple comming harmes with sorrowes past?
Long since my voice is hoarce, and throte is sore,
  With cries to skies, and curses to the ground,
  But more I plaine, I feele my woes the more.
Ah where was first that cruell cunning found,
  To frame of Earth a vessell of the minde,
  Where it should be to selfe-destruction bound?
What needed so high sprites such mansions blind?
  Or wrapt in flesh what do they here obtaine,
  But glorious name of wretched humaine-kind?
Balles to the starres, and thralles to Fortunes raigne;
  Turnd from themselves, infected with their cage,
  Where death is feard, and life is held with paine.
Like players pla'st to fill a filthy stage,
  Where chaunge of thoughts one foole to other shewes,
  And all but jests, save onely sorrowes rage.
The child feeles that; the man that feeling knowes,
  With cries first borne, the presage of his life,
  Where wit but serves, to have true tast of woes.
A Shop of shame, a Booke where blots be rife
  This bodie is: this bodie so composed,
  As in it selfe to nourish mortall strife.
So divers be the Elements disposed
 . In this weake worke, that it can never be
  Made uniforme to any state reposed.
Griefe onely makes his wretched state to see
  (Even like a toppe which nought but whipping moves)
  This man, this talking beast, this walking tree.
Griefe is the stone which finest judgement proves:
  For who grieves not hath but a blockish braine,
  Since cause of griefe no cause from life removes.

How long wilt thou with monefull musicke staine
  The cheerefull notes these pleasant places yeeld,
  Where all good haps a perfect state maintaine?

Plangus.   *Curst be good haps, and curst be they that build*
      Their hopes on haps, and do not make despaire
      For all these certaine blowes the surest shield.
  Shall I that saw Eronaes *shining haire*
      Torne with her hands, and those same hands of snow
      With losse of purest blood themselves to teare?
  Shall I that saw those brests, where beauties flow,
      Swelling with sighes, made pale with mindes disease,
      And saw those eyes (those Sonnes) such shoures to shew,
  Shall I, whose eares her mournefull words did seaze,
      Her words in syrup laid of sweetest breath,
      Relent those thoughts, which then did so displease?
  No, no: Despaire my dayly lesson saith,
      And saith, although I seeke my life to flie,
      Plangus *must live to see* Eronaes *death.*
  Plangus *must live some helpe for her to trie*
      Though in despaire, so Love *enforceth me;*
      Plangus *doth live, and must* Erona *dye?*
  Erona *dye? O heaven (if heaven there be)*
      Hath all thy whirling course so small effect?
      Serve all thy starrie eyes this shame to see?
  Let doltes in haste some altars faire erect
      To those high powers, which idly sit above,
      And vertue do in greatest need neglect.

Basilius.   *O man, take heed, how thou the Gods do move*
      To irefull wrath, which thou canst not resist.
      Blasphemous words the speaker vaine do prove.
  Alas while we are wrapt in foggie mist
      Of our selfe-love (so passions do deceave)
      We thinke they hurt, when most they do assist.
  To harme us wormes should that high Justice leave
      His nature? nay, himselfe? for so it is.
      What glorie from our losse can he receave?
  But still our dazeled eyes their way do misse,
      While that we do at his sweete scourge repine,
      The kindly way to beate us to our blisse.
  If she must dye, then hath she past the line
      Of lothsome dayes, whose losse how canst thou mone,
      That doost so well their miseries define?

But such we are with inward tempest blowne
Of mindes quite contrarie in waves of will :
We mone that lost, which had we did bemone.

And shall shee dye? shall cruell fier spill   Plangus.
Those beames that set so many harts on fire?
Hath she not force even death with love to kill?
Nay even cold Death enflamde with hot desire
Her to enjoy, where joy it selfe is thrall,
Will spoile the earth of his most rich attire.
Thus Death becomes a rivall to us all,
And hopes with foule embracements her to get,
In whose decay Vertues faire shrine must fall.
O Vertue weake, shall death his triumph set
Upon thy spoiles, which never should lye waste?
Let Death first dye; be thou his worthy let.
By what eclipse shall that Sonne be defaste?
What myne hath erst throwne downe so faire a tower?
What sacriledge hath such a saint disgra'st?
The world the garden is, she is the flower
That sweetens all the place; she is the guest
Of rarest price, both heav'n and earth her bower.
And shall (ô me) all this in ashes rest?
Alas, if you a Phœnix *new will have*
Burnt by the Sunne, she first must build her nest.
But well you know, the gentle Sunne would save
Such beames so like his owne, which might have might
In him, the thoughts of Phaëtons *damme to grave.*
Therefore, alas, you use vile Vulcans *spight,*
Which nothing spares, to melt that Virgin-waxe
Which while it is, it is all Asias *light.*
O Mars, *for what doth serve thy armed axe?*
To let that wit-old beast consume in flame
Thy Venus *child, whose beautie* Venus *lackes?*
O Venus *(if her praise no envy frames,*
In thy high minde) get her thy husbands grace.
Sweete speaking oft a currish hart reclaimes.   „
O eyes of mine, where once she saw her face,
Her face which was more lively in my hart;
O braine, where thought of her hath onely place;

O hand, which toucht her hand when she did part;
O lippes, that kist her hand with my teares sprent;
O toonge, then dumbe, not daring tell my smart;
O soule, whose love in her is onely spent,
   What ere you see, thinke, touch, kisse, speake, or love,
   Let all for her, and unto her be bent.

Basilius. *Thy wailing words do much my spirits move,*
   They uttred are in such a feeling fashion,
   That sorrowes worke against my will I prove.
Me-thinkes I am partaker of thy passion,
   And in thy case do glasse mine owne debilitie:
   Selfe-guiltie folke most prone to feele compassion.
Yet Reason saith, Reason should have abilitie,
   To hold these worldly things in such proportion,
   As let them come or go with even facilitie.
But our Desires tyrannicall extortion
   Doth force us there to set our chiefe delightfulnes,
   Where but a baiting place is all our portion.
But still, although we faile of perfeƈt rightfulnes,
   Seeke we to tame the childish superfluities:
   Let us not winke though void of purest sightfulnes.
For what can breed more peevish incongruities,
   Then man to yeeld to female lamentations?
   Let us some grammar learne of more congruities.

Plangus. *If through mine eares pearce any consolation*
   By wise discourse, sweete tunes, or Poets fiƈtion;
   If ought I cease these hideous exclamations,
While that my soule, she, she lives in affliƈtion;
   Then let my life long time on earth maintained be,
   To wretched me, the last worst malediƈtion.
Can I, that know her sacred parts restrained be,
   For any joy, know fortunes vile displacing her,
   In morall rules let raging woes contained be?
Can I forget, when they in prison placing her,
   With swelling hart in spite and due disdainfulnes
   She lay for dead, till I helpt with unlasing her?
Can I forget, from how much mourning plainfulnes
   With Diamond in window-glasse she graved,
   Erona dye, and end thy ougly painefulnes?

Can I forget in how straunge phrase she craved
  That quickly they would her burne, drowne, or smother,
  As if by death she onely might be saved?
Then let me eke forget one hand from other :
  Let me forget that Plangus *I am called :*
  Let me forget I am sonne to my mother,
But if my memory must thus be thralled
  To that strange stroke which conquer'd all my senses,
  Can thoughts still thinking so rest unappalled?

Basilius.

Who still doth seeke against himselfe offences,
  What pardon can availe? or who employes him
  To hurt himselfe, what shields can be defenses?
Woe to poore man : ech outward thing annoyes him
  In divers kinds ; yet as he were not filled,
  He heapes in inward griefe, which most destroyes him.
Thus is our thought with paine for thistles tilled :
  Thus be our noblest parts dryed up with sorrow :
  Thus is our mind with too much minding spilled.
One day layes up stuffe of griefe for the morrow :
  And whose good haps do leave him unprovided,
  Condoling cause of friendship he will borrow.
Betwixt the good and shade of good divided,
  We pittie deeme that which but weakenes is :
  So are we from our high creation slided.
But Plangus *lest I may your sicknesse misse*
  Or rubbing hurt the sore, I here doo end.
  The asse did hurt when he did thinke to kisse.

When *Zelmane* had read it over, marveyling verie much of 3
the speeche of *Eronas* death, and therefore desirous to know
further of it, but more desirous to heare *Philoclea* speake, Most
excellent Ladie (said she) one may be little the wiser for reading
the Dialogue, since it nether sets foorth what this *Plangus* is, nor
what *Erona* is, nor what the cause should be which threatens her
with death, and him with sorow : therefore I woulde humbly
crave to understand the particular discourse thereof : because (I
must confesse) some thing in my travaile I have heard of this
strange matter, which I would be glad to find by so sweet an
authoritie confirmed. The trueth is (answered *Philoclea*) that

231

after he knew my father to be Prince of this countrie, while he
hoped to prevaile something with him in a great request he made
unto him, he was content to open fully unto him the estate both
of himselfe, and of that Ladie; which with my sisters help (said
she) who remembers it better then I, I will declare unto you:
and first of *Erona*, (being the chiefe Subject of this discourse)
this storie (with more teares and exclamations then I liste to
spende about it) he recounted.

CHAP. 13.

Erona [1]*irreligious gainst Love,* [2]*must love the base* Antiphilus, [3]*is
loved, pursued, and beleaguered by the great* Tiridates. [4]*The
two Greeke Princes ayde her.* [5]*They combatte with two
Kings;* Antiphilus *with* Plangus; *they conquerors, he prisoner.*
[6]Eronas *hard-choice to redeeme him.* [7]Tiridates *slaine,* Antiphilus *delivered,* Artaxia *chased by the two Princes,* [8]*and her
hate to them.*

1 OF late there raigned a King in *Lycia*, who had for the
blessing of his mariage, this onely daughter of his, *Erona*;
a Princesse worthie for her beautie, as much praise, as beautie
may be praise-worthy. This Princesse *Erona*, being 19. yeres
of age, seeing the countrie of *Lycia* so much devoted to *Cupid*,
as that in every place his naked pictures & images were superstitiously adored (ether moved therūto, by the esteeming that
could be no Godhead, which could breed wickednes, or the
shamefast consideration of such nakednes) procured so much of
her father, as utterly to pull downe, and deface all those statues
and pictures. Which how terriblie he punished (for to that the
Lycians impute it) quickly after appeared.

2 For she had not lived a yeare longer, when she was striken
with most obstinate Love, to a yong man but of mean parentage,
in her fathers court, named *Antiphilus*: so meane, as that he was
but the sonne of her Nurse, & by that meanes (without other
desert) became knowen of her. Now so evill could she conceale
her fire, and so wilfully persevered she in it, that her father
offering her the mariage of the great *Tiridates*, king of *Armenia*

(who desired her more then the joyes of heaven) she for *Antiphilus*
sake refused it. Many wayes her father sought to withdrawe
her from it; sometimes perswasions, sometimes threatnings;
once hiding *Antiphilus*, & giving her to understand that he was
fled the countrie: Lastly, making a solemne execution to be
done of another, under the name of *Antiphilus*, whom he kept
in prison. But nether she liked perswasions, nor feared threateninges, nor changed for absence: and when she thought him dead,
she sought all meanes (as well by poyson as by knife) to send her
soule, at least, to be maried in the eternall church with him.
This so brake the tender fathers hart, that (leaving things as he
found them) he shortly after died. Then foorthwith *Erona*
(being seazed of the crowne, and arming her will with authoritie)
sought to advance her affection to the holy title of matrimonie.

But before she could accōplish all the solēnities, she was 3
overtakē with a war the King *Tiridates* made upon her, only
for her person; towards whom (for her ruine) Love had kindled
his cruel hart; indeed cruell & tyrannous: for (being far too
strōg in the field) he spared not man, woman, and child, but (as
though there could be found no foile to set foorth the extremitie
of his love, but extremity of hatred) wrote (as it were) the sonets
of his Love, in the bloud, & tuned thē in the cries of her subjects; although his fair sister *Artaxia* (who would accōpany him
in the army) sought all meanes to appease his fury: till lastly,
he besieged *Erona* in her best citie, vowing to winne her, or
lose his life. And now had he brought her to the point ether
of a wofull consent, or a ruinous deniall; whē there came
thether (following the course which Vertue & Fortune led thē)
two excellent yoūg Princes, *Pyrocles* and *Musidorus*, the one
Prince of *Macedō*, the other of *Thessalia*: two princes, as *Plāgus*
said, (and he witnessed his saying with sighes & teares) the most
acconplished both in body & mind, that the Sun ever lookt upon.
While *Philoclea* spake those words, O sweete wordes (thought
Zelmane to her self) which are not onely a praise to me, but a
praise to praise it selfe, which out of that mouth issueth.

These 2. princes (said *Philoclea*) aswel to help the weaker 4
(especially being a Ladie) as to save a Greeke people from being
ruined by such, whom we call and count Barbarous, gathering
together such of the honestest *Lycians*, as woulde venture their
lives to succour their Princesse: giving order by a secreat

message they sent into the Citie, that they should issue with all force at an appointed time; they set upon *Tiridates* campe, with so well-guided a fiercenes, that being of both sides assaulted, he was like to be overthrowen: but that this *Plangus* (being Generall of *Tiridates* hors-men) especially ayded by the two mightie men, *Euardes* and *Barzanes*, rescued the foot-men, even almost defeated: but yet could not barre the Princes (with their suc-coures both of men and victuall) to enter the Citie.

5 Which when *Tiridates* found would make the war long, (which length seemed to him worse then a languishing con-sumption) he made a challenge of three Princes in his retinue, against those two Princes and *Antiphilus*: and that thereupon the quarrell should be decided; with compact, that neither side should helpe his felow: but of whose side the more overcame, with him the victorie should remaine. *Antiphilus* (though *Erona* chose rather to bide the brunt of warre, then venture him, yet) could not for shame refuse the offer, especially since the two strangers that had no interest in it, did willingly accept it: besides that, he sawe it like enough, that the people (werie of the miseries of war) would rather give him up, if they saw him shrinke, then for his sake venture their ruine: considering that the challengers were farre of greater worthinesse then him selfe. So it was agreed upon; and against *Pyrocles* was *Euardes*, King of *Bithinia*; *Barzanes* of *Hircania*, against *Musidorus*, two men, that thought the world scarse able to resist them: & against *Antiphilus* he placed this same *Plangus*, being his own cousin germain, & sonne to the King of *Iberia*. Now so it fell out that *Musidorus* slewe *Barzanes*, & *Pyrocles Euardes*; which victory those Princes esteemed above all that ever they had: but of the other side *Plãgus* tooke *Antiphilus* prisoner: under which colour (as if the matter had bene equal, though indeed it was not, the greater part being overcome of his side) *Tiridates* continued his war: & to bring *Erona* to a cõpelled yeelding, sent her word, that he would the third morrow after, before the walles of the towne strike of *Antiphilus* head; with-out his suite in that space were graunted: adding withall (because he had heard of her desperate affectiõ) that if in the meane time she did her selfe any hurt, what tortures could be devised should be layed upon *Antiphilus*.

6 Then lo if *Cupid* be a God, or that the tyranny of our own

thoughts seeme as a God unto us. But whatsoever it was, then
it did set foorth the miserablenes of his effectes: she being drawne
to two contraries by one cause. For the love of him cõmaunded
her to yeeld to no other: the love of him cõmaunded
him to preserve his life: which knot might well be cut, but
untied it could not be. So that Love in her passions (like a right
makebate) whispered to both sides arguments of quarrell. What
(said he of the one side) doost thou love *Antiphilus*, ô *Erona*? and
shal *Tiridates* enjoy thy bodie? with what eyes wilt thou looke
upon *Antiphilus*, when he shall know that another possesseth
thee? But if thou wilt do it, canst thou do it? canst thou force
thy hart? Thinke with thy selfe, if this man have thee, thou
shalt never have more part of *Antiphilus* thẽ if he were dead.
But thus much more, that the affectiõ shalbe gnawing, & the
remorse still present. Death perhaps will coole the rage of thy
affection: where thus, thou shalt ever love, and ever lacke.
Thinke this beside, if thou marrie *Tiridates*, *Antiphilus* is so excellent a man, that long he cannot be from being in some high
place maried: canst thou suffer that too? If an other kill him,
he doth him the wrong: if thou abuse thy body, thou doost him
the wrong. His death is a worke of nature, and either now,
or at another time he shall die. But it shalbe thy worke, thy
shamefull worke, which is in thy power to shun, to make him
live to see thy faith falsified, and his bed defiled. But when
Love had well kindled that parte of her thoughts, then went he
to the other side. What (said he) O *Erona*, and is thy Love of
Antiphilus come to that point, as thou doost now make it a question, whether he shall die, or no? O excellent affection, which for
too much love, will see his head of. Marke well the reasons of
the other side, and thou shalt see, it is but love of thy selfe which
so disputeth. Thou canst not abide *Tiridates*: this is but love
of thy selfe: thou shalt be ashamed to looke upõ him afterward;
this is but feare of shame, & love of thy selfe: thou shalt want
him as much then; this is but love of thy selfe: he shalbe
married; if he be well, why should that grieve thee, but for love
of thy selfe? No, no, pronounce these wordes if thou canst, let
Antiphilus die. Then the images of each side stood before her
understanding; one time she thought she saw *Antiphilus* dying:
an other time she thought *Antiphilus* saw her by *Tiridates*
enjoyed: twenty times calling for a servaunt to carry message

of yeelding, but before he came the minde was altered. She blusht when she considered the effect of granting; she was pale, whē she remēbred the fruits of denial. As for weeping, sighing, wringing her hāds, & tearing her haire, were indifferēt of both sides. Easily she wold have agreed to have broken al disputatiōs with her owne death, but that the feare of *Antiphilus* furder torments staied her. At lēgth, evē the evening before the day apointed of his death, the determinatiō of yeelding prevailed, especially, growing upō a message of *Antiphilus*; who with all the conjuring termes he could devise, besought her to save his life, upon any cōdition. But she had no sooner sent her messenger to *Tiridates*, but her mind changed, and she went to the two yong Princes, *Pyrocles* & *Musidorus*, & falling downe at their feet, desired thē to trie some way for her deliverance; shewing her selfe resolved, not to over-live *Antiphilus*, nor yet to yeeld to *Tiridates*.

7 They that knew not what she had done in private, prepared that night accordingly: & as sometimes it fals out, that what is incōstancy, seemes cūning; so did this chāge indeed stand in as good steed as a witty dissimulatiō. For it made the King as reckles, as them diligēt: so that in the dead time of the night, the Princes issued out of the towne; with whō she would needs go, either to die her self, or reskew *Antiphilus*, having no armour, nor weapon, but affection. And I cannot tell you how, by what devise (though *Plangus* at large described it) the conclusion was, the wonderfull valour of the two Princes so prevailed, that *Antiphilus* was succoured, and the King slaine. *Plangus* was then the chiefe man left in the campe; and therefore seeing no other remedie, cōveied in safety into her country *Artaxia*, now 8 Queene of *Armenia*; who with true lamētations, made known to the world, that her new greatnes did no way cōfort her in respect of her brothers losse, whō she studied all meanes possible to revenge upon every one of the occasioners, having (as she thought) overthrowne her brother by a most abominable treason. In somuch, that being at home, she proclaimed great rewards to any private man, and her selfe in mariage to any Prince, that would destroy *Pyrocles* and *Musidorus*. But thus was *Antiphilus* redeemed, and (though against the consent of all her nobility) married to *Erona*; in which case the two Greeke Princes (being called away by an other adventure) left them.

CHAP. 14.

[1]Philocleas *narration broken of by* Miso. [2]*Her old-wives tale*, [3]*and ballad against* Cupid. [4]*Their drawing cuts for tales.* [5]Mopsas *tale of the old cut :* [6]*cut of by the Ladies to returne to their stories.*

BUt now me thinkes as I have read some Poets, who when [1] they intĕd to tell some horrible matter, they bid men shun the hearing of it: so if I do not desire you to stop your eares frō me, yet may I well desire a breathing time, before I am to tell the execrable treason of *Antiphilus*, that brought her to this misery; and withall wish you al, that frō al mankind indeed you stop your eares. O most happy were we, if we did set our loves one upon another. (And as she spake that worde, her cheekes in red letters writ more, then her tongue did speake.) And therefore since I have named *Plangus*, I pray you sister (said she) helpe me with the rest, for I have helde the stage long inough; and if it please you to make his fortune knowne, as I have done *Eronas*, I will after take hart againe to go on with his falshood; & so betweene us both, my Ladie *Zelmane* shall understand both the cause and parties of this Lamentation. Nay I beshrow me then (said *Miso*) I wil none of that, I promise you, as lŏg as I have the governmĕt, I will first have my tale, & thē my Lady *Pamela*, my Lady *Zelmane*, & my daughter *Mopsa* (for *Mopsa* was then returned frō *Amphialus*) may draw cuts, & the shortest cut speake first. For I tell you, and this may be suffred, when you are married you wil have first, and last word of your husbands. The Ladies laughed to see with what an eger earnestnesse she looked, having threatning not onely in her Ferret eies, but while she spake, her nose seeming to threaten her chin, & her shaking lims one to threaten another. But there was no remedy, they must obey : & *Miso* (sitting on the groūd with her knees up, & her hands upon her knees) tuning her voice with many a quavering cough, thus discoursed unto thē. I tel you [2] true (said she) whatsoever you thinke of me, you will one day be as I am; & I, simple though I sit here, thought once my pennie as good silver, as some of you do: and if my father had not plaid the hasty foole (it is no lie I tell you) I might have

had an other-gaines husbãd, thẽ *Dametas*. But let that passe,
God amend him: and yet I speake it not without good cause.
You are ful of your tittle tattling of *Cupid*: here is *Cupid*, &
there is *Cupid*. I will tell you now, what a good old womã told
me, what an old wise mã told her, what a great learned clerke
told him, and gave it him in writing; and here I have it in my
praier booke. I pray you (said *Philoclea*) let us see it, & read it.
No hast but good (said *Miso*) you shal first know how I came by
it. I was a young girle of a seven and twenty yeare old, & I
could not go thorow the streate of our village, but I might heare
the young mẽ talke; O the pretie little eies of *Miso*; O the fine
thin lips of *Miso*; O the goodly fat hands of *Miso*: besides,
how well a certaine wrying I had of my necke, became me.
Then the one would wincke with one eye, & the other cast
daiseys at me: I must cõfesse, seing so many amorous, it made
me set up my peacocks tayle with the hiest. Which when this
good old womã perceived (O the good wold woman, well may
the bones rest of the good wold womã) she cald me to her into
her house. I remember full well it stood in the lane as you go
to the Barbers shop, all the towne knew her, there was a great
losse of her : she called me to her, and taking first a soppe of
wine to comfort her hart (it was of the same wine that comes
out of *Candia*, which we pay so deere for now a daies, and in
that good worlde was very good cheape) she cald me to her;
Minion said she, (indeed I was a pretie one in those daies
though I say it) I see a nũber of lads that love you; Wel (said
she) I say no more: doo you know what Love is? With that
she broght me into a corner, where ther was painted a foule fiẽd
I trow : for he had a paire of hornes like a Bull, his feete cloven,
as many eyes upon his bodie, as my gray-mare hath dappels, &
for all the world so placed. This mõster sat like a hãgman upõ
a paire of gallowes, in his right hand he was painted holding a
crowne of Laurell, in his left hand a purse of mony, & out of
his mouth honge a lace of two faire pictures, of a mã & a womã,
& such a coũtenance he shewed, as if he would perswade folks
by those aluremẽts to come thither & be hanged. I, like a tẽder
harted wench, skriked out for feare of the divell. Well (sayd
she) this same is even Love: therefore do what thou list with all
those fellowes, one after another; & it recks not much what
they do to thee, so it be in secreat; but upon my charge, never

love none of them. Why mother (said I) could such a thing
come frõ the belly of the faire *Fenus?* for a few dayes before, our
(priest betweene him & me) had tolde me the whole storie of
Venus. Tush (said she) they are all deceaved: and therewith
gave me this Booke, which she said a great maker of ballets had
given to an old painter, who for a litle pleasure, had bestowed
both booke and picture of her. Reade there (said she) & thou
shalt see that his mother was a cowe, and the false *Argus* his
father. And so she gave me this Booke, & there now you may
reade it. With that the remembrance of the good old woman,
made her make such a face to weepe, as if it were not sorrow,
it was the carkasse of sorrow that appeared there. But while
her teares came out, like raine falling upon durtie furrowes, the
latter end of her praier booke was read among these Ladies,
which contained this.

POore Painters oft with silly Poets joyne,
  To fill the world with strange but vaine conceits :
One brings the stuffe, the other stamps the coine,
Which breeds nought else but gloses of deceits.
  Thus Painters Cupid paint, thus Poets do
  A naked god, young blind, with arrowes two.
Is he a God, that ever flies the light ?
Or naked he, disguis'd in all untruth ?
If he be blind, how hitteth he so right ?
How is he young, that tam'de old Phœbus youth ?
  But arrowes two, and tipt with gold or leade :
  Some hurt accuse a third with horny head.
No, nothing so ; an old false knave he is
By Argus got on Io, then a cow :
What time for her Juno her Jove did misse,
And charge of her to Argus did allow.
  Mercury kill'd his false sire for this act,
  His damme a beast was pardon'd beastly fact.
With fathers death, and mothers guiltie shame,
With Joves disdaine at such a rivals seed,
The wretch compell'd a runnagate became,
And learn'd what ill a miser state doth breed,
  To lye, faine, gloze, to steale, pry, and accuse,
  Naught in himselfe ech other to abuse.

Yet beares he still his parents stately gifts,
A horned head, cloven foote, and thousand eyes,
Some gazing still, some winking wilye shiftes,
With long large eares where never rumour dyes.
 His horned head doth seeme the heaven to spight:
 His cloven foote doth never treade aright.
Thus halfe a man, with man he dayly haunts,
Cloth'd in the shape which soonest may deceave:
Thus halfe a beast, ech beastly vice he plants,
In those weake harts that his advice receave.
 He proules ech place stil in new colours deckt,
 Sucking ones ill, another to infeɛt.
To narrow brests he comes all wrapt in gaine:
To swelling harts he shines in honours fire:
To open eyes all beauties he doth raine;
Creeping to ech with flattering of desire.
 But for that Loves desire most rules the eyes,
 Therein his name, there his chiefe triumph lyes.
Millions of yeares this old drivell Cupid *lives;*
While still more wretch, more wicked he doth prove:
Till now at length that Jove *him office gives,*
(At Junos *suite who much did* Argus *love)*
 In this our world a hang-man for to be,
 Of all those fooles that will have all they see.

4   These Ladies made sport at the description and storie of
Cupid. But *Zelmane* could scarce suffer those blasphemies (as
she tooke them) to be read, but humbly besought *Pamela* she
would perfourme her sisters request of the other part of the storie.
Noble Lady (answered she, beautifying her face with a sweete
smiling, and the sweetnes of her smiling with the beautie of her
face) since I am borne a Princes daughter, let me not give example of disobedience. My governesse will have us draw cuts,
and therefore I pray you let us do so: and so perhaps it will
light upon you to entertaine this company with some storie of
your owne; and it is reason our eares should be willinger to
heare, as your tongue is abler to deliver. I will thinke
(answered *Zelmane*) excellent Princesse my tongue of some
value, if it can procure your tongue thus much to favour
me. But *Pamela* pleasantly persisting to have fortune their

judge, they set hands, and *Mopsa* (though at the first for squeamishnes going up & downe, with her head like a boate in a storme) put to her golden gols among them, and blind Fortune (that saw not the coulor of them) gave her the preheminence: and so being her time to speake (wiping her mouth, as there was good cause) she thus tumbled into her matter. In time past (sayd she) there was a King, the mightiest man in all his country, that had by his wife, the fairest daughter that ever did eate pappe. Now this King did keepe a great house, that every body might come and take their meat freely. So one day, as his daughter was sitting in her window, playing upon a harpe, as sweete as any Rose; and combing her head with a combe all of precious stones, there came in a Knight into the court, upŏ a goodly horse, one haire of gold, & the other of silver; *and so* the Knight casting up his eyes to the window, did fall into such love with her, that he grew not worth the bread he eate; till many a sorry day going over his head, with Dayly Diligence and Grisly Grones, he wan her affection, so that they agreed to run away togither. *And so in May, when all true hartes rejoyce,* they stale out of the Castel, without staying so much as for their breakfast. Now forsooth, as they went togither, often all to kissing one another, the Knight told her, he was brought up among the water Nymphes, who had so bewitched him, that if he were ever askt his name, he must presently vanish away: and therefore charged her upon his blessing, that she never aske him what he was, nor whether he would. *And so* a great while she kept his commandement; til once, passing through a cruell wildernes, as darke as pitch; her mouth so watred, that she could not choose but aske him the question. And then, he making the greevousest cŏplaints that would have melted a tree to have heard them, vanisht quite away: & she lay down, casting forth as pitifull cries as any shrich-owle. But having laien so, (wet by the raine, and burnt by the Sun) five dayes, & five nights, she gat up and went over many a high hil, & many a deepe river; till she came to an Aunts house of hers; and came, & cried to her for helpe: and she for pittie gave her a Nut, and bad her never open her Nut, til she was come to the extremest misery that ever tongue could speake of. *And so* she went, & she went, & never rested the evening, wher she wĕt in the morning; til she came to a second Aunt; and she gave her another Nut.

5

6   Now good *Mopsa* (said the sweete *Philoclea*) I pray thee at
my request keepe this tale, till my marriage day, & I promise
thee that the best gowne I weare that day shalbe thine. *Mopsa*
was very glad of the bargaine, especially that it shuld grow a
festival Tale: so that *Zelmane*, who desired to finde the uttermost what these Ladies understood touching her selfe, and
having understood the danger of *Erona* (of which before she
had never heard) purposing with her selfe (as soone as this
pursuit she now was in, was brought to any effect) to succour
her, entreated againe, that she might know as well the story of
Plangus, as of *Erona*. *Philoclea* referred it to her sisters per-
fecter remēbrāce, who with so sweet a voice, and so winning a
grace, as in themselves were of most forcible eloquence to
procure attention, in this maner to their earnest request soone
condiscended.

CHAP. 15.

[1] Plangus-*his parentage.* [2] *His trick of youth,* [3] *espied,* [4] *& turned
over by, and to his old father.* [5] *An inveagling-womans arts.*
[6] *A guilty stepmothers divellish practises against* Plangus.
[7] *Her ministers false informations.* [8] Plangus *perplexities.*
[9] *His fathers jelousies. The Queenes complots* [10] *to feede the
ones suspicion,* [11] *& work the others overthrow.* [12] Plangus
taken; [13] *delivered flieth:* [14] *is pursued with old hate, & new
treason.* [15] *Yet must he serve abroad, while a new heire is
made at home.* [16] *This story broken off by* Basilius.

1   THe father of this Prince *Plangus* as yet lives, and is King
of *Iberia:* a man (if the judgement of *Plangus* may be
accepted) of no wicked nature, nor willingly doing evill, without himselfe mistake the evill, seeing it disguised under some
forme of goodnesse. This Prince, being married at the first to
a Princesse (who both from her auncesters, and in her selfe
was worthy of him) by her had this son, *Plangus*. Not long
after whose birth, the Queene (as though she had perfourmed
the message for which she was sent into the world) returned
again unto her maker. The King (sealing up al thoughts of

love under the image of her memorie) remained a widdower many yeares after; recompencing the griefe of that disjoyning from her, in conjoyning in himselfe both a fatherly and a motherly care toward her onely child, *Plangus*. Who being growne to mans age, as our owne eies may judge, could not but fertilly requite his fathers fatherly education.

This Prince (while yet the errors in his nature were excused 2 by the greenenes of his youth, which tooke all the fault upon it selfe) loved a private mans wife of the principal Citie of that Kingdome, if that may be called love, which he rather did take into himselfe willingly. then by which he was takē forcibly. It sufficeth, that the yong man perswaded himself he loved her: she being a woman beautiful enough, if it be possible, that the outside onely can justly entitle a beauty. But finding such a chase as onely fledde to be caught, the young Prince broght his affectiõ with her to that point, which ought to engrave remorse in her harte, & to paint shame upon her face. And so possest he his desire without any interruption; he constantly favouring her, and she thinking, that the enameling of a Princes name, might hide the spots of a broken wedlock. But as I have seene one that was sick of a sleeping disease, could not be made wake, but with pinching of him: so out of his sinfull sleepe his minde (unworthie so to be loste) was not to be cald to it selfe, but by a sharpe accident.

It fell out, that his many-times leaving of the court (in 3 undue times) began to be noted; and (as Princes eares be manifolde) from one to another came unto the King; who (carefull of his onely sonne) sought, and found by his spies (the necessarie evill servauntes to a King) what it was, whereby he was from his better delights so diverted.

Whereupon, the King (to give his fault the greater blow) 4 used such meanes, by disguising himselfe, that he found them (her husband being absent) in her house together: which he did, to make him the more feelingly ashamed of it. And that way he tooke, laying threatnings upon her, and upon him reproaches. But the poore young Prince (deceived with that young opinion, that if it be ever lawfull to lie, it is for ones Lover,) employed all his witte to bring his father to a better opinion. And because he might bende him from that (as he counted it) crooked conceit of her, he wrested him, as much as he coulde possiblie, to the other side: not sticking with prodigall protestations to set foorth her chastitie; not denying his own attempts, but thereby the more extolling her vertue. His Sophistrie prevayled, his father beleeved; and so beleeved, that ere long (though he were alredy stept into the winter of his age) he founde himselfe warme in those desires, which were in his sonne farre more excusable. To be short, he gave him-selfe over unto it; and (because he would avoide the odious comparison of a yong rivall) sent away his sonne with an armie, to the subduing of a Province lately rebelled against him, which he knewe could not be a lesse worke, thē of three or foure yeares. Wherein he behaved him so worthilie, as even to this country the fame therof came, long before his own cŏming: while yet his father had a speedier succes, but in a far unnobler conquest. For while *Plangus* was away, the old man (growing onely in age & affectiŏ) folowed his suite with all meanes of unhonest servants, large promises, and each thing els that might help to countervaile his owne unlovelines.

5   And she (whose husband about that time died) forgetting the absent *Plangus,* or at lest not hoping of him to obtaine so aspiring a purpose, lefte no arte unused, which might keepe the line from breaking, wherat the fishe was alredy taken; not drawing him violently, but letting him play himself upon the hooke, which he had greedely swalowed. For, accompanying her mourning with a dolefull countenaunce, yet neither for-getting hansomnes in her mourning garments, nor sweetenes in her dolefull countenance; her wordes were ever seasoned with sighes; and any favour she shewed, bathed in teares, that affection might see cause of pity; and pity might perswade cause of affection. And being growen skilfull in his humors, she was no lesse skilfull in applying his humors: never suffering his feare to fall to a despaire, nor his hope to hasten to an assurance: she was content he should thinke that she loved him; and a certaine stolne looke should sometimes (as though it were against her will) bewray it: But if thereupon he grewe bolde, he straight was encountred with a maske of vertue. And that which seemeth most impossible unto me, (for as neere as I can I repeate it as *Plangus* tolde it) she could not onely sigh when she would, as all can doo; & weep when she would, as (they say) some can doo; but (being most impudent in her

hart) she could, when she would, teach her chekes blushing, and make shamefastnes the cloake of shamelesnes. In summe, to leave out many particularities which he recited, she did not onely use so the spurre, that his Desire ran on, but so the bit, that it ran on, evē in such a careere as she would have it; that within a while, the king, seeing with no other eyes but such as she gave him, & thinking no other thoghts but such as she taught him; having at the first liberall measure of favors then shortned of thē, when most his Desire was inflamed; he saw no other way but mariage to satisfie his longing, and her mind (as he thought) loving, but chastly loving. So that by the time *Plangus* returned from being notably victorious of the Rebels, he foūd his father, not only maried, but alredy a father of a sonne & a daughter by this womā. Which though *Plăgus* (as he had every way just cause) was grieved at; yet did his grief never bring forth ether cōtemning of her, or repining at his father. But she (who besides she was growen 6 a mother, and a stepmother, did read in his eies her owne fault, and made his conscience her guiltines) thought still that his presence caried her condēnation: so much the more, as that she (unchastly attempting his wōted fācies) foūd (for the reverēce of his fathers bed) a bitter refusall: which breeding rather spite then shame in her, or if it were a shame, a shame not of the fault, but of the repulse, she did not onely (as hating him) thirst for a revenge, but (as fearing harm from him) endevoured to doo harme unto him. Therefore did she trie the uttermost of her wicked wit, how to overthrow him in the foundation of his strength, which was, in the favour of his father: which because she saw strong both in nature and desert, it required the more cūning how to undermine it. And therfore (shunning the ordinary trade of hireling sycophants) she made her praises of him, to be accusations; and her advauncing him, to be his ruine. For first with words (neerer admiration then liking) she would extoll his excellēcies, the goodlines of his shape, the power of his witte, the valiantnes of his courage, the fortunatenes of his successes: so as the father might finde in her a singular love towardes him: nay, she shunned not to kindle some fewe sparkes of jelousie in him. Thus having gotten an opinion in his father, that she was farre from meaning mischiefe to the sonne, then fell she to praise

him with no lesse vehemencie of affection, but with much
more cunning of malice. For then she sets foorth the liberty
of his mind, the high flying of his thoughts, the fitnesse in him
to beare rule, the singular love the Subjects bare him; that it
was doubtfull, whether his wit were greater in winning their
favors, or his courage in employing their favours: that he was
not borne to live a subject-life, each action of his bearing in it
Majestie, such a Kingly entertainement, such a Kingly magnificence, such a Kingly harte for enterprises: especially remembring those vertues, which in a successor are no more
honoured by the subjects, then suspected of the Princes. Then
would she by putting-of objectiõs, bring in objectiõs to her
husbands head, alredy infected with suspitiõ. Nay (would she
say) I dare take it upon my death, that he is no such sonne, as
many of like might have bene, who loved greatnes so well, as
to build their greatnes upon their fathers ruine. Indeed Ambition, like Love, can abide no lingring, & ever urgeth on his
own successes; hating nothing, but what may stop thẽ. But
the Gods forbid, we should ever once dreame of any such thing
in him, who perhaps might be content, that you & the world
should know, what he can do: but the more power he hath
to hurte, the more admirable is his praise, that he wil not
hurt. Then ever remembring to strengthen the suspition of
his estate with private jelousie of her love, doing him excessive
honour when he was in presence, and repeating his pretie
speaches and graces in his absence; besides, causing him to be
imployed in all such dangerous matters, as ether he should perish
in them, or if he prevailed, they should increase his glory:
which she made a weapon to woũd him, untill she found that
suspition began already to speake for it selfe, and that her
husbands eares were growne hungry of rumours, and his eies
prying into every accident.

7   Then tooke she help to her of a servant neere about her
husband, whom she knew to be of a hasty ambitiõ, and such a
one, who wanting true sufficiencie to raise him, would make a
ladder of any mischiefe. Him she useth to deale more plainely
in alleaging causes of jealousie, making him know the fittest
times when her husband already was stirred that way. And
so they two, with divers wayes, nourished one humour, like
Musitians, that singing divers parts, make one musicke. He

sometime with fearefull countenaúnce would desire the King
to looke to himselfe; for that all the court and Cittie were full
of whisperings, and expectation of some suddaine change, upon
what ground himselfe knew not. Another time he would
counsell the King to make much of his sonne, and holde his
favour, for that it was too late now to keepe him under. Now
seeming to feare himselfe, because (he said) *Plangus* loved none
of them that were great about his father. Lastly, breaking
with him directly (making a sorrowful countenance, & an
humble gesture beare false witnesse for his true meaning) that
he foūd, not only souldiery, but people weary of his government, & al their affections bent upon *Plangus*. Both he and
the Queene concurring in strange dreames, & each thing else,
that in a mind (already perplexed) might breed astonishment:
so that within a while, all *Plangus* actions began to be translated
into the language of suspition.

Which though *Plangus* foūd, yet could he not avoid, even 8
cōtraries being driven to draw one yoke of argumēt: if he were
magnificēt, he spent much with an aspiring intent: if he spared,
he heaped much with an aspiring intent: if he spake curteously,
he angled the peoples harts: if he were silent, he mused upon
some daungerous plot. In summe, if he could have turned
himself to as many formes as *Proteus*, every forme should have
bene made tedious.

But so it fell out, that a meere trifle gave thē occasion of 9
further proceeding. The King one morning, going to a vine-
yard that lay a long the hill where his castle stood, he saw a
vine-labourer, that finding a bowe broken, tooke a branch of
the same bowe for want of another thing, and tied it about the
place broken. The King asking the fellow what he did, Marry
(said he) I make the sonne binde the father. This word
(finding the King alredy supersticious through suspitiō) amazed
him streight, as a presage of his owne fortune: so that, returning, and breaking with his wife how much he misdoubted his
estate, she made such gaine-saying answeres, as while they
strave, strave to be overcome. But even while the doubtes
most boiled, she thus nourished them.

She under-hand dealt with the principall mē of that coūtry, 10
that at the great Parliamēt (which was then to be held) they
should in the name of all the estates perswade the King (being

now stept deeply into old age) to make *Plangus*, his associate in
governmẽt with him : assuring thẽ, that not only she would
joine with them, but that the father himself would take it
kindly; chargeing thẽ not to acquaint *Plangus* withal; for that
perhaps it might be harmeful unto him, if the King should find,
that he wer a party. They (who thought they might do it,
not only willingly, because they loved him, & truly, because
such indeed was the minde of the people, but safely, because
she who ruled the King was agreed therto) accõplished her
coũsell: she indeed keeping promise of vehement perswading
the same: which the more she & they did, the more she knew
her husbãd would fear, & hate the cause of his feare. *Plangus*
foũd this, & hũbly protested against such desire, or wil to
accept. But the more he protested, the more his father thought
he dissẽbled, accoũting his integritie to be but a cũning face of
falshood: and therfore delaying the desire of his subjeĉts,
attended some fit occasion to lay hands upon his sonne: which
his wife thus brought to passe.

11   She caused that same minister of hers to go unto *Plãgus*, &
(enabling his words with great shew of faith, & endearing them
with desire of secresie) to tell him, that he found his ruine
conspired by his stepmother, with certain of the noble men of
that coũtry, the King himselfe giving his consent, and that few
daies should passe, before the putting it in praĉtize: with all
discovering the very truth indeed, with what cunning his stepmother had proceeded. This agreing with *Plangus* his owne
opiniõ, made him give him the better credit: yet not so far, as
to flie out of his country (according to the naughty fellowes
persuasion) but to attend, and to see further. Wherupon the
fellow (by the direĉtion of his mistresse) told him one day, that
the same night, about one of the clocke, the King had appointed
to have his wife, & those noble mẽ together, to deliberate of
their manner of proceeding against *Plangus*: & therfore offered
him, that if himselfe would agree, he would bring him into a
place where he should heare all that passed; & so have the
more reason both to himselfe, and to the world, to seeke his
safetie. The poore *Plãgus* (being subjeĉt to that only disadvantage of honest harts, credulitie) was perswaded by him: &
arming himself (because of his late going) was closely conveied
into the place appointed. In the meane time his stepmother

making all her gestures cunningly counterfait a miserable afflictiõ, she lay almost groveling on the flower of her chãber, not suffering any body to comfort her; untill they calling for her husband, and he held of with long enquiry, at length, she told him (even almost crying out every word) that she was wery of her life, since she was brought to that plunge, either to conceale her husbãds murther, or accuse her sonne, who had ever bene more deare, then a sonne unto her. Then with many interruptions and exclamations she told him, that her sonne *Plangus* (solliciting her in the old affection betweene them) had besought her to put her helping hand to the death of the King; assuring her, that though all the lawes in the world were against it, he would marrie her when he were King.

She had not fully said thus much, with many pitifull 12 digressiõs, whẽ in comes the same fellow, that brought *Plãgus*: & runing himself out of breath, fell at the Kings feet, beseeching him to save himself, for that there was a man with sword drawen in the next roome. The King affrighted, wẽt out, & called his gard, who entring the place, foũd indeed *Plangus* with his sword in his hand, but not naked, but stãding suspiciously inough, to one already suspicious. The King (thinking he had put up his sworde because of the noise) never tooke leasure to heare his answer, but made him prisoner, meaning the next morning to put him to death in the market place.

But the day had no sooner opened the eies & eares of his 13 friends & followers, but that there was a little army of them, who came, and by force delivered him; although nũbers on the other side (abused with the fine framing of their report) tooke armes for the King. But *Plangus*, though he might have used the force of his friends to revenge his wrong, and get the crowne; yet the naturall love of his father, and hate to make their suspition seeme just, caused him rather to choose a volũtarie exile, thẽ to make his fathers death the purchase of his life: & therefore went he to *Tiridates*, whose mother was his fathers sister, living in his Court eleven or twelve yeares, ever hoping by his intercession, and his owne desert, to recover his fathers grace. At the end of which time, the warre of *Erona* happened, which my sister with the cause thereof discoursed unto you.

But his father had so deeply engraved the suspicion in his 14 hart, that he thought his flight rather to proceed of a fearefull guiltines, then of an humble faithfulnes; & therfore continued his hate, with such vehemencie, that he did ever hate his Nephew *Tiridates*, and afterwards his neece *Artaxia*, because in their Court he received countenance, leaving no meanes unattēpted of destroying his son; among other, employing that wicked servant of his, who undertooke to empoyson him. But his cūning disguised him not so well, but that the watchful servāts of *Plāgus* did discover him. Wherupō the wretch was taken, & (before his wel-deserved execution) by torture forced to confesse the particularities of this, which in generall I have told you.

15 Which cōfession autentically set downe (though *Tiridates* with solemne Embassage sent it to the King) wrought no effeᘓt. For the King having put the reines of the government into his wives hande, never did so much as reade it; but sent it streight by her to be considered. So as they rather heaped more hatred upon *Plangus*, for the death of their servaunt. And now finding, that his absence, and their reportes had much diminished the wavering peoples affeᘓtion towardes *Plangus*, with advauncing fit persons for faᘓtion, and graunting great immunities to the commons, they prevailed so farre, as to cause the sonne of the second wife, called *Palladius*, to be proclaymed successour, and *Plangus* quite excluded: so that *Plangus* was driven to continue his serving *Tiridates*, as he did in the warre against *Erona*, and brought home *Artaxia*, as my sister tolde you; when *Erona* by the treason of *Antiphilus*, But at that word she stopped. For *Basilius* (not able longer to abide their absence) came sodainly among them, and with smiling countenance (telling *Zelmane* he was affraid she had stollen away his daughters) invited them to follow the Sunnes counsel in going then to their lodging; for indeed the Sun was readie to set. They yeelded, *Zelmane* meaning some other time to understand the storie of *Antiphilus* treason, and *Eronas* daunger, whose case she greatly tendred. But *Miso* had no sooner espied *Basilius*, but that as spitefully, as her rotten voice could utter it, she set forth the sawcinesse of *Amphialus*. But *Basilius* onely attended what *Zelmanes* opinion was, who though she hated *Amphialus*, yet the nobilitie of her courage prevailed over it, and she desired he might be pardoned that youthfull error;

considering the reputation he had, to be one of the best knights in the world; so as hereafter he governed himselfe, as one remembring his fault. *Basilius* giving the infinite tearmes of praises to *Zelmanes* both valour in conquering, and pittifulnesse in pardoning, commanded no more words to be made of it, since such he thought was her pleasure.

CHAP. 16.

[1] *The cumber of* Zelmanes *love and lovers.* [2] Gynecias *love-lamentations.* [3] Zelmanes *passions* [4] *& sonet.* [5] Basilius-*his wooing, and* Zelmanes *answeres.* [6] Philoclea *feed atturney to plead her fathers cause.*

S O brought he them up to visite his wife, where betweene [1] her, & him, the poore *Zelmane* receaved a tedious entertainemẽt; oppressed with being loved, almost as much, as with loving. *Basilius* not so wise in covering his passion, could make his toong go almost no other pace, but to runne into those immoderate praises, which the foolish Lover thinkes short of his Mistres, though they reach farre beyond the heavens. But *Gynecia* (whome womanly modestie did more outwardly bridle) yet did oftentimes use the advantage of her sexe in kissing *Zelmane,* as she sate upon her bedde-side by her; which was but still more and more sweete incense, to cast upon the fire wherein her harte was sacrificed: Once *Zelmane* could not stirre, but that, (as if they had bene poppets, whose motion stoode onely upon her pleasure) *Basilius* with serviceable steppes, *Gynecia* with greedie eyes would follow her. *Basilius* mind *Gynecia* well knew, and could have found in her hart to laugh at, if mirth could have borne any proportion with her fortune. But all *Gynecias* actions were interpreted by *Basilius,* as proceeding from jealousie of his amorousnesse. *Zelmane* betwixt both (like the poore childe, whose father while he beates him, will make him beleeve it is for love; or like the sicke man, to whom the Phisition sweares, the ill-tasting wallowish medicine he profers, is of a good taste) their love was hatefull, their courtesie troublesome, their presence cause of her absence thence, where not onely her light, but her life consisted. Alas (thought she to her selfe) deare *Dorus*, what ods is there betweene thy destiny & mine? For thou hast to doo in thy pursuite but with shepherdish folkes, who trouble thee with a little envious care, and affected diligence. But I (besides that I have now *Miso*, the worst of thy divels, let loose upon me) am waited on by Princes, and watched by the two wakefull eyes of Love and Jealousie. Alas, incomparable *Philoclea*, thou ever seest me, but dost never see me as I am: thou hearest willingly all that I dare say, and I dare not say that which were most fit for thee to heare. Alas who ever but I was imprisoned in libertie, and banished being still present? To whom but me have lovers bene jailours, and honour a captivitie?

2   But the night comming on with her silent steps upon thẽ, they parted ech from other (if at lest they could be parted, of whom every one did live in another) and went about to flatter sleepe with their beds, that disdained to bestow it selfe liberally upon such eies which by their will would ever be looking: and in lest measure upon *Gynecia*, who (when *Basilius* after long tossing was gotten a sleepe, and the cheereful comfort of the lights removed from her) kneeling up in her bed, began with a soft voice, and swolne hart, to renue the curses of her birth; & thẽ in a maner embracing her bed; Ah chastest bed of mine (said she) which never heretofore couldst accuse me of one defiled thought, how canst thou now receave this desastred changeling? Happie, happie be they onely which be not: and thy blessednes onely in this respect thou maist feele, that thou hast no feeling. With that she furiously tare off great part of her faire haire: Take here ô forgotten vertue (said she) this miserable sacrifice; while my soule was clothed with modestie, that was a comely ornament: now why should nature crowne that head, which is so wicked, as her onely despaire is, she cannot be enough wicked? More she would have said, but that *Basilius* (awaked with the noise) tooke her in his armes, & begã to cõfort her; the good-man thinking, it was all for a jealous love of him: which humor if she would a litle have maintained, perchance it might have weakned his new conceaved fancies. But he finding her answeres wandring frõ the purpose, left her to her selfe (glad the next morning to take the advãtage of a sleepe, which a little before day, overwatched

with sorow, her teares had as it were sealed up in her eyes) to have the more conference with *Zelmane*, who baited on this fashion by these two lovers, & ever kept from any meane to declare herselfe, found in her selfe a dayly encrease of her violent desires; like a river the more swelling, the more his current is stopped.

The chiefe recreation she could find in her anguish, was 3 somtime to visite that place, where first she was so happy as to see the cause of her unhap. There would she kisse the ground, and thanke the trees, blisse the aier, & do dutifull reverence to every thing that she thought did accompany her at their first meeting: then returne again to her inward thoughts; somtimes despaire darkning all her imaginations, sometimes the active passion of Love cheering and cleering her invention, how to unbar that combersome hinderance of her two ill-matched lovers. But this morning *Basilius* himself gave her good occasion to go beyond them. For having combd and trickt himself more curiously, then any time fortie winters before, comming where *Zelmane* was, he found her given over to her musicall muses, to the great pleasure of the good old *Basilius*, who retired himselfe behinde a tree, while she with a most sweete voice did utter these passionate verses.

LOved I am, and yet complaine of Love: 4
    As loving not, accus'd, in Love I die.
When pittie most I crave, I cruell prove:
Still seeking Love, love found as much I flie.
    Burnt in my selfe, I muse at others fire:
What I call wrong, I doo the same, and more:
Bard of my will, I have beyond desire:
I waile for want, and yet am chokte with store.
    This is thy worke, thou God for ever blinde:
Though thousands old, a Boy entit'led still.
Thus children doo the silly birds they finde,
With stroking hurt, and too much cramming kill.
    Yet thus much Love, O Love, I crave of thee:
    Let me be lov'd, or els not loved be.

Basilius made no great haste from behind the tree, till he 5 perceaved she had fully ended her musick. But then loth to loose the pretious fruite of time, he presented himselfe unto her, falling downe upon both his knees, and holding up his hands, as the old governesse of *Danae* is painted, when she sodainly saw the goldē shoure, O heavēly womã, or earthly Goddesse (said he) let not my presence be odious unto you, nor my humble suit seeme of small weight in your eares. Vouchsafe your eies to descend upon this miserable old-mã, whose life hath hitherto bene maintained but to serve as an encrease of your beautiful triumphs. You only have over throwne me, & in my bondage cōsists my glory. Suffer not your owne worke to be despised of you: but looke upon him with pittie, whose life serves for your praise. *Zelmane* (keeping a coūtenãce ascanses she understood him not) told him, It became her evil to suffer such excessive reverence of him, but that it worse became her to correct him, to whom she owed duetie: that the opinion she had of his wisedome was such, as made her esteeme greatly of his words; but that the words themselves sounded so, as she could not imagine what they might intend. Intend? (said *Basilius*, proud that that was brought in question) what may they intend, but a refreshing of my soule, and a swaging of my heat, and enjoying those your excellencies, wherein my life is upheld, and my death threatned? *Zelmane* lifting up her face as if she had receaved a mortall injurie of him, And is this the devotion your ceremonies have bene bent unto? said she: Is it the disdaine of my estate, or the opinion of my lightnesse, that have emboldned such base fancies towards me? enjoying quoth you? now little joy come to them that yeeld to such enjoying. Poore *Basilius* was so appalled, that his legges bowed under him; his eyes lookt as though he would gladly hide himself; and his old blood going to his hart, a generall shaking all over his bodie possessed him. At length with a wanne mouth; he was about to give a stammering answere, when it came into *Zelmanes* head by this devise to make her profite of his folly; and therefore with a relented countenance, thus said unto him. Your words (mightie Prince) were unfit either for me to heare, or you to speake: but yet the large testimonie I see of your affection makes me willing to suppresse a great number of errors. Onely thus much I thinke good to say, that the same words in my Ladie *Philocleas* mouth, as from one woman to another (so as there were no other bodie by) might have had a better grace; and perchance have found a gentler receipt.

Basilius (whose senses by Desire were held open, and conceipt was by Love quickned) heard scarcely halfe her answere out, but that (as if speedie flight might save his life) he turned away, and ran with all the speede his bodie would suffer him, towardes his daughter *Philoclea* : whom he found at that time duetifully watching by her mother, and *Miso* curiouslie watching her; having left *Mopsa* to doo the like service to *Pamela*. *Basilius* foorthwith calling *Philoclea* aside, (with all the conjuring words which Desire could endite, and authoritie utter) besought her she would preserve his life, in whŏ her life was begonne; she would save his graye haires from rebuke, and his aged mind from despaire; that if she were not cloyed with his companie, and that she thought not the earth over-burdened with him, she would coole his fierie griefe, which was to be done but by her breath. That in fine, whatsoever he was, he was nothing but what it pleased *Zelmane*; all the powers of his spirite depending of her : that if she continued cruell, he could no more sustaine his life, then the earth remaine fruitefull in the Sunnes continuall absence. He concluded, she should in one payment requite all his deserts : and that she needed not disdaine any service (though never so meane) which was warranted by the sacred name of a father. *Philoclea* more glad then ever she had knowen her selfe, that she might by this occasion, enjoy the private conference of *Zelmane*, yet had so sweete a feeling of vertue in her minde, that she would not suffer a vile colour to be cast over her faire thoughts; but with humble grace answered her father : That there needed nether promise nor perswasion to her, to make her doo her uttermost for her fathers service. That for *Zelmanes* favour, she would in all vertuous sort seeke it towards him : and that as she woulde not pearce further into his meaning, then himselfe should declare, so would she interprete all his doinges to be accomplished in goodnes : and therfore desired, (if otherwise it were) that he woulde not imparte it to her, who then should be forced to beginne (by true obedience) a shew of disobedience : rather perfourming his generall commandement, which had ever beene, to embrace vertue, then any new particular, sprong out of passion, and contrarie to the former. *Basilius* content to take that, since he could have no more (thinking it a great point, if by her meanes, he could get but a more free accesse unto *Zelmane*) allowed her reasons, & took her proffer thākfully, desiring onely a speedy returne of comfort. *Philoclea* was parting, and *Miso* streight behind her, like *Alecto* following *Proserpina*. But *Basilius* forced her to stay, though with much a doo, she being sharp-set upon the fulfilling of a shrewde office, in over-looking *Philoclea*: and so said to *Basilius*, that she did as she was comanded, and could not answere it to *Gynecia*, if she were any whitte from *Philoclea*: telling him true, that he did evill to take her charge from her. But *Basilius*, (swearing he would put out her eyes, if she stird a foote to trouble his daughter) gave her a stoppe for that while.

CHAP. 17.

[1] Zelmanes *teares,* [2] *and tearefull dittie.* [3] Philoclea *enters conference with her.* [4] *She shues, and shewes her selfe Prince* Pyrocles. [5] Philoclea *feares much, but loves more.* [6] *Their conclusion,* [7] *with reentrie to their intermitted historiologie.*

SO away departed *Philoclea,* with a new field of fancies for her travayling mind. For well she sawe, her father was growen her adverse partie, and yet her fortune such, as she must favour her Rivall; and the fortune of that fortune such, as neither that did hurt her, nor any contrarie meane helpe her.

I   But she walkt but a little on, before she saw *Zelmane* lying upon a banke, with her face so bent over *Ladon,* that (her teares falling into the water) one might have thought, that she began meltingly to be metamorphosed to the under-running river. But by and by, with speech she made knowen, as well that she lived, as that she sorrowed. Faire streames (said she) that do vouchsafe in your cleerenes to represent unto me my blubbered face, let the tribute-offer of my teares unto you, procure your stay a while with me, that I may beginne yet at last, to finde some thing that pities me: and that all thinges of comfort and pleasure doo not flie away from me. But if the

violence of your spring commaund you to haste away, to pay
your dueties to your great prince, the Sea, yet carrie with you
these fewe wordes, and let the uttermost ends of the world
know them. A Love more cleer then your selves, dedicated to
a Love (I feare) more cold then your selves, with the cleerenes
layes a night of sorow upon me; and with the coldenes en-
flames a worlde of fire within me. With that she tooke a
willowe stick, and wrote in a sandie banke these fewe verses.

O*Ver these brookes trusting to ease mine eyes,*   2
  (Mine eyes even great in labour with their teares)
I layde my face; my face wherein there lyes
Clusters of clowdes, which no Sunne ever cleares.
  In watry glasse my watrie eyes I see:
  Sorrowes ill easde, where sorrowes painted be.

My thoughts imprisonde in my secreat woes,
With flamie breathes doo issue oft in sound:
The sound to this strange aier no sooner goes,
But that it dooth with Echoes *force rebound.*
  And make me heare the plaints I would refraine:
  Thus outward helps my inward griefes maintaine.

Now in this sande I would discharge my minde,
And cast from me part of my burdnous cares:
But in the sand my tales foretolde I finde,
And see therein how well the writer fares.
  Since streame, aier, sand, mine eyes and eares conspire:
  What hope to quench, where each thing blowes the fire?

And assoon as she had written them (a new swarme of 3
thoughts stinging her mind) she was ready with her foot to
give the new-borne letters both death and buriall. But
Philoclea (to whom delight of hearing and seeing was before a
stay from interrupting her) gave her self to be seen unto her,
with such a lightning of Beauty upŏ *Zelmane,* that nether she
could looke on, nor would looke of. At last *Philoclea* (having
a little mused how to cut the threede even, betweene her owne
hopelesse affection, and her fathers unbridled hope) with eyes,
cheekes, and lippes, (whereof each sange their parte, to make
up the harmonie of bashfulnesse) began to say, My Father to

whom I owe my self, & therefore, When *Zelmane* (making a womanish habite to be the Armour of her boldnesse, giving up her life to the lippes of *Philoclea*, and taking it againe by the sweetenesse of those kisses) humbly besought her to keepe her speach for a while within the Paradise of her minde. For well she knew her fathers errãd, who should soon receive a sufficient answere. But now she demaunded leave not to loose this long sought-for commoditie of time, to ease her harte thus farre, that if in her agonies her destinie was to be condemned by *Philocleas* mouth, at lest *Philoclea* might know, whom she had condemned. *Philoclea* easily yeelded to graunt her owne desire: and so making the greene banke the situation, and the river the prospect of the most beautiful buildings of Nature, *Zelmane* doubting how to beginne, though her thoughts already had runne to the ende, with a minde fearing the unworthinesse of every worde that should be presented to her eares, at length brought it forth in this manner.

4   Most beloved Ladie, the incomparable excellencies of your selfe, (waited-on by the greatnesse of your estate) and the importaunce of the thing (whereon my life consisteth) doth require both many ceremonies before the beginning, and many circumstaunces in the uttering my speech, both bolde, and fearefull. But the small opportunitie of envious occasion (by the malicious eie hateful Love doth cast upon me) and the extreme bent of my affection (which will eyther breake out in wordes, or breake my harte) compell me, not onely to embrace the smallest time, but to passe by respects due unto you, in respect of your poore caitifes life, who is now, or never to be preserved. I doo therefore vowe unto you, hereafter never more to omit all dutifull forme: doo you onely now vouchsafe to heare the matter of a minde most perplexed. If ever the sound of Love have come to your eares, or if ever you have understood, what force it hath had to conquere the strongest hartes, and change the most setled estates : receive here an example of those straunge Tragedies; one, that in him selfe conteineth the particularities of all those misfortunes: and from hencefoorth beleeve that such a thing may be, since you shall see it is. You shall see (I say) a living image, and a present storie of what Love can doo, when he is bent to ruine.

But alas, whether goest thou my tongue? or how doth my

harte consent to adventure the revealing his neerest touching secrete? But peace Feare, thou commest too late, when already the harme is taken. Therefore I say againe, O onely Princesse, attend here a miserable miracle of affection. Behold here before your eyes *Pyrocles*, Prince of *Macedon*, whome you onely have brought to this game of Fortune, and unused *Metamorphosis*: whome you onely have made neglect his countrie, forget his Father, and lastly, forsake to be *Pyrocles*: the same *Pyrocles*, who (you heard) was betrayed by being put in a ship, which being burned, *Pyrocles* was drowned. O most true presage: for these traytors, my eyes, putting me in a shippe of Desire, which dayly burneth, those eyes (I say) which betraied me, will never leave till they have drowned me. But be not, be not, (most excellent Lady) you that Nature hath made to be the Load-starre of comfort, be not the Rocke of shipwracke: you whome vertue hath made the Princesse of felicitie, be not the minister of ruine: you, whom my choyse hath made the Goddesse of my safetie, O let not, let not, from you be powred upon me destruction. Your faire face hath manie tokens in it of amazement at my wordes: thinke then what his amazement is, from whence they come: since no wordes can carry with them the life of the inward feeling. I desire, that my desire may be waied in the ballances of Honour, and let Vertue hold them. For if the highest Love in no base person may aspire to grace, then may I hope your beautie will not be without pittie. If otherwise you be (alas but let it never be so) resolved, yet shall not my death be comfortles, receiving it by your sentence.

The joy which wrought into *Pygmalions* mind, while he 5 found his beloved image was softer, & warmer in his folded armes, till at length it accoplished his gladnes with a perfect womans shape (still beautified with the former perfections) was even such, as by each degree of *Zelmanes* wordes creepingly entred into *Philoclea*: till her pleasure was fully made up with the manifesting of his being; which was such as in hope did over-come Hope. Yet Doubt would faine have playd his parte in her minde, and cald in question, how she should be assured that *Zelmane* was *Pyrocles*. But Love streight stood up & deposed, that a lie could not come from the mouth of *Zelmane*. Besides, a certain sparke of honour, which rose in her well-disposed minde, made her feare to be alone with him, with whom alone she desired to be (with all the other cõtradictions growing in those minds, which nether absolutly clime the rocke of Vertue, nor freely sinke into the sea of Vanitie) but that sparke soone gave place, or at lest gave no more light in her mind, then a cãdle doth in the Sunnes presence. But even sicke with a surfet of joy, and fearefull of she knewe not what (as he that newly findes huge treasures, doubtes whether he sleepe or no; or like a fearfull Deere, which then lookes most about, when he comes to the best feede) with a shrugging kinde of tremor through all her principall partes, she gave these affectionate wordes for answere. Alas, how painefull a thing it is to a devided minde to make a wel-joyned answere? how harde it is to bring inwarde shame to outward confession? and what handsomnes trow you can be observed in that speeche, which is made one knowes not to whom? Shall I say ô Zelmane? Alas your wordes be against it. Shall I say Prince Pyrocles? wretch that I am, your shew is manifest against it. But this, this I may well say; If I had continued as I ought, Philoclea, you had either never bene, or ever bene Zelmane: you had either never attempted this change, set on with hope, or never discovered it, stopt with despaire. But I feare me, my behaviour ill governed, gave you the first comfort: I feare me, my affection ill hid, hath givẽ you this last assurance: I feare indeed, the weakenesse of my government before, made you thinke such a maske would be gratefull unto me: & my weaker governmẽt since, makes you to pull of the visar. What shall I doo then? shal I seeke far-fetched inventions? shall I labour to lay marble coulours over my ruinous thoughts? or rather, though the purenes of my virgin-minde be stained, let me keepe the true simplicitie of my word. True it is, alas, too true it is, ô Zelmane (for so I love to call thee, since in that name my love first began, and in the shade of that name my love shall best lie hidden,) that even while so thou wert, (what eye bewitched me I know not) my passions were fitter to desire, then to be desired. Shall I say then, I am sory, or that my love must be turned to hate, since thou art turned to Pyrocles? how may that wel be, since when thou wert Zelmane, the despaire thou mightest not be thus, did most torment me. Thou hast then the victorie: use it with vertue. Thy vertue

wan me; with vertue preserve me. Doost thou love me?
keepe me then still worthy to be beloved.

Then held she her tongue, and cast downe a self-accusing 6
looke, finding, that in her selfe she had (as it were) shot out of
the bow of her affeĉtiõ, a more quick opening of her minde,
then she minded to have done. But *Pyrocles* so caried up with
joy, that he did not envy the Gods felicitie, presented her with
some jewels of right princely value, as some litle tokens of his
love, & qualitie: and withall shewed her letters from his father
King *Euarchus*, unto him, which even in the Sea had amongst
his jewels bene preserved. But little needed those proofes to
one, who would have fallen out with her selfe, rather then
make any contrarie conjeĉtures to *Zelmanes* speeches; so thaŧ
with such imbracements, as it seemed their soules desired to
meete, and their harts to kisse, as their mouthes did: which
faine *Pyrocles* would have sealed with the chiefe armes of his
desire, but *Philoclea* commaunded the contrary; and yet they
passed the promise of mariage.

And then at *Philocleas* entreaty, who was willing to pur- 7
loine all occasions of remayning with *Zelmane*, she tolde her the
storie of her life, from the time of their departing from *Erona*,
for the rest she had already understood of her sister. For (saide
she) I have understood, how you first in the companie of your
Noble cousin *Musidorus* parted from *Thessalia*, and of divers
adventures, which with no more daunger then glory you passed
through, till your comming to the succour of the Queene
Erona; and the ende of that warre (you might perceive by my
selfe) I had understood of the Prince *Plangus*. But what since
was the course of your doings, until you came, after so many
viĉtories, to make a conquest of poore me, that I know not, the
fame thereof having rather shewed it by pieces; then delivered
any full forme of it. Therefore, deere *Pyrocles* (for what can
mine eares be so sweetly fed with as to heare you of you) be
liberall unto me of those things which have made you indeede
pretious to the worlde, and now doubt not to tell of your perils;
for since I have you here out of them, even the remembraunce
of them is pleasaunt. *Pyrocles* easily perceived she was content
with kindnesse, to put of occasion of further kindnesse; wherein
Love shewed himselfe a cowardly boy, that durst not attempt
for feare of offending. But rather Love prooved him selfe

valiant, that durst with the sworde of reverent dutie gaine-stand
the force of so many enraged desires. But so it was, that
though he knewe this discourse was to entertaine him from a
more streight parley, yet he durst not but kisse his rod, and
gladly make much of the entertainement which she allotted
unto him: and therefore with a desirous sigh chastning his
brest for too much desiring, Sweete Princesse of my life (said
he) what Trophees, what Triumph, what Monuments, what
Histories may ever make my fame yeeld so sweete a Musicke
to my eares, as that it pleaseth you to lend your minde to the
knowledge of any thing touching *Pyrocles*, onely therefore of
value, because he is your *Pyrocles*? And therefore grow I now
so proud, as to thinke it worth the hearing, since you vouchsafe
to give it hearing. Therefore (onely height of my hope)
vouchsafe to know, that after the death of *Tiridates*, and setling
Erona in her governement; for setled we left her, howsoever
since (as I perceived by your speech the last day) the ungrateful
treason of her ill-chosen husband overthrew her (a thing in
trueth never till this time by me either heard, or suspected) for
who could thinke without having such a minde as *Antiphilus*,
that so great a beautie as *Eronas* (indeed excellent) could not
have held his affection? so great goodnes could not have bound
gratefulnesse? and so high advancement could not have satisfied
his ambition? But therefore true it is, that wickednesse may well
be compared to a bottomlesse pit, into which it is farre easier
to keepe ones selfe from falling, then being fallen, to give ones
selfe any stay from falling infinitely. But for my Cosen, and
me, upon this cause we parted from *Erona*.

CHAP. 18.

[1] Anaxius-*his surcuidrie*; [2] *and challenge to* Pyrocles, *accepted.*
[3] *The execution of Ladies done on a Light-of-love.* [4] Pyrocles-
his intercession in the cause. [5] *The lewd parts of that light
lecher.* [6] *His scoffing excuses.* [7] Didos *revenge on him stopped,*
[8] *and his revenge on her stayed by* Pyrocles.

[1] Euardes (the brave & mighty Prince, whom it was my
fortune to kill in the cōbat for *Erona*) had three
Nephewes, sonnes to a sister of his; all three set among the

foremost rãcks of Fame for great minds to attẽpt, and great force to perfourme what they did attempt; especially the eldest, by name *Anaxius*; to whom al men would willingly have yeelded the height of praise, but that his nature was such, as to bestow it upon himselfe, before any could give it. For of so unsupportable a pride he was, that where his deede might well stirre envie, his demeanor did rather breed disdain. And if it be true that the *Gyants* ever made war against heaven, he had bene a fit ensigne-bearer for that company. For nothing seemed hard to him, though impossible; and nothing unjust, while his liking was his justice. Now he in these wars had flatly refused his aid; because he could not brooke, that the worthy Prince *Plãgus* was by his cosen *Tiridates* preferred before him. For allowing no other weights, but the sword & speare in judging of desert, how-much he esteemed himselfe before *Plangus* in that, so much would he have had his allowance in his service.

But now that he understood that his uncle was slaine by 2 me, I thinke rather scorne that any should kil his uncle, then any kindnesse (an un-used guest to an arrogant soule) made him seeke his revenge; I must confesse in manner gallant enough. For he sent a challenge to me to meete him at a place appointed, in the confines of the kingdome of *Lycia*; where he would prove upon me, that I had by some trecherie overcome his uncle, whom els many hundreds such as I, could not have withstood. Youth & successe made me willing enough to accept any such bargaine; especially, because I had heard that your cosen *Amphialus* (who for some yeares hath universally borne the name of the best Knight in the world) had divers times fought with him, & never bene able to master him; but so had left him, that every man thought *Anaxius* in that one vertue of curtesie far short of him, in al other his match; *Anaxius* stil deeming himselfe for his superiour. Therefore to him I would goe, and I would needs goe alone, because so I understood for certaine, he was; and (I must confesse) desirous to do something without the company of the incomparable Prince *Musidorus*, because in my hart I acknowledge that I owed more to his presence, then to any thing in my self, whatsoever before I had done. For of him indeed (as of any worldly cause) I must grant, as received, what ever there is, or may be good in me. He taught me by word, and best by example, giving me in him so lively an Image of vertue, as ignorance could not cast such mist over mine eyes, as not to see, and to love it, and all with such deare friendship and care, as (ô heavens) how cã my life ever requite unto him? which made me indeed find in my selfe such a kind of depending upon him, as without him I found a weakenesse, and a mistrustfulnes of my selfe, as one strayed from his best strength, when at any time I mist him. Which humour perceiving to over-rule me, I strave against it; not that I was unwilling to depend upon him in judgemẽt, but by weakenesse I would not; which though it held me to him, made me unworthy of him. Therfore I desired his leave, and obtained it: such confidence he had in me, preferring my reputation before his owne tendernesse; and so privately went from him, he determining (as after I knew) in secreat maner, not to be far from the place, where we appointed to meete, to prevent any foule play that might be offered unto me. Full loth was *Erona* to let us depart from her, (as it were) forefeeling the harmes which after fell to her. But I, (ridde fully from those combers of kindnesse, and halfe a dayes journey in my way toward *Anaxius*) met an adventure, (though in it selfe of small importance) I will tell you at large, because by the occasion thereof I was brought to as great comber and danger, as lightly any might escape.

3   As I past through a Laund (ech side whereof was so bordred both with high tymber trees, and copses of farre more humble growth, that it might easily bring a solitarie minde to looke for no other companions then the wild burgesses of the forrest) I heard certaine cries, which comming by pawses to mine eares from within the wood of the right hand, made me well assured by the greatnesse of the crie, it was the voice of a man, though it were a verie unmanlike voice, so to crie. But making mine eare my guide, I left not many trees behind me, before I saw at the bottome of one of them a gentle-man bound (with many garters) hand & foot, so as well he might tomble and tosse, but neither runne nor resist he could. Upõ him (like so many Eagles upon an Oxe) were nine Gentle-women; truely such, as one might well enough say, they were hansome. Each of them helde bodkins in their handes, wherewith they continually pricked him, having bene before-hand unarmed of

any defence from the wast upward, but onely of his shirte: so as the poore man wept and bled, cryed and prayed, while they sported themselves in his paine, and delighted in his prayers, as the arguments of their victorie.

I was moved to compassion, and so much the more that he straight cald to me for succour, desiring me at lest to kill him, to deliver him from those tormenters. But before my-self could resolve, much lesse any other tell what I would resolve, there came in cholericke hast towards me about sevẽ or eight knights; the foremost of which willed me to get me away, and not to trouble the Ladies, while they were taking their due revenge, but with so over-mastring a maner of pride, as truly my hart could not brooke it: & therfore (answering them, that how I would have defended him from the Ladies I knew not, but from them I would) I began a combate first with him particularly, and after his death with the others (that had lesse good maners) joyntly. But such was the end of it, that I kept the fielde with the death of some, and flight of others. In so much as the women (afraid, what angrie victorie would bring forth) ranne away; saving onely one; who was so flesht in malice, that neither during, nor after the fight, she gave any truce to her crueltie, but still used the little instrument of her great spight, to the well-witnest paine of the impatient patient: and was now about to put out his eies, which all this while were spared, because they should do him the discomfort of seeing who prevailed over him. When I came in, and after much ado, brought her to some conference, (for some time it was before she would harken, more before she would speake; & most, before she would in her speech leave off that remembrance of her bodkin) but at length whẽ I puld off my head-peece, and humbly entreated her pardon, or knowledge why she was cruell; out of breath more with choller (which increased in his owne exercise) thẽ with the paine she tooke, much to this purpose she gave her griefe unto my knowledge. Gentleman (said she) much it is against my will to forbeare any time the executing of my just revẽge upon this naughtie creature, a man in nothing, but in deceaving women; But because I see you are young, and like enough to have the power (if you would have the mind) to do much more mischiefe, then he,

I am content upon this bad subject to reade a lecture to your vertue.

5   This man called *Pamphilus*, in birth I must confesse is noble (but what is that to him, if it shalbe a staine to his deade auncestors to have left such an off[s]pring?) in shape as you see not uncomely (indeed the fit maske of his disguised falshood) in conversation wittily pleasant, and pleasantly gamesome; his eyes full of merie simplicitie, his words of hartie companablenesse; and such a one, whose head one would not think so stayed, as to thinke mischievously: delighted in al such things, which by imparting their delight to others, makes the user therof welcome; as, Musicke, Daunsing, Hunting, Feasting, Riding, & such like. And to conclude, such a one, as who can keepe him at armes ende, neede never wish a better cõpaniõ. But under these qualities lies such a poysonous addar as I will tell you. For by those gifts of Nature and Fortune (being in all places acceptable) he creepes, nay (to say truely) he flies so into the favour of poore sillie women, that I would be too much ashamed to confesse, if I had not revenge in my hande, as well as shame in my cheekes. For his hart being wholy delighted in deceiving us, we could never be warned, but rather, one bird caught, served for a stale to bring in more. For the more he gat, the more still he shewed, that he (as it were) gave away to his new mistresse, whẽ he betrayed his promises to the former. The cunning of his flatterie, the readines of his teares, the infinitenes of his vowes, were but among the weakest threedes of his nette. But the stirring our owne passions, and by the entrance of them, to make himselfe Lord of our forces; there lay his Masters part of cunning, making us now jealous, now envious, now proud of what we had, desirous of more; now giving one the triumph, to see him that was Prince of many, Subject to her; now with an estranged looke, making her feare the losse of that minde, which indeede could never be had: never ceasing humblenes and diligence, till he had imbarked us in some such disadvantage, as we could not return dry-shod; and then suddenly a tyrant, but a craftie tyrant. For so would he use his imperiousnes, that we had a delightfull feare, and an awe which made us loath to lose our hope. And, which is strangest (when sometimes with late repentance I thinke of it)

266

I must confesse, even in the greatest tempest of my judgemẽt was I never driven to think him excellent, and yet so could set my minde, both to gette and keepe him, as though therein had laien my felicitie: like them I have seene play at the ball, growe extremely earnest, who shoulde have the ball, and yet every one knew it was but a ball. But in the end, the bitter sauce of the sport was, that we had ether our hartes broken with sorrow, or our estates spoyled with being at his direction, or our honours for ever lost, partly by our owne faults, but principally by his faultie using of our faults. For never was there man that could with more scornefull eyes beholde her, at whose feete he had lately laine, nor with a more unmanlike braverie use his tongue to her disgrace, which lately had song Sonets of her praises: being so naturally inconstant, as I marvell his soule findes not some way to kill his bodie, whereto it had beene so long united. For so hath he dealt with us (unhappie fooles,) as we could never tell, whether he made greater haste after he once liked, to enjoy, or after he once enjoyed, to forsake. But making a glorie of his own shame, it delighted him to be challenged of unkindnesse: it was a triumph unto him to have his mercie called for: and he thought the fresh colours of his beautie were painted in nothing so well, as in the ruines of his Lovers: yet so farre had we engaged our selves, (unfortunate soules) that we listed not complaine, since our complaintes could not but carrie the greatest accusation to our selves. But everie of us (each for her selfe,) laboured all meanes how to recover him, while he rather daily sent us companions of our deceipt, then ever returned in any sound and faithfull manner. Till at length he concluded all his wronges with betrothing himselfe to one (I must confesse) worthie to be liked, if any worthinesse might excuse so unworthie a change-ablenesse; leaving us nothing but remorse for what was past, and despaire of what might followe. Then indeede, the common injurie made us all joyne in friendshippe, who till that time, had employed our endevours one against the other. For, we thought nothing was a more condemning of us, then the justifying of his love to her by mariage: then Despaire made Feare valiant, and Revenge gave Shame countenance: whereupon, we (that you saw here) devised how to get him among us alone: which he (suspecting no such matter of them, whom he had by often abuses he thought made tame to be still abused) easilie gave us opportunitie to doo.

6   And a man may see, even in this, how soone Rulers growe proude, and in their pride foolish: he came with such an authoritie among us, as if the Planets had done inough for us, that by us once he had beene delighted. And when we began in courteous manner, one after the other, to lay his unkindnesse unto him, he seeing himselfe confronted by so many (like a resolute Orator,) went not to deniall, but to justifie his cruell falshoode, and all with such jestes, and disdainfull passages, that if the injurie could not be made greater, yet were our conceiptes made the apter to apprehende it.

Among other of his answeres (forsooth) I shall never forgette, how he woulde proove it was no inconstancie to chaunge from one Love to an other, but a great constancie; and contrarie, that which we call constancie, to be most changeable. For (said he) I ever loved my Delight, & delighted alwayes in what was Lovely: and where-soever I founde occasion to obtaine that, I constantly folowed it. But these constant fooles you speak of, though their Mistres grow by sicknes foule, or by fortune miserable, yet stil will love her, and so committe the absurdest inconstancie that may be, in changing their love from fairenes to foulenesse, and from lovelines to his contrarie; like one not content to leave a friend, but will streight give over himself to his mortall enemie: where I (whom you call inconstant) am ever constant; to Beautie, in others; and Delight in my self. And so in this jollie scoffing braverie he went over us all, saying, He left one, because she was over-waiwarde; another, because she was too soone woon; a third, because she was not merie inough; a fourth, because she was over-gamesome; the fifth, because she was growen with griefe subject to sicknesse; the sixt, because she was so foolish, as to be jelous of him; the seventh, because she had refused to carie a letter for him, to another that he loved; the eight, because she was not secrete; the ninth, because she was not liberall: but to me, who am named *Dido*, (and indeede have mette with a false *Ænæas*) to me, I say, (ô the ungratefull villaine) he could finde no other fault to object, but that (perdie) he met with many fayrer.

7   But when he had thus plaide the carelesse Prince, we

(having those servants of ours in readines, whom you lately so manfully overcame) laide holde of him; beginning at first but that trifling revenge, in which you found us busie; but meaning afterwardes to have mangled him so, as should have lost his credit for ever abusing more. But as you have made my fellowes flie away, so for my part the greatnesse of his wrong overshadowes in my judgement the greatnesse of any daunger. For was it not inough for him, to have deceived me, & through the deceipt abused me, & after the abuse forsaken me, but that he must now, of al the company, & before all the company lay want of beautie to my charge? Many fairer? I trow evẽ in your judgemẽt, Sir, (if your eies do not beguile me) not many fairer; & I know (whosoever saies the cõtrary) there are not many fairer. And of whom should I receive this reproch, but of him, who hath best cause to know there are not many fairer? And therefore how-soever my fellowes pardon his injuries, for my parte I will ever remember, & remember to revenge this scorne of al scornes. With that she to him afresh; & surely would have put out his eies (who lay muet for shame, if he did not sometimes crie for feare) if I had not lept from my horse, & mingling force with intreaty, staied her furie.

But, while I was perswading her to meekenes, comes a number of his friends, to whom he forthwith cried, that they should kill that womã, that had thus betraied and disgraced him. But then I was faine to forsake the ensigne; under which I had before served, and to spend my uttermost force in the protecting of the Ladie; which so well prevailed for her, that in the ende there was a faithfull peace promised of all sides. And so I leaving her in a place of securitie (as she thought) went on my journey towards *Anaxius*, for whom I was faine to stay two daies in the apointed place, he disdaining to waite for me, till he was sure I were there.

CHAP. 19.

[1] *The monomachie betweene* Anaxius *and* Pyrocles; [2] *adjourned by*
Pyrocles *to resuccour* Dido. [3] *The course of* Didos *daunger.*
[4] *The miserablenesse of her father.* [5] *His carlish entertaine-*
ment to Pyrocles; [6] *and his treason against him.* [7] Pyrocles
hard bestead. [8] *succoured by* Musidorus: [9] *both saved by the*
King *of* Iberia. [10] *The execution of the traitors, and death of*
Dido.

[1]   I Did patientlie abide his angrie pleasure, till about that
space of time he came (indeede, according to promise)
alone: and (that I may not say too little, because he is wont to
say too much) like a man, whose courage was apt to clime over
any daunger. And assoone as ever he came neere me, in fit
distaunce for his purpose, he with much fury, (but with fury
skilfully guided) ran upon me; which I (in the best sort I
could) resisted, having kept my selfe ready for him, because
I had understood, that he observed but few complements in
matters of armes, but such as a proud anger did indite unto
him. And so putting our horses into a full careere, we hit ech
other upon the head with our Launces: I think he felte my
blowe; for my parte (I must confesse) I never received the
like: but I thinke though my senses were astonished, my
minde forced them to quicken themselves, because I had
learned of him, how little favour he is woont to show in any
matter of advantage. And indeede he was turned, and comming
upon me with his sworde drawne, both our staves having bene
broken at that encounter. But I was so ready to answere him,
that truely I know not who gave the first blowe. But whosoever gave the first, it was quickly seconded by the second.
And indeed (excellentest Ladie) I must say truely, for a time it
was well fought betweene us; he undoubtedly being of singular
valour, (I would to God, it were not abased by his too much
loftinesse) but as by the occasion of the combate, winning and
loosing ground, we chaunged places, his horse happened to
come upon the point of the broken speare, which fallen to the
ground chaunced to stand upward; so as it lighting upon his
hart, the horse died. He driven to dismount, threatned, if I

did not the like, to doo as much for my horse, as Fortune had done for his. But whether for that, or because I would not be beholding to Fortune for any part of the victorie, I descended.

So began our foote-fight in such sort, that we were well entred to bloud of both sides, when there comes by, that unconstant *Pamphilus*, whom I had delivered (easie to be knowne, for he was bare faced) with a dozen armed men after him; but before him he had *Dido* (that Ladie, who had most sharpely punished him) riding upon a palfrey, he following her with most unmanlike crueltie; beating her with wandes he had in his hande, she crying for sense of payne, or hope of succour: which was so pittifull a sight unto me, that it mooved me to require *Anaxius* to deferre our combate, till an other day, and now to perfourme the duties of Knighthood in helping this distressed Ladie. But he that disdaines to obey any thing but his passion (which he cals his mind) bad me leave of that thought; but when he had killed me, he would then (perhaps) go to her succour. But I well finding the fight would be long betweene us (longing in my hart to deliver the poore *Dido*) giving him so great a blowe, as somewhat staied him, (to terme it a right) I flatly ran away from him toward my horse, who trotting after the cõpanie, in mine armour I was put to some paine, but that use made me nimble unto it. But as I followed my horse, *Anaxius* followed me: but his prowde harte did so disdaine that exercise, that I had quickly over-run him, & over-taken my horse; being (I must cõfesse) ashamed to see a number of country folks, who happened to passe thereby, who hallowed & howted after me as at the arrantest coward, that ever shewed his shoulders to his enemie. But when I had leapt on my horse (with such speedy agility, that they all cried, O see how feare gives him wings) I turned to *Anaxius*, & aloud promised him to returne thether again, as soone as I had relieved the injuried Ladie. But he railing at me, with all the base wordes angry contempt could endite; I said no more, but, *Anaxius*, assure thy self, I nether feare thy force, nor thy opinion. And so using no weapon of a Knight as at that time, but my spurres, I ranne in my knowledge after *Pamphilus*, but in al their conceipts from *Anaxius*, which as far as I could heare, I might well heare testified with such laughters and games, that I was some few times moved to turne backe againe.

3 But the Ladies misery over-balanced my reputation so that after her I went, & with six houres hard riding (through so wild places, as it was rather the cunning of my horse sometimes, then of my selfe, so rightly to hit the way) I overgat thẽ a little before night, neere to an old il-favoured castle, the place where I perceived they meant to perfourme their unknightly errand. For there they began to strip her of her clothes, when I came in among them, & running through the first with a laũce, the justnesse of the cause so enhabled me against the rest (falsharted in their owne wrong doing) that I had, in as short time almost as I had bene fighting with only *Anaxius*, delivered her from those injurious wretches: most of whom carried newes to the other world, that amongst men secret wronges are not alwaies left unpunished. As for *Pamphilus*, he having once seene, & (as it should seeme) remembred me, even from the beginning began to be in the rereward, and before they had left fighting, he was too far of to give them thanks for their paines. But when I had delivered to the Ladie a ful libertie, both in effe ct, & in opinion, (for some time it was before she could assure her selfe she was out of their handes, who had layd so vehement apprehension of death upon her) she then tolde me, how as she was returning toward her fathers, weakely accompanied (as too soone trusting to the falshood of reconcilement) *Pamphilus* had set upon her, and killing those that were with her, carried her selfe by such force, and with such mãner as I had seene, to this place, where he meant in cruell and shamefull manner to kill her, in the sight of her owne Father; to whom he had already sent worde of it, that out of his castle windowe (for this castle, she said, was his) he might have the prospe ct of his onely childes destru ction, if my comming, whom (she said) he feared (as soone as he knew me by the armour) had not warraunted her from that neere approching crueltie. I was glad I had done so good a deede for a Gentlewoman not unhandsome, whome before I had in like sorte helped. But the night beginning to perswade some retiring place, the Gentlewoman, even out of countenaunce before she began her speach, much after this manner invited me to lodge that night with her father.

4 Sir (said she) how much I owe you, can be but abased by wordes, since the life I have, I holde it now the second time of

you: and therefore neede not offer service unto you, but onely to remember you, that I am your servaunt: and I would, my being so, might any way yeeld any small contentment unto you. Now onely I can but desire you to harbour your selfe this night in this castle; because the time requires it; and in truth this countrie is very daungerous for murthering theeves, to trust a sleeping life among them. And yet I must confesse, that as the love I beare you makes me thus invite you, so the same love makes me ashamed to bring you to a place, where you shalbe so (not spokẽ by ceremonie but by truth) miserably entertained. With that she tolde me, that though she spake of her father (whom she named *Chremes*) she would hide no truth from me, which was in summe, that as he was of all that region the man of greatest possessions, and riches, so was he either by nature, or an evill received opinion, given to sparing, in so unmeasurable a sorte, that he did not onely barre him selfe from the delightfull, but almost from the necessarie use thereof; scarsely allowing him selfe fitte sustenaunce of life, rather then he would spende of those goods, for whose sake onely he seemed to joye in life. Which extreame dealing (descending from himselfe upon her) had driven her to put her selfe with a great Lady of that countrie, by which occasion she had stumbled upon such mischance, as were little for the honour either of her, or her familie. But so wise had he shewed himselfe therein, as while he found his daughter maintained without his cost, he was content to be deafe to any noise of infamie: which though it had wronged her much more then she deserved, yet she could not denie, but she was driven thereby to receave more then decent favours. She concluded, that there at lest I should be free from injuries, & should be assured to her-wards to abound as much in the true causes of welcomes, as I should want of the effects thereof.

I, who had acquainted my selfe to measure the delicacie of foode and rest, by hunger and wearinesse, at that time well stored of both, did not abide long entreatie; but went with her to the Castle: which I found of good strength, having a great mote rounde about it; the worke of a noble Gentleman, of whose unthriftie sonne he had bought it. The bridge drawne up, where we were faine to crie a good while before we coulde have answeare, and to dispute a good while before answeare would bee brought to acceptance. At length a willingnesse, rather then a joy to receave his daughter, whome hee had lately seene so neere death, and an opinion rather brought into his heade by course, because he heard himselfe called a father; rather then any kindnesse that hee found in his owne harte, made him take us in; for my part by that time growne so wearie of such entertainement, that no regard of my selfe, but onely the importunitie of his daughter made me enter. Where I was met with this *Chremes*, a driveling old fellow, leane, shaking both of head and hands, alredie halfe earth, and yet then most greedie of Earth: who scarcely would give me thankes for that I had done, for feare I suppose, that thankefulnesse might have an introduction of reward. But with a hollow voice, giving me a false welcome, I might perceave in his eye to his daughter, that it was hard to say, whether the displeasure of her company did not over-way the pleasure of her owne comming. But on he brought me, into so bare a house, that it was the picture of miserable happinesse, and rich beggerie (served onely by a company of rusticall villaines, full of sweate and dust, not one of them other, then a labourer) in summe (as he counted it) profitable drudgerie: and all preparations both for foode and lodging such, as would make one detest nigardnesse, it is so sluttish a vice. His talke nothing but of his povertie, for feare belike lest I should have proved a young borrower. In summe, such a man, as any enemy could not wish him worse, then to be himselfe. But there that night bidde I the burthen of being a tedious guest to a loathsome host; over-hearing him sometimes bitterly warne his daughter of bringing such costly mates under his roofe: which she grieving at, desired much to know my name, I thinke partly of kindnesse to remember who had done some-thing for her, and partly because she assured her selfe I was such a one as would make even his miser-minde contented, with what he had done. And accordingly she demaunded my name, and estate, with such earnestnesse, that I whom Love had not as then so robbed me of my selfe, as to be another then I am, told her directly my name and condition: whereof she was no more gladde then her father, as I might well perceave by some ill-favoured cheerefulnesse, which then first began to wrinckle it selfe in his face.

But the causes of their joyes were farre different; for as the 6 shepheard and the butcher both may looke upon one sheepe with pleasing conceipts, but the shepheard with minde to profite himselfe by preserving, the butcher with killing him: So she rejoyced to finde that mine owne benefits had tyed me to be her friend, who was a Prince of such greatnesse, and lovingly rejoyced: but his joy grew, (as I to my danger after perceived) by the occasion of the Queene *Artaxias* setting my head to sale, for having slaine her brother *Tiridates*; which being the summe of an hundreth thousand crownes (to whosoever brought me alive into her hands) that old wretch, (who had over-lived all good nature) though he had lying idly by him much more then that, yet above all things loving money, for monies owne sake determined to betray me, so well deserving of him, for to have that which he was determined never to use. And so knowing that the next morning I was resolved to go to the place where I had left *Anaxius*, he sent in all speed to a Captaine of a Garrison hard by; which though it belonged to the King of *Iberia*, (yet knowing the Captaines humor to delight so in riotous spending; as he cared not how he came by the meanes to maintaine it) doubted not, that to be halfe with him in the gaine, he would play his quarters part in the treason. And therefore that night agreeing of the fittest places where they might surprise me in the morning, the old caitiffe was growne so ceremonious, as he would needs accompanie me some myles in my way; a sufficient token to me, if Nature had made me apte to suspect; since a churles curtesie rathely comes but either for gaine, or falshood. But I suffered him to stumble into that point of good manner: to which purpose he came out with all his clownes, horst upon such cart-jades, and so furnished, as in good faith I thought with my selfe, if that were thrift, I wisht none of my friends or subjectes ever to thrive. As for his daughter (the gentle *Dido*) she would also (but in my conscience with a farre better minde) prolong the time of farewell, as long as he.

So we went on togither: he so old in wickednes, that he 7 could looke me in the face, and freely talke with me, whose life he had alreadie contracted for: till comming into the falling of a way which ledde us into a place, of each-side whereof men might easily keepe themselves undiscovered, I was encompassed sodainly by a great troupe of enimies, both of horse and foote, who willed me to yeelde my selfe to the Queene *Artaxia*. But they coulde not have used worse eloquence to have perswaded my yeelding, then that; I knowing the little good will *Artaxia* bare me. And therefore making necessitie and justice my best sword and shield, I used the other weapons I had as well as I could; I am sure to the little ease of a good number, who trusting to their number more then to their valure, and „ valewing money higher then equitie, felt, that guiltlesnesse is not alwayes with ease oppressed. As for *Chremes*, he withdrew himselfe, yet so guilding his wicked conceipts with his hope of gaine, that he was content to be a beholder, how I should be taken to make his pray.

8   But I was growne so wearie, that I supported my selfe more with anger then strength, when the most excellent *Musidorus* came to my succour; who having followed my trace as well as he could, after he had found I had left the fight with *Anaxius*, came to the niggards Castell, where he found all burnd and spoiled by the countrie people, who bare mortall hatred to that covetous man, and now tooke the time, when the castell was left almost without garde, to come in, and leave monuments of their malice therein: which *Musidorus* not staying either to further, or impeach, came upon the spurre after me (because with one voice many told him, that if I were in his company, it was for no good meant unto me) and in this extremitie found me. But when I saw that Cosen of mine, me thought my life was doubled, and where before I thought of a noble death, I now thought of a noble victorie. For who can feare that hath *Musidorus* by him? who, what he did there for me, how many he killed, not straunger for the number, then for the straunge blowes wherwith he sent them to a weldeserved death, might well delight me to speake off, but I should so holde you too long in every particular. But in trueth, there if ever, and ever, if ever any man, did *Musidorus* shew himselfe second to none in able valour.

9   Yet what the unmeasurable excesse of their number woulde have done in the ende I knowe not, but the triall thereof was cutte off by the chaunceable comming thither of the King of *Iberia*, that same father of that worthy *Plangus*, whom it hath pleased you somtimes to mention: who, (not yeelding over to

old age his country delights, especially of hauking) was at that time (following a Merline) brought to see this injurie offred unto us: and having great numbers of Courtiers waiting upon him, was straight known by the souldiers that assaulted us, to be their King, and so most of them with-drew themselves.

He by his authoritie knowing of the Captaines owne con- 10 strained confession, what was the motive of this mischievous practise; misliking much such violēce should be offred in his countrie to men of our ranke: but chiefely disdaining it should be done in respect of his Niece, whom (I must confesse wrong-fully) he hated, because he interpreted that her brother and she had maintained his sonne *Plangus* against him, caused the Cap-taines head presently to be striken off, and the old bad *Chremes* to be hanged: though truely for my part, I earnestly laboured for his life, because I had eaten of his bread. But one thing was notable for a conclusion of his miserable life, that neither the death of his daughter, who (alas the poore Gentlewoman) was by chaunce slaine among his clownes, while she over-boldly for her weake sex sought to hold thē from me, nor yet his owne shamefull ende was so much in his mouth as he was ledde to execution, as the losse of his goods, and burning of his house: which often, with more laughter then teares of the hearers, he made pittifull exclamations upon.

CHAP. 20.

[1] *The two Princes passage to the* Iberian *Court.* [2] Andromanas *omniregencie.* [3] *Her parti-love to them both.* [4] *Her faire and foule meanes to inveigle them.* [5] Palladius *love to* Zel-mane. [6] Zelmanes *love to* Pyrocles, *and practise with her Lover to release her beloved.*

THis justice thus done, and we delivered, the King indeede 1 in royall sorte invited us to his Court, not farre thence: in all points entertaining us so, as truely I must ever acknow-ledge a beholdingnesse unto him: although the streame of it fell out not to be so sweet as the spring. For after some dayes being there (curing our selves of such wounds as we had received, while I, causing diligent search to be made of *Anaxius*, could learne nothing, but that he was gone out of the countrie, boasting in everie place, how he had made me run away) we were brought to receive the favour of acquaintāce with this Queene *Andromana*, whom the Princesse *Pamela* did in so lively colours describe the last day, as still me thinkes the figure therof possesseth mine eyes, confirmed by the knowledge my selfe had.

2   And therefore I shall neede the lesse to make you know what kinde of woman she was; but this onely, that first with the rarenes of affection, and after with the very use of directing, she had made her selfe so absolute a maister of her husbands minde, that a-while he would not, and after, he could not tell how to govern, without being governed by her: but finding an ease in not understanding, let loose his thoughtes wholly to pleasure, entrusting to her the entire conduct of all his royall affaires. A thing that may luckely fall out to him that hath the blessing, to match with some Heroicall minded Ladie. But in him it was nether guided by wisdome, nor followed by Fortune, but thereby was slipte insensiblie into such an estate, that he lived at her undiscreete discretion: all his subjectes having by some yeares learned, so to hope for good, and feare of harm, onely frõ her, that it should have neded a stronger vertue thē his, to have unwound so deeply an entred vice. So that either not striving (because he was contented) or contented (because he would not strive) he scarcelie knewe what was done in his owne chamber, but as it pleased her Instrumentes to frame the relation.

3   Now we being brought knowen unto her (the time that we spent in curing some very dangerous wounds) after once we were acquainted, (and acquainted we were sooner then our selves expected) she continuallie almost haunted us, till (and it was not long a doing) we discovered a most violent bent of " affection: and that so strangely, that we might well see, an " evill minde in authoritie, dooth not onely folow the sway of " the desires alreadie within it, but frames to it selfe new desires, not before thought of. For, with equall ardour she affected us both: and so did her greatnes disdaine shamefastnes, that she was content to acknowledge it to both. For, (having many times torne the vaile of modestie) it seemed, for a laste delight,

that she delighted in infamy: which often she had used to her
husbands shame, filling all mens eares (but his) with reproch;
while he (hoodwinkt with kindnes) lest of al mē knew who
strake him. But her first degree was, by setting foorth her
beauties, (truely in nature not to be misliked, but as much
advāced to the eye, as abased to the judgemēt by arte) thereby
to bring us (as willingly-caught fishes) to bite at her baite.
And thereto had she that scutchion of her desires supported by
certain badly-diligēt ministers, who oftē cloyed our eares with
her praises, & would needs teach us a way of felicitie by seeking
her favor. But when she found, that we were as deaf to thē,
as dumb to her; then she listed no lōger stay in the suburbs of
her foolish desires, but diretly entred upŏ thē; making her
self an impudent suter, authorizing her selfe very much with
making us see that all favor & power in that realm, so depēded
upon her, that now (being in her hands) we were ether to
keep, or lose our liberty, at her discretiŏ; which yet she so
tēpred, as that we might rather suspet, thē she threatē. But
whē our woūds grew so, as that they gave us leave to travell,
& that she found we were purposed to use all meanes we could
to depart thence, she (with more & more importunatnes) craved
that, which in all good maners was ether of us to be desired, or
not granted. Truely (most faire & every way excellēt Lady)
you would have wondred to have seene, how before us she
would confes the contentiŏ in her own mind, between that
lovely (indeed most lovely) broūnes of *Musidorus* his face, &
this colour of mine, which she (in the deceivable stile of
affetion) would intitle beautifull: how her eyes wandered (like
a glutton at a feast) from the one to the other; and how her
wordes would beginne halfe of the sentence to *Musidorus*, &
end the other half to *Pyrocles*: not ashamed (seeing the friendshippe betweene us) to desire either of us to be a mediator to
the other; as if we should have played a request at Tennis
betweene us: and often wishing, that she might be the angle,
where the lines of our friendshippe might meet; and be the
knotte which might tie our hartes together. Which proceeding of hers I doo the more largely set before you
(most deare Lady) that by the foyle therof, you may see the
noblenes of my desire to you, & the warrantablenes of your
favour to me.

4   At that *Philoclea* smiled, with a little nod. But (saide *Pyrocles*) when she perceived no hope by suite to prevaile, then (perswaded by the rage of affection, and encouraged by daring to doo any thing) she founde meanes to have us accused to the King, as though we went about some practise to overthrowe him in his owne estate. Which, because of the straunge successes we had in the kingdomes of *Phrigia, Pontus* & *Galatia*) seemed not unlikely to him, who (but skimming any thing that came before him) was disciplined to leave the through-handling of all, to his gentle wife: who foorthwith caused us to be put in prison, having (while we slept) deprived us of our armour: a prison, indeede injurious, because a prison, but els well testifying affection, because in all respectes as commodious, as a prison might be: and indeede so placed, as she might at all houres, (not seene by many, though she cared not much how many had seene her) come unto us. Then fell she to sause her desires with threatnings, so that we were in a great perplexitie, restrained to so unworthie a bondage, and yet restrained by Love, which (I cannot tell how) in noble mindes, by a certain duety, claimes an answering. And how much that love might moove us, so much, and more that faultines of her mind removed us; her beautie being balanced by her shamelesnes. But that which did (as it were) tie us in captivitie, was, that to graunt, had ben wickedly injurious to him, that saved our lives: and to accuse a Ladie that loved us, of her love unto us, we esteemed almost as dishonorable: & but by one of those waies we sawe no likelihood of going out of that place, where the words would be injurious to your eares, which should expresse the manner of her suite: while yet many times earnestnes died her cheekes with the colour of shamefastnes; and wanton languishing borrowed of her eies the downe-cast looke of modestie. But we in the meane time far from loving her, and often assuring her, that we would not so recompence her husbandes saving of our lives; to such a ridiculous degree of trusting her, she had brought him, that she caused him sende us worde, that upon our lives, we should doo whatsoever she commaunded us: good man, not knowing any other, but that all her pleasures bent to the preservation of his estate. But when that made us rather pittie, then obey his folly, then fel she to servile entreating us, as though force could have bene the

schoole of Love, or that an honest courage would not rather strive against, then yeelde to injurie. All which yet could not make us accuse her, though it made us almost pine awaie for spight, to loose any of our time in so troublesome an idlenesse.

But while we were thus full of wearinesse of what was past, and doubt of what was to follow, Love (that I thinke in the course of my life hath a sporte sometimes to poison me with roses, sometimes to heale me with wormewood) brought forth a remedy unto us: which though it helped me out of that distres, alas the cõclusion was such, as I must ever while I live, think it worse then a wracke, so to have bene preserved. This King by this Queene had a sonne of tender age, but of great expectation, brought up in the hope of themselves, & already acceptation of the inconstant people, as successour of his fathers crowne: whereof he was as worthy, considering his partes, as unworthie, in respect of the wrong was therby done against the most worthy *Plangus*: whose great desertes now either forgotten, or ungratefully remembred, all men set their sayles with the favourable winde, which blewe on the fortune of this young Prince, perchaunce not in their harts, but surely not in their mouths, now giving *Plangus* (who some yeares before was their only chãpion) the poore cõfort of calamitie, pittie. This youth therefore accounted Prince of that regiõ, by name *Palladius*, did with vehement affection love a young Ladie, brought up in his fathers court, called *Zelmane*, daughter to that mischievously unhappie Prince *Plexirtus* (of whom already I have, and sometimes must make, but never honorable mention) left there by her father, because of the intricate changeablenes of his estate; he by the motherside being halfe brother to this Queene *Andromana*, and therefore the willinger committing her to her care. But as Love (alas) doth not alwaies reflect it selfe, so fel it out that this *Zelmane*, (though truely reason there was inough to love *Palladius*) yet could not ever perswade her harte to yeelde thereunto: with that paine to *Palladius*, as they feele, that feele an unloved love. Yet loving indeede, and therefore constant, he used still the intercession of diligéce and faith, ever hoping, because he would not put him selfe into that hell, to be hopelesse: untill the time of our being come, and captived there, brought foorth this ende, whiche truely deserves of me a further degree of sorrow then teares.

6   Such was therein my ill destinie, that this young Ladie *Zelmane* (like some unwisely liberall, that more delight to give presentes, then pay debtes) she chose (alas for the pittie) rather to bestowe her love (so much undeserved, as not desired) upon me, then to recōpence him, whose love (besides many other things) might seeme (even in the court of Honour) justly to claime it of her.   But so it was (alas that so it was) whereby it came to passe, that (as nothing doth more naturally follow his cause, then care to preserve, and benefite doth follow unfained affeċtion) she felt with me, what I felte of my captivitie, and streight laboured to redresse my paine, which was her paine: which she could do by no better meanes, then by using the helpe therein of *Palladius*: who (true Lover) considering what, and not why, in all her commaundementes; and indeed she concealing from him her affeċtion (which she intituled compassion,) immediatly obeyed to imploy his uttermost credite to relieve us: which though as great, as a beloved son with a mother, faulty otherwise, but not hard-harted toward him, yet it could not prevaile to procure us libertie.   Wherefore he sought to have that by praċtise, which he could not by praier.   And so being allowed often to visit us (for indeed our restraints were more, or lesse, according as the ague of her passion was either in the fit, or intermission) he used the opportunitie of a fit time thus to deliver us.

CHAP. 21.

[1] *The cause of the* Iberian *yearely justes.*   [2] *Queene* Helens *prayses.*   [3] *The prize borne by her Knights, which* Palladius *and the Princes set them to reverse.*   [4] *The inventions and aċtions of seven tilters.*   [5] Palladius *and the Princes entry into the field, honour in it, and flight from it.*   [6] Andromanas *pursuite of them* [7] *to the death of her sonne* [8] *and her selfe.*

1   THe time of the maryinge that Queene was every year, by the extreame love of her husband, & the serviceable love of the Courtiers, made notable by some publike honours, which

indeede (as it were) proclaymed to the worlde, how deare she was to the people. Among other, none was either more grate-full to the beholders, or more noble in it selfe, then justs, both with sword and launce, mainteined for a seven-night together: wherein that Nation dooth so excell, bothe for comelines and hablenes, that from neighbour-countries they ordinarily come, some to strive, some to learne, and some to behold.

This day it happened that divers famous Knights came 2 thither frõ the court of *Helen*, Queene of *Corinth*; a Ladie, whom Fame at that time was so desirous to honor, that she borrowed all mens mouthes to joyne with the sounde of her Trumpet. For as her beautie hath wonne the prize from all women, that stande in degree of comparison (for as for the two sisters of *Arcadia*, they are farre beyond all conceipt of com-parison) so hath her government bene such, as hath bene no lesse beautifull to mens judgements, then her beautie to the eiesight. For being brought by right of birth, a woman, a yong woman, a faire woman, to governe a people, in nature mutinously prowde, and alwaies before so used to hard governours, as they knew not how to obey without the sworde were drawne. Yet could she for some yeares, so carry her selfe among them, that they found cause in the delicacie of her sex, of admiration, not of cõtempt: & which was notable, even in the time that many countries were full of wars (which for old grudges to *Corinth* were thought still would conclude there) yet so hãdled she the matter, that the threatens ever smarted in the threatners; she using so straũge, and yet so well-succeeding a temper, that she made her people by peace, warlike; her courtiers by sports, learned; her Ladies by Love, chast. For by continuall martiall exercises without bloud, she made them perfeĉt in that bloudy art. Her sportes were such as caried riches of Knowledge upõ the streame of Delight: & such the behaviour both of her selfe, and her Ladies, as builded their chastitie, not upon waywardnes, but by choice of worthines: So as it seemed, that court to have bene the mariage place of Love and Vertue, & that her selfe was a *Diana* apparelled in the garments of *Venus*. And this which Fame onely delivered unto me, (for yet I have never seene her) I am the willinger to speake of to you, who (I knowe) knowe her better, being your neere neighbour, because you may see by her example (in her

selfe wise, and of others beloved) that neither follie is the cause
of vehement Love, nor reproch the effect. For never (I thinke)
was there any woman, that with more unremoveable deter-
minatiŏ gave her selfe to the coūcell of Love, after she had
once set before her mind the worthines of your cousin *Amphialus*; & yet is nether her wisedome doubted of, nor honour
blemished. For (O God) what doth better become wisdome,
then to discerne, what is worthy the loving? what more agreable to goodnes, then to love it so discerned? and what to
greatnesse of hart, then to be constant in it once loved? But
at that time, that Love of hers was not so publikely knowne,
as the death of *Philoxenus*, and her search of *Amphialus* hath
made it: but then seemed to have such leasure to sende thither
diverse choyse Knights of her court, because they might bring
her, at lest the knowledge, perchaunce the honour, of that
Triumph.

3   Wherein so they behaved themselves as for three daies they
caried the prize; which being come from so farre a place to
disgrace her servaunts, *Palladius* (who himselfe had never used
armes) persuaded the Queene *Andromana* to be content (for the
honour sake of her court) to suffer us two to have our horse
and armour, that he with us might undertake the recoverie of
their lost honour: which she graunted; taking our oth to go
no further then her sonne, and never to abandon him. Which
she did not more for saving him, then keeping us: and yet not
satisfied with our oth, appointed a band of horsemen to have
eye, that we should not go beyond appointed limits. We were
willing to gratifie the young Prince, who (we saw) loved us.
And so the fourth day of that exercise, we came into the fielde:
where (I remember) the manner was, that the forenoone they
should run at tilt, one after the other: the afternoone in a
broad field, in manner of a battell, till either the strangers, or
that countrie Knights wan the field.

4   The first that ran was a brave Knight, whose devise was to
come in, all chayned with a Nymph leading him: his *Impresa*
was

Against him came forth an *Iberian*
whose manner of entring was, with bagpipes in steed of
trumpets; a shepheards boy before him for a Page, and by him
a dosen apparelled like shepherds for the fashion, though rich in

stuffe, who caried his launces, which though strong to give a launcely blow indeed, yet so were they couloured with hooks neere the mourn, that they pretily represēted shephooks. His own furniture was drest over with wooll, so enriched with Jewels artificially placed, that one would have thought it a mariage betweene the lowest and the highest. His *Impresa* was a sheepe marked with pitch, with this word *Spotted to be knowne.* And because I may tell you out his conceipt (though that were not done, till the running for that time was ended) before the Ladies departed from the windowes, among them there was one (they say) that was the *Star*, wherby his course was only directed. The shepherds attending upõ *PHILISIDES* went amõg thē, & sãg an eclogue; one of thē answering another, while the other shepheards pulling out recorders (which possest the place of pipes) accorded their musick to the others voice. The Eclogue had great praise: I onely remember sixe verses, while having questioned one with the other, of their fellow-shepheards sodaine growing a man of armes, and the cause of his so doing, they thus said.

M *E thought some staves he mist: if so, not much amisse:*
  For where he most would hit, he ever yet did misse.
One said he brake acrosse; full well it so might be:
For never was there man more crossely crost then he.
But most cryed, O well broke: O foole full gaily blest:
Where failing is a shame, and breaking is his best.

Thus I have digrest, because his maner liked me wel: But when he began to run against *Lelius*, it had neere growne (though great love had ever bene betwixt them) to a quarrell. For *Philisides* breaking his staves with great commendation, *Lelius* (who was knowne to be second to none in the perfection of that Art) ranne ever over his head, but so finely to the skilfull eyes, that one might well see, he shewed more knowledge in missing, then others did in hitting. For with so gallant a grace his staffe came swimming close over the crest of the Helmet, as if he would represent the kisse, and not the stroke of *Mars.* But *Philisides* was much moved with it, while he thought *Lelius* would shew a contempt of his youth: till *Lelius* (who therefore would satisfie him, because he was his friend) made him know, that to such bondage he was for so many courses tyed by her, whose disgraces to him were graced by her excellency, and whose injuries he could never otherwise returne, then honours.

But so by *Lelius* willing-missing was the odds of the *Iberian* side, and continued so in the next by the excellent rūning of a Knight, though fostred so by the *Muses*, as many times the verie rustick people left both their delights and profites to harken to his songs; yet could he so well perfourme all armed sports, as if he had never had any other pen, then a Launce in his hand. He came in like a wild man; but such a wildnes, as shewed his eye-sight had tamed him, full of withered leaves, which though they fell not, still threatned falling. His *Impresa* was, a mill-horse still bound to goe in one circle; with this word, *Data fata sequutus.* But after him the *Corinthian* Knights absolutely prevailed, especially a great noble man of *Corinth*; whose devise was to come without any devise, all in white like a new knight, as indeed he was; but so new, as his newnes shamed most of the others long exercise. Then another from whose tent I remember a birde was made flie, with such art to carry a written embassage among the Ladies, that one might say, If a live bird, how so taught? if a dead bird, how so made? Then he, who hidden, man and horse in a great figure lively representing the *Phœnix:* the fire tooke so artificially, as it consumed the birde, and left him to rise as it were, out of the ashes thereof. Against whom was the fine frosen Knight, frosen in despaire; but his armor so naturally representing Ice, and all his furniture so lively answering therto, as yet did I never see any thing that pleased me better.

5 But the delight of those pleasing sights have carried me too farre in an unnecessary discourse. Let it then suffice (most excellent Ladie) that you know the *Corinthians* that morning in the exercise (as they had done the dayes before) had the better; *Palladius* neither suffring us, nor himselfe to take in hand that partie till the afternoone; when we were to fight in troopes, not differing otherwise from earnest, but that the sharpenesse of the weapons was taken away. But in the triall *Palladius* (especially led by *Musidorus*, and somewhat aided by me) himselfe truely behaving himselfe nothing like a beginner, brought the honor to rest it selfe that night of the *Iberian* side: And the next day, both morning, and after-noone being kept

by our party, He (that saw the time fitte for that deliverie he intended) called unto us to follow him; which we both bound by oth, and willing by good-wil, obeyed: and so the gard not daring to interrupt us (he commanding passage) we went after him upon the spur to a little house in a forrest neere by: which he thought would be the fittest resting place, till we might go further from his mothers fury, whereat he was no lesse angry, & ashamed, then desirous to obay *Zelmane*.

But his mother (as I learned since) understanding by the 6 gard her sonnes convaying us away (forgetting her greatnes, & resining modesty to more quiet thoughts) flew out from her place, and cried to be accompanied, for she her-selfe would follow us. But what she did (being rather with vehemency of passion, then conduct of reason) made her stumble while she ran, & by her owne confusion hinder her owne desires. For so impatiently she commanded, as a good while no body knew what she cõmanded; so as we had gotten so far the start, as to be alredy past the confines of her kingdome before she overtooke us: and overtake us she did in the kingdome of *Bythinia*, not regarding shame, or daunger of having entred into anothers dominions: but (having with her about a three score hors-men) streight commaunded to take us alive, and not to regard her sonnes threatening therein: which they attempted to do, first by speach, & then by force. But neither liking their eloquence, nor fearing their might, we esteemed few swordes in a just defence, able to resist any unjust assaulters. And so *Musidorus* incredible valour (beating downe all lets) made both me, and *Palladius*, so good way, that we had little to doo to overcome weake wrong.

And now had the victorie in effect without bloud, when 7 *Palladius* (heated with the fight, and angrie with his mothers fault) so pursued our assaylers, that one of them (who as I heard since had before our comming bene a speciall minion of *Andromanas*, and hated us for having dispossest him of her hart) taking him to be one of us, with a traiterous blow slew his yoũg Prince: who falling downe before our eyes, whom he specially had delivered, judge (sweetest Lady) whether anger might not be called justice in such a case: once, so it wroght in us, that many of his subjects bodies we left there dead, to wait on him more faithfully to the other world.

8   All this while disdaine, strengthened by the furie of a
furious love, made *Andromana* stay to the last of the combat:
& whẽ she saw us light down, to see what help we might do to
the helplesse *Palladius*, she came runing madly unto us, then no
lesse threatning, when she had no more power to hurt.   But
when she perceived it was her onely sonne that lay hurt, and
that his hurt was so deadly, as that alredy his life had loste the
use of the reasonable, and almost sensible part; then onely did
misfortune lay his owne ouglinesse upon his faulte, and make
her see what she had done, and to what she was come:
especiallie, finding in us rather detestation then pittie (considering the losse of that young Prince) and resolution presently
to depart, which stil she laboured to stay.   But deprived of all
comfort, with eyes full of death, she ranne to her sonnes dagger,
and before we were aware of it (who else could have stayed it)
strake her selfe a mortall wound.   But then her love, though
not her person, awaked pittie in us, and I went to her, while
Musidorus labored about *Palladius*.   But the wound was past
the cure of a better surgeon then my selfe, so as I could but
receave some few of her dying words; which were cursings of
her ill set affection, and wishing unto me many crosses &
mischances in my love, whẽsoever I should love, wherin I
feare, and only feare that her prayer is from above granted.   But
the noise of this fight, & issue thereof being blazed by the
country people to some noble-mẽ there-abouts, they came
thither, and finding the wrong offered us, let us go on our
journey, we having recommended those royal bodies unto thẽ
to be conveyed to the King of *Iberia*.   With that *Philoclea*,
seeing the teares stand in his eyes with remembrance of
Palladius, but much more of that which therupon grew, she
would needs drinke a kisse from those eyes, and he sucke
another from her lippes; whereat she blushed, & yet kissed
him againe to hide her blushing.   Which had almost brought
Pyrocles into another discourse, but that she with so sweete a
rigor forbad him, that he durst not rebell, though he found it a
great war to keepe that peace, but was faine to go on his storie:
for so she absolutely badde him, and he durst not know how to
disobey.

CHAP. 22.

[1] *A new complaint of* Pamphilus *new change,* [2] *to a gracelesse curtisan.* [3] Zelmane *loves, and as a Page serves* Pyrocles. [4] *The two Princes policie to reconcile two warring brothers.* [5] *The unbrotherly brave combat of* Tydeus *and* Telenor. [6] Plexirtus *his viperine unkindnes to the kindest* Leonatus. [7] *His conquest by the two brothers,* [8] *and his dogtrick to destroy them by themselves.* [9] *The regreete of the dying brothers.*

SO (said he) parting from that place before the Sunne had much abased himselfe of his greatest height, we sawe sitting upon the drie sandes (which yeelded at that time a verie hotte reflection) a faire Gentlewoman, whose gesture accused her of much sorow, & every way shewed she cared not what paine she put her body to, since the better parte (her minde) was laide under so much agonie: and so was she dulled withall, that we could come so neare, as to heare her speeches, and yet she not perceive the hearers of her lamentation. But wel we might understand her at times, say, Thou doost kill me with thy unkind falshood: and, It greeves me not to die, but it greeves me that thou art the murtherer: neither doth mine owne paine so much vexe me, as thy errour. For God knowes, it would not trouble me to be slaine for thee, but much it tormĕts me to be slain by thee. Thou art untrue *Pamphilus*, thou art untrue, and woe is me therefore. How oft didst thou sweare unto me, that the Sun should loose his light, and the rocks runne up and down like little kiddes, before thou wouldst falsifie thy faith to me? Sunne therefore put out thy shining, & rockes runne mad for sorrow, for *Pamphilus* is false. But alas, the Sun keepes his light, though thy faith be darckned; the rockes stand still, though thou change like the wethercocke. O foole that I am, that thought I coulde graspe water, and binde the winde. I might well have knowẽ thee by others, but I would not; & rather wished to learne poison by drinking it my selfe, while my love helped thy wordes to deceive me. Well, yet I would thou hadst made a better choise, when thou didst forsake thy unfortunate *Leucippe*. But it is no matter, *Baccha* (thy new mistres) will revenge my wrongs. But do not *Baccha*, let *Pamphilus* live happie, though I die.

2   And much more to such like phrase she spake, but that
I (who had occasion to know some-thing of that *Pamphilus*)
stept to comfort her: & though I could not doo that, yet I
gotte thus much knowledge of her, that this being the same
Leucippe, to whom the unconstante *Pâphilus* had betrothed
himselfe, which had moved the other Ladies to such indignation as I tolde you: nether her woorthinesse (which in truthe
was great) nor his owne suffering for her (which is woont to
endeare affection) could fetter his ficklenes, but that before his
mariage-day appointed, he had taken to wife that *Baccha*, of
whom she complayned; one, that in divers places I had heard
before blazed, as the most impudentlie unchaste woman of all
Asia; and withall, of such an imperiousnes therein, that she
would not stick to employ them (whom she made unhappie
with her favour) to draw more companions of their follie: in
the multitude of whom she did no lesse glorie, then a Captaine
would doo, of being followed by brave souldiers: waiwardly
proud; and therefore bold, because extreamely faultie: and yet
having no good thing to redeeme both these, and other unlovely
parts, but a little beautie, disgraced with wandring eyes, and
unwaied speeches; yet had *Pamphilus* (for her) left *Leucippe*, and
withall, left his faith: *Leucippe*, of whom one looke (in a cleere
judgement) would have bene more acceptable, then all her
kindenesses so prodigallie bestowed.   For my selfe, the remembrance of his crueltie to *Dido*, joyned to this, stirred me to
seeke some revenge upon him, but that I thought, it shoulde
be a gayne to him to lose his life, being so matched: and
therefore (leaving him to be punished by his owne election) we
conveyed *Leucippe* to a house thereby, dedicated to *Vestall*
Nunnes, where she resolved to spende all her yeares (which
her youth promised shoulde be many) in bewayling the wrong,
and yet praying for the wrong-dooer.

3   But the next morning, we (having striven with the Sunnes
earlines) were scarcely beyond the prospect of the high turrets
of that building, when there overtoke us a young Gentleman,
for so he seemed to us, but indeede (sweete Ladie) it was the
faire *Zelmane*, *Plexirtus* daughter; whom unconsulting affection
(unfortunately borne to me-wards) had made borrowe so much
of her naturall modestie, as to leave her more-decent rayments,
and taking occasion of *Andromanas* tumultuous pursuing us, had

apparrelled her selfe like a Page, with a pittifull crueltie cutting
of her golden haire, leaving nothing, but the short curles, to
cover that noble head, but that she ware upon it a faire head-
peece, a shielde at her back, and a launce in her hand, els
disarmed. Her apparrell of white, wrought upon with broken
knots, her horse, faire & lustie, which she rid so, as might shew
a fearefull boldnes, daring to doo that, which she knew that she
knew not how to doo: and the sweetnes of her countenance
did give such a grace to what she did, that it did make hansome
the unhansomnes, and make the eye force the minde to beleeve,
that there was a praise in that unskilfulnesse. But she straight
approached me, and with fewe words (which borowed the help
of her countenance to make themselves understood) she desired
me to accept her in my service; telling me, she was a noble-
mans sonne of *Iberia*, her name *Daiphantus*, who having seene
what I had done in that court, had stolne from her father, to
follow me. I enquired the particularities of the maner of
Andromanas following me, which by her I understood, she
hiding nothing (but her sexe) from me. And still me thought
I had seen that face, but the great alteration of her fortune,
made her far distant from my memorie: but liking very well
the yong Gentleman, (such I tooke her to be) admitted this
Daiphantus about me: who well shewed, there is no service
like his, that serves because he loves. For, though borne of
Princes bloud, brought up with tenderest education, unapt to
service (because a woman) & full of thoughts (because in a
strange estate;) yet Love enjoyned such diligence, that no
apprentise, no, no bondslave could ever be by feare more
readie at all commaundementes, then that yong Princesse was.
How often (alas) did her eyes say unto me, that they loved? and
yet, I (not looking for such a matter) had not my conceipt open,
to understand them. How oftē would she come creeping to
me, betweene gladnes to be neere me, & feare to offend me?
Truly I remember, that then I marvailing, to see her receive
my cōmandements with sighes, and yet do them with cheerefulnes: sometimes answering me in such riddles, as I then
thought childish in experiēce: but since returning to my
remēbrance, they have come more neere unto my knowledge:
& pardon me (onely deare Lady) that I use many words: for
her affection to me deserves of me an affectionate speach.

4   In such sort did she serve me in that kingdom of *Bythinia*, for two moneths space. In which time we brought to good end, a cruell warre long maintained betweene the King of *Bythinia* and his brother. For my excellent cousin, and I (dividing our selves to either side) found meanes (after some triall we had made of our selves) to get such credite with them, as we brought them to as great peace betweene thēselves, as love towards us, for having made the peace. Which done, we intended to returne through the Kingdome of *Galatia*, towarde *Thrace*, to ease the câre of our father and mother, who (we were sure) first with the shipwracke; and then with the other daungers we dayly past, should have litle rest in their thoughts, till they saw us.

5   But we were not entred into that Kingdome, whē by the noise of a great fight, we were guided to a pleasaunt valey, which like one of those Circusses, which in great cities some-where doth give a pleasant speĉtacle of rūning horses; so of either side stretching it selfe in a narrow length was it hemd in by wooddy hilles; as if indeed Nature had meant therein to make a place for beholders. And there we behelde one of the cruellest fights betweene two Knights, that ever hath adorned the martial storie. So as I must côfesse, a while we stood wondring, another while delighted with the rare bravery therof; till seing such streames of bloud, as threatned a drowning of life, we galloped towarde them to part them. But we were prevented by a dosen armed Knights, or rather villains, who using this time of their extreame feeblenesse, all together set upon them. But common daunger brake of particular discorde, so that (though with a dying weakenes) with a lively courage they resisted, and by our help drave away, or slue those murdering attempters: among whom we hapt to take alive the principall. But going to disarme those two excellent Knights, we found with no lesse wonder to us, then astonishment to themselves, that they were the two valiaunt, and indeede famous Brothers, *Tydeus* and *Telenor*; whose adventure (as afterwarde we made that ungratious wretch confesse) had thus fallen out.

6   After the noble Prince *Leonatus* had by his fathers death succeeded in the kingdome of *Galatia*, he (forgetting all former injuries) had received that naughtie *Plexirtus* into a streight

degree of favour, his goodnesse being as apt to be deceived, as the others crafte was to deceive.   Till by plaine proofe finding, that the ungratefull man went about to poyson him, yet would not suffer his kindnesse to be overcome, not by justice it selfe: but calling him to him, used wordes to this purpose.   *Plexirtus* (said he) this wickednesse is founde by thee.   No good deedes of mine have bene able to keepe it downe in thee.   All men counsell me to take away thy life, likely to bring foorth nothing, but as daungerous, as wicked effects.   But I cannot finde it in my harte, remembring what fathers sonne thou arte.   But since it is the violence of ambition, which perchaunce puls thee from thine owne judgement, I will see, whether the satisfying that, may quiet the ill working of thy spirites.   Not farre hence is the great cittie of *Trebisonde*; which, with the territorie about it, aunciently pertained unto this crowne, now unjustly possessed, and as unjustly abused by those, who have neither title to holde it, nor vertue to use it.   To the conquest of that for thy selfe I will lende thee force, and give thee my right.   Go therfore, and with lesse unnaturalnesse glut thy ambition there; and that done, if it be possible, learne vertue.

Plexirtus, mingling forsworne excuses with false-meant 7 promises, gladly embraced the offer: and hastilie sending backe for those two Brothers (who at that time were with us succouring the gratious Queen *Erona*) by their vertue chiefly (if not onely) obteyned the conquest of that goodly dominion. Which indeede done by them, gave them such an authoritie, that though he raigned, they in effect ruled, most men honouring them, because they onely deserved honour; and many, thinking therein to please *Plexirtus*, considering how much he was bound unto them: while they likewise (with a certaine sincere boldenesse of selfe-warranting friendship) accepted all openly and plainely, thinking nothing should ever by *Plexirtus* be thought too much in them, since all they were, was his.

But he (who by the rules of his own mind, could cõstrue no 8 other end of mẽs doings, but self seking) sodẽly feared what they could doo; and as sodainely suspected, what they would doo, and as sodainely hated them, as having both might, and minde to doo.   But dreading their power, standing so strongly in their owne valour, & others affection, he durst not take open way against them: and as harde it was to take a secrete, they being so continually followed by the best, & every way hablest of that region: and therfore used this divelish sleight (which I wil tel you) not doubting (most wicked man) to turne their owne friēdship toward him to their owne destruction. He, (knowing that they wel knew, there was no friendship betweene him and the new King of *Pontus*, never since he succoured *Leonatus* and us, to his overthrow) gave them to understand that of late there had passed secrete defiance betweene them, to meete privately at a place apointed. Which though not so fit a thing for men of their greatnes, yet was his honour so engaged, as he could not go backe. Yet faining to find himself weake by some counterfait infirmitie, the day drawing neere, he requested each of them to go in his stead; making either of thē sweare, to keep the matter secret, ever ech frō other, delivering the selfe same particularities to both, but that he told *Tydeus*, the King would meet him in a blew armour; & *Telenor*, that it was a black armour: & with wicked subtiltie (as if it had bene so apointed) caused *Tydeus* to take a black armour, & *Telenor* a blew; appointing them waies how to go, so as he knew they should not meet, til they came to the place appointed, where each had promised to keep silence, lest the King should discover it was not *Plexirtus:* and there in await had he laied these murtherers, that who overlived the other, should by them be dispatched: he not daring trust more then those, with that enterprise, and yet thinking them too few, till themselves by themselves were weakened.

9   This we learned chiefly, by the chiefe of those way-beaters, after the death of those worthie brothers, whose love was no lesse, then their valour: but well we might finde much thereof by their pitifull lamentation, when they knew their mismeeting, and saw each other (in despite of the Surgerie we could doo unto them) striving who should runne fastest to the goale of death: each bewailing the other, and more dying in the other, then in himselfe: cursing their owne hands for doing, and their breastes for not sooner suffering: detesting their unfortunately-spent time in having served so ungrateful a Tyraunt: and accusing their folly in having beleeved, he could faithfully love, who did not love faithfulnes: wishing us to take heed, how we placed our good wil upon any other ground, then proofe of vertue: since length of acquaintance, mutuall secrecies, nor

height of benefits could binde a savage harte ; no man being
good to other, that is not good in himself. Then (while any
hope was) beseeching us to leave the cure of him that besought,
and onely looke to the other. But when they found by themselves, and us, no possibilitie, they desired to be joined; and so
embracing and craving that pardon each of other, which they
denied to themselves, they gave us a most sorrowfull spectacle
of their death; leaving fewe in the world behind them, their
matches in any thing, if they had soone inough knowne the
ground and limits of friendship. But with wofull hartes, we
caused those bodies to be conveyed to the nexte towne of
Bythinia, where we learning thus much (as I have tolde you)
caused the wicked Historian to coclude his history, with his
owne well-deserved death.

CHAP. 23.

[1] Zelmanes *griefe for* Plexirtus *fault.* [2] Otaves, *and his Gyants
warre on* Pontus. [3] Plexirtus *endaungered, needes helpe of the
dead brothers.* [4] Zelmane *thought-sicke, unmaskes her selfe.*
[5] *Her dying teares* [6] *and last requestes.* [7] Musidorus *to*
Pontus, Pyrocles *hardly partes to save* Plexirtus. [8] *The
sourse and course of his deaths-doome,* [9] *stayed by* Pyrocles.
[10] *The combat of* Pontus *well ended.* [11] *The* Asian *Princes
meeting, to honour the two* Greekes.

Ut then (I must tell you) I found such wofull countenances [1]
in *Daiphantus*, that I could not but much marvaile
(finding them continew beyond the first assault of pittie) how
the cause of strangers (for further I did not conceive) could so
deeply pearce. But the truth indeed is, that partly with the
shame & sorrow she tooke of her fathers faultinesse, partly with
the feare, that the hate I coceived against him, would utterly
disgrace her in my opinion, whensoever I should know her, so
vehemently perplexed her, that her fayre colour decaied; and
dayly, and hastily grew into the very extreme working of
sorowfulnesse : which oft I sought to learne, & helpe. But
she, as fearefull as loving, still concealed it; and so decaying

295

still more and more, in the excellencie of her fairenesse, but that whatsoever weakenesse took away, pitie seemed to adde: yet still she forced her selfe to waite on me, with such care and diligence, as might well shew had bene taught in no other schoole, but Love.

2   While we returning againe to embarke our selves for *Greece*, understood that the mighty *Otaves* (brother to *Barzanes* slaine by *Musidorus*, in the battaile of the six Princes) had entred upŏ the kingdome of *Pontus*, partly upon the pretences he had to the crowne, but principally, because he would revenge upon him (whom he knew we loved) the losse of his brother: thincking (as indeede he had cause) that wheresoever we were, hearing of his extremitie, we would come to relieve him; in spite whereof he doubted not to prevaile, not onely upon the confidence of his owne vertue and power, but especially because he had in his cŏpany two mighty *Giants*, sonnes to a couple whom we slue in the same realme: they having bene absent at their fathers death, and now returned, willingly entered into his service, hating (more then he) both us, and that King of *Pontus*. We therefore withall speede went thetherwarde, but by the way this fell out, which whensoever I remember without sorrow, I must forget withall, all humanitie.

3   Poore *Daiphantus* fell extreme sick, yet would needs conquere the delicacie of her constitution, and force her selfe to waite on me: till one day going towarde *Pontus*, we met one, who in great hast went seeking for *Tydeus* & *Telenor*, whose death as yet was not knowne unto the messenger; who (being their servaunt and knowing how deerely they loved *Plexirtus*) brought them word, how since their departing, *Plexirtus* was in pre[se]nt daunger of a cruel death, if by the valiantnesse of one of the best Knightes of the world, he were not reskewed: we enquired no further of the matter (being glad he should now to his losse finde what an unprofitable treason it had bene unto him, to dismember himselfe of two such friendes) and so let the messenger part, not sticking to make him know his masters destruction, by the falshood of *Plexirtus*.

4   But the griefe of that (finding a bodie alreadie brought to the last degree of weakenesse) so overwhelmed the little remnant of the spirits left in *Daiphantus*, that she fell sodainely into deadly soundings; never comming to her selfe, but that withall

she returned to make most pittifull lamentations; most straunge unto us, because we were farre from ghessing the ground thereof. But finding her sicknesse such, as beganne to print death in her eyes, we made al hast possible to convey her to the next towne: but before we could lay her on a bed, both we, & she might find in herselfe, that the harbinger of over-hastie death, had prepared his lodging in that daintie body, which she undoubtedly feeling, with a weake chearefulnes, shewed côfort therin; and then desiring us both to come neere her, & that no bodie els might be present; with pale, and yet (even in palenes) lovely lippes, Now or never, and never indeed, but now it is time for me (said she) to speake: and I thanke death which gave me leave to discover that, the suppressing whereof perchance hath bene the sharpest spur, that hath hasted my race to this end. Know then my Lords, and especially you my Lord and master, *Pyrocles*, that your page *Daiphantus* is the unfortunat *Zelmane*, who for your sake caused my (as unfortunate) lover, and cosen, *Palladius*, to leave his fathers court, and côsequently, both him & my Aunt his mother, to loose their lives. For your sake my selfe have become, of a Princesse a Page: and for your sake have put off the apparell of a woman, & (if you judge not more mercifully) modestie. We were amazed at her speach, and thẽ had (as it were) new eyes givẽ us to perceve that which before had bene a present strãger to our minds. For indeed, we forthwith knew it to be the face of *Zelmane*, whõ before we had knowen in the court of *Iberia*. And sorrow and pittie laying her paine upon me, I comforted her the best I could by the tendernes of good-will, pretending indeed better hope then I had of her recovery.

But she that had inward ambassadors from the tyrãt that 5 should shortly oppresse her. No, my deere master (said she) I neither hope nor desire to live. I know you would never have loved me (& with that she wept) nor, alas, had it bene reason you should, considering manie wayes my unworthines. It sufficeth me that the strange course I have takẽ, shall to your remembrance, witnesse my love: and yet this breaking of my harte, before I would discover my paine, will make you (I hope) think I was not altogether unmodest. Thinke of me so, deare Master, and that thought shal be my life: and with that, languishingly looking upon me; And I pray you (said she) even by these dying eies of mine (which are onely sorrie to dye, because they shall lose your sight) and by these pouled lockes of mine (which while they were long, were the ornament of my sex, now in their short curles, the testimonie of my servitude) and by the service I have done you (which God knowes hath beene full of love) thinke of me after my death with kindnes, though ye cannot with love. And whensoever ye shall make any other Ladie happie with your placed affectiõ, if you tell her my folly, I pray you speake of it, not with scorne, but with pitie. I assure you (deare Princesse of my life, for how could it be otherwise?) her words and her manners, with the lively consideration of her love, so pearced me, that I, though I had diverse griefes before, yet me thought I never felt till then, how much sorow enfeebleth all resolution. For I coulde not chuse, but yeeld to the weakenes of abundant weeping; in trueth with such griefe, that I could willingly at that time have chaunged lives with her.

6 But when she saw my teares, O God (said she) howe largely am I recompenced for my losses? why then (said shee) I may take boldnesse to make some requests unto you. I besought her to doo, vowing the performance, though my life were the price therof. She shewed great joy : The first (said she) is this, that you will pardon my father the displeasure you have justly conceived against him, and for this once succour, him out of the daunger wherin he is: I hope he will amende: and I pray you, whensoever you remember him to be the faultie *Plexirtus*, remember withall that he is *Zelmanes* father. The second is, that when you come into *Greece*, you will take unto your selfe this name (though unlucky) of *Daiphantus*, and vouchsafe to be called by it: for so shal I be sure, you shall have cause to remember me : and let it please your noble cousin to be called *Palladius*, that I doo that right to that poore Prince, that his name may yet live upon the earth in so excellent a person: and so betwene you, I trust sometimes your unluckie page shall be (perhaps with a sigh) mencioned. Lastly, let me be buried here obscurely, not suffering my friends to knowe my fortune, till (when you are safely returned to your own countrie) you cause my bones to be conveied thither, and laid (I beseech you) in some place, where your selfe vouchsafe sometimes to resort. Alas, small petitions for

such a suter; which yet she so earnestly craved, that I was faine to sweare the accomplishment. And then kissing me, & often desiring me not to condemne her of lightnesse, in mine armes she delivered her pure soule to the purest place: leaving me as full of agonie, as kindnes, pitie, and sorow could make an honest harte. For I must confesse for true, that if my starres had not wholy reserved me for you, there els perhaps I might have loved, & (which had bene most strange) begun my love after death: whereof let it be the lesse marvaile, because somwhat shee did resemble you: though as farre short of your perfectiõ, as her selfe dying, was of her flourishing: yet somthing there was, which (when I saw a picture of yours) brought againe her figure into my remẽbrance, and made my harte as apte to receive the wounde, as the power of your beauty with unresistable force to pearce.

But we in wofull (& yet privat) manner burying her, per- 7 formed her commandement: & then enquiring of her fathers estate, certainly learned that he was presentlie to be succoured, or by death to passe the neede of succour. Therfore we determined to divide our selves; I, according to my vowe, to helpe him, and *Musidorus* toward the King of *Pontus*, who stood in no lesse need then immediate succour, and even readie to depart one from the other, there came a messenger from him, who after some enquirie found us, giving us to understand, that he trusting upon us two, had apointed the combat betweene him & us, against *Otaves*, and the two *Gyants*. Now the day was so accorded, as it was impossible for me both to succour *Plexirtus*, & be there, where my honour was not onely gaged so far, but (by the straunge working of unjust fortune) I was to leave the standing by *Musidorus*, whom better then my selfe I loved, to go save him whom for just causes I hated. But my promise given, & given to *Zelmane*, & to *Zelmane* dying, prevailed more with me, then my friendship to *Musidorus*: though certainely I may affirme, nothing had so great rule in my thoughts as that. But my promise caried me the easier, because *Musidorus* himselfe would not suffer me to breake it. And so with heavy mindes (more careful each of others successe, thẽ of our owne) we parted; I towarde the place, where I understood *Plexirtus* was prisoner to an auncient Knight, absolutely governing a goodly Castle, with a large territory about it, whereof he acknowledged no other soveraigne, but himselfe: whose hate to *Plexirtus*, grew for a kinsman of his, whŏ he malitiously had murdered, because in the time that he raigned in *Galatia*, he foŭd him apt to practise for the restoring of his vertuous brother *Leonatus*. This old Knight, still thirsting for revenge, used (as the way to it) a pollicie, which this occasion I will tell you, prepared for him. *Plexirtus* in his youth had maried *Zelmanes* mother, who dying of that only child-birth, he a widdower, and not yet a King, haunted the Court of *Armenia*; where (as he was comming to winne favour) he obteined great good liking of *Artaxia*, which he pursued, till (being called home by his father) he falsly got his fathers kingdome; and then neglected his former love: till thrown out of that (by our meanes) before he was deeply rooted in it, and by and by again placed in *Trebisonde*, understanding that *Artaxia* by her brothers death was become Queen of *Armenia*, he was hotter then ever, in that pursuit, which being understood by this olde Knight, he forged such a letter, as might be written from *Artaxia*, entreating his present (but very privie) repaire thether, giving him faithfull promise of presente mariage: a thing farre from her thought, having faithfully, and publiquely protested, that she would never marrie any, but some such Prince who woulde give sure proofe, that by his meanes we were destroyed. But he (no more wittie to frame, then blinde to judge hopes) bitte hastely at the baite, and in private maner poasted toward her, but by the way he was met by this Knight, far better accompanied, who quickly laid holde of him, & condemned him to death, cruell inough, if any thing may be both cruell and just. For he caused him to be kept in a miserable prison, till a day appointed, at which time he would deliver him to be devoured by a monstrous beast, of most ugly shape, armed like a *Rhinoceros*, as strong as an Elephant, as fierce as a Lion, as nimble as a Leopard, and as cruell as a Tigre: whom he having kept in a strong place, from the first youth of it, now thought no fitter match, then such a beastly monster with a monstrous Tyrant: proclaiming yet withall, that if any so well loved him, as to venture their lives against this beast, for him, if they overcame, he should be saved: not caring how many they were (such confidence he had in the monsters strength) but especially hoping to entrappe therby the great courages of

Tydeus and *Telenor*, whom he no lesse hated, because they had bene principall instruments of the others power.

I dare say, if *Zelmane* had knowen what daunger I should 9 have passed, she would rather have let her father perishe, then me to have bidden that adventure. But my word was past, and truely, the hardnes of the enterprise, was not so much a bitte, as a spurre unto me; knowing well, that the jorney of " high honor lies not in plaine wayes. Therefore, going thether, and taking sufficient securitie, that *Plexirtus* should be delivered if I were victorious, I undertooke the combatte: and (to make shorte, excellent Ladie, and not trouble your eares with re-counting a terrible matter) so was my weakenes blessed from above, that without dangerous wounds I slewe that monster, which hundreds durste not attempt: to so great admiration of many (who from a safe place might looke on) that there was order given, to have the fight, both by sculpture and picture, celebrated in most parts of *Asia.* And the olde nobleman so well liked me, that he loved me; onely bewayling, my vertue had beene imployed to save a worse monster then I killed: whom yet (according to faith given) he delivered, and accom-panied me to the kingdome of *Pontus*, whether I would needes in all speede go, to see whether it were possible for me (if per-chance the day had bene delaied) to come to the combat. But that (before I came) had bene thus finished.

The vertuous *Leonatus* understanding two so good friends of 10 his were to be in that danger, would perforce be one him selfe: where he did valiantly, and so did the King of *Pontus.* But the truthe is, that both they being sore hurt, the incomparable *Musidorus* finished the combat by the death of both the Giants, and the taking of *Otaves* prisoner. To whom as he gave his life, so he gotte a noble friend: for so he gave his worde to be, and he is well knowen to thinke him selfe greater in being subject to that, then in the greatnes of his principalitie.

But thither (understanding of our being there) flocked great 11 multitudes of many great persons, and even of Princes; especially those, whom we had made beholding unto us: as, the Kings of *Phrygia, Bythinia,* with those two hurte, of *Pontus* and *Galatia,* and *Otaves* the prisoner, by *Musidorus* set free; and thither came *Plexirtus* of *Trebisonde,* and *Antiphilus,* then King of *Lycia;* with as many mo great Princes, drawen ether by our reputation, or by willingnes to acknowledge them selves obliged unto us, for what we had done for the others. So as in those partes of the world, I thinke, in many hundreds of yeares, there was not seene so royall an assemblie: where nothing was let passe to doo us the highest honors, which such persons (who might commaund both purses and inventions) could perfourme. All from all sides bringing unto us right royall presents (which we to avoide both unkindnes, and importunitie, liberally received,) & not content therewith, would needes accept, as from us, their crownes, and acknowledge to hold them of us: with many other excessive honors, which would not suffer the measure of this short leisure to describe unto you.

CHAP. 24.

[1] *The causes and provisions of the Princes embarking for* Arcadia. [2] Plexirtus *his treason against them disclosed by one*, [3] *attempted by another of his ministers.* [4] *Sedition and slaughter in the shippe about it.* [5] *Their shipwrack by fire.* [6] Pyrocles *fight with the Captaine, and escape from sea.* [7] *The amarous concluding the olde, and beginning a newe storie, both broken of by* Miso.

BUt wee quickely aweary thereof, hasted to *Greece*-ward, led thither partly with the desire of our parents, but hastened principally, because I understoode that *Anaxius* with open mouth of defamation had gone thither to seeke mee, and was nowe come to *Peloponnesus* where from Court to Court he made enquyrie of me, doing yet himselfe so noble deedes, as might hap to aucthorize an ill opinion of me. We therefore suffred but short delayes, desiring to take this countrey in our way, so renowmed over the worlde, that no Prince coulde pretend height, nor begger lownesse, to barre him from the sound thereof: renowmed indeede, not so much for the ancient prayses attributed thereunto, as for the having in it *Argalus* and *Amphialus* (two knights of such rare prowes, as we desired especially to know) and yet by farre, not so much for that, as without suffering of comparison for the beautie of you and your sister, which makes all indifferent judges, that speake thereof, account this countrie as a temple of deities. But these causes indeed moving us to come by this land, we embarked our selves in the next porte, whether all those Princes (saving *Antiphilus*, who returned, as he pretended, not able to tarry long from *Erona*) conveied us. And there found we a ship most royally furnished by *Plexirtus*, who made all thinges so proper (as well for our defence, as ease) that all the other Princes greatly commended him for it: who (seeming a quite altered man) had nothing but repētance in his eies, friendship in his gesture, & vertue in his mouth: so that we who had promised the sweete *Zelmane* to pardon him, now not onely forgave, but began to favour; perswading our selves with a youthfull credulitie, that perchance things were not so evil as we tooke them, & as it were desiring our owne memorie, that it might be so. But so were we licensed from those Princes, truly not without teares, especially of the vertuous *Leonatus*, who with the king of *Pōtus*, would have come with us, but that we (in respect of the ones young wife, & both their new settled kingdomes) would not suffer it. Then would they have sent whole fleets to guard us: but we, that desired to passe secretely into *Greece*, made them leave that motion, when they found that more ships, then one, would be displeasing unto us. But so cōmitting our selves to the uncertaine discretiō of the wind, we (then determining as soone as we came to *Greece*, to take the names of *Daiphantus* and *Palladius*, as well for our owne promise to *Zelmane*, as because we desired to come unknowne into *Greece*) left the *Asian* shore full of Princely persons, who even upon their knees, recommended our safeties to the devotion of their chiefe desires: among whom none had bene so officious (though I dare affirme, all quite contrarie to his unfaithfulnes) as *Plexirtus*.

So having sailed almost two daies, looking for nothing but when we might looke upon the land, a grave man (whom we had seene of great trust with *Plexirtus*, and was sent as our principall guide) came unto us, and with a certaine kinde manner, mixt with shame, and repentaunce, began to tell us, that he had taken such a love unto us (considering our youth and fame) that though he were a servaunt, and a servaunt of such trust about *Plexirtus*, as that he had committed unto him

2

even those secretes of his hart, which abhorde all other knowledge; yet he rather chose to reveale at this time a most
pernitious counsell, then by concealing it bring to ruin those,
whom he could not choose but honour. So went he on, and
tolde us, that *Plexirtus* (in hope thereby to have *Artaxia*,
endowed with the great Kingdome of *Armenia*, to his wife) had
given him order, when we were neere *Greece*, to finde some
opportunitie to murder us, bidding him to take us a sleepe,
because he had seene what we could do waking. Now sirs
(said he) I would rather a thousand times loose my life, then
have my remembrance (while I lived) poysoned with such a
mischiefe : and therefore if it were onely I, that knewe herein
the Kings order, then should my disobedience be a warrant of
your safetie. But to one more (said he) namely the Captaine
of the shippe, *Plexirtus* hath opened so much touching the
effect of murdering you, though I think, laying the cause
rather upon old grudge, then his hope of *Artaxia*. And my
selfe, (before the consideration of your excellencies had drawne
love and pittie into minde) imparted it to such, as I thought
fittest for such a mischiefe. Therefore, I wishe you to stand
upon your garde, assuring you, that what I can doo for your
safetie, you shall see (if it come to the pushe) by me perfourmed. We thanked him, as the matter indeed deserved,
and from that time would no more disarme our selves, nor the
one sleepe without his friendes eyes waked for him : so that it
delaied the going forwarde of their bad enterprize, while they
thought it rather chaunce, then providence, which made us so
behave our selves.

3   But when we came within halfe a daies sayling of the
shore, soone they saw it was speedily, or not at all to be done.
Then (and I remember it was about the first watch in the
night) came the Captaine and whispered the Councellour in the
eare : But he (as it should seem) disswading him from it, the
Captaine (who had bene a pyrate from his youth, and often
blouded in it) with a lowde voice sware, that if *Plexirtus* bad
him, he would not sticke to kill God him selfe. And therewith cald his mates, and in the Kings name willed them to
take us, alive or dead; encouraging thẽ with the spoile of us,
which he said, (& indeed was true) would yeeld many exceeding rich jewels. But the Councellour (according to his promise)

commanded them they should not cõmit such a villany, protesting that he would stãd betweene them and the Kings anger therein. Wherewith the Captaine enraged: Nay (said he) thẽ we must begin with this traitor him selfe: and therewith gave him a sore blow upon the head, who honestly did the best he could to revenge himselfe.

But then we knew it time rather to encounter, then waite 4 for mischiefe. And so against the Captaine we went, who straight was environned with most parte of the Souldiers and Mariners. And yet the truth is, there were some, whom either the authoritie of the councellour, doubt of the Kings minde, or liking of us, made draw their swords of our side: so that quickly it grew a most confused fight. For the narrownesse of the place, the darkenesse of the time, and the uncertainty in such a tumult how to know friẽds from foes, made the rage of swordes rather guide, then be guided by their maisters. For my cousin and me, truly I thinke we never perfourmed lesse in any place, doing no other hurte, then the defence of our selves, and succouring them who came for it, drave us to: for not discerning perfectlie, who were for, or against us, we thought it lesse evill to spare a foe, then spoyle a friend. But from the hiest to the lowest parte of the shippe there was no place lefte, without cries of murdring, and murdred persons. The Captaine I hapt a while to fight withall, but was driven to parte with him, by hearing the crie of the Councellour, who received a mortall wounde, mistaken of one of his owne side. Some of the wiser would call to parley, & wish peace, but while the wordes of peace were in their mouthes, some of their auditours gave them death for their hire. So that no man almost could conceive hope of living, but being lefte alive: and therefore every one was willing to make him selfe roome, by dispatching almost any other: so that the great number in the ship was reduced to exceeding few, when of those few the most part weary of those troubles leapt into the boate, which was fast to the ship: but while they that were first, were cutting of the rope that tied it, others came leaping in, so disorderly, that they drowned both the boate, and themselves.

But while even in that little remnant (like the children of 5 *Cadmus*) we continued still to slay one an other, a fire, which (whether by the desperate malice of some, or intention to separate, or accidentally while all things were cast up and downe) it should seeme had taken a good while before, but never heeded of us, (who onely thought to preserve, or revenge) now violently burst out in many places, and began to maister the principall partes of the ship. Then necessitie made us see, that, a common enimy sets at one a civill warre : for that little all we were (as if we had bene waged by one man to quench a fire) streight went to resist that furious enimie by all art and labour: but it was too late, for already it did embrace and devoure from the sterne, to the wast of the ship: so as labouring in vaine, we were driven to get up to the prowe of the ship, by the worke of nature seeking to preserve life, as long as we could: while truely it was a straunge and ougly sight, to see so huge a fire, as it quickly grew to be, in the Sea, and in the night, as if it had come to light us to death. And by and by it had burned off the maste, which all this while had prowdly borne the sayle (the winde, as might seeme, delighted to carrie fire and bloud in his mouth) but now it fell over boord, and the fire growing neerer us, it was not onely terrible in respect of what we were to attend, but insupportable through the heat of it.

6   So that we were constrained to bide it no longer, but disarming and stripping our selves, and laying our selves upon such things, as we thought might help our swimming to the lande (too far for our owne strength to beare us) my cousin and I threw our selves into the Sea. But I had swomme a very little way, when I felt (by reason of a wound I had) that I should not be able to bide the travaile, and therefore seeing the maste (whose tackling had bene burnt of) flote cleare from the ship, I swamme unto it, and getting on it, I found mine owne sworde, which by chaunce, when I threw it away (caught by a peece of canvas) had honge to the maste. I was glad, because I loved it well; but gladder, when I saw at the other end, the Captaine of the ship, and of all this mischiefe; who having a long pike, belike had borne him selfe up with that, till he had set him selfe upon the mast. But when I perceived him, Villaine (said I) doost thou thinke to overlive so many honest men, whom thy falsehood hath brought to destruction? with that bestriding the mast, I gat by little and little towards him, after such a manner as boies are wont (if ever you saw that

sport) when they ride the wild mare. And he perceiving my intention, like a fellow that had much more courage then honestie, set him selfe to resist. But I had in short space gotten within him, and (giving him a sound blowe) sent him to feede fishes. But there my selfe remainde, untill by pyrates I was taken up, and among them againe taken prisoner, and brought into *Laconia*.

But what (said *Philoclea*) became of your cousin *Musidorus*? 7 Lost said *Pyrocles*. Ah my *Pyrocles*, said *Philoclea*, I am glad I have takē you. I perceive you lovers do not alwaies say truely: as though I know not your cousin *Dorus*, the sheepeheard? Life of my desires (saide *Pyrocles*) what is mine, even to my soule is yours: but the secret of my friend is not mine. But if you know so much, then I may truely say, he is lost, since he is no more his owne. But I perceive, your noble sister & you are great friends, and well doth it become you so to be. But go forward deare *Pyrocles*, I lōg to heare out till your meeting me: for there to me-warde is the best part of your storie. Ah sweet *Philoclea* (said *Pyrocles*) do you thinke I can thinke so precious leysure as this well spent in talking. Are your eyes a fit booke (thinke you) to reade a tale upon? Is my love quiet inough to be an historian? Deare Princesse, be gracious unto me. And then he faine would have remembred to have forgot himselfe. But she, with a sweetly disobeying grace, desired that her desire (once for ever) might serve, that no spotte might disgrace that love which shortly she hoped shold be to the world warrantable. Faine he would not have heard, til she threatned anger. And then the poore lover durst not, because he durst not. Nay I pray thee, deare *Pyrocles* (said she) let me have my story. Sweet Princesse (said he) give my thoughts a litle respite: and if it please you, since this time must so be spoiled, yet it shall suffer the lesse harme, if you vouchsafe to bestow your voice, and let me know, how the good Queene *Erona* was betraied into such dāger, and why *Plangus* sought me. For in deede, I should pitie greatly any mischance fallen to that Princesse. I will, said *Philoclea* smiling, so you give me your worde, your handes shall be quiet auditours. They shal, said he, because subject. Then began she to speake, but with so prettie and delightfull a majestie, when she set her counten-aunce to tell the matter, that *Pyrocles* could not chuse but rebell so far, as to kisse her. She would have puld her head away, and speake, but while she spake he kist, and it seemed he fedde upon her wordes: but shee gate away. Howe will you have your discourse (said she) without you let my lips alone? He yeelded and tooke her hand. On this (said he) will I revenge my wrong: and so began to make much of that hand, when her tale, & his delight were interrupted by *Miso*: who taking her time, while *Basilius* backe was turned, came unto them: and told *Philoclea*, she deserved she knewe what, for leaving her mother, being evill at ease, to keepe companie with straungers. But *Philoclea* telling her, that she was there by her fathers commandemẽt, she went away muttering, that though her back, and her shoulders, and her necke were broken, yet as long as her tongue would wagge, it should do her errand to her mother.

CHAP. 25.

[1] *Gynecias divining dreame.* [2] *Her passionate jelousie in actions,* [3] *speach, and* [4] *song described* [5] *Her troubling Philoclea and* Zelmane, [6] *The rebels troubling her.* [7] *Rebels resisted by* Zelmane. [8] Zelmane *assisted by* Dorus. [9] Dorus *and* Zelmanes *five memorable strokes.*

[1] SO went up *Miso* to *Gynecia*, who was at that time miserably vexed with this manner of dreame. It seemed unto her to be in a place full of thornes, which so molested her, as she could neither abide standing still, nor treade safely going forward. In this case she thought *Zelmane*, being upon a faire hill, delightfull to the eye, and easie in apparance, called her thither: whither with much anguish being come, *Zelmane* was vanished, and she found nothing but a dead bodie like unto her husband, which seeming at the first with a strange smell to infect her, as she was redie likewise within a while to die, the dead bodie, she thought, tooke her in his armes, and said, *Gynecia*, leave all; for here is thy onely rest.

[2] With that she awaked, crying very loud, *Zelmane, Zelmane*. But remembring her selfe, and seeing *Basilius* by, (her guiltie conscience more suspecting, then being suspected) she turned

her call, and called for *Philoclea*. *Miso* forthwith like a valiant shrew, (looking at *Basilius*, as though she would speake though she died for it) tolde *Gynecia*, that her daughter had bene a whole houre togither in secrete talke with *Zelmane*: And (sayes she) for my part I coulde not be heard (your daughters are brought up in such awe) though I tolde her of your pleasure sufficiently. *Gynecia*, as if she had heard her last doome pronounced agaynst her, with a side-looke and chaunged countenance, O my Lorde (said she) what meane you to suffer these yong folkes together? *Basilius* (that aymed nothing at the marke of her suspition) smilingly tooke her in his armes, sweete wife (said he) I thanke you for your care of your childe: but they must be youthes of other mettall, then *Zelmane*, that can endaunger her. O but; cryed *Gynecia*, and therewith she stayed: for then indeede she did suffer a right conflict, betwixt the force of love, and rage of jealousie. Manie times was she about to satisfie the spite of her minde, and tell *Basilius*, how she knewe *Zelmane* to be farre otherwise then the outwarde appearance. But those many times were all put backe, by the manifolde objections of her vehement love. Faine she would have barde her daughters happe, but loth she was to cut off her owne hope. But now, as if her life had bene set uppon a wager of quicke rysing, as weake as she was, she gat up; though *Basilius*, (with a kindnesse flowing onely from the fountaine of unkindnesse, being in deede desirous to winne his daughter as much time as might be) was loth to suffer it, swearing he sawe sickenesse in her face, and therefore was loath she should adventure the ayre.

But the great and wretched Ladie *Gynecia*, possessed with those devils of Love and Jealousie, did rid herselfe from her tedious husbande: and taking no body with her, going toward thẽ; O Jealousie (said she) the phrensie of wise folkes, the well-wishing spite, and unkinde carefulnesse, the selfe-punishment for others faults, and selfe-miserie in others happinesse, the cousin of envie, daughter of love, & mother of hate, how couldest thou so quietly get thee a seate in the unquiet hart of *Gynecia*, *Gynecia* (said she sighing) thought wise, and once vertuous? Alas it is thy breeders power which plantes thee there: it is the flaming agonie of affection, that works the chilling accesse of thy fever, in such sort, that nature gives place; the growing

of my daughter seemes the decay of my selfe; the blessings of
a mother turne to the curses of a cõpetitor; and the faire face of
Philoclea, appeares more horrible in my sight, then the image
of death. Then remembred she this song, which she thought
tooke a right measure of her present mind.

> WYth two strange fires of equall heate possest,
>   The one of Love, the other Jealousie,
> Both still do worke, in neither finde I rest:
> For both, alas, their strengthes together tie:
> The one aloft doth holde, the other hie.
>   Love wakes the jealous eye least thence it moves:
>   The jealous eye, the more it lookes, it loves.

4
> These fires increase: in these I dayly burne:
> They feede on me, and with my wings do flie:
> My lovely joyes to dolefull ashes turne:
> Their flames mount up, my powers prostrate lie:
> They live in force, I quite consumed die.
>   One wonder yet farre passeth my conceate:
>   The fuell small: how be the fires so great?

5   But her unleasured thoughtes ran not over the ten first
wordes; but going with a pace, not so much too fast for her
bodie, as slowe for her minde, she found them together, who
after *Misos* departure, had left their tale, and determined what
to say to *Basilius*. But full abashed was poore *Philoclea*, (whose
conscience nowe began to knowe cause of blushing) for first
salutation, receyving an eye from her mother, full of the same
disdainefull scorne, which *Pallas* shewed to poore *Arachne*,
that durst contende with her for the prize of well weaving:
yet did the force of love so much rule her, that though for
Zelmanes sake she did detest her, yet for *Zelmanes* sake she used
no harder words to her, then to bid her go home, and
accompany her solitarie father.

6   Then began she to display to *Zelmane* the storehouse of her
deadly desires, when sodainly the confused rumor of a mutinous
multitude gave just occasion to *Zelmane* to breake of any such
conference, (for well she found, they were not friendly voices
they heard) and to retire with as much diligence as conveniently
they could, towards the lodge. Yet before they could winne

the lodge by twentie paces, they were overtaken by an unruly sort of clownes, and other rebels, which like a violent floud, were caried, they themselves knewe not whether. But assoone as they came within perfect discerning these Ladies, like enraged beastes, without respect of their estates, or pitie of their sexe, they began to runne against them, as right villaines, thinking abilitie to doo hurt, to be a great advancement: yet so many as they were, so many almost were their mindes, all knitte together onely in madnes. Some cried, Take; some, Kill; some, Save: but even they that cried save, ran for companie with them that meant to kill. Everie one commaunded, none obeyed, he only seemed chief Captain, that was most ragefull.

Zelmane (whose vertuous courage was ever awake) drew out 7 her sword, which upon those il-armed churls giving as many wounds as blowes, & as many deathes almost as wounds (lightning courage, and thundering smart upon them) kept them at a bay, while the two Ladies got thẽselves into the lodge: out of the which, *Basilius* (having put on an armour long untried) came to prove his authoritie among his subjects, or at lest, to adventure his life with his deare mistresse, to whõ he brought a shield, while the Ladies tremblingly attended the issue of this dangerous adventure. But *Zelmane* made them perceive the ods betweene an Eagle and a Kight, with such a nimble stayednes, and such an assured nimblenes, that while one was running backe for feare, his fellow had her sword in his guts.

And by and by was both her harte and helpe well encreased 8 by the comming of *Dorus*, who having been making of hurdles for his masters sheepe, hearde the horrible cries of this madde multitude; and having streight represented before the eies of his carefull love, the perill wherein the soule of his soule might be, he went to *Pamelas* lodge, but found her in a cave hard by, with *Mopsa* and *Dametas*, who at that time would not have opened the entrie to his father. And therfore leaving them there (as in a place safe, both for being strong, and unknowen) he ranne as the noise guyded him. But when he saw his friend in such danger among them, anger and contempt (asking no counsell but of courage) made him roome among them, with no other weapon but his sheephooke, and with that over-throwing one of the villaines, took away a two-hand sword from him, and withall, helpt him from ever being ashamed of losing it. Then lifting up his brave head, and flashing terror into their faces, he made armes & legs goe complaine to the earth, how evill their masters had kept them. Yet the multitude still growing, and the verie killing wearying them (fearing, lest in long fight they should be conquered with cõquering) they drew back toward the lodge; but drew back in such sort, that still their terror went forwarde: like a valiant mastiffe, whom when his master pulles backe by the taile from the beare (with whom he hath alreadie interchanged a hatefull imbracement) though his pace be backwarde, his gesture is foreward, his teeth and eyes threatening more in the retiring, then they did in the advancing: so guided they themselves homeward, never stepping steppe backward, but that they proved themselves masters of the ground where they stept.

9   Yet among the rebels there was a dapper fellowe, a tayler by occupation, who fetching his courage onelie from their going back, began to bow his knees, & very fencer-like to draw neere to *Zelmane*. But as he came within her distãce, turning his swerd very nicely about his crown, *Basilius*, with a side blow, strake of his nose. He (being a suiter to a seimsters daughter, and therfore not a little grieved for such a disgrace) stouped downe, because he had hard, that if it were fresh put to, it would cleave on againe. But as his hand was on the grounde to bring his nose to his head, *Zelmane* with a blow, sent his head to his nose. That saw a butcher, a butcherlie chuffe indeed (who that day was sworn brother to him in a cup of wine) & lifted up a great leaver, calling *Zelmane* all the vile names of a butcherly eloquence. But she (letting slippe the blowe of the leaver) hitte him so surely on the side of his face, that she lefte nothing but the nether jawe, where the tongue still wagged, as willing to say more, if his masters remẽbrance had served. O (said a miller that was halfe dronke) see the lucke of a good fellow, and with that word, ran with a pitchforke at *Dorus*: but the nimblenes of the wine caried his head so fast, that it made it over-runne his feet, so that he fell withall, just betwene the legs of *Dorus*: who setting his foote on his neck (though he offered two milche kine, and foure fatte hogs for his life) thrust his sword quite through, from one eare to the other; which toke it very unkindlie, to feele such newes

before they heard of them, in stead of hearing, to be put to such feeling. But *Dorus* (leaving the miller to vomit his soul out in wine and bloud) with his two-hand sword strake of another quite by the waste, who.the night before had dreamed he was growen a couple, and (interpreting it he should be maried) had bragd of his dreame that morning among his neighbors. But that blow astonished quite a poore painter, who stood by with a pike in his handes. This painter was to counterfette the skirmishing betwene the *Centaures* and *Lapithes*, and had bene very desirous to see some notable wounds, to be able the more lively to expresse them; and this morning (being caried by the streame of this companie) the foolish felow was even delighted to see the effe{ct of blowes. But this last, (hapning neere him) so amazed him, that he stood still, while *Dorus* (with a turne of his sword) strake of both his hands. And so the painter returned, well skilled in wounds, but with never a hand to performe his skill.

CHAP. 26.

[1] Zelmanes *confident attempt to appease the mutinie.* [2] *A bone of division cast by her,* [3] *and caught by them.* [4] *Her pacificatorie oration.* [5] *The acceptation and issue of it.*

IN this manner they recovered the lodge, and gave the rebels [1] a face of wood of the out-side. But they then (though no more furious, yet more couragious when they saw no resister) went about with pickaxe to the wall, and fire to the gate, to gette themselves entrance. Then did the two Ladies mixe feare with love, especially *Philoclea*, who ever caught hold of *Zelmane*, so (by the follie of love) hindering the help which she desired. But *Zelmane* seeing no way of defence, nor time to deliberate (the number of those villaines still encreasing, and their madnesse still encreasing with their number) thought it onely the meanes to goe beyond their expe{ctation with an unused boldenesse, and with danger to avoide danger: and therfore opened againe the gate, and (*Dorus* and *Basilius* standing redie for her defence) she issued againe among them. The blowes she had dealt before (though all in generall were hastie) made each of them in particular take breath, before they brought them sodainly over-neere her, so that she had time to gette up to the judgement-seate of the Prince, which (according to the guise of that countrie) was before the gate. There she paused a while, making signe with her hand unto them, & withall, speaking aloud, that she had something to say unto them, that would please them. But she was answered a while with nothing but shouts and cries; and some beginning to throw stones at her, not daring to approach her. But at length, a young farmer (who might do most among the countrie sort, and was caught in a little affection towardes *Zelmane*) hoping by this kindenesse to have some good of her, desired them, if they were honest men, to heare the woman speake. Fie fellowes, fie, (said he) what will all the maides in our towne say, if so many tall men shall be afraide to heare a faire wench? I sweare unto you by no little ones, I had rather give my teeme of oxen, then we should shewe our selves so uncivill wights. Besides, I tell you true, I have heard it of old men counted wisdome, to heare much, & say little. His sententious speech so prevailed, that the most parte began to listen. Then she, with such efficacie of gracefulnes, & such a quiet magnanimitie represented in her face in this uttermost perill, as the more the barbarous people looked, the more it fixed their looks upon her, in this sorte began unto them.

2   It is no small comfort unto me (said she) having to speake something unto you for your owne behoofs, to find that I have to deale with such a people, who shew indeed in theselves the right nature of valure, which as it leaves no violence unattempted, while the choller is nourished with resistance; so when the subject of their wrath, doth of it self unloked-for offer it self into their hands, it makes the at lest take a pause before they determine cruelty. Now then first (before I come to the principall matter) have I to say unto you; that your Prince *Basilius* himselfe in person is within this Lodge, & was one of the three, whõ a few of you went about to fight withall: (& this she said, not doubting but they knew it well inough; but because she would have them imagine, that the Prince might think that they did not know it) by him am I sent unto you, as frõ a Prince to his well approved subjects, nay as from a father to beloved children, to know what it is that hath bred

just quarrell among you, or who they be that have any way wrõged you? what it is with which you are displeased, or of which you are desirous? This he requires: and indeed (for he knowes your faithfulnes) he commaunds you presently to set downe, & to choose among your selves some one, who may relate your griefes or demaundes unto him.

This (being more then they hoped for from their Prince) **3** asswaged well their furie, & many of them consented (especially the young farmer helping on, who meant to make one of the demaũds that he might have *Zelmane* for his wife) but when they began to talke of their grieves, never Bees made such a cõfused hũming: the towne dwellers demanding putting downe of imposts: the country felowes laying out of cõmons: some would have the Prince keepe his Court in one place, some in another. Al cried out to have new coũcellors: but when they should think of any new, they liked thẽ as well as any other, that they could remẽber, especially they would have the treasure so looked unto, as that he should never neede to take any more subsidies. At length they fel to direct contrarieties. For the Artisans, they would have corne & wine set at a lower price, and bound to be kept so stil: the plowmen, vine-laborers, & farmers would none of that. The coũtrimen demaunded that every man might be free in the chief townes: that could not the Burgesses like of. The peasãts would have the Gentlemẽ destroied, the Citizens (especially such as Cookes, Barbers, & those other that lived most on Gentlemen) would but have them refourmed. And of ech side were like divisions, one neighbourhood beginning to find fault with another. But no confusion was greater then of particular mens likings and dislikings: one dispraising such a one, whõ another praised, & demanding such a one to be punished, whom the other would have exalted. No lesse ado was there about choosing him, who should be their spokes-man. The finer sort of Burgesses, as Marchants Prentises, & Clothworkers, because of their riches, disdaining the baser occupations, & they because of their number as much disdaining them: all they scorning the countrimens ignoraunce, & the countrymen suspecting as much their cũning: So that *Zelmane* (finding that their united rage was now growne, not only to a dividing, but to a crossing one of another, & that the mislike growne among thẽselves did

wel allay the heat against her) made tokẽs againe unto thẽ (as
though she tooke great care of their wel doing, and were afraid
of their falling out) that she would speake unto thẽ. They now
growne jealous one of another (the stay having ingẽdred divisiõ,
& divisiõ having manifested their weaknes) were willing inough
to heare, the most part striving to show themselves willinger
then their fellowes: which *Zelmane* (by the acquaintaunce she
had had with such kinde of humors) soone perceiving, with an
angerles bravery, & an unabashed mildnes, in this manner spake
unto them.

4   An unused thing it is, & I think not heretofore seene, ô
Arcadians, that a womã should give publike coũsel to men, a
strãger to the coũtry people, & that lastly in such a presence by
a private person, the regall throne should be possessed.   But
the straungenes of your action makes that used for vertue, which
your violent necessitie imposeth.   For certainely, a woman may
well speake to such men, who have forgottẽ al manlike government: a straunger may with reason instruct such subjects, that
neglect due points of subjection: and is it marvaile this place
is entred into by another, since your owne Prince (after thirtie
yeares government) dare not shew his face unto his faithfull
people?   Heare therfore ô *Arcadians*, & be ashamed: against
whõ hath this rage bene stirred? whether have bene bent these
mãfull weapons of yours?   In this quiet harmles lodge are
harbourd no *Argians* your ancient enimies, nor *Laconians* your
now feared neighbours.   Here be nether hard landlords, nor
biting usurers.   Here lodge none, but such as either you have
great cause to love, or no cause to hate: here being none,
besides your Prince, Princesse, and their children, but my self.
Is it I then, ô *Arcadians*, against whom your anger is armed?
Am I the marke of your vehemẽt quarrell? if it be so, that
innocencie shall not be a stop for furie; if it be so, that the law
of hospitalitie (so long & holily observed among you) may not
defend a straunger fled to your armes for succour: if in fine it
be so, that so many valiaunt mens courages can be enflamed to
the mischiefe of one silly woman; I refuse not to make my life
a sacrifice to your wrath.   Exercise in me your indignatiõ, so
it go no further, I am content to pay the great favours I have
received amõg you, with my life, not ill deserving I present it
here unto you, ô *Arcadians*, if that may satisfie you; rather

thẽ you (called over the world the wise and quiet *Arcadians*)
should be so vaine, as to attempt that alone, which all the rest
of your countrie wil abhor; thẽ you should shew your selves
so ungratefull, as to forget the fruite of so many yeares peaceable government; or so unnaturall, as not to have with the
holy name of your naturall Prince, any furie over-maistred.
For such a hellish madnes (I know) did never enter into your
harts, as to attẽpt any thing against his person; which no successor, though never so hatefull, wil ever leave (for his owne
sake) unrevenged.   Neither can your wonted valour be turned
to such a basenes, as in stead of a Prince, delivered unto you by
so many roiall ancestors, to take the tyrannous yoke of your
fellow subjeſt, in whom the innate meanes will bring forth
ravenous covetousnes, and the newnes of his estate, suspeſtfull
cruelty.   Imagine, what could your enimies more wish unto
you, then to see your owne estate with your owne handes undermined?   O what would your fore-fathers say, if they lived at
this time, & saw their ofspring defacing such an excellent
principalitie, which they with so much labour & bloud so
wisely have establisht?   Do you thinke them fooles, that saw
you should not enjoy your vines, your cattell, no not your
wives & children, without government; and that there could
be no government without a Magistrate, and no Magistrate
without obedience, and no obediẽce where every one upon his
owne private passion, may interprete the doings of the rulers?
Let your wits make your present exãple to you.   What
sweetnes (in good faith) find you in your present condition?
what choise of choise finde you, if you had lost *Basilius*? under
whose ensigne would you go, if your enimies should invade
you?   If you cannot agree upon one to speake for you, how
wil you agree upõ one to fight for you?   But with this feare of
I cannot tel what, one is troubled, and with that passed wrong
another is grieved.   And I pray you did the Sunne ever bring
you a fruitfull harvest, but that it was more hote then pleasant?
Have any of you childrẽ, that be not sometimes cumbersome?
Have any of you fathers, that be not sometime weerish?
What, shall we curse the Sonne, hate our children, or disobey
our fathers?   But what need I use these wordes, since I see in
your countenances (now vertuously settled) nothing els but love
and dutie to him, by whom for your only sakes the governmẽt

317

is embraced. For al what is done, he doth not only pardon
you, but thanke you; judging the action by the minds, & not
the minds by the actiõ. Your grieves, and desires, whatsoever,
& whensoever you list, he wil consider of, and to his consideration it is reason you should refer them. So then, to cõclude;
the uncertainty of his estate made you take armes; now you
see him well, with the same love lay them downe. If now you
end (as I know you will) he will make no other account of this
matter, but as of a vehement, I must cõfesse over-vehement
affection: the only continuaunce might prove a wickednes.
But it is not so, I see very wel, you begã with zeale, & wil
end with reverẽce.

5   The action *Zelmane* used, being beautified by nature and
apparelled with skill, her gestures beyng such, that as her
wordes did paint out her minde, so they served as a shadow, to
make the picture more lively and sensible, with the sweete
cleernesse of her voice, rising & falling kindly as the nature of
the worde, and efficacie of the matter required, altogether in
such admirable person, whose incomparable valour they had
well felte, whose beautie did pearce through the thicke dulnes
of their senses, gave such a way unto her speach through the
rugged wildernesse of their imaginations, who (besides they
were striken in admiration of her, as of more then a humane
creature) were coold with taking breath, and had learned
doubts out of leasure, that in steed of roaring cries, there was
now heard nothing, but a cõfused muttring, whether her saying
were to be followed, betwixt feare to pursue, & lothnesse to
leave: most of them could have bene cõtent, it had never bene
begun, but how to end it (each afraid of his companion,) they
knew not, finding it far easier to tie then to loose knots. But
Zelmane thinking it no evil way in such mutinies, to give the
mutinous some occasiõ of such service, as they might thinke (in
their own judgement) would countervaile their trespasse, withal,
to take the more assured possession of their mindes, which she
feared might begin to waver, Loiall *Arcadians* (said she) now do
I offer unto you the manifesting of your duties: all those that
have taken armes for the Princes safetie, let thẽ turne their
backs to the gate, with their weapons bent against such as
would hurt his sacred person. O weak trust of the many-
headed multitude, whom inconstancie onely doth guide to well

doing: who can set confidence there, where company takes
away shame, and ech may lay the fault of his fellow? So said
a craftie felow among them, named *Clinias*, to himselfe, when
he saw the worde no sooner out of *Zelmanes* mouth, but that
there were some shouts of joy, with, God save *Basilius*, and
divers of them with much jollity growne to be his guard, that
but litle before mēt to be his murderers.

CHAP. 27.

[1] *A verball craftie coward purtrayed in* Clinias. [2] *His first raising,
and with the first, relenting in this mutinie,* [3] *punished by the
farmer.* [4] *The uprore reenforced, & weakned by themselves.*
[5] Clinias-*his* Sinon-*like narration of this drüken rebellions
original.* [6] *The kings order in it.*

THis *Clinias* in his youth had bene a scholler so farre, as to 1
learne rather wordes then maners, and of words rather
plentie then order; and oft had used to be an actor in Tragedies, where he had learned, besides a slidingnesse of language,
acquaintance with many passions, and to frame his face to
beare the figure of them: long used to the eyes and eares of
men, and to recken no fault, but shamefastnesse; in nature, a
most notable Coward, and yet more strangely then rarely
venturous in privie practises.

This fellowe was become of neere trust to *Cecropia*, 2
Amphialus-his mother, so that he was privy to al the mischievous devises, wherewith she went about to ruine *Basilius*,
and his children, for the advauncing of her sonne: and though
his education had made him full of tongue, yet his love to be
doing, taught him in any evill to be secret; and had by his
mistresse bene used (ever since the strange retiring of *Basilius*)
to whisper rumors into the peoples eares: and this time (finding
great aptnes in the multitude) was one of the chiefe that set
them in the uprore (though quite without the cōsent of
Amphialus, who would not for all the Kingdoms of the world so
have advētured the life of *Philoclea*.) But now perceiving the
flood of their furie began to ebbe, he thought it policie to take

the first of the tide, so that no mã cried lowder then he, upon *Basilius*. And som of the lustiest rebels not yet agreeing to the rest, he caused two or three of his mates that were at his cõmandement to lift him up, & then as if he had had a prologue to utter, he began with a nice gravitie to demand audience. But few attending what he said, with vehement gesture, as if he would teare the stars from the skies, he fell to crying out so lowde, that not onely *Zelmane*, but *Basilius* might heare him. O unhappie men, more madde then the Giants that would have plucked *Jupiter* out of heaven, how long shal this rage continue? why do you not all throw downe your weapons, and submit your selves to our good Prince, our good *Basilius*, the *Pelops* of wisdom, & *Minos* of all good governmẽt? when will you begin to beleve me, and other honest and faithfull subjects, that have done all we could to stop your furie?

3   The farmer that loved *Zelmane* could abide him no longer. For as at the first he was willing to speake of cõditions, hoping to have gotten great soverainties, & among the rest *Zelmane*: so now perceiving, that the people, once any thing downe the hill from their furie, would never stop till they came to the bottom of absolute yeelding, and so that he should be nearer feares of punishment, then hopes of such advancement, he was one of them that stood most against the agreement: and to begin withall, disdaining this fellow should play the preacher, who had bin one of the chiefest make-bates, strake him a great wound upon the face with his sword. The cowardly wretch fell down, crying for succour, & (scrambling through the legs of them that were about him) gat to the throne, where *Zelmane* tooke him, and comforted him, bleeding for that was past, and quaking for feare of more.

4   But as soone as that blow was given (as if *Æolus* had broke open the doore to let all his winds out) no hand was idle, ech one killing him that was next, for feare he should do as much to him. For being divided in minds & not divided in cõpanies, they that would yeeld to *Basilius* were intermingled with thẽ that would not yeeld. These men thinking their ruine stood upõ it; those men to get favor of their Prince, converted their ungracious motion into their owne bowels, & by a true judgement grew their owne punishers. None was sooner killed thẽ those that had bene leaders in the disobedience: who by being

so, had taught them, that they did leade disobediēce to the same leaders. And many times it fel out that they killed them that were of their owne faction, anger whetting, and doubt hastening their fingers. But then came downe *Zelmane*; and *Basilius* with *Dorus* issued, and somtimes seeking to draw together those of their party, somtimes laying indifferently among them, made such havocke (amōg the rest *Zel-mane* striking the farmer to the hart with her sworde, as before she had done with her eyes) that in a while all they of the contrary side were put to flight, and fled to certaine woods upon the frontiers; where feeding coldly, and drinking onely water, they were disciplined for their dronken riots; many of them being slaine in that chase, about a score onely escaping. But when these late rebels, nowe souldiers, were returned from the chase, *Basilius* calling them togither, partly for policy sake, but principally because *Zelmane* before had spoken it (which was to him more thē a divine ordinance) he pronounced their generall pardon, willing them to returne to their houses, and therafter be more circūspect in their proceedings: which they did most of them with share-marks of their folly. But imagining *Clinias* to be one of the chiefe that had bred this good alteration, he gave him particular thanks, and withall willed him to make him know, how this frenzie had entred into the people.

Clinias purposing indeede to tell him the trueth of al, saving 5 what did touch himself, or *Cecropia*, first, dipping his hand in the blood of his woūd, Now by this blood (said he) which is more deare to me, then al the rest that is in my body, since it is spent for your safety: this tōgue (perchance unfortunate, but never false) shall not now begin to lie unto my Prince, of me most beloved. Then stretching out his hand, and making vehement countenāces the ushers to his speches, in such maner of tearms recounted this accident. Yesterday (said he) being your birth-day, in the goodly greene two mile hence before the city of *Enispus*, to do honour to the day, were a four or five thousand people (of all conditions, as I thinke) gathered together, spending al the day in dancings and other exercises: and when night came, under tents and bowes making great cheare, and meaning to observe a wassaling watch all that night for your sake. *Bacchus* (the learned say) was begot with thunder: I think, that made him ever since so full of stur & debate. *Bacchus* indeed it was which soũded the first trũpet to this rude alarũ. For that barbarous opinion being generally among them, to thinke with vice to do honor, & with activitie in beastlines to shew abundãce of love, made most of thẽ seeke to shew the depth of their affectiõ in the depth of their draught. But being once wel chafed with wine (having spent al the night, & some peece of the morning in such revelling) & imboldned by your absented maner of living, there was no matter their eares had ever heard of that grew not to be a subject of their winie conference. I speake it by proofe : for I take witnes of the gods (who never leave perjuries unpunished) that I oftẽ cried out against their impudency, & (whẽ that would not serve) stopt mine eares, because I wold not be partaker of their blasphemies, till with buffets they forced me to have mine eares & eies defiled. Publike affairs were mingled with private grudges, neither was any man thought of wit, that did not pretende some cause of mislike. Rayling was counted the fruite of freedome, and saying nothing had his uttermoste prayse in ignoraunce. At the length, your sacred person (alas why did I live to heare it ? alas how do I breath to utter it ? But your cõmandement doth not onely enjoine obedience, but give me force : your sacred person (I say) fell to be their table-talke : a proud word swelling in their stomacks, & disdainfull reproches against so great a greatnes, having put on the shew of greatnes in their little mindes : till at length the very un-brideled use of words having increased fire in their mindes (which God knowes thought their knowledge notable, because they had at all no knowledge to cõdemne their own want of knowledge) they descended (O never to be forgotten presump-tion) to a direct mislike of your living from among them. Whereupon it were tedious to remember their far-fetched constructions. But the summe was, you disdained them : and what were the pompes of your estate, if their armes mainteyned you not ? Who woulde call you a Prince, if you had not a people ? When certaine of them of wretched estates, and worse mindes (whose fortunes, change could not impaire) began to say, that your government was to be looked into ; how the great treasures (you had levied amõg thẽ) had bene spent ; why none but great men & gentlemen could be admitted into

counsel, that the cõmons (forsooth) were to plain headed to say
their opiniõs: but yet their blood & sweat must maintain all.
Who could tell whether you were not betraied in this place,
where you lived? nay whether you did live or no? Therefore
that it was time to come & see; and if you were here, to know
(if *Arcadia* were growne lothsome in your sight) why you did
not ridde your selfe of the trouble? There would not want
those that would take so faire a cumber in good part. Since
the Countrie was theirs, and the governement an adherent to
the countrie, why should they not consider of the one, as well
as inhabite the other? Nay rather (said they) let us beginne
that, which all *Arcadia* will followe. Let us deliver our Prince
from daunger of practises, and our selves from want of a Prince.
Let us doo that, which all the rest thinke. Let it be said, that
we onely are not astonished with vaine titles, which have their
force but in our force. Lastly, to have saide & heard so much,
was as dãgerous, as to have attẽpted: & to attẽpt they had the
name of glorious liberty with them. These words being spokẽ
(like a furious storme) presently caried away their wel inclined
braines. What I, and some other of the honester sort could
do, was no more, then if with a puffe of breath, one should goe
about to make a saile goe against a mightie winde: or, with
one hand, stay the ruine of a mightie wall. So generall grewe
this madnes among them, there needed no drumme, where each
man cried, each spake to other that spake as fast to him, and
the disagreeing sounde of so many voices, was the chiefe token
of their unmeete agreement. Thus was their banquette turned
to a battaile, their winie mirthes to bloudie rages, and the happie
prayers for your life, to monstrous threatning of your estate;
the solemnizing your birth-day, tended to have been the cause
of your funerals. But as a dronken rage hath (besides his
wickednes) that follie, that the more it seekes to hurt, the lesse
it considers how to be able to hurt: they never weyed how to
arme thẽselves, but tooke up every thing for a weapon, that
furie offered to their handes. Many swordes, pikes, and billes
there were: others tooke pitchforkes and rakes, converting
husbandrie to souldierie: some caught hold of spittes (thinges
serviceable for life) to be the instruments of death. And there
was some such one, who held the same pot wherein he drank
to your health, to use it (as he could) to your mischiefe. Thus

armed, thus governed, forcing the unwilling, and hartening the willing, adding furie to furie, and encreasing rage with running, they came headlong towarde this lodge: no man (I dare say) resolved in his own hart, what was the uttermost he would doo when he came hether. But as mischief is of such nature, that it cannot stand but with strengthning one evill by an other, and so multiplie in it selfe, till it come to the highest, and then fall with his owne weight: so to their mindes (once passed the bounds of obedience) more and more wickednes opened it selfe, so that they who first pretended to preserve you, then to reforme you, (I speak it in my conscience, and with a bleeding hart) now thought no safetie for them, without murdering you. So as if the Gods (who preserve you for the preservation of *Arcadia*) had not shewed their miraculous power, and that they had not used for instruments, both your owne valour (not fit to be spoken of by so meane a mouth as mine) and some (I must confesse) honest minds, (whõ alas why should I mention, since what we did, reached not the hundred part of our duetie?) our hands (I tremble to think of it) had destroyed all that, for which we have cause to rejoyce that we are *Arcadians*.

6   With that the fellow did wring his hands, & wrang out teares: so as *Basilius*, that was not the sharpest pearcer into masked minds, toke a good liking to him; & so much the more as he had tickled him with praise in the hearing of his mistres. And therfore pitying his woũd, willed him to get him home, and looke well unto it, & make the best search he could, to know if there were any further depth in this matter, for which he should be well rewarded. But before he went away, certain of the shepheards being come (for that day was appointed for their pastorals) he sent one of them to *Philanax*, and an other to other principal noble-men, and cities there abouts, to make through-inquirie of this uprore, and withall, to place such garrisons in all the townes & villages neere unto him, that he might thereafter keep his solitary lodge in more security, upõ the making of a fire, or ringing of a bell, having them in a redines for him.

CHAP. 28.

¹ *The praises of* Zelmanes *act.* ² Dametas *his caroll for saving himself, and his charge.* ³ Basilius *his conference with* Phi¹anax *of the Oracle (the ground of all this storie.)* ⁴ *His wrong-construction of it.* ⁵ *His hymne to* Apollo. ⁶ *His courting turnde over to tale-telling.*

THis, *Clinias* (having his eare one way when his eye was 1 an other) had perceived; & therefore hasted away, with mind to tell *Cecropia* that she was to take some speedie resolution, or els it were daunger those examinations would both discover, & ruine her: and so went his way, leaving that little companie with embracements, and praising of *Zelmanes* excellent proceeding, to shew, that no decking sets foorth any thing so" much, as affection. For as, while she stoode at the discretion of those indiscreete rebelles, everie angrie countenance any of them made, seemed a knife layde upon their owne throates; so unspeakable was now their joy, that they saw (besides her safetie & their owne) the same wrought, and safely wrought by her meanes, in whom they had placed all their delights. What examples *Greece* could ever alledge of witte and fortitude, were set in the ranke of trifles, being compared to this action.

But as they were in the midst of those unfained ceremonies, 2 a Gitterne, ill-played on, accompanied with a hoarce voice (who seemed to sing maugre the Muses, and to be merie in spite of Fortune) made them looke the way of the ill-noysed song. The song was this.

> A *Hatefull cure with hate to heale:*
>   *A blooddy helpe with blood to save:*
> *A foolish thing with fooles to deale:*
> *Let him be bold that bobs will have.*
>   *But who by meanes of wisdome hie*
>   *Hath sav'd his charge? it is even I.*
>
> *Let other deck their pride with skarres,*
> *And of their wounds make brave lame showes:*
> *First let them die, then passe the starres,*
> *When rotten Fame will tell their blowes.*
>   *But eye from blade, and eare from crie:*
>   *Who hath sav'd all? it is even I.*

They had soone found it was *Dametas,* who came with no
lesse lifted up countenance, then if he had passed over the
bellies of all his enemies: so wise a point he thought he had
perfourmed, in using the naturall strength of a cave. But
never was it his dooing to come so soone thence, till the coast
were more assuredly cleare: for it was a rule with hin , that
after a great storme there ever fell a fewe droppes before it be
"fully finished. But *Pamela* (who had now experienced how
much care doth sollicite a Lovers hart) used this occasion of
going to her parents and sister, indeed aswel for that cause, as
being unquiet, till her eye might be assured, how her shepheard
had gone through the daunger. But *Basilius* with the sight of
Pamela (of whom almost his head otherwise occupied, had left
the wonted remembrance) was sodainly striken into a devout
kind of admiration, remembring the oracle, which (according
to the fauning humour of false hope) he interpreted now his
owne to his owne best, and with the willing blindnesse of
affection (because his minde ran wholly upon *Zelmane*) he
thought the Gods in their oracles did principally minde her.

3   But as he was deepely thinking of the matter, one of the
shepheards tolde him, that *Philanax* was already come with a
hundred horse in his company. For having by chaunce rid not
farre of the little desert, he had heard of this uprore, and so
was come upon the spurre (gathering a company of Gentlemen
as fast as he could) to the succour of his Master. *Basilius* was
glad of it; but (not willing to have him, nor any other of the
Noble men, see his Mistresse) he himselfe went out of the
Lodge, and so giving order unto him of placing garrisons, and
examining these matters; and *Philanax* with humble earnestnesse beginning to entreate him to leave of his solitarie course
(which already had bene so daungerous unto him) Well (said
Basilius) it may be ere long I wil cōdiscend unto your desire.
In the meane time, take you the best order you can to keepe
me safe in my solitarinesse. But, (said he) doo you remember,
how earnestly you wrote unto me, that I should not be moved
by that Oracles authoritie, which brought me to this resolution?
Full well Sir (answered *Philanax*) for though it pleased you not
as then to let me knowe, what the Oracles words were, yet all
Oracles holding (in my conceipt) one degree of reputatiơ, it
suffised me to know, it was but an Oracle, which led you frō

your owne course. Well (said *Basilius*) I will now tell you the wordes; which before I thought not good to doo; because when al the events fall out (as some already have done) I may charge you with your incredulitie. So he repeated them in this sorte.

THy elder care shall from thy carefull face
    By princely meane be stolne, and yet not lost.
Thy yonger shall with Natures blisse embrace
An uncouth love, which Nature hateth most.
Both they themselves unto such two shall wed,
Who at thy beer, as at a barre, shall plead;
Why thee (a living man) they had made dead.
In thy owne seate a forraine state shall sit.
And ere that all these blowes thy head doo hit,
Thou, with thy wife, adultry shall commit.

For you forsoth (said he) when I told you, that some supernaturall cause sent me strange visiõs, which being cõfirmed with presagious chaunces, I had gone to *Delphos*, & there received this answere: you replied to me, that the onely supernaturall causes were the humors of my body, which bred such melancholy dreames; and that both they framed a mind full of conceipts, apt to make presages of things, which in thẽselves were meerly chaungeable: & with all as I say, you remẽber what you wrot unto me, touching authoritie of the Oracle: but now I have some notable triall of the truth therof, which herafter I wil more largly cõmunicate unto you. Only now, know that the thing I most feared is alredy performed; I mean that a forraine state should possesse my throne. For that hath ben done by *Zelmane*, but not as I feared, to my ruine, but to my preservatiõ. But whẽ he had once named *Zelmane*, that name was as good as a pully, to make the clocke of his praises run on in such sort, that (*Philanax* found) was more exquisite then the only admiration of vertue breedeth: which his faithful hart inwardly repining at, made him shrinke away as soone as he could, to go about the other matters of importance, which *Basilius* had enjoyned unto him.

Basilius returned into the Lodge, thus by him selfe construing the oracle, that in that he said, his elder care should by Princely meane be stolne away from him, and yet not lost, it was now perfourmed, since *Zelmane* had as it were robd from him the care of his first begotten childe, yet was it not lost, since in his harte the ground of it remained. That his younger should with Natures blisse embrace the love of *Zelmane*, because he had so commaunded her for his sake to doo; yet shoulde it be with as much hate of Nature, for being so hatefull an opposite to the jealousie hee thought her mother had of him. The sitting in his seate he deemed by her already perfourmed: but that which most côforted him, was his interpretation of the adulterie, which he thought he should commit with *Zelmane*, whom afterwards he should have to his wife. The point of his daughters marriage, because it threatned his death withall, he determined to prevent, with keeping them unmaried while he lived. But having as he thought, gotten thus much understanding of the Oracle, he determined for three daies after to perfourme certaine rites to *Apollo*: and even then began with his wife and daughters to singe this Hymne, by them yearely used.

5   A Pollo *great, whose beames the greater world do light,*
      And in our little world do cleare our inward sight,
  Which ever shine, though hid from earth by earthly shade,
  Whose lights do ever live, but in our darkenesse fade;
  Thou God, whose youth was deckt with spoiles of Pythös *skin:*
"*(So humble knowledge can throw downe the snakish kinne)*
Latonas sonne, *whose birth in paine and travaile long*
Doth teach, to learne the good what travailes do belong:
"*In travaile of our life (a short but tedious space)*
While brickle houreglas runnes, guide thou our panting pace:
Give us foresightfull mindes: give us minds to obaye
What foresight tels; our thoughts upon thy knowledge staye.
Let so our fruites grow up, that nature be maintainde:
But so our hartes keepe downe, with vice they be not stainde.
Let this assured holde our judgements overtake,
"*That nothing winnes the heaven, but what doth earth forsake.*

6   Assone as he had ended his devotion (all the priviledged shepheards being now come) knowing well inough he might lay all his care upon *Philanax*, he was willing to sweeten the tast of this passed tumult, with some rurall pastimes. For which while the shepheards prepared themselves in their best

mãner, *Basilius* tooke his daughter *Philoclea* aside, and with such hast, as if his eares hunted for wordes, desired to know how she had found *Zelmane*. She humbly answered him, according to the agreement betwixt them, that thus much for her sake *Zelmane* was content to descend from her former resolutiõ, as to heare him, whẽsoever he would speake; & further then that (she said) as *Zelmane* had not graunted, so she nether did, nor ever would desire. *Basilius* kist her with more then fatherly thanks, and straight (like a hard-kept warde new come to his lands) would faine have used the benefite of that graunt, in laying his sicknes before his onely physition. But *Zelmane* (that had not yet fully determined with her selfe, how to beare her selfe toward him) made him in a few words understand, that the time in respect of the cõpanie was unfit for such a parley, & therfore to keep his braines the busier, letting him understand what she had learned of his daughters, touching *Eronas* distresse (whom in her travaile she had knowne, and bene greatly beholding to) she desired him to finish the rest, for so far as *Plãgus* had told him; Because she said (& she said truly) she was full of care for that Ladie, whose desart (onely except an over-base choise) was nothing agreable to misfortune. *Basilius* glad that she would commaund him any thing, but more glad, that in excusing the unfitnesse of that time, she argued an intention to graunt a fitter, obeyed her in this manner.

CHAP. 29.

[1] Antiphilus *his base-borne pride borne high by flatterie.* [2] *His unkinde hating the loving* Erona, *and fond loving of hating* Artaxia. [3] Artaxias *trap to take them both.* [4] *The mans weakenesse, and the womans strength in bearing captivitie.* [5] Plangus *love to her, employed by her to save* Antiphilus, [6] *who againe betraies himselfe and them.* [7] *His execution by women.* [8] Plangus *hardy attempts to save* Erona. [9] *The conditions of her death.* [10] *Her sorrow for* Antiphilus, [11] *and* Plangus *travaile for her: with his crosses, and course therein.*

Madame (said he) it is very true, that since yeares enhabled me to judge what is, or is not to be pitied, I never saw anything that more moved me to justifie a vehemẽt compassion in my self, then the estate of that Prince, whom strong against al his owne afflictions (which yet were great, as I perceave you have heard) yet true and noble love had so pulled downe, as to lie under sorrow for another. In so much as I could not temper my long idle pen in that subject, which I perceive you have seene. But then to leave that unrepeated, which I finde my daughters have told you, It may please you to understäd, since it pleaseth you to demaüd, that *Antiphilus* being crowned, & so left by the famous Princes *Musidorus* & *Pyrocles* (led thěce by the challenge of *Anaxius*, who is now in these provinces of *Greece*, making a dishonorable enquirie after that excellent prince *Pyrocles* alreadie perished) *Antiphilus* (I say) being crowned, and delivered from the presence of those two, whose vertues (while they were present, good schoolmasters) suppressed his vanities, he had not strěgth of mind enough in him to make long delay, of discovering what maner of man he was. But streight like one caried up to so hie a place, that he looseth the discerning of the ground over which he is; so was his mind lifted so far beyöd the levell of his owne discourse, that remembring only that himselfe was in the high seate of a King, he coulde not perceive that he was a king of reasonable creatures, who would quickly scorne follies, and repine at injuries. But imagining no so true propertie of sovereigntie, as to do what he listed, and to list whatsoever pleased his fansie, he quickly made his kingdome a Teniscourt, where his subjects should be the balles; not in truth cruelly, but licenciously abusing them, presuming so far upon himselfe, that what he did was liked of every bodie: nay, that his disgraces were favours, and all because he was a King. For in Nature not able to conceyve the bonds of great matters (suddenly borne into an unknowne Ocean of absolute power) he was swayed withall (he knewe not howe) as everie winde of passions puffed him. Whereto nothing helped him better, then that poysonous sugar of flatterie: which some used, out of the innate basenesse of their hart, straight like dogges fawning uppon the greatest; others secretely hating him, and disdayning his great rising so suddenly, so undeservedly (finding his humour) bent their exalting him only to his overthrow; like the bird that caries the shell-fish high, to breake him the easier with his fall. But his minde (being an apt matter to receive what forme their amplifying speeches woulde lay upon it) daunced so prettie a musicke to their false measure, that he thought himselfe the wysest, the woorthyest, and best beloved, that ever gave honour to a royall tytle. And being but obscurely borne, he had found out unblushing pedegrees, that made him not onely of the blood royall, but true heyre, unjustly dispossest by *Eronas* auncestours. And like the foolish birde, that when it so hides the heade that it sees not it selfe, thinkes no bodie else sees it : so did he imagine, that no bodie knew his basenesse, while he himselfe turned his eyes from it.

Then vainenesse (a meager friend to gratefulnesse) brought 2 him so to despise *Erona*, as of whom he had received no benefit, that within halfe a yeeres mariage he began to pretend barren-nesse: and making first an unlawfull law of having mo wives then one, he still keeping *Erona*, under-hãd, by message sought *Artaxia*, who no lesse hating him, then loving (as unluckie a choise) the naughtie King *Plexirtus*, yet to bring to passe what he purposed, was content to train him into false hopes, till alreadie his imagination had crowned him King of *Armenia*, & had made that, but the foundation of more, and more mon-archies; as if fortune had only gottẽ eies to cherish him. In which time a great assembly of most part of al the Princes of *Asia* being to do honour to the never sufficiently praised *Pyrocles* & *Musidorus*, he would be one not to acknowledge his obligation (which was as great as any of the others,) but looking to have bene yong master among those great estates, as he was amõg his abusing underlings. But so many valorous Princes, in-deed farre neerer to disdaine him then otherwise, he was quickly (as standing upon no true ground, inwardly) out of countenance with himselfe, till his seldom-cõfortlesse flatterers (perswading him, it was envie & feare of his expeĉted greatnes) made him hast away frõ that company, & without further delay appointed the meeting with *Artaxia*; so incredibly blinded with the over-bright shining of his roialty, that he could thinke such a Queene could be content to be joined-patent with an other to have such an husband. Poore *Erona* to all this obeied, either vehemẽcy of affeĉtion making her stoop to so overbase a servitude, or astonished with an unlooked-for fortune, dull to any behoofeful resolutiõ, or (as many times it falles out even in great harts when they can accuse none but thẽselves) desperatly bent to maintaine it. For so went she on in that way of her love, that (poore Lady) to be beyond all other examples of ill-set affection, she was brought to write to *Artaxia*, that she was content, for the publike good, to be a second wife, and yeeld the first place to her: nay to extoll him, and even woo *Artaxia* for him.

3　But *Artaxia* (mortally hating them both for her brothers sake) was content to hide her hate, til she had time to shewe it: and pretending that all her grudge was against the two paragons of vertue, *Musidorus* & *Pyrocles*, even met them halfe way in excusing her brothers murder, as not being principall actors; and of the other-side, driven to what they did by the ever-pardonable necessitie: and so well handled the matter, as, though she promised nothing, yet *Antiphilus* promised himselfe all that she woulde have him thinke. And so a solemne enterview was appointed. But (as the Poets say) *Hymen* had not there his saffron-coloured cote. For *Artaxia* laying men secretly (and easily they might be secret, since *Antiphilus* thought she overran him in love) when he came even readie to embrace her, shewing rather a countenaunce of accepting then offering, they came forth, and (having much advauntage both in number, valure, and fore-preparation) put all his companie to the sword; but such as could flie away. As for *Antiphilus* she caused him and *Erona* both to be put in irons, hasting backe toward her brothers tombe, upõ which she ment to sacrifice them; making the love of her brother stand betwene her and all other motions of grace, from which by nature she was alienated.

4　But great diversitie in them two quickely discovered it selfe for the bearing of that affliction. For *Antiphilus* that had no greatnesse but outwarde, that taken away, was readie to fall faster then calamitie could thrust him; with fruitlesse begging (where reason might well assure him his death was resolved) and weake bemoning his fortune, to give his enemies a most pleasing musique, with manie promises, and protestations, to as little purpose, as from a little minde. But *Erona* sadde in-deede, yet like one rather used, then new fallen to sadnesse (as who had the joyes of her hart alreadie broken) seemed rather to welcome then to shunne that ende of miserie, speaking little, but what she spake was for *Antiphilus*, remembring his guiltlesnesse, being at that time prisoner to *Tiridates*, when the valiant princes slue him: to the disgrace of men, shewing that there are women more wise to judge what is to be expected, and more constant to beare it when it is happened.

But her witte endeared by her youth, her affliction by her 5 birth, and her sadnesse by her beautie, made this noble prince *Plangus*, who (never almost from his cousin *Artaxia*) was nowe present at *Eronaes* taking, to perceyve the shape of lovelinesse more perfectly in wo, then in joyfulnesse (as in a picture which receives greater life by the darkenesse of shadowes, then by more glittering colours) and seeing to like; and liking to love; and loving straight to feele the most incident effects of love, to serve and preserve. So borne by the hastie tide of short leysure, he did hastily deliver together his affection, and affectionate care. But she (as if he had spoken of a small matter, when he mencioned her life, to which she had not leisure to attend) desired him if he loved her, to shew it, in finding some way to save *Antiphilus*. For her, she found the world but a wearisom stage unto her, where she played a part against her will: and therefore besought him, not to cast his love in so unfruitfull a place, as could not love it selfe: but for a testimonie of constancie, and a sutablenes to his word, to do so much comfort to her minde, as that for her sake *Antiphilus* were saved. He tolde me how much he argued against her tendering him, who had so ungratefully betraied her, and foolishly cast away himselfe. But perceiving she did not only bend her very goodwits to speake for him against her-selfe, but when such a cause could be allied to no reasõ, yet love would needs make it-self a cause, & barre her rather frõ hearing, then yeeld that she should yeeld to such arguments: he likewise in whõ the power of Love (as they say of spirits) was subject to the love in her, with griefe cõsented, & (though backwardly) was diligẽt to labor the help of *Antiphilus*: a man whom he not onely hated, as a traitour to *Erona*, but envied as a possessor of *Erona*. Yet Love sware, his hart, in spite of his hart, should make him become a servant to his rivall. And so did he, seeking all the meanes of perswading *Artaxia*, which the authority of so neere, and so vertuous a kinsmã would give unto him. But she to whom the eloquence of hatred had given revenge the face of delight, rejected all such motions;

but rather the more closely imprisoning them in her chiefe citie, where she kept them with intention at the birth-day of *Tiridates* (which was very nere) to execute *Antiphilus*, & at the day of his death (which was about halfe a yeere after) to use the same rigor towar[d]s *Erona*. *Plangus* much grieved (because much loving) attempted the humors of the *Lycians*, to see, whether they would come in with forces to succor their Princesse. But there the next inheritor to the crowne (with the true play that is used in the game of kingdŏs) had no sooner his mistres in captivity, but he had usurped her place, & making her odious to her people, because of the unfit eleĉtiŏ she had made, had so left no hope there: but which is worse, had sent to *Artaxia*, perswading the justicing her, because that unjustice might give his title the name of justice. Wãting that way, *Plangus* praĉtised with some deere friends of his, to save *Antiphilus* out of prison, whose day because it was much neerer then *Eronaes*, & that he wel found, she had twisted her life upŏ the same threed with his, he determined first to get him out of prison : & to that end having prepared al matters as wel as in such case he could, where *Artaxia* had set many of *Tiridates* old servants to have well-marking eyes, he cŏferred with *Antiphilus*, as (by the auĉthoritie he had) he found meanes to do; & agreed with him of the time and maner, how he should by the death of some of his jaylors escape.

6   But all being well ordered, and *Plangus* willinglie putting himselfe into the greatest danger, *Antiphilus* (who, like a bladder, sweld redie to breake, while it was full of the winde of prosperitie, that being out, was so abjeĉted, as apt to be trode on by every bodie) when it came to the point, that with some hazard, he might be in apparant likelihoode to avoide the uttermost harm, his harte fainted, and (weake foole, neither hoping, nor fearing as he should) gat a conceite, that with bewraying his praĉtise, he might obtaine pardon : and there-fore, even a little before *Plangus* should have come unto him, opened the whole praĉtise to him that had the charge, with unpittyed teares idly protesting, he had rather die by *Artaxias* commaundement, then against her will escape : yet begging life upon any the hardest, and wretchedest conditions that she woulde lay upon him. His keeper provided accordingly, so that when *Plangus* came, he was like, himself to have bene

entrappud: but that finding (with a luckie in-sight) that it was discovered, he retired; and (calling his friendes about him) stood upon his guard, as he had good cause. For, *Artaxia* (accounting him most ungrateful considering that her brother and she, had not onely preserved him against the malice of his father, but ever used him much liker his birth, then his fortune) sent forces to apprehend him. But he among the martiall men had gotten so great love, that he could not onely keepe himself from the malice, but worke in their mindes a compassion of *Eronas* adversitie.

But for the succour of *Antiphilus* he could gette no bodie to 7 joyne with him, the contempt of him having not bene able to qualifie the hatred; so that *Artaxia* might easilie upon him perfourme her will; which was (at humble suite of all the women of that citie) to deliver him to their censure, who mortally hating him for having made a lawe of *Polygamie*, after many tortures, forste him to throwe himselfe from a high *Pyramis*, which was built over *Tiridates* tombe, and so to end his fallse-harted life, which had planted no strong thought in him, but that he could be unkinde.

But *Plangus* well perceiving that *Artaxia* staied onely for 8 the appointed day, that the faire *Eronas* bodie, (consumed to ashes) should make a notorious testimonie, how deepely her brothers death was engraven in her brest, he assembled good numbers of friendes, whõ his vertue (though a stranger) had tied unto him, by force to give her libertie. Contrariwise, *Artaxia*, to whom Anger gave more courage then her sexe did feare, used her regall authoritie (the most she could) to suppresse that sedition, and have her will: which (she thought) is the most princely thing that may be. But *Plangus*, who indeede (as all men witnes) is one of the best captains (both for policie and valour) that are trained in the schoole of *Mars*, in a conflict overthrew *Artaxias* power, though of far greater number: and there toke prisoner a base sonne of her brothers, whom she deerly affected, & then sent her word that he should run the same race of fortune (whatsoever it was) that *Erona* did: & happy was that threatning for her; for els *Artaxia* had hastened the day of her death, in respecte of those tumults.

But now (some principal noble-mẽ of that countrie inter- 9 posing thẽselves) it was agreed, that all persons els fullie pardoned, and all prisoners (except *Erona*) delivered, she should be put into the hands of a principall nobleman, who had a castle of great strength, upon oath, that if by the day two yeare frõ *Tiridates* death, *Pyrocles* and *Musidorus* did not in person combat, & overcome two knights, whõ she appointed to maintain her quarrell against *Erona* and them, of having by treason destroyed her brother, that thẽ *Erona* should be that same day burned to ashes: but if they came, and had the victorie, she should be delivered; but upon no occasion, neither freed, nor executed, till that day. And hereto of both sides, all toke solemne oath, and so the peace was concluded; they of *Plangus* partie forcing him to agree, though he himselfe the sooner condiscended, knowing the courtesie of those two excellent Princes, not to refuse so noble a quarrell, and their power such, as two more (like the other two) were not able to resist. But *Artaxia* was more, and upon better ground, pleased with this action; for she had even newly received newes frõ *Plexirtus*, that upon the sea he had caused them both to perish, and therefore she held her selfe sure of the match.

10   But poore *Plangus* knew not so much, and therefore seeing his partie (as most times it falles out in like case) hungry of conditions of peace, accepted them; & then obteined leave of the Lord, that indifferently kept her, to visite *Erona*, whom he founde full of desperate sorowe, not suffering, neither his un-woorthinesse, nor his wronges, nor his death (which is the naturall conclusion of all worldly acts) either to cover with forgetfulnes, or diminish with consideration, the affection she had borne him: but even glorying in affliction, and shunning all comforte, she seemed to have no delight, but in making her selfe the picture of miserie. So that when *Plangus* came to her, she fell in deadlie traunces, as if in him she had seene the death of *Antiphilus*, because he had not succoured him: and yet (her vertue striving) she did at one time acknowledge her selfe bound, and professe her selfe injured; in steede of allowing the conclusion they had made, or writing to the Princes (as he wisht her to doo) craving nothing but some speedie death to followe, her (in spite of just hate) beloved *Antiphilus*.

11   So that *Plangus* having nothing but a ravisht kisse from her hande at their parting, went away towarde *Greece*, whether-ward he understoode the Princes were embarked. But by the

way it was his fortune to intercept letters, written by *Artaxia* to *Plexirtus*: wherein she signified her accepting him to her husband, whom she had ever favoured, so much the rather, as he had perfourmed the conditions of her mariage, in bringing to their deserved end, her greatest enemies: withall, thanking the sea, in such tearmes, as he might well perceive, it was by some treason wrought in *Plexirtus* shippe. Whereupon (to make more diligent search) he tooke shippe himselfe, and came into *Laconia*, enquiring, and by his enquirie finding, that such a shippe was indeede with fight, and fire, perished, none (almost) escaping. But for *Pyrocles* and *Musidorus*, it was assuredly determined that they were cast away: for the name of such Princes (especially in *Greece*) would quickly els have bene a large witnesse to the contrarie. Full of griefe with that, for the losse of such, who left the world poor of perfection: but more sorie for *Eronas* sake, who now by them could not be relieved. A new advertisement from *Armenia* overtooke him, which multiplied the force of his anguish. It was a message from the Nobleman who had *Erona* in ward, giving him to understäd, that since his departure, *Artaxia* (using the benefite of time) had besieged him in his castell, demaunding present delivery of her, whom yet for his faith given, he would not, before the day appointed, if possibly he could resist, which he foresaw, lög he should not do for want of victuall, which he had not so wisely provided, because he trusted upon the generall oth taken for two yeares space: & therfore willed him to make hast to his succour, & come with no small forces; for all they that were of his side in *Armenia*, were consumed, & *Artaxia* had encreased her might by mariage of *Plexirtus*, who now crowned King there, stickt not to glory in the murder of *Pyrocles* and *Musidorus*, as having just cause thereto, in respect of the deaths of his sister *Andromana*, her sonne his nephew, and his own daughter *Zelmane*, all whose losse he unjustly charged them withal, & now openly stickt not to cöfesse, what a revenge his wit had brought forth. *Plangus* much astonished herewith, bethought himselfe what to doo. For to returne to *Armenia* was vaine, since his friends there were utterly overthrowne. Thē thought he of going to his father; but he had already (even since the death of his stepmother, & brother) attempted the recovering his favour, &

337

all in vaine. For they, that had before joined with *Andromana* to do him the wrong, thought now no life for thē if he returned, & therfore kept him stil (with new forged suspicions) odious to his father. So that *Plangus* reserving that for a worke of longer time, then the saving of *Erona* could beare, determined to go to the mighty and good King *Euarchus*: who lately having (to his eternall fame) fully, not onely conquered his enimies, but established good government in their countries, he hoped he might have present succour of him, both for the justnes of the cause, & revenge of his childrens death, by so hainous a treason murthered. Therefore with diligence he went to him; & by the way (passing through my country) it was my hap to find him, the most overthrowne mā with griefe, that ever I hope to see againe. For stil it seemed he had *Erona* at a stake before his eies; such an apprehension he had taken of her daunger; which in despite of all the comfort I could give him, he poured out in such lamentations, that I was moved not to let him passe, till he had made full declaration, which by peeces my daughters & I have delivered unto you. Fayne he would have had succour of my selfe, but the course of my life being otherwise bent, I onely accompanied him with some that might safely guide him to the great *Euarchus*: for my parte having had some of his speeches so feelingly in my memory, that at an idle time (as I tolde you) I set them downe Dialogue-wise, in such manner as you have seene. And thus, excellent Ladie, I have obeyed you in this storie; wherein if it well please you to consider, what is the straunge power of Love, and what is due to his authoritie, you shall exercise therein the true noblenesse of your judgement, and doo the more right to the unfortunate Historian. *Zelmane* (sighing for *Eronaes* sake, yet inwardly comforted in that she assured her selfe, *Euarchus* would not spare to take in hande the just delivering of her, joyned with the just revenge of his childrens losse) having now what she desired of *Basilius*, to avoide his further discourses of affection, encouraged the shepheards to begin, whom she saw all ready for them.

The second Eclogues.

THe rude tumulte of the *Enispians* gave occasion to the
honest shepheards to beginne their pastorals this day
with a daûce, which they called the skirmish betwixt *Reason*
and *Passion*. For seven shepheards (which were named the
Reasonable shepheards) joined thẽselves; foure of them making
a square, and the other two going a litle wide of either side,
like winges for the maine battell; and the seventh man formost, like the forlorne hope to begin the skirmish. In like
order came out the seven appassionated shepheards; all keeping
the pase of their foote by their voice, and sundry consorted
instrumẽts they held in their armes. And first, the formost of
Reasonable side began to sing.

R.   *Thou Rebell vile, come, to thy master yelde.*
 And the other that met with him answered.
P.   *No, Tyrant, no: mine, mine shall be the fielde.*
Reason. *Can* Reason *then a Tyraunt counted be?*
Passion. *If* Reason *will, that* Passions *be not free.*
R.   *But* Reason *will, that* Reason *governe most.*
P.   *And* Passion *will, that* Passion *rule the rost.*
R.   *Your will is will; but* Reason *reason is.*
P.   *Will hath his will, when* Reasons *will doth misse.*
R.   *Whom* Passion *leades unto his death is bent.*
P.   *And let him die, so that he die content.*
R.   *By nature you to* Reason *faith have sworne.*
P.   *Not so, but fellowlike together borne.*
R.   *Who* Passion *doth ensue, lives in annoy.*
P.   *Who* Passion *doth forsake, lives void of joy.*
R.   *Passion is blinde, and treades an unknowne trace.*
P.   *Reason hath eyes to see his owne ill case.*
 Then as they approched neerer, the two of *Reasons* sides, as
if they shot at the other, thus sange.
R.   *Dare* Passions *then abide in* Reasons *light?*
P.   *And is not* Reason *dimde with* Passions *might?*
R.   *O foolish thing, which glory doth destroye.*
P.   *O glorious title of a foolish toye.*
R.   *Weakenes you are, dare you with our strength fight?*
P.   *Because our weaknes weakeneth all your might.*

R.   *O sacred* Reason, *helpe our vertuous toiles.*
P.   *O* Passion, *passe on feeble* Reasons *spoiles.*
R.   *We with ourselves abide a daily strife.*
P.   *We gladly use the sweetnes of our life.*
R.   *But yet our strife sure peace in end doth breede.*
P.   *We now have peace, your peace we doo not neede.*

Then did the two square battailes meete, & in steed of
fighting embrace one another, singing thus.

R.   *We are too strong: but* Reason *seekes no blood.*
P.   *Who be too weake, do feigne they ·be too good.*
R.   *Though we cannot orecome, our cause is just.*
P.   *Let us orecome, and let us be unjust.*
R.   *Yet* Passion, *yeeld at length to* Reasons *stroke.*
P.   *What shall we winne by taking* Reasons *yoke?*
R.   *The joyes you have shall be made permanent.*
P.   *But so we shall with griefe learne to repent.*
R.   *Repent indeed, but that shall be your blisse.*
P.   *How know we that, since present joyes we misse?*
R.   *You know it not: of* Reason *therefore know it.*
P.   *No* Reason *yet had ever skill to show it.*
R. P.   *Then let us both to heavenly rules give place,*
          Which Passions *skill, and* Reason *do deface.*

THen embraced they one another, and came to the King,
who framed his praises of thẽ according to *Zelmanes*
liking; whose unrestrained parts, the minde & eie, had their
free course to the delicate *Philoclea*, whose looke was not short
in well requiting it, although she knew it was a hatefull sight
to her jealous mother. But *Dicus* (that had in this time taken
a great liking of *Dorus* for the good partes he found above his
age in him) had a delight to taste the fruites of his wit, though
in a subject which he him selfe most of all other despised: and
so entred to speach with him in the manner of this following
Eclogue.

Dicus.   Dorus.

Dicus.   DOrus, *tell me, where is thy wonted motion*
          To make these woods resounde thy lamentation?
Thy sainte is dead, or dead is thy devotion.

For who doth holde his love in estimation,
To witnes, that he thinkes his thoughts delicious,
Thinks to make ech thing badge of his sweet passion.

  But what doth make thee Dicus *so suspicious*   Dorus.
Of my due faith, which needs must be immutable?
Who others vertue doubt, themselves are vicious.
  Not so; although my mettall were most mutable,
Her beames have wrought therin most faire impression:
To such a force some chaunge were nothing sutable.

  The harte well set doth never shunne confession: Dicus.
If noble be thy bandes, make them notorious:
Silence doth seeme the maske of base oppression.
  Who glories in his love, doth make Love glorious:
But who doth feare, or bideth muet wilfully,
Showes, guilty harte doth deeme his state opprobrious.
  Thou then, that framste both words & voice most skilfully,
Yeeld to our eares a sweet and sound relation,
If Love tooke thee by force, or caught thee guilefully.

  If Sunnie beames shame heav'nly habitation;   Dorus.
If three-leav'd grasse seeme to the sheepe unsavorie,
Then base and sower is Loves most high vocation.
  Or if sheepes cries can helpe the Sunnes owne braverie,
Then may I hope, my pipe may have abilitie,
To helpe her praise, who decks me in her slaverie.
  No, no: no wordes ennoble selfe-nobilitie.
As for your doubts; her voice was it deceaved me,
Her eye the force beyond all possibilitie.

  Thy words well voic'd, well gra'ste had almost heaved me   Dicus.
Quite from my selfe to love Loves contemplation;
Till of these thoughts thy sodaine ende bereaved me.
  Goe on therefore, and tell us, by what fashion
In thy owne proofe he gets so straunge possession,
And how possest he strengthens his invasion?

  Sight is his roote, in thought is his progression,   Dorus.
His childhood woonder, prenticeship attention,
His youth delight, his age the soules oppression:

Doubte is his sleepe, he waketh in invention;
Fancie his foode, his clothing is of carefulnes;
Beautie his boote, his play lovers dissention:
  His eyes are curious search, but vailde with warefulnesse:
His wings desire oft clipt with desperation:
Largesse his hands could never skill of sparefulnesse.
  But how he doth by might, or by persuasion
To conquere, and his conquest how to ratifie,
Experience doubts, and schooles holde disputation.

Dicus. *But so thy sheepe may thy good wishes satisfie*
With large encrease, and wooll of fine perfection,
So she thy love, her eyes thy eyes may gratifie,
  As thou wilt give our soules a deare refection,
By telling how she was, how now she framed is
To helpe, or hurt in thee her owne infection.

Dorus. *Blest be the name, wherewith my mistres named is:*
Whose wounds are salves, whose yokes please more then pleasure doth:
Her staines are beames; vertue the fault she blamed is.
  The hart, eye, eare here onely find his treasure doth:
All numbring artes her endlesse graces number not:
Time, place, life, wit scarcely her rare gifts measure doth.
  Is she in rage? so is the Sunne in sommer hot,
Yet harvest brings. Doth she alas absent herselfe?
The Sunne is hid; his kindly shadows cumber not.
  But when to give some grace she doth content herselfe,
O then it shines; then are the heav'ns distributed,
And Venus seemes, to make up her, she spent herselfe.
  Thus then (I say) my mischiefes have contributed
A greater good by her divine reflection;
My harmes to me, my blisse to her attributed,
  Thus she is framde: her eyes are my direction;
Her love my life; her anger my destruction.
Lastly what so she is, that's my protection.

Dicus. *Thy safetie sure is wrapped in destruction:*
For that construction thine owne wordes do beare.
A man to feare a womans moodie eye,
Makes Reason lie a slave to servile Sense.
A weake defence where weakenesse is thy force:
So is remorse in follie dearely bought.

If I had thought to heare blasphemous wordes,   Dorus.
My brest to swords, my soule to hell have solde
I rather would, then thus mine eares defile
With words so vile, which viler breath doth breed.
O heards take heed; for I a woolfe have found;
Who hunting round the strongest for to kill,
His breast doth fill with earth of others joyes,
And loden so puls downe, puld downe destroyes.
O sheepheards boyes, eschue these tongues of venome,
Which do envenome both the soule and senses.
Our best defenses are to flie these adders.
O tongues like ladders made to clime dishonour,
Who judge that honour, which hath scope to slander.

Dorus you wander farre in great reproches;   Dicus.
So love encroches on your charmed reason,
But it is season for to end our singing.
Such anger bringing: as for me, my fancie
  In sicke-mans frenzie rather takes compassion,
Then rage for rage: rather my wish I send to thee,
Thou soone may have some helpe, or change of passion.
  She oft her lookes, the starres her favour bend to thee:
Fortune store, Nature health, Love grant perswasion.
  A quiet mind none but thy selfe can lend to thee,   ,,
Thus I commend to thee all our former love,

Well do I prove, errour lies oft in zeale,   ,, Dorus.
Yet it is seale, though errour, of true hart.   ,,
Nought could impart such heates to friendly mind.
But for to find thy words did her disgrace,
Whose onely face the little heaven is,
  Which who doth misse his eyes are but delusions,
Barr'd from their chiefest object of delightfulnesse,
Throwne on this earth the Chaos of confusions.
  As for thy wish to my enraged spitefulnesse,
The lovely blowne with rare reward, my prayer is   *
Thou mayest love her that I may see thy sightfulnesse.
  The quiet mind (whereof my selfe empairer is,
As thou doest thinke) should most of all disquiet me
Without her love, then any mind who fairer is.
  Her onely cure from surfet-woes can diet me:

343

She holdes the ballance of my contentation:
Her cleared eyes, nought els, in stormes can quiet me.
  Nay rather then my ease discontentation
Should breed to her, let me for aye dejeĉted be
From any joy, which might her griefe occasion.
  With so sweete plagues my happie harmes infeĉted be:
Paine willes me die, yet will of death I mortifie:
For though life irkes, in life my loves proteĉted be.
  Thus for ech change my changelesse hart I fortifie.

W Hen they had ended to the good pleasing of the assistants,
especially of *Zelmane,* who never forgat to give due
cŏmēdations to her friend *Dorus,* the more to advance him in
his pursute (although therein he had brought his matters to a
more wished conclusion then yet she knew of) out starte a
jolly yonker, his name was *Nico,* whose tongue had borne a
very itching silence all this while.   And having spied one *Pas,*
a mate of his, as mad as himselfe (both indeed lads to clime any
tree in the world) he bestowed this maner of salutation upon
him, and was with like reverence requited.

Nico.   Dorus.

Nico.   A Nd are you there old Pas? in troth I ever thought,
           Among us all we should find out some thing of nought.

Pas.   And I am here the same, so mote I thrive and thee,
Despairde in all this flocke to find a knave, but thee.

Nico.   Ah now I see, why thou art in thy selfe so blind:
Thy gray-hood hides the thing, that thou despairst to find.

Pas.   My gray-hood is mine owne, all be it be but gray,
Not like the scrippe thou stol'ste, while Dorcas sleeping lay.

Nico.   Mine was the scrippe: but thou, that seeming raid with love,
Didst snatch from Cosmas hand her greeny wroughtē glove.

Pas.   Ah foole; so Courtiers do. But who did lively skippe,
When for a treene-dish stolne, thy father did thee whippe?

Nico.   In deed the witch thy dam her crouch from shoulder spred,
For pilfring Lalus lambe, with crouch to blesse thy head.

My *voice the lambe did winne*, Menalcas *was our judge:* Pas.
Of *singing match was made, whence he with shame did trudge.*

Couldst thou make Lalus *flie? so nightingales avoide*, Nico.
When with the kawing crowes their musicke is annoide.

Nay like to nightingales the other birds give eare: Pas.
My pipe and song made him both pipe and song forsweare.

I thinke it well: such voice would make one musicke hate: Nico.
But if I had bene there, th'adst met another mate.

Another sure as is a gander from a goose: Pas.
But still when thou dost sing, me thinkes a colt is loose.

Well aimed by my hat: for as thou sangst last day; Nico.
The neighbours all did crie, alas what asse doth bray?

But here is Dicus *old; let him then speake the woord,* Pas.
To whether with best cause the Nymphes faire flowers affoord.

Content: but I will lay a wager hereunto, Nico.
That profit may ensue to him that best can do.
I have (and long shall have) a white great nimble cat,
A king upon a mouse, a strong foe to the rat,
Fine eares, long taile he hath, with Lions curbed clawe,
Which oft he lifteth up, and stayes his lifted pawe,
Deepe musing to himselfe, which after-mewing showes,
Till with lickt beard, his eye of fire espie his foes.
If thou (alas poore if) do winne, then winne thou this,
And if I better sing, let me thy Cosma *kisse.*

Kisse her? now mayst thou kisse. I have a better match; Pas.
A prettie curre it is; his name iwis is Catch,
No eare nor taile he hath, least they should him disgrace,
A ruddie haire his cote, with fine long speckled face:
He never musing standes, but with himselfe will play
Leaping at every flie, and angrie with a flea:
He eft would kill a mouse, but he disdaines to fight,
And makes our home good sport with dauncing bolt upright.
This is my pawne; the price let Dicus *judgement show:*
Such oddes I willing lay; for him and you I know.

Sing then my lads, but sing with better vaine then yet, Dicus.
Or else who singeth worst, my skill will hardly hit.

THE COUNTESSE OF PEMBROKES

Nico.
> *Who doubts but* Pas *fine pipe againe will bring*
> *The aunciant prayse to* Arcad *shepheards skill?*
> Pan *is not dead, since* Pas *beginnes to sing.*

Pas.
> *Who evermore will love* Apollos *quill,*
> *Since* Nico *doth to sing so widely gape?*
> Nico *his place farre better furnish will.*

Nico.
> *Was not this he, who did for* Syrinx *scape*
> *Raging in woes teach pastors first to plaine?*
> *Do you not heare his voice, and see his shape?*

Pas.
> *This is not he that failed her to gaine,*
> *Which made a Bay, made Bay a holy tree:*
> *But this is one that doth his musicke staine.*

Nico.
> *O Faunes, O Fairies all, and do you see,*
> *And suffer such a wrong? a wrong I trowe,*
> *That* Nico *must with* Pas *compared be?*

Pas.
> *O Nymphes, I tell you newes, for* Pas *you knowe:*
> *While I was warbling out your woonted praise,*
> Nico *would needes with* Pas *his bagpipe blowe.*

Nico.
> *If never I did faile your holy-dayes,*
> *With daunces, carols, or with barlybreake:*
> *Let* Pas *now know, how* Nico *makes the layes.*

Pas.
> *If each day hath bene holy for your sake,*
> *Unto my pipe, O Nimphes, helpe now my pipe,*
> *For* Pas *well knowes what layes can* Nico *make.*

Nico.
> *Alas how oft I looke on cherries ripe,*
> *Me thinkes I see the lippes my* Leuca *hath,*
> *And wanting her, my weeping eyes I wipe.*

Pas.
> *Alas, when I in spring meete roses rathe,*
> *And thinke from* Cosmas *sweet red lips I live,*
> *I leave mine eyes unwipte my cheekes to bathe.*

Nico.
> *As I of late, neer bushes usde my sive,*
> *I spied a thrush where she did make her nest,*
> *That will I take, and to my* Leuca *give.*

Pas.
> *But long have I a sparrow gailie drest,*
> *As white as milke, and comming to the call,*
> *To put it with my hand in* Cosmas *brest.*

346

I oft doo sue, and Leuca *saith, I shall,*   Nico.
But when I did come neere with heate and hope,
She ranne away, and threw at me a ball.

Cosma *once said, she left the wicket ope,*   Pas.
For me to come, and so she did: I came,
But in the place found nothing but a rope.

When Leuca *dooth appeare, the Sunne for shame*   Nico.
Dooth hide himselfe: for to himselfe he sayes,
If Leuca *live, she darken will my fame.*

When Cosma *doth come forth, the Sun displaies*   Pas.
His utmost light: for well his witte doth know,
Cosmas *faire beames emblemish much his raies.*

Leuca *to me did yester-morning showe*   Nico.
In perfect light, which could not me deceave,
Her naked legge, more white then whitest snowe.

But yesternight by light I did receave   Pas.
From Cosmas *eyes, which full in darkenes shine,*
I sawe her arme, where purest Lillies cleave.

She once starke nak'd did bathe a little tine;   Nico.
But still (me thought) with beauties from her fell,
She did the waters wash, and make more fine.

She once, to coole her selfe, stood in a well,   Pas.
But ever since that well is well besought,
And for Rose-water sould of rarest smell.

To rivers banke, being on walking brought,   Nico.
She bad me spie her babie in the brooke,
Alas (said I) this babe dooth nurce my thought.

As in a glasse I held she once did looke,   Pas.
I said, my hands well paide her for mine eyes,
Since in my hands selfe goodly sight she tooke.

O if I had a ladder for the skies,   Nico.
I would climbe up, and bring a prettie starre,
To weare upon her neck, that open lies.

O if I had Apollos *golden carre,*   Pas.
I would come downe, and yeeld to her my place,
That (shining now) she then might shine more farre.

347

Nico.
> *Nothing (O Leuca) shall thy fame deface,*
> *While shepheards tunes be heard, or rimes be read,*
> *Or while that shepheards love a lovely face.*

Pas.
> *Thy name (O Cosma) shall with praise be spread,*
> *As farre as any shepheards piping be:*
> *As farre as Love possesseth any head.*

Nico.
> *Thy monument is layd in many a tree,*
> *With name engrav'd: so though thy bodie die,*
> *The after-folkes shall wonder still at thee.*

Pas.
> *So oft these woods have heard me Cosma crie,*
> *That after death, to heav'n in woods resound,*
> *With Echoes help, shall Cosma, Cosma flie.*

Nico.
> *Peace, peace good Pas, thou weeriest even the ground*
> *With sluttish song: I pray thee learne to blea,*
> *For good thou mayst yet proove in sheepish sound.*

Pas.
> *My father hath at home a prettie Jay,*
> *Goe winne of him (for chattering) praise or shame:*
> *For so yet of a conquest speake thou may.*

Nico.
> *Tell me (and be my Pan) the monsters name,*
> *That hath foure legs, and with two onely goes,*
> *That hath foure eyes, and onely two can frame.*

Pas.
> *Tell me (and Phœbus be) what monster growes*
> *With so strong lives, that bodie cannot rest*
> *In ease, untill that bodie life forgoes.*

Dicus.
> *Enough, enough: so ill hath done the best,*
> *That since the having them to neither's due,*
> *Let cat and dog fight which shall have both you.*

SOme speech there streight grew among the hearers, what they should meane by the riddles of the two monsters. But *Zelmane*, whose harte better delighted in wailefull ditties, as more according to her fortune, she desired *Lamon*, he would againe repeate some other lamentation of the still-absent *Strephon* and *Klaius*. *Basilius* (as soone as he understood *Zelmanes* pleasure) commaunded *Lamon* upon paine of his life (as though every thing were a matter of life and death, that pertained to his mistresse service) immediately to sing it: who with great cunning, varying his voice according to the diversitie of the persons, began this Dizaine, answered in that kinde of verse, which is called the Crowne.

Strephon.   Klaius.

I Joye in griefe, and doo detest all joyes: Strephon.
   Despise delight, and tyrde with thought of ease
I turne my minde to all formes of annoyes,
And with the chaunge of them my fancie please.
I studie that which may me most displease,
And in despite of that displeasures might,
Embrace that most, that most my soule destroyes.
Blinded with beames, fell darkenes is my sight:
Dole on my ruine feedes, with sucking smarte,
I thinke from me, not from my woes to parte.

I thinke from me, not from my woes to parte, Klaius.
   And loth this time, calld life, nay thinke, that life
Nature to me for torment did emparte;
Thinke, my harde haps have blunted deaths sharpe knife,
Not sparing me, in whom his workes be rife:
And thinking this, thinke Nature, Life, and Death
Place Sorrowes triumph on my conquered brest:
Whereto I yeeld, and seeke none other breath,
But from the sent of some infectious grave:
Nor of my fortune ought, but mischieve crave.

Nor of my fortune ought but mischiefe crave, Strephon.
   And seeke to nourish that, which now contaynes
All what I am: if I my selfe will save,
Then must I save, what in me chiefly raignes,
Which is the hatefull web of Sorowes paines.
Sorow then cherish me, for I am sorowe:
No being now, but sorowe I can have:
Then decke me as thine owne; thy helpe I borowe,
Since thou my riches arte, and that thou haste
Enough to make a fertill minde lie waste.

Enough to make a fertill minde lie waste Klaius.
   Is that huge storme, which powres it selfe on me:
Hailestones of teares, of sighes a monstrous blast,

349

Thunders of cries; lightnings my wilde lookes be,
The darkened heav'n my soule which nought can see;
The flying sprites which trees by rootes up teare
Be those despaires, which have my hopes quite wast.
The diffrence is; all folkes those stormes forbeare:
But I cannot; who then my selfe should flie
So close unto my selfe my wrackes doo lie.

Strephon.

So close unto my selfe my wrackes doo lie;
Both cause, effect, beginning, and the ende
Are all in me: what helpe then can I trie?
My ship, my selfe; whose course to love doth bende,
Sore beaten doth her mast of Comforte spende:
Her cable, Reason, *breakes from anchor,* Hope:
Fancie, her tackling, torne away doth flie:
Ruine, the winde, hath blowne her from her scope:
Brused with waves of Cares, *but broken is*
On rocke, Despaire, *the buriall of my blisse.*

Klaius.

On rocke, Despaire, *the buriall of my blisse*
I long doo plowe with plough of deepe Desire:
The seed Fast-meaning *is, no truth to misse:*
I harowe it with Thoughts, *which all conspire*
Favour to make my chiefe and onely hire.
But, woe is me, the yeare is gone about,
And now I faine would reape, I reape but this,
Hate fully growne, Absence *new sprongen out.*
So that I see, although my sight empaire,
Vaine is their paine, who labour in Despaire.

Strephon.

Vaine is their paine, who labour in Despaire.
For so did I, when with my angle, Will,
I sought to catch the fish Torpedo *faire.*
Ev'n then Despaire *did* Hope *already kill:*
Yet Fancie *would perforce employ his skill,*
And this hath got; the catcher now is caught,
Lamde with the angle, which it selfe did beare,
And unto death, quite drownde in Dolours, *brought*
To death, as then disguisde in her faire face.
Thus, thus I had, alas, my losse in chase.

350

Thus, thus I had, alas, my losse in chase, Klaius
  When first that crowned Basiliske *I knewe,*
  Whose footesteps I with kisses oft did trace,
  Till by such hap, as I must ever rewe,
  Mine eyes did light upon her shining hewe,
  And hers on me, astonisht with that sight.
  Since then my harte did loose his wonted place,
  Infected so with her sweet poysons might,
  That, leaving me for dead, to her it went:
  But ah her flight hath my dead reliques spent.

But ah her flight hath my dead reliques spent, Strephon.
  Her flight from me, from me, though dead to me,
  Yet living still in her, while her beames lent
  Such vitall sparke, that her mine eyes might see.
  But now those living lights absented be,
  Full dead before, I now to dust should fall,
  But that eternall paines my soule should hent,
  And keepe it still within this body thrall:
  That thus I must, while in this death I dwell,
  In earthly fetters feele a lasting hell.

In earthly fetters feele a lasting hell Klaius.
  Alas I doo; from which to finde release,
  I would the earth, I would the heavens fell.
  But vaine it is to thinke these paines should cease,
  Where life is death, and death cannot breed peace.
  O faire, ô onely faire, from thee, alas,
  These foule, most foule, distresses to me fell;
  Since thou from me (ô me) ô Sunne didst passe.
  Therefore esteeming all good blessings toyes
  I joy in griefe, and doo detest all joyes.

I joye in griefe, and doo detest all joyes. Strephon
  And now an ende, (ô Claius) *now an ende*
  For even the hearbes our mournefull musique stroyes,
  And from our burning breath the trees doo bende.

SO wel did *Lamons* voice expresse the passiõs of those
  shepheards, that all the Princely beholders were striken
in a silent cõsideration of them; indeed every one making, that

he heard of another the balãce of his own troubles. And *Basilius* perceiving such melancholique musique best consorted to the humor of his mistresse, entreated againe the young melancholy shepheard, that he would emparte some part of the sorow his coũtenaunce so well witnessed unto them. Which he in parte to satisfie, began an Eclogue betwixt himself and the *Echo*: framing his voice in those deserte places, as what words he would have the *Echo* replie, unto those he would singe higher then the rest, and so kindly framed a disputation betwixt himselfe and it. Which with these *Hexameters* in the following order he uttered.

Echo.

FAire rocks, goodly rivers, sweet woods, when shall I see peace? *Peace.*
   Peace? who debars me my tongue? who is it that comes me so
   nie? *I.*
O I doo know what guest I doo meete: it is Echo. *T'is* Echo.
Well mett Echo; *aproch, and tell me thy will too.* *I will too.*
Echo, *what doo I get yeelding my sprite to my grieves?* *Grieves.*
What medicine may I finde for a paine that drawes me to death? *Death.*
O pois'nous medicine: what worse to me can be then it? *It.*
In what state was I then, when I tooke this deadly disease? *Ease.*
And what maner a minde, which had to that humor a vaine? *Vaine.*
Hath not reason enough vehemence the desire to reprove? *Prove.*
Oft prove I: but what salve, when Reason seeks to be gone? *One.*
O what is it? what is it, that may be a salve to my love? *Love.*
What doo lovers seeke for, long seeking for t' enjoye? *Joye.*
What be the joyes, for which t'enjoye they went to the paines? *Paines.*
Then to an earnest love what doth best victorie lende? *Ende.*
Ende? but I can never ende: Love will not give me the leave. *Leave.*
How be the mindes disposde, that cannot taste the Physicke? *Sicke.*
Yet say againe th'advice for th'ils that I tolde thee. *I told thee.*
Doth th'infected wretch of his ill th'extremitie know? *No.*
But if he know not his harmes, what guids hath he whilst he be
   blind? *Blinde.*
What blinde guides can he have that leades to a fancie? *A fancie.*
Can fancies wante eyes? or he fall that steppeth aloft? *Oft.*
What causes first made these torments on me to light? *Light.*
Can then a cause be so light, that forceth a man to goe die? *I.*
Yet tell, what light thing I had in me to drawe me to die? *Eye.*
Eie-sight made me to yeeld: but what first pearst to my eyes? *Eyes.*

Eyes hurters ? eyes hurte ? but what from them to me falls ?   Falls.
But when I first did fall, what brought most fall to my harte ?   Arte.
Arte ? what can be that arte, which thou doost meane by thy speach?   Speach.
What be the fruites of speaking arte, what growes by the wordes ?   Wordes.
O much more then wordes : those wordes serv'd more me to blesse.   Lesse.
O when shall I be knowne, where most to be known I doo long ?   Longe.
Long be thy woes for such bad newes : how recks she my thoughts ?   Oughts.
Then, then what doo I gayne, since unt' her will I doo winde ?   Winde.
Winde, tempests, and stormes : yet in ende what gives she desire ?   Ire.
Silly rewarde : yet above women hath she a title.   A tittle.
What great name may I give to so heav'nly a woman ?   A wo-man.
Woe, but seems to me joye, that agrees to my thought so.   I thought so.
Thinke so : for of my desired blisse it is onely the course.   Course.
Curst be thy selfe for cursing that, which leades me to joyes.   Toyes.
What be the sweete creatures where lowly demaundes be not harde?   Harde.
Harde to be gott, but got constant, to be helde very steeles.   Eeles.
How be they helde unkinde ? speake, for th' hast narrowly pry'de.   Pride.
How can pride come there since springs of beautie be thence ?   Thence.
Horrible is this blasphemie unto the most holie.   O lye.
Thou li'st, false Echo; *their mindes, as vertue, be juste.*   Juste.
Mockst thou those Diamonds, which onely be matcht by the Godds ?   Odds.
Odds ? what an odds is there, since them to the heav'ns I preferre ?   Erre.
Tell yet againe, how name ye the goodly made evill ?   A devill.
Devill ? in hell where such Devill is, to that hell I doo goe.   Goe.

AFter this well placed *Echo,* the other shepheards were offring themselves to have continued the sports: But the night had so quietly spent most part of her selfe, that the King for that time licensed them : & so bringing *Zelmane* to her lodging, who would much rather have done the same for *Philoclea,* of all sides they went to counterfait a sleep in their beds, for a true one their agonies could not afoord them. Yet there lay they (for so might they be most solitarie) for the foode of their thoughts, till it was neere noone the next day. After which *Basilius* was to continue his *Apollo* devotions, and the other to meditate upon their private desires.

The end of the second Booke.

THE THIRDE BOOKE

OF THE COUNTESSE OF
PEMBROKES ARCADIA.

CHAP. I.

Dorus-*his* [1] *faire and* [2] *foule weather in his love.* [3] *His forlorne agonies.* [4] *His doubts to write,* [5] *and* Pamelaes *to reade,* [6] *his elegie.*

1 THis last dayes daunger, having made *Pamelaes* love discerne, what a losse it should have suffered, if *Dorus* had bene destroyed, bredde such tendernesse of kindnes in her toward him: that she coulde no longer keepe Love from looking through her eyes, and going forth in her words; whom before as a close prisoner she had to her hart onely committed; so as finding not only by his speeches & letters, but by the pitifull oratiō of a languishing behavior, & the easily discyphered character of a sorowful face, that Despair began nowe to threaten him destruction, she grewe content both to pitie him, and let him see she pityed him: as well by making her owne beautifull beames thawe away the former icinesse of her behaviour, as by entertaining his discourses (whensoever he did use them) in the third person of *Musidorus*; to so farre a degree, that in the ende she said, that if she had bene the Princesse, whom that disguised Prince had vertuously loved, she would have requited his faith with faithfull affection: „finding in her hart, that nothing could so hartily love as vertue: with many mo words to the same sense of noble favour, & chast plainnesse. Which when at the first it made that expected blisse shine upon *Dorus*; he was like one frozen with extremitie of colde, over-hastily brought to a great fire, rather oppressed, then relieved with such a lightning of felicitie. But after the strength of nature had made him able to feel the sweetnesse of joyfulnes, that again being a child of Passion, & never acquainted with mediocrity, could not set boūds upon his happines, nor be cōtent to give Desire a kingdome, but that

354

it must be an unlimited Monarchy. So that the ground he stood upon being over-high in happines, & slipperie through affection, he could not hold himselfe frō falling into such an error, which with sighs blew all cōfort out of his brest, & washt away all cheerfulnes of his cheere, with teares. For this favour filling him with hope, Hope encouraging his desire, & Desire considering nothing, but oportunitie: one time (*Mopsa* being called away by her mother, & he left alone with *Pamela*) the sudden occasion called Love, & that never staid to aske Reasons leave; but made the too-much loving *Dorus* take her in his armes, offering to kisse her, and, as it were, to establish a trophee of his victorie.

But she, as if she had bin ready to drinke a wine of excellent **2** tast & colour, which suddenly she perceived had poison in it, so did she put him away frō her: loking first unto heaven, as amazed to find herselfe so beguiled in him; then laying the cruel punishment upon him of angry Love, and lowring beautie, shewing disdain, & a despising disdain, Away (said she) unworthy man to love, or to be loved. Assure thy selfe, I hate my selfe for being so deceived; judge then what I doo thee, for deceiving me. Let me see thee no more, the only fall of my judgement, and staine of my conscience. With that she called *Mopsa*, not staying for any answer (which was no other, but a flood of tears, which she semed not to mark (much lesse to pity) & chid her for having so left her alone.

It was not an amazement, it was not a sorrow, but it was **3** even a death, which then laid hold of *Dorus*: which certainly at that instant would have killed him, but that the feare to tary longer in her presence (contrary to her cōmandement) gave him life to cary himselfe away frō her sight, and to run into the woods, where, throwing himselfe downe at the foot of a tree, he did not fall to lamentation (for that proceeded of pitying) or grieving for himselfe (which he did no way) but to curses of his life, as one that detested himselfe. For finding himselfe not onely unhappy, but unhappie after being falne from all happinesse: and to be falne from all happines, not by any misconceiving, but by his own fault, and his fault to be done to no other but to *Pamela*: he did not tender his owne estate, but despised it; greedily drawing into his minde, all conceipts which might more and more torment him. And so remained he two dayes in the woods, disdaining to give his bodie food, or his mind comfort, loving in himselfe nothing, but the lcve of her. And indeed that love onely strave with the fury of his anguish, telling it, that if it destroyed *Dorus*, it should also destroy the image of her that lived in *Dorus*: and when the thought of that was crept in unto him, it begã to win of him some cõpassion to the shrine of the image, & to bewaile not for himselfe (whõ he hated) but that so notable a love should perish. Thẽ began he onely so farre to wish his owne good, as that *Pamela* might pardon him the fault, though not the punishment: & the uttermost height he aspired unto, was, that after his death, she might yet pittie his error, and know that it proceeded of love, and not of boldnesse.

4   That conceipt found such friendship in his thoughts, that at last he yelded, since he was banished her presẽce, to seeke some meanes by writing to shew his sorrow, & testifie his repentance. Therfore getting him the necessarie instruments of writing, he thought best to coũterfaite his hand (fearing that as alreadie she knew his, she would cast it away as soone as she saw it) and to put it in vers, hoping, that would draw her on to read the more, chusing the *Elegiac* as fittest for mourning. But pen did never more quakingly performe his office; never was paper more double moistned with inke & teares; never words more slowly maried together, & never the *Muses* more tired, then now with changes & rechanges of his devises: fearing howe to ende, before he had resolved how to begin, mistrusting ech word, condemning eche sentence. This word was not significant, that word was too plain: this would not be cõceived; the other would be il conceived. Here Sorow was not inough expressed; there he seemed too much for his owne sake to be sory. This sentence rather shewed art, then passion; that sentence rather foolishly passionate, then forcibly moving. At last, marring with mending, and putting out better, then he left, he made an end of it; & being ended, & diverse times ready to teare it: till his reason assuring him, the more he studied, the worse it grew, he folded it up, devoutly invoking good acceptation unto it; and watching his time, when they were all gone one day to dinner (saving *Mopsa*) to the other lodge, stale up into *Pamelaes* chamber, and in her stãdish (which first he kissed; and craved of it a safe and friendly

keeping) left it there, to be seene at her next using her inke
(himselfe returning againe to be true prisoner to desperate
sorrow) leaving her standish upon her beds head, to give her
the more occasion to marke it: which also fell out.

For she finding it at her after noone-returne, in another 5
place then she left it, opened it. But when she saw the letter,
her hart gave her from whence it came. And therefore clapping
it to againe, she went away from it, as if it had bin a con-
tagious garment of an infected person: and yet was not long
away, but that she wished she had read it, though she were
loth to reade it. Shall I (said she) second his boldnesse so
farre, as to reade his presumptuous letters? And yet (said she)
he sees me not to growe the bolder thereby: And how can I
tell, whether they be presumptuous? The paper came from
him, and therefore not worthie to be receyved; and yet the
paper (she thought) was not guiltie. At last, she concluded, it
were not much amisse to looke it over, that she might out of
his wordes picke some further quarrell against him. Then she
opened it, and threwe it away, and tooke it up againe, till (ere
she were aware) her eyes woulde needes reade it, conteining
this matter.

U Nto a caitife wretch, whom long affliction holdeth,   6
    and now fully beleeves helpe to be quite perished ;
Grant yet, grant yet a looke, to the last monumēt of his anguish,
   O you (alas so I find) cause of his onely ruine.
Dread not a whit (O goodly cruell) that pittie may enter
   into thy hart by the sight of this Epistle I send :
And so refuse to behold of these strange wounds the recitall,
   least it might th' allure home to thy selfe to returne,
(Unto thy selfe I do meane those graces dwell so within thee,
   gratefulnes, sweetnes, holy love, hartie regard)
Such thing cannot I seeke (Despaire hath giv'n me my answer
   despaire most tragicall clause to a deadly request)
Such thing cānot he hope, that knowes thy determinat hardnes ;
   hard like a rich marble : hard, but a faire Diamond.
Can those eyes that of eyes drownd in most harty flowing teares,
   (teares and teares of a man) had no returne to remorse ;
Can those eyes now yeeld to the kind conceit of a sorow,
   which inke onely relates, but ne laments, ne replies?

Ah, that, that I do I not conceive (though that to my blisse were)
  more then Nestors *yeares, more then a Kings diademe.*
Ah, that, that I do not cōceive ; to the heavē when a mouse climes
  then may I hope t'atchieve grace of a heavenly tiger.
But, but alas, like a man cōdemn'd doth crave to be heard speake
  not that he hopes for amends of the desaster he feeles,
But finding th' approch of death with an ougly relenting,
  gives an adieu to the world, as to his onely delight :
Right so my boiling hart, enflam'de with fire of a faire eye,
  bubling out doth breath signes of his hugie dolours :
Now that he finds to what end his life and love be reserved,
  and that he hence must part where to live onely he lov'd.
O faire, O fairest, are such thy triumphs to thy fairnesse ?
  can death beautie become ? must be such a monument ?
Must I be onely the marke, shall prove that Vertue is angrie ?
  shall prove that fiercenes can with a white dove abide ?
Shall to the world appeare that faith and love be rewarded
  with mortall disdaine, bent to unendly revenge ?
Unto revenge ?   O sweete, on a wretch wilt thou be revenged ?
  shall such high Plannets ende to the losse of a worme ?
And to revenge who doo bend, would in that kind be revenged,
  as th' offence was done, and goe beyond if he can.
All my' offence was Love : with Love then must I be chastned,
  and with more, by the lawes that to Revenge doo belong.
If that love be a fault, more fault in you to be lovely :
  Love never had me opprest, but that I saw to be lov'd.
You be the cause that I lov'd : what Reason blameth a shadowe,
  that with a body't goes ? since by a body it is.
If that Love you did hate, you should your beautie have hidden:
  you should those faire eyes have with a veile covered.
But foole, foole that I am, those eyes would shine frō a dark cave.
  what veiles then doo prevaile, but to a more miracle ?
Or those golden lockes, those lockes which lock me to bondage,
  torne you should disperse unto the blasts of a winde.
But foole, foole that I am, tho I had but a hair of her head foūd,
  ev'n as I am, so I should unto that haire be a thrall.
Or with fair hāds-nailes (ô hād which nailes me to this death)
  you should have your face (since Love is ill) blemished.
O wretch, what do I say ? should that faire face be defaced ?
  should my too-much sight cause so true a Sunne to be lost ?

First let Cimmerian *darknes be my onel' habitacion:*
  first be mine eyes pulde out, first be my braine perished;
Ere that I should consent to doo such excessive a dammage
  unto the earth, by the hurt of this her heavenly jewell.
O no: but such love you say you could have afoorded,
  as might learne Temp'rance voyde of a rages events.
O sweet simplicitie: from whence should Love so be learned?
  unto Cupid *that boy shall a* Pedante *be found?*
Well: but faultie I was: Reason to my Passion yeelded,
  Passion unto my rage, Rage to a hastie revenge.
But what's this for a fault, for which such fault is abolisht,
  such faith, so staineles, inviolate, violent?
Shall I not? ô may I not thus yet refresh the remembrance,
  what sweete joyes I had once, and what a place I did hold?
Shall I not once object, that you, you graunted a favour
  unto the man, whom now such miseries you awarde?
Bẽd your thoghts to the dear sweet words which thẽ to me giv'n were:
  think what a world is now, think who hath altred her hart.
What? was I then worthie such good, now worthie such evill?
  now fled, then cherished? then so nie, now so remote?
Did not a rosed breath, from lips more rosie proceeding,
  say, that I should well finde in what a care I was had?
With much more: now what doo I finde, but Care to abhor me,
  Care that I sinke in griefe, Care that I live banished?
And banished doo I live, nor now will seeke a recov'rie,
  since so she will, whose will is to me more then a lawe.
If then a man in most ill case may give you a farewell;
  farewell, long farewell, all my woe, all my delight.

CHAP. 2.

[1]*The young Ladies mette:* [2]*invited to the countrie-wenches sports,* [3]*goe thether,* [4]*there are taken, and thence caried to* Amphialus *castle.* [5]*Their entertainement there.* [6]Cecropias *auricular confession of her proud cariage in prosperitie,* [7]*and ambitious practises in adversitie.* [8]Amphialus *his affection in these actions.*

WHat this would have wrought in her, she her selfe could not tell: for, before her Reason could moderate the disputation betwene Favour & Faultines, her sister, and *Miso,*

called her downe to entertaine *Zelmane,* who was come to visite
the two sisters; about whom, as about two Poles, the Skie of
Beautie was turned: while *Gynecia* wearied her bed with her
melancholie sicknes, and made *Misos* shrewdnesse (who like a
sprite, sette to keep a treasure, barde *Zelmane* from any further
conference) to be the Lieutenant of her jealousie: Both she and
her husband, driving *Zelmane* to such a streit of resolution,
either of impossible graunting, or dangerous refusing, as the
best escape she had, was (as much as she coulde) to avoyde
their companie. So as, this day, being the fourth day after the
uprore, (*Basilius* being with his sicke wife, conferring upon such
examinations, as *Philanax,* and other of his noble-men had
made of this late seditiŏ, all touching *Cecropia* with vehemĕt
suspition of giving either flame or fuell unto it) *Zelmane* came
with her bodie, to find her mind, which was gone long before
her, & had gotten his seate in *Philoclea:* who now with a
bashfull cheerefulnesse (as though she were ashamed, that she
could not choose but be glad) joyned with her sister, in making
much of *Zelmane.*

2   And so as they sate devising how to give more feathers to
the winges of Time, there came to the lodge dore, sixe maides,
all in one liverie of skarlette petticotes, which were tuckt up
almoste to their knees, the petticoates them selves beinge in
many places garnished with leaves, their legges naked, saving
that above the anckles they had little black silke laces, upon
which did hang a few silver belles: like which they had a little
above their elbowes, upon their bare armes. Upon their haire
they ware garlands of roses and gilliflowers; and the haire was
so drest, as that came againe above the garlandes; enterchaung-
ing a mutuall covering: so as it was doubtfull, whether the
haire drest the garlandes, or the garlandes drest the haire.
Their breasts liberall to the eye: the face of the formoste
of them, in excellencie faire; and of the rest lovely, if not
beautifull: and beautifull would have bene, if they had not
suffered greedy *Phœbus,* over-often, and harde, to kisse them.
Their countenaunces full of a gracefull gravitie; so as the
gesture matcht with the apparell, it might seem a wanton
modestie, and an entising sobernes. Each of them had an
instrument of musick in their hands, which consorting their
wel-pleasing tunes, did charge each eare with unsensiblenes,

that did not lende it selfe unto them. The Musicke entring alone into the lodge, the Ladies were all desirous to see from whence so pleasant a guest was come: and therefore went out together; where, before they coulde take the paines to doubt, much lesse to aske the question of their qualitie, the fairest of them (with a gay, but yet discreete demeanour) in this sort spake unto them. Most excellent Ladies, (whose excellencies have power to make cities envie these woods, and solitarines to be accounted the sweetest companie) vouchsafe our message your gracious hearing, which as it comes from Love, so comes it from lovely persons. The maides of all this coast of *Arcadia*, understanding the often accesse that certaine shepheards of these quarters, are allowed to have in this forbidden place; and that their rurall sports are not disdained of you, have bene stird with emulation to them, and affection to you, to bring forth some thing, which might as well breede your contentment: and therefore hoping that the goodnes of their intention, & the hurtlesnes of their sex shall excuse the breach of the commandemēt in cōming to this place unsent for, they chose out us, to invite both your princely parents, & your selves, to a place in the woods about half a mile hence: where they have provided some such sports, as they trust your gratious acceptatiõs will interpret to be delitefull. We have bene at the other lodge, but finding them there, busied in weightier affaires, our trust is, that you yet will not denie the shining of your eies upõ us.

The Ladies stood in some doubte, whether they should goe 3 or not, lest *Basilius* might be angry withall. But *Miso* (that had bene at none of the pastorals, and had a great desire to lead her old senses abroad to some pleasure) told them plainely, they should nor will nor choose, but go thether, and make the honest countrie people know, that they were not so squeamish as folkes thought of them. The Ladies glad to be warranted by her authoritie; with a smiling humblenesse obeied her: *Pamela* only casting a seeking looke, whether she could see *Dorus* (who poore wretch wandred halfe mad for sorrow in the woods, crying for pardon of her, who could not heare him) but indeed was grieved for his absence, having given the wound to him through her owne harte. But so the three Ladies & *Miso* went with those six *Nymphes*, conquering the length of the way with the force of musique, leaving only *Mopsa* behind, who disgraced weeping with her countenaunce, because her mother would not suffer her to shewe her newskoured face among them. But the place apointed (as they thought) met them halfe in their way, so well were they pleased with the sweete tunes and prettie conversation of their inviters. There founde they in the midst of the thickest part of the wood, a litle square place, not burdened with trees, but with a boord covered, & beautified with the pleasantest fruites, that Sunburnd *Autumne* could deliver unto thẽ. The maids besought the Ladies to sit downe, and tast of the swelling grapes, which seemed great with child of *Bacchus*: & of the divers coloured plums, which gave the eye a pleasant tast before they came to the mouth. The Ladies would not shew to scorne their provision, but eat, and dranke a little of their coole wine, which seemed to laugh for joy to come to such lips.

4 But after the collation was ended, and that they looked for the cõming foorth of such devises, as were prepared for them, there rusht out of the woods twentie armed men, who round about environed them, & laying hold of *Zelmane* before she could draw her sword, and taking it from her, put hoods over the heads of all fower, and so muffled, by force set them on horsebacke and carried them away; the sisters in vaine crying for succour, while *Zelmanes* harte was rent in peeces with rage of the injurie, and disdaine of her fortune. But when they had caried them a foure or five mile further, they lefte *Miso* with a gagge in her mouth, and ʰound hande and foote, so to take her fortune: and brought the three Ladies (by that time that the Night seemed with her silence to conspire to their treason) to a castle about ten mile of from the Lodges: where they were fayne to take a boate whiche wayted for them. For the castle stood in the midst of a great lake, uppon a high rocke, where partly by Arte, but principallie by Nature, it was by all men esteemed impregnable.

5 But at the Castle gate their faces were discovered, and there were mett with a great number of torches, after whome the sisters knewe their aunt in lawe, *Cecropia*. But that sight increased the deadly terrour of the Princesses, looking for nothing but death, since they were in the power of the wicked *Cecropia*: who yet came unto them, making curtesie the outside

362

of mischiefe, and desiring them not to be discomforted: for they were in a place dedicated to their service. *Philoclea* (with a looke where Love shined through the miste of Feare) besought her to be good unto them, having never deserved evill of her. But *Pamelas* high harte disdayning humblenesse to injurie, Aunt, (said she) what you have determined of us I pray you doo it speedily: for my part I looke for no service, where I finde violence.

But *Cecropia* (using no more wordes with them) conveyed them all three to severall lodgings (*Zelmanes* harte so swelling with spite, that she coulde not bring foorth a worde) and so lefte them: first taking from them their knives, because they should do themselves no hurte, before she had determined of them: and then giving such order that they wanted nothing but libertie, & comfort, she went to her sonne, who yet kept his bed, because of his wound he had received of *Zelmane,* & told him, whom now he had in his power. *Amphialus* was but even then returned from far countries, where he had wonne immortall fame, both of courage & curtesie, when he met with the Princesses, and was hurt by *Zelmane,* so as he was utterly ignorant of all his mothers wicked devises; to which he would never have consented, being (like a rose out of a brier) an excellent sonne of an evill mother: and now when he heard of this, was as much amazed, as if he had seen the Sunne fall to the earth. And therefore desired his mother that she would tell him the whole discourse, how all these matters had happened.

Sonne (said she) I will doo it willingly, and since all is done 6 for you, I will hide nothing from you. And howsoever I might be ashamed to tell it strangers, who would thinke it wickednesse, yet what is done for your sake (how evill soever to others) to you is vertue. To begin then even with the beginning, this doting foole *Basilius* that now raignes, having lived unmarried till he was nigh threescore yeares old (and in all his speaches affirming, and in all his dooings assuring, that he never would marrie) made all the eyes of the country to be bent upon your father, his onely brother (but then younger by thirty yeares) as upon the undoubted successour: being indeed a man worthy to raigne, thinking nothing enough for himselfe: where this goose (you see) puts downe his head, before there be any thing neere to touch him. So that he holding place and estimation as heyre of *Arcadia*, obteyned me of my father the King of *Argos*, his brother helping to the conclusion, with protesting his bachelerly intention: for else you may be sure the King of *Argos*, nor his daughter would have suffered their Royall bloud to be stained with the base name of subjection. So that I came into this countrie as apparant Princesse therof, and accordingly was courted, and followed of all the Ladies of this countrie. My porte and pompe did well become a King of *Argos* daughter: in my presence their tongues were turned into eares, & their eares were captives unto my tongue. Their eyes admired my Majestie, & happy was he or she, on whom I would suffer the beames thereof to fall. Did I goe to church? it seemed the very Gods wayted for me, their devotions not being solemnized till I was ready. Did I walke abroad to see any delight? Nay, my walking was the delight it selfe: for to it was the concourse; one thrusting upon another, who might shewe him selfe most diligent and serviceable towardes me: my sleepes were inquired after, and my wakings never unsaluted: the very gate of my house full of principall persons, who were glad, if their presents had receaved a gratefull acceptation. And in this felicitie wert thou borne, the very earth submitting it selfe unto thee to be troden on as by his Prince; and to that passe had my husbandes vertue (by my good helpe) within short time brought it, with a plot we laide, as we should not have needed to have waited the tedious worke of a naturall end of *Basilius*; when the heavẽs (I thinke envying my great felicity) thẽ stopt thy fathers breath, whẽ he breathed nothing. but power and soveraigntie. Yet did not thy orphancie, or my widdowhood, deprive us of the delightfull prospect, which the hill of honour dooth yeeld, while expectation of thy succession did bind dependencies unto us.

7   But before, (my sonne) thou wert come to the age to feele the sweetnesse of authoritie, this beast (whom I can never name with patience) falsely and foolishly married this *Gynecia*, then a young girle, and brought her to sit above me in al feasts, to turne her shoulder to me-ward in all our solemnities. It is certaine, „ it is not so great a spite to be surmounted by straungers, as by ones owne allies. Thinke then what my minde was, since withall there is no question: The fall is greater from the first

to the second, then from the second to the undermost. The rage did swell in my harte, so much the more as it was faine to be suppressed in silēce, & disguised with humblenes. But above al the rest, the griefe of grieves was, whē with these daughters (now thy prisoners) she cut of al hope of thy successiō. It was a tedious thing to me; that my eies should looke lower then any bodies, that (my selfe being by) anothers voice then mine, should be more respeƈted. But it was insupportable unto me, to think that not only I, but thou shouldst spend al thy time in such misery, & that the Sun should see my eldest son lesse then a Prince. And though I had ben a sainƈt I could not choose, finding the chaūge this chaūge of fortune bred unto me, for now frō the multitude of followers, silēce grew to be at my gate, & absēce in my presence. The guesse of my mind could prevaile more before, then now many of my earnest requests. And thou (my deare sonne) by the fickle multitude no more then any ordinary person (borne of the mud of the people) regarded. But I (remēbring that in all miseries „ weeping becomes fooles, and praƈtize wise folks) have tried „ divers meanes to pull us out of the mire of subjeƈtiō. And though many times Fortune failed me, yet did I never faile my self. Wild beasts I kept in a cave hard by the lodges, which I caused by night to be fed in the place of their pastorals, I as then living in my house hard by the place, and against the houre they were to meete (having kept the beasts without meate) then let them loose, knowing that they would seeke their food there, and devoure what they founde. But blind Fortune hating sharpe-sighted inventions, made them unluckily to be killed. After, I used my servant *Clinias* to stir a notable tumult of country people: but those louts were too grosse instruments for delicate conceits. Now lastly, finding *Philanax-* his examinations grow daungerous, I thought to play double or quit; & with a sleight I used of my fine-witted wēch *Artesia*, with other maids of mine, would have sent these good inheritrixes of *Arcadia*, to have pleaded their cause before *Pluto*, but that over-fortunatly for thē, you made me know the last day how vehemently this childish passion of love doth torment you. Therfore I have brought them unto you, yet wishing rather hate thē love in you. For Hate often begetteth viƈtory; Love " commonly is the instrument of subjeƈtion. It is true, that I would also by the same practise have entrapped the parents, but my maids failed of it, not daring to tary long about it. But this sufficeth, since (these being taken away) you are the undoubted inheritor, and *Basilius* will not long over-live this losse.

8   O mother (said *Amphialus*) speake not of doing them hurt, no more then to mine eies, or my hart, or if I have any thing more deare then eyes, or hart unto me. Let others finde what sweetnesse they will in ever fearing, because they are ever feared: for my part, I will thinke my selfe highly intitled, if I may be once by *Philoclea* accepted for a servant. Well (said *Cecropia*) I would I had borne you of my minde, as well as of my body: then should you not have suncke under base weakenesses. But since you have tied your thoughts in so wilfull a knot, it is happie I have brought matters to such a passe, as you may both enjoy affection, and uppon that build your soveraigntie. Alas (said *Amphialus*) my hart would faine yeeld you thanks for setting me in the way of felicitie, but that feare killes them in me, before they are fully borne. For if *Philoclea* be displeased, how can I be pleased? if she count it unkindnes, shal I give tokens of kindnes? perchance she côdemnes me of this action, and shall I triumph? perchance she drownes nowe the beauties I love with sorrowful teares, and where is then my rejoicing? You have reason (said *Cecropia* with a feined gravitie) I will therefore send her away presently, that her contentment may be recovered. No good mother (said *Amphialus*) since she is here, I would not for my life constraine presence, but rather would I die then côsent to absence. Prety intricat follies (said *Cecropia*) but get you up, & see how you can prevaile with her, while I go to the other sister. For after we shal have our hands full to defend our selves, if *Basilius* hap to besiege us. But remembring herself, she turned back, & asked him what he woulde have done with *Zelmane*, since nowe he might be revenged of his hurt. Nothing but honorably, answered *Amphialus*, having deserved no other of me, especially being (as I heare) greatly cherished of *Philoclea*. And therefore I could wish they were lodged together. O no „ (said *Cecropia*) company confirmes resolutiôs, & lonelines breeds „ a werines of ones thoughts, and so a sooner consenting to reasonable profers.

CHAP. 3.

[1] Amphialus *addressing him to* Philoclea.   [2] *Her melancholie habit.*
[3] *His humble sute.*   [4] *Her pitifull answere:* [5] *and his compassionate replie.*   [6] *Their parting with cold comfort.*

BUt *Amphialus* (taking of his mother *Philocleas* knives, which [1] he kept as a relique, since she had worne them) gat up, and calling for his richest apparell, nothing seemed sumptuous inough for his mistresses eyes: and that which was costly, he feared were not daintie: and though the invention were delicat, he misdoubted the making. As carefull he was too of the colour; lest if gay, he might seeme to glorie in his injury, and her wrong; if mourning, it might strike some evill presage unto her of her fortune. At length he tooke a garment more rich then glaring, the ground being black velvet, richly embrodered with great pearle, & precious stones, but they set so among certaine tuffes of cypres, that the cypres was like blacke clowds, through which the starrs might yeeld a darke luster. About his necke he ware a brode & gorgeous coller; whereof the pieces enterchangeably answering; the one was of Diamonds and pearle, set with a white enamell, so as by the cunning of the workman it seemed like a shining ice, and the other piece being of Rubies, and Opalles, had a fierie glistring, which he thought pictured the two passions of Feare and Desire, wherein he was enchayned. His hurt (not yet fully well) made him a little halt, but he strave to give the best grace he could unto his halting.

And in that sort he went to *Philocleas* chamber: whome he [2] found (because her chamber was over-lightsome) sitting of that side of her bedde which was from the windowe; which did cast such a shadow upon her, as a good Painter woulde bestowe uppon *Venus*, when under the trees she bewayled the murther of *Adonis*: her handes and fingers (as it were) indented one within the other: her shoulder leaning to her beds head, and over her head a scarfe, which did eclipse almost halfe her eyes, which under it fixed their beames upon the wall by, with so steddie a maner, as if in that place they might well chaunge, but not mende their object: and so remayned they a good while after his comming in, he not daring to trouble her, nor she perceyving him, till that (a little varying her thoughts something quickening her senses) she heard him as he happed to stirre his upper garment: and perceyving him, rose up, with a demeanure, where in the booke of Beautie there was nothing to be read but Sorrow: for Kindnesse was blotted out, and Anger was never there.

3　But *Amphialus* that had entrusted his memorie with long and forcible speeches, found it so locked up in amazement, that he could pike nothing out of it, but the beseeching her to take what was don in good part, and to assure herselfe there was nothing but honour meant unto her person.　But she making no other aunswere, but letting her handes fall one from the other, which before were joyned (with eyes something cast aside, and a silent sigh) gave him to understande, that considering his dooings, she thought his speech as full of incongruitie, as her aunswere would be voyde of purpose: whereuppon he kneeling downe, and kissing her hande, (which she suffered with a countenaunce witnessing captivitie, but not kindnesse) he besought her to have pitie of him, whose love went beyonde the boundes of conceite, much more of uttering: that in her handes the ballance of his life or death did stande; whereto the least motion of hers woulde serve to determine, she being indeede the mistresse of his life, and he her eternall slave; and with true vehemencie besought her that he might heare her speake, whereupon she suffered her sweete breath to turne it selfe into these kind of words.

4　Alas cousin, (saide she) what shall my tongue be able to doo, which is infourmed by the eares one way, and by the eyes another?　You call for pittie, and use crueltie; you say, you love me, and yet do the effectes of enmitie.　You affirme your death is in my handes, but you have brought me to so neere a degree to death, as when you will, you may lay death upon me: so that while you say I am mistresse of your life, I am not mistresse of mine owne.　You entitle your selfe my slave, but I am sure I am yours.　If then violence, injurie, terror, and depriving of that which is more dear then life it selfe, libertie, be fit orators for affection, you may expect that I will be easily perswaded.　But if the nearenesse of our kinred breede any remorse in you, or there be any such thing in you, which you call love towarde me, then let not my fortune be disgraced with the name of imprisonment : let not my hart waste it selfe by being vexed with feeling evill, and fearing worse. Let not me be a cause of my parents wofull destruction; but restore me to my selfe; and so doing I shall account I have receyved my selfe of you. And what I say for my selfe, I say for my deare sister, and my friend *Zelmane* : for I desire no wel being, without they may be partakers. With that her teares rained downe from her heavenly eyes, and seemed to water the sweet and beautifull flowers of her face.

But *Amphialus* was like the poore woman, who loving a 5 tame Doe she had, above all earthly things, having long played withall, and made it feede at her hand and lappe, is constrained at length by famine (all her flocke being spent, and she fallen into extreeme povertie) to kill the Deare, to sustaine her life. Manie a pitifull looke doth she cast upon it, and many a time doth she draw backe her hand before she can give the stroke. For even so *Amphialus* by a hunger-sterved affection, was compelled to offer this injurie, and yet the same affection made him with a tormenting griefe, thinke unkindnesse in himselfe, that he could finde in his hart any way to restraine her freedome. But at length, neither able to grant, nor denie, he thus answered her. Deare ladie (said he) I will not say unto you (how justly soever I may do it) that I am neither author, nor accessarie unto this your withholding. For since I do not redres it, I am as faulty as if I had begun it. But this I protest unto you (and this protestation of mine, let the heavens heare, and if I lie, let them answer me with a deadly thunderbolt) that in my soule I wish I had never seene the light, or rather, that I had never had a father to beget such a child, thē that by my meanes those eyes should overflow their owne beauties, then by my meanes the skie of your vertue should be overclowded with sorrow. But woe is me, most excellent Ladie, I finde my selfe most willing to obey you : neither truely doo mine eares receave the least word you speak, with any lesse reverence, then as absolute, and unresistable commaundements. But alas, that Tyrant Love, (which now possesseth the holde of all my life and reason) will no way suffer it. It is Love, it is Love, not I, which disobey you. What then shall I say? but that I, who am redie to lie under your feete, to venture, nay to loose my life at your least commandement: I am not the staye of your freedome, but Love, Love, which ties you in your owne knots. It is you your selfe, that imprison your selfe: it is your beautie which makes these castle-walles embrace you: it is your owne eyes, which reflect upon themselves this injurie. Then is there no other remedie, but that you some way vouchsafe to satisfie this Loves vehemencie; which (since it grewe in your selfe) without question you shall finde it (far more then I) tractable.

But with these wordes *Philoclea* fell to so extreame a quaking, and her lively whitenesse did degenerate to so dead a palenesse, that *Amphialus* feared some daungerous traunce: so that taking her hande, and feelinge that it (which was woonte to be one of the chiefe firebrands of *Cupid*) had all the sense of it wrapt up in coldnes, he began humblie to beseech her to put away all feare, and to assure herselfe upon the vowe he made thereof unto God, and her selfe, that the uttermost forces he would ever employ to conquere her affection, should be Desire, and Desert. That promise brought *Philoclea* againe to her selfe, so that slowly lifting up her eyes upon him, with a countenaunce ever courteous, but then languishing, she tolde him, that he should doo well to do so, if indeede he had ever tasted what true love was: for that where now she did beare him good will, she should (if he tooke any other way) hate, and abhor the very thought of him: offering him withall, that though his mother had taken away her knives, yet the house of Death had so many doores, as she would easilie flie into it, if ever she founde her honor endaungered.

6   *Amphialus* having the colde ashes of Care cast upon the coales of Desire, leaving some of his mothers Gentlewomen to waite upon *Philoclea*, himselfe indeede a prisoner to his prisoner, and making all his authoritie to be but a footestoole to Humblenes, went from her to his mother. To whom with words which Affection endited, but Amazement uttered, he delivered what had passed betwene him and *Philoclea*: beseeching her to trie what her perswasions could doo with her, while he gave order for all such things as were necessarie against such forces, as he looked dayly *Basilius* would bring before his castle. His mother bade him quiette him selfe, for she doubted not to take fitte times. But that the best way was, first to let her owne Passion a little tire it selfe.

CHAP. 4.

[1] Amphialus *warlike preparations.* [2] *His justification.* [3] *His fortifications.* [4] *His Arte of men.* [5] *His Love-passions, and passionate complaints.*

SO they calling *Clinias*, and some other of their counsell, 1 advised upon their present affaires. First, he dispatched privat letters to al those principall Lords and gentlemen of the country, whõ he thought ether alliance, or friendship to himselfe might drawe; with speciall motions from the generall considera- tion of duetie : not omitting all such, whom either youthfull age, or youth-like mindes did fill with unlimited desires : besides such, whom any discontentment made hungry of change, or an over-spended wante, made want a civill warre : to each (accord- ing to the counsell of his mother) conforming himselfe after their humors. To his friends, friendlines ; to the ambitious, great expectations ; to the displeased, revenge ; to the greedie, spoyle : wrapping their hopes with such cunning, as they rather seemed given over unto them as partakers : then promises sprong of necessitie. Then sent he to his mothers brother, the King of *Argos :* but he was as then so over-laide with warre himselfe, as from thence he could attend small succour.

But because he knewe, how violently rumors doo blow the 2 sailes of popular judgemẽts, & how few there be, that can dis- cerne betweene trueth and truthlikenes, betweene showes and substance ; he caused a justification of this his action to be written, wherof were sowed abroad many copies, which with some glosses of probabilitie, might hide indeede the foulenes of his treason; and from true common-places, fetch downe most false applications. For, beginning how much the duetie which is owed to the countrie, goes beyond all other dueties, since in it selfe it conteines them all, and that for the respect therof, not onely all tender respects of kinred, or whatsoever other friendshippes, are to be laide aside, but that even long-helde opinions (rather builded upon a secreate of governement, then any groũd of truthe) are to be forsaken. He fell by degrees to shew, that since the ende whereto any thing is directed, is ever to be of more noble reckning, then the thing thereto directed :

that therefore, the weale-publicke was more to be regarded, then any person or magistrate that thereunto was ordeined. The feeling consideration whereof, had moved him (though as nere of kinne to *Basilius* as could be, yet) to set principally before his eyes, the good estate of so many thousands, over whom *Basilius* raigned: rather then so to hoodwinke himselfe with affection, as to suffer the realme to runne to manifest ruine. The care whereof, did kindly appertaine to those, who being subalterne magistrates and officers of the crowne, were to be employed as frō the Prince, so for the people; and of all other, especiallie himselfe, who being descended of the Royall race, and next heire male, Nature had no soner opened his eyes, but that the soyle where-upon they did looke, was to looke for at his hands a continuall carefulnes: which as frō his childhood he had ever caried; so now finding that his uncle had not only givē over al care of government, but had put it into the hands of *Philanax*, (a man neither in birth comparable to many, nor for his corrupt, prowde, and partiall dealing, liked of any) but beside, had set his daughters (in whom the whole estate, as next heires thereunto, had no lesse interest thē himselfe) in so unfit & il-guarded a place, as it was not only dāgerous for their persons, but (if they should be conveied to any forraine country) to the whole common-wealth pernicious: that therfore he had brought them into this strōg castle of his, which way, if it might seem strange, they were to consider, „that new necessities require new remedies: but there they should be served & honored as belonged to their greatnes, until by the generall assembly of the estates, it should be determined how they should to their best (both private, and publique) advantage be matched; vowing all faith & duty both to the father & children, never by him to be violated. But if in the meane time, before the estates could be assēbled, he were assailed, he would thē for his own defence take armes: desiring all, that either tendred the dangerous case of their country, or in their harts loved justice, to defēd him in this just actiō. And if the Prince should commaund them otherwise, yet to know, that therein he was no more to be obeied, then if he should call for poison to hurt himself withall: since all that was done, was done for his service, howsoever he might (seduced by *Philanax*) interpret of it: he protesting, that what soever he should doo for his owne defence, should be against *Philanax*, & no way against *Basilius*.

To this effect, amplified with arguments and examples, and 3 painted with rhetoricall colours, did he sow abroad many discourses: which as they prevayled with some of more quicke then sounde conceipte, to runne his fortune with him; so in many did it breed a coolenesse, to deale violently against him, and a false-minded neutralitie to expect the issue. But besides the waies he used to weaken the adverse partie, he omitted nothing for the strengthning of his owne. The chiefe trust whereof (because he wanted men to keepe the field) he reposed in the suretie of his castle; which at lest would winne him much time, the mother of many mutations. To that therfore he bent his outward & inward eyes, striving to make Art strive with Nature, to whether of them two that fortification should be most beholding. The seat Nature bestowed, but Arte gave the building: which as his rocky hardnesse would not yeeld to undermining force, so to opẽ assaults he tooke counsell of skill, how to make all approches, if not impossible, yet difficult; as well at the foot of the castle, as round about the lake, to give unquiet lodgings to thẽ, whom onely enmitie would make neighbors. Then omitted he nothing of defence, as wel simple defence, as that which did defend by offending, fitting instrumẽts of mischiefe to places, whence the mischiefe might be most liberally bestowed. Nether was his smallest care for victuals, as wel for the providing that which should suffice both in store & goodnesse, as in well preserving it, and wary distributing it, both in quantitie, and qualitie; spending that first which would keepe lest.

But wherein he sharpned his wits to the pearcingest point, 4 was touching his men (knowing them to be the weapon of weapons, & master-spring (as it were) which makes all the rest to stir; and that therefore in the Arte of man stood the quintessence, & ruling skill of all prosperous governement, either peaceable, or military) he chose in number as many as without pestring (and so daunger of infection) his victuall would seem for two yeare to maintaine; all of hable bodies, and some few of able mindes to direct, not seeking many commaunders, but contenting himselfe, that the multitude should have obeying wills, every one knowing whom he should commaund, and whom he should obey, the place where, and the matter wherein; distributing each office as neere as he could, to the disposition of the person that should exercise it : knowing no love, daunger, nor discipline can sodainly alter an habite in nature. Therfore would he not employ the stil mã to a shifting practise, nor the liberall man to be a dispenser of his victuals, nor the kind-harted man to be a punisher: but would exercise their vertues in sorts, where they might be profitable, employing his chief care to know thẽ all particularly, & throughly, regarding also the cõstitutiõ of their bodies; some being able better to abide watching, some hũger, some labour, making his benefit of ech hability, & not forcing beyond power. Time to every thing by just proportiõ he allotted, & as well in that, as in every thing els, no small errour winckt at, lest greater should be animated. Even of vices he made his profite, making the cowardly *Clinias* to have care of the watch, which he knew his own feare would make him very wakefully performe. And before the siege began, he himselfe caused rumors to be sowed, and libels to be spread against himselfe, fuller of mallice, then witty persuasion : partly, to knowe those that would be apt to stumble at such motions, that he might cull them from the faithfuller band ; but principally, because in necessitie they should not know when any such thing were in earnest attempted, whether it were, or not, of his owne invention. But even then (before the enemies face came neere to breed any terrour) did he exercise his men dayly in all their charges, as if Daunger had presently presented his most hideous presence: him selfe rather instructing by example, then precept ; being neither more sparing in travaile, nor spẽding in diet, then the meanest souldier : his hand and body disdaining no base matters, nor shrinking from the heavy.

5 The onely ods was, that when others tooke breath, he sighed; and when others rested, he crost his armes. For Love passing thorow the pikes of Daũger, & tumbling it selfe in the dust of Labour, yet still made him remember his sweete desire, and beautifull image. Often when he had begun to commaund one, somewhat before halfe the sentence were ended, his inward guest did so entertaine him, that he would breake it of, and a prettie while after end it, when he had (to the marvaile of the standers by) sent himself in to talke with his own thoughts.

Sometimes when his hand was lifted up to some thing, as if with the sight of *Gorgons* head he had bene sodainely turned into a stone, so would he there abide with his eyes planted, and handes lifted, till at length, comming to the use of himself, he would looke about whether any had perceived him; then would he accuse, and in himselfe condemne all those wits, that durst affirme Idlenesse to be the well-spring of Love. O, would he say, al you that affect the title of wisdome, by ungratefull scorning the ornaments of Nature, am I now piping in a shaddow? or doo slouthfull feathers now enwrap me? Is not hate before me, and doubte behinde me? is not daunger of the one side, and shame of the other? And doo I not stande upon paine, and travaile, and yet over all, my affection triumphes? The more I stirre about urgent affaires, the more me thinks the very stirring breeds a breath to blow the coales of my love: the more I exercise my thoughts, the more they encrease the appetite of my desires. O sweet *Philoclea* (with that he would cast up his eies wherin some water did appeare, as if they would wash themselves against they should see her) thy heavenly face is my Astronomie; thy sweet vertue, my sweet Philosophie: let me profite therein, and farewell all other cogitations. But alas, my mind misgives me, for your planets beare a contrarie aspect unto me. Woe, woe is me, they threaten my destruction: and whom doo they threaten this destruction? even him that loves them; and by what means will they destroy, but by loving them? O deare (though killing) eyes, shall death head his darte with the golde of *Cupids* arrowe? Shall death take his ayme from the rest of Beautie? O beloved (though hating) *Philoclea*, how if thou beest mercifull, hath crueltie stolne into thee? Or how if thou beest cruell, doth crueltie looke more mercifull then ever Mercie did? Or alas, is it my destinie that makes Mercie cruell? Like an evill vessell which turnes sweete licour to sowernes; so when thy grace fals upon me, my wretched constitution makes it become fiercenesse. Thus would he exercise his eloquence, when she could not heare him, and be dumbe-striken, when her presence gave him fit occasion of speaking: so that his witte could finde out no other refuge, but the comfort and counsell of his mother, desiring her (whose thoughts were unperplexed) to use for his sake the most prevailing manners of intercession.

CHAP. 5.

[1] *Suttle* Cecropia *visites sad* Philoclea. [2] *The shamelesse Aunts shrewd temptations to love and mariage. The modest neeces maidenly resistance.*

[1] CEcropia seing her sonnes safetie depende thereon, (though her pride much disdained the name of a desire) tooke the charge upon her, not doubting the easie conquest of an unexpert virgin, who had alreadie with subtiltie and impudencie begun to undermine a monarchy. Therfore, waighing *Philocleas* resolutions by the counterpease of her own youthful thoughts, which she then called to minde, she doubted not at least to make *Philoclea* receive the poyson distilled in sweete liquour, which she with little disguising had drunke up thirstily. Therefore she went softly to *Philocleas* chamber, & peeping through the side of the doore, then being a little open, she sawe *Philoclea* sitting lowe upon a cushion, in such a given-over manner, that one would have thought, silence, solitarinesse, and melancholie were come there, under the ensigne of mishap, to conquere delight, and drive him from his naturall seate of beautie: her teares came dropping downe like raine in Sunshine, and she not taking heede to wipe the teares, they ranne downe upon her cheekes, and lips, as upon cherries which the dropping tree bedeweth. In the dressing of her haire and apparell, she might see neither a careful arte, nor an arte of carelesnesse, but even left to a neglected chaunce, which yet coulde no more unperfect her perfections, then a Die anie way cast, could loose his square-nesse.

[2] *Cecropia* (stirred with no other pitie, but for her son) came in, and haling kindnesse into her countenance, What ayles this sweete Ladie, (said she) will you marre so good eyes with weeping? shall teares take away the beautie of that complexion, which the women of *Arcadia* wish for, and the men long after? Fie of this peevish sadnesse ; in sooth it is untimely for your age. Looke upon your owne bodie, and see whether it deserve to pine away with sorrow : see whether you will have these hands (with that she tooke one of her hands and kissing it, looked uppon it as if she were enamoured with it) fade from

their whitenesse, which makes one desire to touch them ; & their softnesse, which rebounds againe a desire to looke on them, and become drie, leane and yellowe, and make everie bodie woonder at the chaunge, and say, that sure you had used some arte before, which nowe you had left? for if the beauties had beene naturall, they woulde never so soone have beene blemished. Take a glasse, and see whether these tears become your eies: although, I must côfesse, those eies are able to make tears comely. Alas Madame (answered *Philoclea*) I know not whether my teares become mine eyes, but I am sure mine eies thus beteared, become my fortune. Your fortune (saide *Cecropia*) if she could see to attire herselfe, would put on her best raiments. For I see, and I see it with griefe, and (to tell you true) unkindnes: you misconster every thing, that only for your sake is attempted. You thinke you are offended, and are indeed defended : you esteeme your selfe a prisoner, and are in truth a mistres : you feare hate, and shall find love. And truely, I had a thing to say to you, but it is no matter, since I find you are so obstinatly melancholy, as that you woo his felowship : I will spare my paines, and hold my peace : And so staied indeede, thinking *Philoclea* would have had a female inquisitivenesse of the matter. But she, who rather wished to unknowe what she knewe, then to burden her hart with more hopeles knowledge, only desired her to have pity of her, and if indeed she did meane her no hurt, then to grant her liberty : for else the very griefe & feare, would prove her unappointed executioners. For that (said *Cecropia*) beleve me upõ the faith of a kings daughter, you shall be free, so soone as your freedome may be free of mortal däger, being brought hither for no other cause, but to prevent such mischiefes as you know not of. But if you thinke indeed to winne me to have care of you, even as of mine owne daughter, then lend your eares unto me, & let not your mind arme it self with a wilfulnesse to be flexible to nothing. But if I speake reason, let Reason have his due reward, persuasion. Then sweet neece (said she) I pray you presuppose, that now, evẽ in the midst of your agonies, which you paint unto your selfe most horrible, wishing with sighes, & praying with vowes, for a soone & safe deliverie. Imagin neece (I say) that some heavenly spirit should appeare unto you, and bid you follow him through the doore, that goes into the garden, assuring you, that

you should therby return to your deare mother, and what
other delights soever your mind esteemes delights: would
you (sweet neece) would you refuse to folow him, & say,
that if he led you not through the chiefe gate, you would
not enjoy your over-desired liberty? Would you not drinke
the wine you thirst for, without it were in such a glasse, as
you especially fancied? tel me (deare neece:) but I wil answer
for you, because I know your reason and will is such, as must
needs conclude, that such nicenesse can no more be in you, to
disgrace such a mind, then disgracefulnesse can have any place
in so faultles a beauty. Your wisdom would assuredly de-
termin, how the marke were hit, not whether the bow were
of Ewe or no, wherein you shot. If this be so, and thus sure
(my deare neece) it is, then (I pray you) imagin, that I am that
same good Angel, who grieving in your griefe, and in truth not
able to suffer, that bitter sighs should be sent foorth with so
sweete a breath, am come to lead you, not only to your desired,
and imagined happines, but to a true and essentiall happines;
not only to liberty, but to libertie with commandement. The
way I will shew you (which if it be not the gate builded hitherto in your private choise, yet shall it be a doore to bring you
through a garden of pleasures, as sweet as this life can bring
foorth; nay rather, which makes this life to be a life: (My son,)
let it be no blemish to him that I name him my son, who was
your fathers own nephew: for you know I am no smal kings
daughter,) my sonne (I say) farre passing the neernesse of his
kinred, with the neernesse of good-will, and striving to match
your matchlesse beautie with a matchlesse affection, doth by
me present unto you the full enjoying of your liberty, so as
with this gift you wil accept a greater, which is, this castell,
with all the rest which you knowe he hath, in honorable
quantitie; and will confirme his gift, and your receipt of both,
with accepting him to be yours. I might say much both for
the person and the matter; but who will crie out the Sun
shines? It is so manifest a profit unto you, as the meanest
judgement must straight apprehend it: so farre is it from the
sharpenesse of yours, therof to be ignorant. Therfore (sweet
neece) let your gratefulnes be my intercession, & your gentlenesse my eloquence, and let me cary comfort to a hart which
greatly needs it. *Philoclea* looked upon her, & cast downe her

eie again. Aunt (said she) I would I could be so much a
mistres of my owne mind, as to yeelde to my cousins vertuous
request: for so I construe of it. But my hart is already set
(and staying a while on that word, she brought foorth afterwards) to lead a virgins life to my death: for such a vow I have
in my selfe devoutly made. The heavens prevent such a
mischiefe (said *Cecropia*.) A vowe, quoth you? no, no, my
deere neece, Nature, when you were first borne, vowed you a
womã, & as she made you child of a mother, so to do your best
to be mother of a child: she gave you beautie to move love;
she gave you wit to know love; she gave you an excellẽt body
to reward love: which kind of liberall rewarding is crowned
with unspeakable felicitie. For this, as it bindeth the receiver,
so it makes happy the bestower: this doth not impoverish, but
enrich the giver. O the sweet name of a mother: O the cõfort
of cõforts, to see your childrẽ grow up, in whõ you are (as
it were) eternized: if you could conceive what a hart-tickling
joy it is to see your own litle ones, with awfull love come
running to your lap, and like litle models of your selfe, still cary
you about them, you would thinke unkindnes in your own
thoughts, that ever they did rebell against the mean unto it.
But perchãce I set this blessednes before your eies, as Captains
do victorie before their souldiers, to which they might come
through many paines, grieves & dangers. No, I am cõtent you
shrinke from this my counsel, if the way to come unto it, be
not most of all pleasant. I know not (answered the sweet
Philoclea, fearing least silence would offend her sullennes) what
contentment you speake of: but I am sure the best you can
make of it, (which is mariage) is a burdenous yoke. Ah, deer
neece (said *Cecropia*) how much you are deceived? A yoke
indeed we all beare, laid upõ us in our creation, which by
mariage is not increased, but thus farre eased, that you have a
yoke-fellow to help to draw through the cloddy cumbers of this
world. O widow-nights, beare witnes with me of the difference. How often alas do I embrace the orfan-side of my bed,
which was wõt to be imprinted by the body of my deare
husband, & with teares acknowledge, that I now enjoy such
a liberty as the banished mã hath; who may, if he list, wãder
over the world, but is ever restrained frõ his most delightful
home? that I have now such a liberty as the seeled dov hath,

which being first deprived of eies, is then by the falconer cast off? For beleve me, neece, beleve me, mans experiēce is womãs best eie-sight. Have you ever seene a pure Rosewater kept in a christal glas; how fine it lokes, how sweet it smels, while that beautifull glasse imprisons it? Breake the prison, and let the water take his owne course, doth it not imbrace dust, and loose all his former sweetenesse, and fairenesse? Truly so are we, if we have not the stay, rather then the restraint of Cristalline mariage. My hart meltes to thinke of the sweete comfortes, I in that happie time received, when I had never cause to care, but the care was doubled: whē I never rejoiced, but that I saw my joy shine in anothers eies. What shall I say of the free delight, which the hart might embrace, without the accusing of the inward conscience, or feare of outward shame? and is a solitary life as good as this? then can one string make as good musicke as a consort: thē can one colour set forth a beautie. But it may be, the generall consideration of mariage dooth not so much mislike you, as the applying of it to him. He is my sōne, I must confesse, I see him with a mothers eyes, which if they doo not much deceive me, he is no such one, over whom Contempt may make any just chalenge. He is comely, he is noble, he is rich ; but that which in it selfe should carie all comelinesse, nobilitie, and riches, he loves you; and he loves you, who is beloved of others. Drive not away his affection (sweete Ladie) and make no other Ladie hereafter proudly bragge, that she hath robbed you of so faithfull and notable a servant. *Philoclea* heard some pieces of her speches, no otherwise then one doth when a tedious pratler cōbers the hearing of a delightful musicke. For her thoughts had left her eares in that captivitie, and conveied themselves to behold (with such eies as imagination could lend thē) the estate of her *Zelmane*: for whō how wel she thought many of those sayings might have ben used with a farre more gratefull acceptation. Therefore listing not to dispute in a matter whereof her selfe was resolute, and desired not to enforme the other, she onely told her, that whilest she was so captived, she could not conceive of any such persuasions (though never so reasonable) any otherwise, then as constraints: and as constraints must needs evē in nature abhor thē, which at her libertie, in their owne force of reason, might more prevaile with her: and so faine would have returned the strength of *Cecropias* perswasions, to have procured freedome.

CHAP. 6.

[1] *Fresh motives to* Philoclea. [2] Cecropias *new fetch to attempt* Pamela. [3] Pamelas *prayer,* [4] *and Sainct-like graces in it.* [5] *Her Auntes fruiteles argumentes.*

BUt neither her wittie wordes in an enemie, nor those [1] wordes, made more then eloquent with passing through such lips, could prevaile in *Cecropia,* no more then her perswasions coulde winne *Philoclea* to disavowe her former vowe, or to leave the prisoner *Zelmane,* for the commaunding *Amphialus.* So that both sides being desirous, and neither graunters, they brake of conference. *Cecropia* sucking up more and more spite out of her deniall, which yet for her sonnes sake, she disguised with a visarde of kindnes, leaving no office unperfourmed, which might either witnes, or endeare her sonnes affection. Whatsoever could be imagined likely to please her, was with liberall diligence perfourmed: Musickes at her windowe, & especially such Musickes, as might (with dolefull embassage) call the mind to thinke of sorow, and thinke of it with sweetnes; with ditties so sensiblie expressing *Amphialus* case, that everie worde seemed to be but a diversifying of the name of *Amphialus.* Daily presents, as it were oblations, to pacifie an angrie Deitie, sent unto her: wherein, if the workmanship of the forme, had striven with the sumptuousnes of the matter, as much did the invention in the application, contende to have the chiefe excellencie: for they were as so many stories of his disgraces, & her perfections; where the richnes did invite the eyes, the fashion did entertaine the eyes, and the device did teach the eyes the present miserie of the presenter himselfe, awefully serviceable: which was the more notable, as his authoritie was manifest. And for the bondage wherein she lived, all meanes used to make knowen, that if it were a bondage, it was a bondage onely knitte in love-knots. But in harte alreadie understanding no language but one, the Musicke wrought indeede a dolefulnes, but it was a dolefulnes to be in his power: the dittie intended for *Amphialus,* she translated to *Zelmane*: the presents seemed so many tedious clogs of a thralled obligation: and his service, the more diligent it was, the more it did exprobrate (as she thought) unto her, her unworthie estate: that even he that did her service, had authoritie of commanding her, onely construing her servitude in his own nature, esteeming it a right, and a right bitter servitude: so that all their shots (how well soever levelled) being carried awrie from the marke, by the storme of her mislike, the Prince *Amphialus* affectionately languished, & *Cecropia* spitefullie cunning, disdained at the barrennes of their successe.

2   Which willingly *Cecropia* woulde have revenged, but that she sawe, her hurte could not be divided from her sonnes mischiefe: wherefore, she bethought her self to attempt *Pamela*, whose beautie being equall, she hoped, if she might be woon, that her sonnes thoughtes would rather rest on a beautifull gratefulnes, then still be tormented with a disdaining beautie. Wherfore, giving new courage to her wicked inventions, and using the more industry, because she had mist in this, & taking even precepts of prevailing in *Pamela*, by her fayling in *Philoclea*, she went to her chamber, & (according to her own ungratious method of a subtile proceeding) stood listning at the dore, because that out of the circũstance of her present behaviour, there might kindly arise a fitte beginning of her intended discourse.

3   And so she might perceave that *Pamela* did walke up and down, full of deep (though patient) thoughts. For her look and countenance was setled, her pace soft, and almost still of one measure, without any passionate gesture, or violent motion: till at length (as it were) awaking, & strengthning her selfe, Well (said she) yet this is the best, & of this I am sure, that how soever they wrõg me, they cannot over-master God. No darknes blinds his eyes, no Jayle barres him out. To whome then else should I flie, but to him for succoure? And therewith kneeling down, euẽ in the same place where she stood, she thus said. O all-seeing Light, and eternal Life of all things, to whom nothing is either so great, that it may resist; or so small, that it is contemned: looke upon my miserie with thine eye of mercie, and let thine infinite power vouchsafe to limite out some proportion of deliverance unto me, as to thee shall seem most convenient. Let not injurie, ô Lord, triumphe over me,

and let my faultes by thy handes be corrected, and make not
mine unjuste enemie the minister of thy Justice. But yet, my
God, if in thy wisdome, this be the aptest chastizement for my
inexcusable follie; if this low bondage be fittest for my over-
hie desires; if the pride of my not-inough humble harte, be thus
to be broken, O Lord, I yeeld unto thy will, and joyfully embrace what sorrow thou wilt have me suffer. Onely thus much
let me crave of thee, (let my craving, ô Lord, be accepted of
thee, since even that proceedes from thee) let me crave, even
by the noblest title, which in my greatest affliction I may give
my selfe, that I am thy creature, & by thy goodnes (which is
thy self) that thou wilt suffer some beame of thy Majestie so to
shine into my mind, that it may still depende confidently upon
thee. Let calamitie be the exercise, but not the overthrowe of
my vertue: let their power prevaile, but prevaile not to destruction: let my greatnes be their praie: let my paine be the
sweetnes of their revenge: let them (if so it seem good unto
thee) vexe me with more and more punishment. But, ô Lord,
let never their wickednes have such a hand, but that I may
carie a pure minde in a pure bodie. (And pausing a while) And
ô most gracious Lord (said she) what ever become of me, preserve the vertuous *Musidorus*.

The other parte *Cecropia* might well heare, but this latter 4
prayer for *Musidorus*, her hart helde it, as so jewel-like a
treasure, that it would scarce trust her owne lippes withall.
But this prayer, sent to heaven, from so heavenly a creature,
with such a fervent grace, as if Devotion had borowed her
bodie, to make of it self a most beautifull representation; with
her eyes so lifted to the skie-ward, that one would have thought
they had begunne to flie thetherward, to take their place amõg
their felow stars; her naked hands raising up their whole
length, & as it were kissing one another, as if the right had
bene the picture of *Zeale*, and the left, of *Humblenesse*, which
both united themselves to make their suites more acceptable.
Lastly, all her senses being rather tokens then instruments of
her inwarde motions, altogether had so straunge a working
power, that even the harde-harted wickednesse of *Cecropia*, if
it founde not a love of that goodnes, yet it felt an abashment
at that goodnes; & if she had not a kindly remorse, yet had
she an yrksome accusation of her owne naughtines, so that she

was put frõ the biasse of her fore-intended lesson. For well she found there was no way at that time to take that mind, but with some, at lest, image of Vertue, and what the figure thereof was her hart knew not.

5   Yet did she prodigally spende her uttermost eloquence, leaving no argument unproved, which might with any force invade her excellent judgement: the justnes of the request being, but for marriage; the worthinesse of the suiter: then her owne present fortune, if she would not onely have amendment, but felicitie: besides falsely making her believe, that her sister would thinke her selfe happie, if now she might have his love which before she contemned: and obliquely touching, what daunger it should be for her, if her sonne should accept *Philoclea* in marriage, and so match the next heire apparant, she being in his powre: yet plentifully perjuring, how extreamely her sonne loved her, and excusing the little shewes he made of it, with the dutifull respect he bare unto her, & taking upõ her selfe that she restrayned him, since she found she could set no limits to his passions. And as she did to *Philoclea*, so did she to her, with the tribute of gifts, seeke to bring her minde into servitude: and all other meanes, that might either establish a beholdingnesse, or at the lest awake a kindnes; doing it so, as by reason of their imprisonment, one sister knew not how the other was wooed; but each might thinke, that onely she was sought. But if *Philoclea* with sweete and humble dealing did avoid their assaults, she with the Majestie of Vertue did beate them of.

CHAP. 7.

[1] *An Allarme to the* Amphialians. [2] *Base cowardise in* Clinias; [3] *brave courage imaged in* Amphialus. [4] *His onset with the death of two friendes his foes.* [5] *The horrour of* Mars-*his game.* [6] *Two deaths taken where they were not lookt for, the third delayed where it was expected.*

[1]   But this day their speach was the sooner broken of, by reason that he, who stood as watche upon the top of the keepe, did not onely see a great dust arise (which the earth sent

up, as if it would strive to have clowdes as well as the aire) but might spie sometimes, especially when the dust (wherein the naked winde did apparaile it self) was caried aside frō them, the shining of armour, like flashing of lightning, wherwith the clowdes did seeme to be with child; which the Sunne guilding with his beames, it gave a sight delightfull to any, but to them that were to abide the terrour. But the watch gave a quick Alarum to the souldiers within, whome practise already having prepared, began each, with unabashed hartes, or at lest countenaunces, to looke to their charge, or obedience, which was allotted unto them.

Onely *Clinias* and *Amphialus* did exceed the bounds of 2 mediocrity: the one in his naturall coldnesse of cowardise, the other in heate of courage. For *Clinias* (who was bold onely in busie whisperings, and even in that whisperingnes rather indeed confident in his cunning, that it should not be bewraied, then any way bolde, if ever it should be bewrayed) now that the enemy gave a dreadful aspect unto the castle, his eyes saw no terror, nor eare heard any martiall sounde, but that they multiplied the hideousnesse of it to his mated minde. Before their comming he had many times felt a dreadfull expectation, but yet his minde (that was willing to ease it selfe of the burden of feare) did somtimes feine unto it selfe possibility of let; as the death of *Baſilius*, the discord of the nobility, & (when other cause fayled him) the nature of chaunce served as a cause unto him: and sometimes the hearing other men speake valiantly, and the quietnesse of his unassailed senses, would make himselfe beleve, that he durst do something. But now, that present daunger did display it selfe unto his eye, & that a daungerous dooing must be the onely meane to prevẽt the dãger of suffering, one that had marked him would have judged, that his eies would have run into him, & his soule out of him; so unkindly did either take a sent of danger. He thought the lake was too shallow, & the walles too thin: he misdouted ech mans treason, and conjectured every possibilitie of misfortune, not onely fore-casting likely perils, but such as all the planets together could scarce have conspired: & already began to arme him selfe, though it was determined he should tarrie within doores; and while he armed himselfe, imagined in what part of the vault he might hide himselfe if the enimies wonne the castle. Desirous he was that every body should do valiantly, but himselfe; and therefore was afraid to shew his feare, but for very feare would have hid his feare; lest it should discõfort others: but the more he sought to disguize it, the more the unsutablenes of a weake brokẽ voice to high brave wordes, and of a pale shaking countenance to a gesture of animating, did discover him.

3   But quite contrarily *Amphialus*, who before the enimies came was carefull, providently diligent, and not somtimes without doubting of the issue; now the nearer danger approched (like the light of a glow-worme) the lesse still it seemed: and now his courage began to boile in choler, and with such impatience to desire to powre out both upõ the enimie, that he issued presently into certaine boates he had of purpose, and carying with him some choise men, went to the fortresse he had upõ the edge of the lake, which he thought would be the first thing, that the enimy would attempt; because it was a passage, which cõmanding all that side of that country, & being lost would stop victuall, or other supply, that might be brought into the castle: & in that fortresse having some force of horsemen, he issued out with two hundred horse, & five hũdred footmen, embushed his footmẽ in the falling of a hill, which was overshadowed with a wood, he with his horsmẽ went a quarter of a mile further; aside hãd of which he might perceave the many troupes of the enimie, who came but to take view where best to encampe themselves.

4   But as if the sight of the enimie had bene a Magnes stone to his courage he could not cõtaine himself, but shewing his face to the enimie, & his backe to his souldiers, used that action, as his onely oration, both of denouncing warre to the one, and persuading help of the other. Who faithfully folowing an example of such authoritie, they made the earth to grone under their furious burden, and the enimies to begin to be angry with thẽ, whom in particular they knew not. Among whom there was a young man, youngest brother to *Philanax*, whose face as yet did not bewray his sex, with so much as shew of haire; of a minde having no limits of hope, nor knowing why to feare; full of jollitie in conversation, and lately growne a Lover. His name was *Agenor*, of all that armie the most beautifull: who having ridden in sportfull conversatiõ among the foremost, all

armed saving that his beaver was up, to have his breath in more freedome, seing *Amphialus* come a pretty way before his cōpany, neither staying the cōmaundement of the captaine, nor recking whether his face were armed, or no, set spurs to his horse, & with youthfull bravery casting his staffe about his head, put it then in his rest, as carefull of comely carying it, as if the marke had ben but a ring, & the lookers on Ladies. But *Amphialus* launce was already come to the last of his descending line, and began to make the full point of death against the head of this young Gentleman, when *Amphialus* perceyving his youth and beautie, Compassion so rebated the edge of Choller, that he spared that faire nakednesse, and let his staffe fall to *Agenors* vamplat: so as both with brave breaking should hurtleslie have perfourmed that match, but that the pittilesse launce of *Amphialus* (angry with being broken) with an unlucky counterbuffe full of unsparing splinters, lighted upon that face farre fitter for the combats of *Venus*; geving not onely a suddaine, but a fowle death, leaving scarsely any tokens of his former beautie: but his hãds abandoning the reynes, and his thighes the saddle, he fell sidewarde from the horse. Which sight comming to *Leontius*, a deere friende of his, who in vayne had lamentably cried unto him to stay, when he saw him beginne his careere, it was harde to say, whether pittie of the one, or revenge of the other, helde as then the soveraigntie in his passions. But while he directed his eye to his friende, and his hande to his enimie, so wrongly-consorted a power could not resist the ready minded force of *Amphialus*: who perceyving his il-directed direction against him, so paide him his debt before it was lent, that he also fell to the earth, onely happy that one place, & one time, did finish both their loves and lives together.

But by this time there had bene a furious meeting of either 5 side: where after the terrible salutation of warlike noyse, the shaking of handes was with sharpe weapons: some launces according to the mettall they mett, and skill of the guider, did staine themselves in bloud; some flew up in pieces, as if they would threaten heaven, because they fayled on earth. But their office was quickly inherited, either by (the Prince of weapons) the sworde, or by some heavy mase, or biting axe; which hunting still the weakest chase, sought ever to light

there, where smallest resistăce might worse prevent mischief.
The clashing of armour, and crushing of staves; the justling
of bodies, the resounding of blowes, was the first part of that
ill-agreeing musicke, which was beautified with the griselinesse
of wounds, the rising of dust, the hideous falles, and grones of
the dying. The verie horses angrie in their maisters anger,
with love and obedience brought foorth the effects of hate and
resistance, and with minds of servitude, did as if they affected
glorie. Some lay deade under their dead maisters, whome
unknightly wounds had unjustly punished for a faithfull dutie.
Some lay uppon their Lordes by like accidents, and in death
had the honour to be borne by them, whō in life they had
borne. Some having lost their commaunding burthens, ranne
scattered about the field, abashed with the madnesse of mankinde. The earth it selfe (woont to be a buriall of men) was
nowe (as it were) buried with men: so was the face thereof
hidden with deade bodies, to whome Death had come masked
in diverse manners. In one place lay disinherited heades, dis-
possessed of their naturall seignories: in an other, whole bodies
to see to, but that their harts wont to be bound all over so close,
were nowe with deadly violence opened: in others, fowler
deaths had ouglily displayed their trayling guttes. There lay
armes, whose fingers yet mooved, as if they woulde feele for
him that made them feele: and legges, which contrarie to
common nature, by being discharged of their burthen, were
growne heavier. But no sworde payed so large a tribute of
soules to the eternall Kingdome, as that of *Amphialus*, who like
a Tigre, from whome a companie of Woolves did seeke to
ravish a newe gotten pray; so he (remembring they came to
take away *Philoclea*) did labour to make valure, strength,
hatred, and choller to answere the proportion of his love, which
was infinit.

6   There died of his handes the olde knight *Æschylus*, who
though by yeares might well have beene allowed to use rather
the exercise of wisedome, then of courage; yet having a lustie
bodie & a merrie hart, he ever tooke the summons of Time in
jest, or else it had so creepingly stollen upon him, that he had
heard scarcely the noise of his feete, and therefore was as fresh
in apparell, and as forwarde in enterprises, as a farre yonger
man: but nothing made him bolder, then a certaine prophecie

had beene tolde him, that he shoulde die in the armes of his sonne, and therefore feared the lesse the arme of an enemie. But nowe, when *Amphialus* sworde was passed through his throate, he thought himselfe abused; but that before he died, his sonne indeede, seeing his father beginne to fall, helde him up in his armes, till a pitilesse souldier of the other side, with a mace brained him, making father and sonne become twinnes in their never againe dying birth. As for *Drialus*, *Memnon*, *Nisus* and *Policrates*; the first had his eyes cut out so, as he could not see to bid the neare following death welcome: the seconde had met with the same Prophet that olde *Æschylus* had, and having founde manie of his speeches true, beleeved this to, that he should never be killed, but by his owne companions: and therefore no man was more valiant then he against an enemie, no man more suspicious of his friends: so as he seemed to sleepe in securitie, when he went to a battell, and to enter into a battaile, when he began to sleepe, such guards he would set about his person; yet mistrusting the verie guardes, that they would murther him. But nowe *Amphialus* helped to unriddle his doubts; for he overthrowing him from his horse, his owne companions comming with a fresh supplie, pressed him to death. *Nisus* grasping with *Amphialus*, was with a short dagger slaine. And for *Policrates*, while he shunned as much as he could, keeping onely his place for feare of punishment, *Amphialus* with a memorable blowe strake of his head, where, with the convulsions of death setting his spurres to his horse, he gave so brave a charge upon the enemie, as it grewe a proverbe, that *Policrates* was onely valiant, after his head was off. But no man escaped so well his handes as *Phebilus* did: for he having long loved *Philoclea*, though for the meannesse of his estate he never durst reveale it, nowe knowing *Amphialus*, setting the edge of a rivall upon the sworde of an enemie, he helde strong fight with him. But *Amphialus* had alreadie in the daungerousest places disarmed him, and was lifting up his sworde to sende him away from him, when he thinking indeede to die, O *Philoclea* (said he) yet this joyes me, that I die for thy sake. The name of *Philoclea* first staied his sworde, and when he heard him out, though he abhorde him much worse then before, yet could he not vouchsafe him the honour of dying for *Philoclea*, but turned his sword another way, doing him no hurt for over-much hatred. But what good did that to poore *Phebilus*, if escaping a valiant hand, he was slaine by a base souldiour, who seeing him so disarmed, thrust him through?

CHAP. 8.

The Basilians reembattelled ¹*first by* Philanax, ⁴*then by the blacke Knight.* ²Ismenus *slaine by* Philanax. ³Philanax *captived by* Amphialus. ⁴*The blacke Knights exploits.* ⁵*His encounter with* Amphialus, *parted by a by-blow.* ⁶*The Amphialians retrait, and departure of the blacke Knight.*

1 THus with the well-followed valure of *Amphialus* were the other almost overthrowne, when *Philanax* (who was the marshal of the army) came in, with newe force renuing the almost decayed courage of his souldiers. For, crying to them (and asking them whether their backes or their armes were better fighters) he himselfe thrust into the presse, and making force and furie waite uppon discretion and governement, he might seeme a brave Lion, who taught his yong Lionets, how in taking of a pray, to joine courage with cunning. Thẽ Fortune (as if she had made chases inow of the one side of that blooddy Teniscourt) went of the other side the line, making as many fall downe of *Amphialus* followers, as before had done of *Philanaxis*; they loosing the ground, as fast as before they had woon it, only leaving them to keepe it, who had lost themselves in keeping it. Then those that had killed, inherited the lot of those that had bene killed; and cruel Death made thẽ lie quietly togither, who most in their lives had sought to disquiet ech other; and many of those first overthrowne, had the comfort to see the murtherers overrun them to *Charons* ferrie.

2 *Codrus, Ctesiphon,* and *Milo,* lost their lives upon *Philanax*-his sword: but no bodies case was more pitied, then of a yong esquire of *Amphialus,* called *Ismenus,* who never abandoning his maister, and making his tender age aspire to actes of the strongest manhoode, in this time that his side was put to the worst, and that *Amphialus*-his valure was the onely stay of them from delivering themselves over to a shamefull flight, he

sawe his masters horse killed under him. Whereupon, asking no advise of no thought, but of faithfulnes and courage, he presently lighted from his owne horse, and with the helpe of some choise and faithfull servants, gat his master up. But in the multitude that came of either side, some to succour, some to save *Amphialus*, he came under the hande of *Philanax*: and the youth perceyving he was the man that did most hurt to his partie, (desirous evĕ to change his life for glorie) strake at him, as he rode by him, and gave him a hurt upon the leg, that made *Philanax* turn towards him; but seing him so yŏg, & of a most lovely presence, he rather toke pity of him; meaning to make him prisoner, & thĕ to give him to his brother *Agenor* to be his companion, because they were not much unlike, neither in yeeres, nor countenance. But as he loked down upon him with that thought, he spied wher his brother lay dead, & his friend *Leontius* by him, evĕ almost under the squiers feet. Thĕ soroing not only his owne sorow, but the past-cŏfort sorow, which he fore-knew his mother would take, (who with many teares, & misgiving sighs had suffred him to go with his elder brother *Philanax*) blotted out all figures of pitie out of his minde, and putting foorth his horse (while *Ismenus* doubled two or three more valiant, then well set blowes) saying to himselfe, Let other mothers bewaile an untimely death as well as mine; he thrust him through. And the boy fearce though beautiful; & beautifull, though dying, not able to keepe his failing feete, fel downe to the earth, which he bit for anger, repining at his Fortune, and as long as he could resisting Death, which might seeme unwilling to; so long he was in taking away his yong struggling soule.

Philanax himselfe could have wished the blow ungiven, when he saw him fall like a faire apple, which some uncourteous bodie (breaking his bowe) should throwe downe before it were ripe. But the case of his brother made him forget both that, and himselfe: so as overhastily pressing uppon the retiring enemies, he was (ere he was aware) further engaged then his owne souldiers could relieve him; were being overthrowne by *Amphialus*, *Amphialus* glad of him, kept head aginst his enemies while some of his men caried away *Philanax*.

But *Philanax*-his men as if with the losse of *Philanax* they had lost the fountaine of their valure, had their courages so dried up in feare; that they began to set honour at their backes, and to use the vertue of pacience in an untimely time: when into the presse comes (as hard as his horse, more afraied of the spurre, then the sword could carie him) a Knight in armor as darke as blacknes coulde make it, followed by none, and adorned by nothing; so far without authoritie that he was without knowledge. But vertue quickly made him knowne, and admiration bred him such authoritie, that though they of whose side he came knew him not, yet they all knew it was fitte to obey him: and while he was followed by the valiantest, he made way for the vilest. For, taking part with the besiegers, he made the *Amphialians* bloud serve for a caparison to his horse, and a decking to his armour. His arme no oftner gave blowes, then the blowes gave wounds, then the wounds gave deathes: so terrible was his force, and yet was his quicknes more forcible then his force, and his judgement more quick then his quicknes. For though the sword went faster then eyesight could follow it, yet his owne judgement went still before it. There died of his hand, *Sarpedon, Plistonax, Strophilus,* and *Hippolitus,* men of great proofe in warres, and who had that day undertaken the guard of *Amphialus.* But while they sought to save him, they lost the fortresses that Nature had placed them in. Thĕ slew he *Megalus,* who was a little before proude, to see himselfe stained in the bloud of his enemies: but when his owne bloud came to be married to theirs, he then felt, that „Crueltie dooth never enjoy a good cheape glorie. After him sent he *Palemon,* who had that daye vowed (with foolish braverie) to be the death of tenne: and nine already he had killed, and was carefull to performe his (almost performed) vowe, when the Blacke Knight helpt him to make up the tenth himselfe.

5 And now the often-changing Fortune began also to chaunge the hewe of the battailes. For at the first, though it were terrible, yet Terror was deckt so bravelie with rich furniture, guilte swords, shining armours, pleasant pensils, that the eye with delight had scarce leasure to be afraide: But now all universally defiled with dust, bloud, broken armours, mangled bodies, tooke away the maske, and sette foorth Horror in his owne horrible manner. But neither could danger be dreadfull to *Amphialus*-his undismayable courage, nor yet seeme ougly to him, whose truely-affected minde, did still paint it over with

the beautie of *Philoclea*. And therefore he, rather enflamed
then troubled with the encrease of dangers, and glad to finde a
woorthie subject to exercise his courage, sought out this newe
Knight, whom he might easilie finde: for he, like a wanton
rich man, that throwes down his neighbours houses, to make
himselfe the better prospecte, so had his sworde made him so
spatious a roome, that *Amphialus* had more cause to wonder at
the finding, then labour for the seeking: which, if it stirred
hate in him, to see how much harme he did to the one side, it
provoked as much æmulation in him, to perceave how much
good he did to the other side. Therefore, they approaching
one to the other, as in two beautifull folkes, Love naturally
stirres a desire of joyning, so in their two courages Hate stirred
a desire of triall. Then began there a combatte betweene
them, worthy to have had more large listes, and more quiet
beholders: for with the spurre of Courage, and the bitte of
Respect, each so guided himselfe, that one might well see, the
desire to overcome, made them not forget how to overcome:
in such time & proportion they did employ their blowes, that
none of *Ceres* servaunts coulde more cunningly place his flaile:
while the lefte foote spurre set forwarde his owne horse, the
right sette backward the contrarie horse, even sometimes by the
advauntage of the enemies legge, while the lefte hande (like him
that helde the sterne) guyded the horses obedient courage: All
done in such order, that it might seeme, the minde was a right
Prince indeede, who sent wise and diligent Lieutenants into
each of those well governed partes. But the more they fought,
the more they desired to fight; and the more they smarted, the
lesse they felte the smarte: and now were like to make a quicke
proofe, to whom Fortune or Valour woulde seeme most friendly,
when in comes an olde Governour of *Amphialus*, alwayes a
good Knight, and carefull of his charge; who giving a sore
wounde to the blacke Knights thigh, while he thought not of
him, with an other blowe slewe his horse under him. *Amphialus*
cried to him, that he dishonoured him: You say well (answered
the olde Knight) to stande now like a private souldier, setting
your credite upon particular fighting, while you may see *Basilius*
with all his hoste, is getting betweene you and your towne.

He looked that way, and found that true indeede, that the
enemie was beginning to encompasse him about, and stoppe his

returne: and therefore causing the retreite to be sounded, his Governour ledde his men homewarde, while he kepte him selfe still hindmoste, as if hee had stoode at the gate of a sluse, to lette the streame goe, with such proportion, as shoulde seeme good unto him: and with so manfull discretion perfourmed it, that (though with losse of many of his men) he returned in him selfe safe, and content, that his enemies had felte, how sharpe the sworde coulde bite of *Philocleas* Lover. The other partie being sorie for the losse of *Philanax*, was yet sorrier when the blacke Knight could not be found. For he having gotten on a horse, whom his dying master had bequeathed to the world, finding himselfe sore hurt, and not desirous to be knowen, had in the time of the enemies retiring, retired away also: his thigh not bleeding bloud so fast, as his harte bledde revenge. But *Basilius* having attempted in vaine to barre the safe returne of *Amphialus*, encamped himselfe as strongly as he could, while he (to his grief) might heare the joy was made in the towne by his owne subjectes, that he had that day sped no better. For *Amphialus* (being well beloved of that people) when they sawe him not vanquished, they esteemed him as victorious, his youth setting a flourishing shew upon his worthinesse, and his great nobilitie ennobling his dangers.

CHAP. 9.

[1]*The Love-divining dreame of* Amphialus *song to* Philoclea. [2]*Philanax his captivitie, and deaths-doome,* [3]*for* Philocleas *sake turnde to life and libertie.* [4]*His loyall answere of his Lords intents.* [5]*Cecropias artes to perswade the sisters.*

BUt the first thing *Amphialus* did, being returned, was to visite *Philoclea*, and first presuming to cause his dreame to be song unto her (which he had seen the night before he fell in love with her) making a fine boy he had, accorde a prettie dolefulnes unto it. The song was this.

[1] *NOw was our heav'nly vaulte deprived of the light*
       With Sunnes depart: and now the darkenes of the night
Did light those beamye stars which greater light did darke:
Now each thing that enjoy'd that firie quickning sparke

(Which life is cald) were mov'd their spirits to repose,
And wanting use of eyes their eyes began to close:
A silence sweet each where with one consent embraste
(A musique sweet to one in carefull musing plaste)
And mother Earth, now clad in mourning weeds, did breath
A dull desire to kisse the image of our death:
When I, disgraced wretch, not wretched then, did give
My senses such reliefe, as they which quiet live,
Whose braines broile not in woes, nor brests with beatings ake,
With natures praise are wont in safest home to take.
Far from my thoughts was ought, whereto their minds aspire,
Who under courtly pompes doo hatch a base desire.
Free all my powers were from those captiving snares,
Which heav'nly purest gifts defile in muddy cares.
Ne could my soule it selfe accuse of such a faulte,
As tender conscience might with furious panges assaulte.
But like the feeble flower (whose stalke cannot sustaine
His weighty top) his top doth downeward drooping leane:
Or as the silly birde in well acquainted nest
Doth hide his head with cares but onely how to rest:
So I in simple course, and unentangled minde
Did suffer drousie lids mine eyes then cleare to blinde;
And laying downe my head, did natures rule observe,
Which senses up doth shut the senses to preserve.
They first their use forgot, then fancies lost their force;
Till deadly sleepe at length possest my living coarse.
A living coarse I lay: but ah, my wakefull minde
(Which made of heav'nly stuffe no mortal chaüge doth blind)
Flew up with freer wings of fleshly bondage free;
And having plaste my thoughts, my thoughts thus placed me.
Me thought, nay sure I was, I was in fairest wood
Of Samothea lande; a lande, which whilom stood
An honour to the world, while Honour was their ende,
And while their line of yeares they did in vertue spende.
But there I was, and there my calmie thoughts I fedd
On Natures sweet repast, as healthfull senses ledd.
Her giftes my study was, her beauties were my sporte:
My worke her workes to know, her dwelling my resorte.
Those lampes of heav'nly fire to fixed motion bound,
The ever-turning spheares, the never-moving ground;

THE COUNTESSE OF PEMBROKES

What essence dest'nie hath; if fortune be or no;
Whence our immortall soules to mortall earth doo flowe:
What life it is, and how that all these lives doo gather,
With outward makers force, or like an inward father.
Such thoughts, me thought, I thought, and straind my single mind
Then void of neerer cares, the depth of things to find.
When lo with hugest noise (such noise a tower makes
When it blowne downe with winde a fall of ruine takes)
(Or such a noise it was, as highest thunders sende,
Or canons thunder-like, all shot togither, lende)
The Moone a sunder rent; whereout with sodaine fall
(More swift then falcons stoope to feeding Falconers call)
There came a chariot faire by doves and sparrowes guided:
Whose stormelike course staid not till hard by me it bided.
I wretch astonisht was, and thought the deathfull doome
Of heaven, of earth, of hell, of time and place was come.
But streight there issued forth two Ladies (Ladies sure
They seemd to me) on whom did waite a Virgin pure:
Straunge were the Ladies weeds; yet more unfit then strange.
The first with cloth's tuckt up as Nymphes in woods do range;
Tuckt up even with the knees, with bowe and arrowes prest:
Her right arme naked was, discovered was her brest.
But heavy was her pace, and such a meagre cheere,
As little hunting minde (God knowes) did there appeere.
The other had with arte (more then our women knowe,
As stuffe meant for the sale set out to glaring showe)
A wanton womans face, and with curld knots had twinde
Her haire, which by the helpe of painters cunning, shinde.
When I such guests did see come out of such a house,
The mountaines great with childe I thought brought foorth a mouse.
But walking forth, the first thus to the second saide,
Venus *come on: said she,* Diane *you are obaide.*
Those names abasht me much, whĕ those great names I hard:
Although their fame (me seemd) from truth had greatly jard.
As I thus musing stood, Diana *cald to her*
The waiting Nymphe, a Nymphe that did excell as farr
All things that earst I sawe, as orient pearles exceed,
That which their mother hight, or els their silly seed.
Indeed a perfect hewe, indeed a sweet consent
Of all those Graces giftes the heavens have ever lent.

And so she was attirde, as one that did not prize
Too much her peerles parts, nor yet could them despise.
But cald, she came apace; a pace wherein did move
The bande of beauties all, the little world of Love.
And bending humbled eyes (ò eyes the Sunne of sight)
She waited mistresse will: who thus disclosd her spright.
Sweet Mira *mine (quoth she) the pleasure of my minde,*
In whom of all my rules the perfect proofe I finde,
To onely thee thou seest we graunt this speciall grace
Us to attend, in this most private time and place.
Be silent therefore now, and so be silent still
Of that thou seest: close up in secrete knot thy will.
She answer'd was with looke, and well perform'd behest:
And Mira *I admirde: her shape sonke in my brest.*
But thus with irefull eyes, and face that shooke with spite
Diana *did begin.* *What mov'd me to invite*
Your presence (sister deare) first to my Moony *spheare,*
And hither now, vouchsafe to take with willing eare.
I know full well you know, what discord long hath raign'd
Betwixt us two; how much that discord foule hath stain'd
Both our estates, while each the other did deprave,
Proofe speakes too much to us that feeling triall have.
Our names are quite forgot, our temples are defac'd:
Our offrings spoil'd, our priest from priesthood are displac'd
Is this the fruite of strife? those thousand churches hie,
Those thousand altars faire now in the dust to lie?
In mortall mindes our mindes but planets names preserve:
No knees once bowed, forsooth, for them they say we serve.
Are we their servants growne? no doubt a noble staye:
Celestiall powers to wormes, Joves *children serve to claye.*
But such they say we be: this praise our discord bred,
While we for mutuall spight a striving passion fed.
But let us wiser be; and what foule discorde brake,
So much more strong againe let fastest concorde make.
Our yeares doo it require: you see we both doo feele
The weakning worke of Times *for ever-whirling wheele.*
Although we be divine, our grandsire Saturne *is*
With ages force decay'd, yet once the heaven was his.
And now before we seeke by wise Apollos *skill*
Our young yeares to renew (for so he saith he will)

THE COUNTESSE OF PEMBROKES

Let us a perfect peace betweene us two resolve:
Which lest the ruinous want of government dissolve;
Let one the Princesse be, to her the other yeeld:
For vaine equalitie is but contentions field.
And let her have the giftes that should in both remaine:
In her let beautie both, and chastnesse fully raigne.
So as if I prevaile, you give your giftes to me:
If you, on you I lay what in my office be.
Now resteth onely this, which of us two is she,
To whom precedence shall of both accorded be.
For that (so that you like) hereby doth lie a youth
(She beckned unto me) as yet of spotlesse truth,
Who may this doubt discerne: for better, witt, then lot
Becommeth us: in us fortune determines not.
This crowne of amber faire (an amber crowne she held)
To worthiest let him give, when both he hath beheld:
And be it as he saith. Venus was glad to heare
Such proffer made, which she well showd with smiling cheere.
As though she were the same, as when by Paris doome
She had chiefe Goddesses in beautie overcome.
And smirkly thus gan say. I never sought debate
Diana deare; my minde to love and not to hate
Was ever apt: but you my pastimes did despise.
I never spited you, but thought you overwise.
Now kindnesse profred is, none kinder is then I:
And so most ready am this meane of peace to trie.
And let him be our judge: the lad doth please me well.
Thus both did come to me, and both began to tell
(For both togither spake, each loth to be behinde)
That they by solemne oth their Deities would binde
To stand unto my will: their will they made me know.
I that was first agast, when first I saw their showe:
Now bolder waxt, waxt prowde, that I such sway must beare:
For neere acquaintance dooth diminish reverent feare.
And having bound them fast by Styx, they should obaye
To all what I decreed, did thus my verdict saye.
How ill both you can rule, well hath your discord taught:
Ne yet for ought I see, your beauties merite ought.
To yonder Nymphe therefore (to Mira I did point)
The crowne above you both for ever I appoint.

398

I would have spoken out: but out they both did crie;
Fie, fie, what have we done? ungodly rebell fie.
But now we needs must yeelde, to that our othes require.
Yet thou shalt not go free (quoth Venus) such a fire
Her beautie kindle shall within thy foolish minde,
That thou full oft shalt wish thy judging eyes were blinde.
Nay then (Diana said) the chastnesse I will give
In ashes of despaire (though burnt) shall make thee live.
Nay thou (said both) shalt see such beames shine in her face
That thou shalt never dare seeke helpe of wretched case.
And with that cursed curse away to heaven they fled,
First having all their giftes upon faire Mira spred.
The rest I cannot tell, for therewithall I wak'd
And found with deadly feare that all my sinewes shak'd.
Was it a dreame? O dreame, how hast thou wrought in me,
That I things erst unseene should first in dreaming see?
And thou ô traytour Sleepe, made for to be our rest,
How hast thou framde the paine wherewith I am opprest?
O cowarde Cupid thus doost thou thy honour keepe,
Unarmde (alas) unwares to take a man asleepe?

Laying not onely the conquests, but the hart of the cõquerour at her feet. *** But she receiving him after her woonted sorrowfull (but otherwise unmoved) mãner, it made him thinke, his good successe was but a pleasant monument of a dolefull buriall: Joy it selfe seeming bitter unto him, since it agreed not to her taste.

Therefore, still craving his mothers helpe to persuade her, 2 he himself sent for *Philanax* unto him, whom he had not onely long hated, but nowe had his hate greatly encreased by the death of his Squire *Ismenus*. Besides he had made him as one of the chiefe causes that mooved him to this rebellion, and therefore was enclined (to colour the better his action, and the more to embrewe the handes of his accomplices by making them guiltie of such a trespasse) in some formall sort to cause him to be executed: being also greatly egged thereunto by his mother, and some other, who long had hated *Philanax*, onely because he was more worthy to be loved then they.

But while that deliberation was handeled, according rather 3 to the humour then the reason of ech speaker, *Philoclea* comming

399

to knowledge of the hard plight wherein *Philanax* stood, she desired one of the gentlewomen appoynted to waite upon her, to goe in her name, and beseech *Amphialus*, that if the love of her had any power of perswasion in his minde, he would lay no further punishment, then imprisonment, uppon *Philanax*. This message was delivered even as *Philanax* was entring to the presence of *Amphialus*, comming (according to the warning was given him) to receyve a judgement of death. But when he with manfull resolution attended the fruite of such a tyrannicall sentence, thinking it wrong, but no harme to him that shoulde die in so good a cause; *Amphialus* turned quite the fourme of his pretended speech, and yeelded him humble thankes, that by his meanes he had come to that happinesse, as to receive a commaundement of his Ladie: and therefore he willingly gave him libertie to returne in safetye whither he would; quitting him, not onely of all former grudge, but assuring him that he would be willing to do him any friendship, and service: onely desiring thus much of him, that he would let him know the discourse and intent of *Basilius*-his proceeding.

4   Truely my Lorde (answered *Philanax*) if there were any such knowne to me, secrete in my maisters counsaile, as that the revealing thereof might hinder his good successe, I shoulde loath the keeping of my blood, with the losse of my faith; and woulde thinke the just name of a traitour a harde purchase of a fewe yeares living. But since it is so, that my maister hath indeede no way of privie practise, but meanes openly and forcibly to deale against you, I will not sticke in fewe wordes to make your required declaration. Then tolde he him in what amaze of amazement, both *Basilius* and *Gynecia* were, when they mist their children and *Zelmane*. Sometimes apt to suspect some practise of *Zelmane*, because she was a straunger; sometimes doubting some reliques of the late mutinie, which doubt was rather encreased, then any way satisfied, by *Miso*: who (being founde, almost deade for hunger, by certaine Countrey-people) brought home worde, with what cunning they were trayned out, and with what violence they were caried away. But that within a fewe dayes they came to knowledge where they were, with *Amphialus*-his owne letters sent abroade to procure confederates in his attempts. That

Basilius his purpose was never to leave the siege of this towne, till he had taken it, and revenged the injurie done unto him. That he meant rather to winne it by time, and famine, then by force of assault: knowing howe valiaunt men he had to deale withall in the towne: that he had sent order, that supplyes of souldiours, pioners, and all things else necessarie, shoulde dayly be brought unto him: so as, my Lorde (sayde *Philanax*) let me nowe, having receyved my life by your grace, let me give you your life and honour by my counsaile; protesting unto you, that I cannot choose but love you, being my maister-his nephewe; and that I wish you well in all causes: but this, you knowe his nature is as apte to forgive, as his power is able to conquere. Your fault passed is excusable, in that Love perswaded, and youth was perswaded. Do not urge the effects of angrie victorie, but rather seeke to obtaine that constantly by courtesie, which you can never assuredly enjoy by violence. One might easily have seene in the cheare of *Amphialus*, that disdainfull choller woulde faine have made the aunswere for him, but the remembraunce of *Philoclea* served for forcible barriers betweene Anger, and angry effects: so as he saide no more, but that he woulde not put him to the trouble to give him any further counsaile: But that he might returne, if he listed, presently. *Philanax* glad to receyve an uncorrupted libertie, humbly accepted his favourable convoy out of the towne; and so departed, not having visited the Princesses, thinking it might be offensive to *Amphialus*, and no way fruit-full to them, who were no way but by force to be relieved.

The poore Ladies indeede, not suffered either to meet together, or to have côference with any other, but such as *Cecropia* had alreadie framed to sing all her songs to her tune, she herselfe omitting no day, and catching holde of everie occasion to moove forwarde her sonnes desire, and remove their knowne resolutions: using the same arguments to the one sister, as to the other; determining that whome she coulde winne first, the other shoulde (without her sonnes knowledge) by poyson be made away. But though the reasons were the same to both, yet the handeling was diverse, according as she sawe their humours to preferre a more or lesse aptnesse of apprehension: this day having used long speech to *Philoclea*, amplifying not a little the great duetifulnesse her sonne had shewed in delivering

Philanax : of whome she coulde get no aunswere, but a silence sealed up in vertue, and so sweetly graced, as that in one instant it caried with it both resistance, and humblenesse.

CHAP. 10.

[1]Pamelas *exercise.* Cecropias *talke with her* [2]*of Beautie* [3]*and the use thereof.* [4]*The Auntes Atheisme* [5]*refuted by the Neeces Divinitie.*

[1] CEcropia threatning in her selfe to runne a more ragged race with her, went to her sister *Pamela :* who that day having wearied her selfe with reading, and with the height of her hart disdaining to keepe companie with any of the Gentlewomen appointed to attende her, whome she accounted her jaylours, was woorking uppon a purse certaine Roses and Lillies, as by the finenesse of the worke, one might see she had borowed her wittes of the sorow that owed them, & lent them wholy to that exercise. For the flowers she had wrought, caried such life in them, that the cuningest painter might have learned of her needle: which with so prety a maner made his careers to & fro through the cloth, as if the needle it selfe would have bene loth to have gone fröward such a mistres, but that it hoped to return thêceward very quickly againe: the cloth loking with many eies upon her, & lovingly embracing the wounds she gave it: the sheares also were at hand to behead the silke, that was growne to short. And if at any time she put her mouth to bite it off, it seemed, that where she had beene long in making of a Rose with her hand, she would in an instant make Roses with her lips; as the Lillies seemed to have their whitenesse, rather of the hande that made them, then of the matter whereof they were made; and that they grew there by the Sünes of her eyes, & were refreshed by the most in discomfort comfortable ayre, which an unwares sigh might bestow upon them. But the colours for the grounde were so well chosen, neither sullenly darke, nor glaringly lightsome, and so well proportioned, as that, though much cunning were in it, yet it was but to serve for an ornament of the principall woorke; that it was not without marvaile to see, howe a minde which could cast a carelesse

semblant upon the greatest conflictes of Fortune, coulde commaunde it selfe to take care for so small matters. Neither had she neglected the daintie dressing of her selfe: but as it had ben her mariage time to Affliction, she rather semed to remember her owne worthinesse, then the unworthinesse of her husband. For well one might perceyve she had not rejected the counsaile of a glasse, and that her handes had pleased themselves, in paying the tribute of undeceyving skill, to so high perfections of Nature.

The sight whereof so diverse from her sister, (who rather 2 suffered sorrow to distresse it selfe in her beautie, then that she would bestow any intertainment of so unwelcome a guest) made *Cecropia* take a suddaine assurednesse of hope, that she should obtaine somewhat of *Pamela*: thinking (according to the squaring out of her own good nature) that beauty, carefully set forth, wold soone prove a signe of an unrefusing harborough. Animated wherewith, she sate downe by *Pamela*: and taking the purse, and with affected curiositie looking upon the worke, Full happie is he (saide she) at least if he knew his owne happinesse, to whom a purse in this maner, and by this hand wrought, is dedicated. In faith he shall have cause to account it, not as a purse for treasure, but as a treasure it selfe, worthie to be pursed up in the purse of his owne hart. And thinke you so indeed (said *Pamela* halfe smiling) I promise you I wrought it, but to make some tedious houres beleeve, that I thought not of them: for else I valued it, but even as a verie purse. It is the right nature (saide *Cecropia*) of Beautie, to woorke unwitting effectes of wonder. Truely (saide *Pamela*) I never thought till nowe, that this outward glasse, intitled Beautie, which it pleaseth you to lay to my (as I thinke) unguiltie charge, was but a pleasaunt mixture of naturall colours, delightfull to the eye, as musicke is to the eare, without any further consequence: since it is a thing, which not onely beastes have; but even stones and trees many of them doo greatly excell in it. That other thinges (answered *Cecropia*) have some portion of it, takes not away the excellencie of it, where indeede it doth excell: since we see, that even those beastes, trees, & stones, are in the name of Beauty only highly praised. But that the beautie of humaine persons be beyond all other things there is great likelihood of reason, since to them onely is given the judgement to discerne Beautie; and among reasonable wights, as it seemes, that our sex hath the

preheminence, so that in that preheminence, Nature counter-
vailes all other liberalities, wherin she may be thought to have
dealte more favourably towarde mankind. How doo men
crowne (thinke you) themselves with glorie, for having either
by force brought others to yeeld to their minde, or with long
studie, and premeditated orations, perswaded what they woulde
have perswaded? and see, a faire woman shall not onely commaund without authoritie, but perswade without speaking. She
shall not neede to procure attention, for their owne eyes will
chaine their eares unto it. Men venture lives to conquere; she
conqueres lives without venturing. She is served, and obeyed,
which is the most notable, not because the lawes so commaund
it, but because they become lawes to thëselves to obey her; not
for her parents sake, but for her owne sake. She neede not dispute, whether to governe by Feare, or by Love, since without
her thinking thereof, their love will bring foorth feare, and their
feare will fortifie their love: and she neede not seeke offensive,
or defensive force, since her lippes may stande for ten thousand
shieldes, and tenne thousand unevitable shot goe from her eyes.
Beautie, Beautie (deare Neece) is the crowne of the feminine
greatnes; which gifte, on whom soever the heavens (therein
most nigardly) do bestowe, without question, she is bound to use
it to the noble purpose, for which it is created: not onely
winning, but preserving; since that indeede is the right happines,
which is not onely in it selfe happie, but can also derive the
happines to another. Certainly Aunt (said *Pamela*) I feare me
you will make me not onely thinke my selfe fairer then ever I
did, but think my fairnes a matter of greater valew then heretofore I coulde imagine it. For I ever (till now) conceaved
these conquests you spake of, rather to proceed from the weakenes of the conquered, then from the strength of the cõquering
power: as they say, the Cranes overthrowe whole battailes of
Pygmees, not so much of their Cranish courage, as because the
other are *Pygmees*: and that we see, young babes think babies
of woonderful excellencie, and yet the babies are but babies.
But since your elder yeares, and abler judgement, finde Beautie
to be worthy of so incomparable estimation, certainly me thinks,
it ought to be held in dearnes, according to the excellencie, and
(no more then we would do of things which we accoũt pretious)
ever to suffer it to be defiled.

Defiled? (said *Cecropia*) Mary God forbid that my speech 3 should tend to any such purpose, as should deserve so foul a title. My meaning is to joyn your beauty to love; your youth to delight. For truely, as colours should be as good as nothing, if there were no eyes to behold them: so is Beauty nothing, without the eye of Love behold it: and therfore, so far is it from defiling it, that it is the only honoring of it, the only preserving of it: for Beauty goes away, devoured by Time, but where remaines it ever flourishing, but in the hart of a true lover? And such a one (if ever there were any) is my son: whose love is so subjected unto you, that rather then breed any offence unto you, it will not delight it selfe in beholding you. Ther is no effect of his love (answered *Pamela*) better pleaseth me then that: but as I have oftē answered you, so, resolutely I say unto you, that he must get my parents consent, & then he shall know further of my mind; for, without that, I know I should offend God. O sweet youth (said *Cecropia*) how untimely subject it is to devotion? No, no sweet neece, let us old folks think of such precise consideratiõs, do you enjoy the heaven of your age, whereof you are sure: and like good housholders, which spend those thinges that will not be kept, so do you pleasantly enjoy that, which else will bring an over-late repentance, whē your glas shall accuse you to your face, what a change there is in you. Do you see how the spring-time is ful of flowers, decking it self with them, & not aspiring to the fruits of *Autumn?* what lesson is that unto you, but that in the april of your age, you should be like *April?* Let not some of thē, for whom alredy the grave gapeth, & perhaps envy the felicity in you, which thēselves cannot enjoy, perswade you to lose the hold of occasiõ, while it may not only be taken, but offers, nay sues to be takē: which if it be not now taken, will never hereafter be overtaken. Your self know, how your father hath refused all offers made by the greatest Princes about you, & wil you suffer your beauty to be hid in the wrinckles of his pevish thoughts? If he be pevish (said *Pamela*) yet is he my father, & how beautiful soever I be, I am his daughter: so as God claimes at my hands obedience, and makes me no judge of his imperfections.

These often replies upon conscience in *Pamela*, made 4

Cecropia thinke, that there was no righter waye for her, then as she had (in her opinion) set her in liking of Beautie, with perswasion not to suffer it to be voide of purpose, so if she coulde make her lesse feeling of those heavenly conceipts, that then she might easilie winde her to her croked bias. Therefore, employing the uttermost of her mischievous witte, and speaking the more earnestly, because she spake as she thought, she thus dealt with her. Deare neece, or rather, deare daughter (if my affection and wishe might prevaile therein) how much dooth it increase (trowe you) the earnest desire I have of this blessed match, to see these vertues of yours knit fast with such zeale of Devotion, indeede the best bonde, which the most politicke wittes have found, to holde mans witte in well doing? For, as children must first by feare be induced to know that, which after (when they doo know) they are most glad of: So are these bug-beares of opinions brought by great Clearkes into the world, to serve as shewelles to keepe them from those faults, whereto els the vanitie of the worlde, and weakenes of senses might pull them. But in you (Neece) whose excellencie is such, as it neede not to be helde up by the staffe of vulgar opinions, I would not you should love Vertue servillie, for feare of I know not what, which you see not: but even for the good effects of vertue which you see. Feare, and indeede, foolish feare, and fearefull ignorance, was the first inventer of those conceates. For, when they heard it thunder, not knowing the naturall cause, they thought there was some angrie body above, that spake so lowde: and ever the lesse they did perceive, the more they did conceive. Whereof they knew no cause that grewe streight a miracle: foolish folks, not marking that the alterations be but upon particular accidents, the universalitie being alwaies one. Yesterday was but as to day, and to morrow will tread the same footsteps of his foregoers: so as it is manifest inough, that all things follow but the course of their own nature, saving only Man, who while by the pregnancie of his imagination he strives to things supernaturall, meane-while he looseth his owne naturall felicitie. Be wise, and that wisedome shalbe a God unto thee; be contented, and that is thy heaven: for els to thinke that those powers (if there be any such) above, are moved either by the eloquence of our prayers, or in a chafe by the folly of our actions; caries asmuch reason as if flies should thinke, that men take great care which of them hums sweetest, and which of them flies nimblest.

She would have spoken further to have enlarged & cõfirmed 5 her discourse: but *Pamela* (whose cheeks were died in the beautifullest graine of vertuous anger, with eies which glistered forth beames of disdaine) thus interrupted her. Peace (wicked woman) peace, unworthy to breathe, that doest not acknowledge the breath-giver; most unworthy to have a tongue, which speakest against him, through whom thou speakest: keepe your affection to your self, which like a bemired dog, would defile with fauning. You say yesterday was as to day. O foolish woman, and most miserably foolish, since wit makes you foolish. What dooth that argue, but that there is a constancie in the everlasting governour? Would you have an inconstant God, since we count a man foolish that is inconstant? He is not seene you say, and would you thinke him a God, who might be seene by so wicked eyes, as yours? which yet might see enough if they were not like such, who for sport-sake willingly hood-wincke themselves to receave blowes the easier. But though I speake to you without any hope of fruite in so rotten a harte, and there be no bodie else here to judge of my speeches, yet be thou my witnesse, O captivitie, that my eares shall not be willingly guiltie of my Creators blasphemie. You saie, because we know not the causes of things, therefore feare was the mother of superstition: nay, because we know that each effect hath a cause, that hath engendred a true & lively devotion. For this goodly worke of which we are, and in which we live, hath not his being by Chaunce; on which opinion it is beyond mervaile by what chaunce any braine could stumble. For if it be eternall (as you would seeme to conceive of it) Eternity, & Chaunce are things unsufferable together. For that is chaunce-able which happeneth; & if it happen, there was a time before it hapned, when it might not have happened; or els it did not happen; and so of chaunceable, not eternall, as now being, thẽ not being. And as absurd it is to thinke that if it had a begin-ning, his beginning was derived frõ Chaunce: for Chaunce could never make all thinges of nothing: and if there were substaunces before, which by chaunce shoulde meete to make up this worke, thereon followes another bottomlesse pitt of absurdities. For then those substaunces must needes have bene from ever, and so eternall: and that eternall causes should bring forth chaunceable effects, is as sensible, as that the Sunne should be the author of darkenesse. Againe, if it were chaunceable, then was it not necessarie; whereby you take away all consequents. But we see in all thinges, in some respect or other, necessitie of consequence: therfore in reason we must needs know that the causes were necessarie.

Lastly, Chaunce is variable, or els it is not to be called Chaunce: but we see this worke is steady and permanent. If nothing but Chaunce had glewed those pieces of this All, the heavie partes would have gone infinitely downewarde, the light infinitely upwarde, and so never have mett to have made up this goodly bodie. For before there was a heaven, or a earth, there was neyther a heaven to stay the height of the rising, nor an earth, which (in respect of the round walles of heaven) should become a centre. Lastly, perfect order, perfect beautie, perfect constancie, if these be the children of Chaunce, or Fortune the efficient of these, let Wisedome be counted the roote of wickednesse, and eternitie the fruite of her inconstancie. But you will say it is so by nature, as much as if you said it is so, because it is so: if you meane of many natures conspiring together, as in a popular governement to establish this fayre estate; as if the Elementishe and ethereall partes should in their towne-house set downe the boundes of each ones office; then consider what followes: that there must needes have bene a wisedome which made them concurre: for their natures beyng absolute contrarie, in nature rather woulde have sought each others ruine, then have served as well consorted partes to such an unexpressable harmonie. For that contrary things should meete to make up a perfectiõ without a force and Wisedome above their powers, is absolutely impossible; unles you will flie to that hissed-out opinion of Chaunce againe. But you may perhaps affirme, that one universall Nature (which hath bene for ever) is the knitting together of these many partes to such an excellent unitie. If you meane a Nature of wisdome, goodnes, & providence, which knowes what it doth, then say you that, which I seeke of you, and cannot conclude those blasphemies, with which you defiled your mouth, & mine eares. But if you meane a

Nature, as we speake of the fire, which goeth upward, it knowes not why: and of the nature of the Sea which in ebbing and flowing seemes to observe so just a daunce, and yet understands no musicke, it is but still the same absurditie subscribed with another title. For this worde, one, being attributed to that which is All, is but one mingling of many, and many ones; as in a lesse matter, when we say one kingdome which conteines many citties; or one cittie which conteines many persons, wherein the under ones (if there be not a superiour power and wisedome) cannot by nature regarde to any preservation but of themselves: no more we see they doo, since the water willingly quenches the fire, and drownes the earth; so farre are they from a conspired unitie: but that a right heavenly Nature indeed, as it were unnaturing them, doth so bridle them.

Againe, it is as absurde in nature that from an unitie many contraries should proceede still kept in an unitie: as that from the number of contrarieties an unitie should arise. I say still, if you banish both a singularitie, and pluralitie of judgement from among them, then (if so earthly a minde can lift it selfe up so hie) doo but conceave, how a thing whereto you give the highest, and most excellent kinde of being (which is eternitie) can be of the base and vilest degree of being, and next to a not-being; which is so to be, as not to enjoy his owne being? I will not here call all your senses to witnes, which can heare, nor see nothing, which yeeldes not most evident evidence of the unspeakeablenesse of that Wisedome: each thing being directed to an ende, and an ende of preservation: so proper effects of judgement, as speaking, and laughing are of mankind.

But what madd furie can ever so enveagle any conceipte, as to see our mortall and corruptible selves to have a reason, and that this universalitie (whereof we are but the lest pieces) should be utterly devoide thereof? as if one should saie, that ones foote might be wise, and him selfe foolish. This hearde I once alledged against such a godlesse minde as yours, who being driven to acknowledge these beastly absurdities, that our bodies should be better then the whole worlde, if it had the knowledge, whereof the other were voide; he sought (not able to answere directly) to shifte it of in this sorte: that if that reason were true, then must it followe also, that the worlde must have in it a spirite, that could write and reade to, and be learned; since that was in us so commendable: wretched foole, not considering that Bookes be but supplies of defects; and so are praysed, because they helpe our want, and therefore cannot be incident to the eternall intelligence, which needes no recording of opinions to confirme his knowledge, no more then the Sunne wants waxe to be the fewell of his glorious lightfulnesse. This worlde therefore cannot otherwise consist but by a minde of Wisedome, whiche governes it, which whether you wil allow to be the Creator thereof, as undoubtedly he is, or the soule and governour thereof, most certaine it is that whether he governe all, or make all, his power is above either his creatures, or his governement. And if his power be above all thinges, then consequently it must needes be infinite, since there is nothing above it to limit it. For beyond which there is nothing, must needes be boundlesse, and infinite: if his power be infinite, then likewise must his knowledge be infinite: for else there should be an infinite proportion of power which he shoulde not know how to use; the unsensiblenesse whereof I thinke even you can conceave: and if infinite, then must nothing, no not the estate of flies (which you with so unsaverie skorne did jest at) be unknowne unto him. For if it were, then there were his knowledge bounded, and so not infinite: if knowledge and power be infinite, then must needs his goodnesse and justice march in the same rancke: for infinitenes of power, & knowledge, without like measure of goodnesse, must necessarily bring foorth destruction and ruine, and not ornament and preservation. Since then there is a God, and an allknowing God, so as he sees into the darkest of all naturall secretes, which is the harte of Man; and sees therein the deepest dissembled thoughts, nay sees the thoughts before they be thought: since he is just to exercise his might, and mightie to performe his justice, assure thy selfe, most wicked woman (that hast so plaguily a corrupted minde, as thou canst not keepe thy sickenesse to thy selfe, but must most wickedly infect others) assure thy selfe, I say, (for what I say dependes of everlasting and unremooveable causes) that the time will come, when thou shalt knowe that power by feeling it, when thou shalt see his wisedome in the manifesting thy ougly shamelesnesse, and shalt onely perceive him to have bene a Creator in thy destruction.

CHAP. 11.

[1] Cecropia *malcontent, still praƐtiseth.* [2] *The besiegers discipline,
and attempts of the besieged.* [3] Phalantus *chalengeth* [4] *by
Letter* Amphialus: [5] *who by Letter accepteth it.* [6] Amphialus
[7] *and* Phalantus *militar accoustrements.* [8] *Their fo-like combate,* [9] *but friendly conclusion.*

THus she saide, thus she ended, with so faire a majestie of 1
unconquered vertue, that captivitie might seeme to have
authoritie over tyrannie: so fowly was the filthinesse of im-
pietie discovered by the shining of her unstayned goodnes, so
farre, as either *Cecropia* saw indeed, or else the guilty amazement of her selfe-accusing conscience, made her eies untrue
judges of their natural objeƐt, that there was a light more then
humaine, which gave a lustre to her perfeƐtions. But *Cecropia,*
like a Batte (which though it have eyes to discerne that there
is a Sunne, yet hath so evill eyes, that it cannot delight in the
Sunne) found a trueth, but could not love it. But as great
persons are woont to make the wrong they have done, to be a
cause to doo the more wrong, her knowledge rose to no higher
point, but to envie a worthier, and her will was no otherwise
bent, but the more to hate, the more she founde her enemie
provided against her. Yet all the while she spake (though with
eyes cast like a horse that woulde strike at the stirrop, and with
colour which blushed through yellownesse) she sate rather still
then quiet, and after her speech rather muttered, then replied:
for the warre of wickednesse in her selfe, brought forth disdainefull pride to resist cunning dissimulation; so as, saying
little more unto her, but that she shoulde have leysure inough
better to bethinke her selfe; she went away repining, but not
repenting: condemning greatly (as she thought) her sonnes
over-feeble humblenesse, and purposing to egge him forward to
a course of violence. For her selfe, determining to deale with
neither of them both any more in maner of a suter: for what
majestie of vertue did in the one, that did silent humblenesse
in the other. But finding her sonne over-apt to lay both con-
demnation, and execution of sorrowe uppon himselfe, she sought
to mitigate his minde with feigned delayes of comforte, who

(having this inward overthrow in himselfe) was the more vexed, that he coulde not utter the rage thereof upon his outward enemies.

2 For *Basilius* taught by the last dayes triall, what daungerous effectes chosen courages can bring forth, rather used the spade, then the sworde; or the sworde, but to defende the spade; girding aboute the whole towne with trenches; which beginning a good way of from the towne, with a number of well directed Pioners, he still caryed before him till they came to a neere distance, where he builded Fortes, one answering the other, in such sort, as it was a prettie consideration in the discipline of warre, to see building used for the instrument of ruine, and the assayler entrenched as if he were besieged. But many sallies did *Amphialus* make to hinder their woorking. But they (exercising more melancholie, then choller in their resolution) made him finde, that if by the advauntage of place, fewe are able to defende themselves from manie, that manie must needes have power, (making themselves strong in seate) to repell fewe; referring the revenge rather to the ende, then a present requitall. Yet oftentimes they dealt some blowes in light skirmishes, eche side having a strong retyring place, and rather fighting with manie alarums, to vexe the enemie, then for anie hope of great successe.

3 Which everie way was a tedious comber to the impacient courage of *Amphialus*: till the fame of this warre, bringing thither diverse, both straungers, and subjects, as well of princely, as noble houses, the gallant *Phalantus*, who restrayned his sportfull delightes as then, to serve *Basilius*, (whome he honoured for receyved honours) when he had spent some time in considering the *Arcadian* manner in marching, encamping, and fighting, and had learned in what points of governement, and obedience their discipline differed from others, and had satisfied his minde in the knowledge, both for the cutting off the enemies helpes, and furnishing ones selfe, which *Basilius* orders coulde deliver unto him, his yong spirites (wearie of wanting cause to be wearie) desired to keepe his valure in knowledge, by some private acte, since the publique policie restrayned him; the rather, because his olde mistresse *Artesia* might see, whome she had so lightly forsaken: and therefore demaunding and obteyning leave of *Basilius*; he caused a

Heraulde to be furnished with apparell of his office, and tokens of a peaceable message, and so sent him to the gate of the towne to demaunde audience of *Amphialus*: who understanding thereof, caused him both safely, and courteously to be brought into his presence: who making lowly reverence unto him, presented his Letters, desiring *Amphialus* that whatsoever they conteyned, he woulde consider that he was onely the bearer, but not the inditer. *Amphialus* with noble gentlenesse assured him both, by honourable speeches, and a demeanure which aunswered for him, that his revenge, whensoever, should sort unto it selfe a higher subject. But opening the Letters, he found them to speake in this maner.

PHalantus of *Corinthe*, to *Amphialus* of *Arcadia*, sendeth the greeting of a hatelesse enemie. The liking of martiall matters without anie mislike of your person, hath brought me rather to the companie, then to the minde of your besiegers: where languishing in idlenesse, I desire to refresh my minde with some exercise of armes, which might make knowne the dooers, with delight of the beholders. Therefore, if there be any Gentleman in your Towne, that eyther for the love of Honour, or honour of his Love, well armed, on horsebacke, with launce, and sworde, will winne another, or loose himselfe, to be a prisoner at discretion of the conquerour, I will to morrowe morning by Sunne rising, with a trumpet and a Squire onely, attende him in like order furnished. The place I thinke fittest, the Iland within the Lake, because it standes so well in the view of your Castell, as that the Ladies may have the pleasure of seeing the combate: which though it be within the commaundement of your Castell, I desire no better securitie, then the promise I make to my selfe of your vertue. I attende your aunswere, and wish you such successe as may be to your honour, rather in yeelding to that which is just, then in main-teyning wrong by much violence.

AMphialus read it with cheerefull countenance, and thinking but a little with himselfe, called for inke and paper, and wrote this aunswere.

AMphialus of *Arcadia*, to *Phalantus* of *Corinthe*, wisheth all his owne wishes, saving those which may be hurtful to another. The matter of your letters so fit for a worthy minde, and the maner so sutable to the noblenesse of the matter, give me cause to thinke howe happie I might accounte my selfe, if I coulde get such a friende, who esteeme it no small happinesse to have mette with so noble an enemie. Your chalenge shall be aunswered, and both time, place, and weapon accepted. For your securitie for any treacherie (having no hostage woorthie to countervaile you) take my woorde, which I esteeme above all respectes. Prepare therefore your armes to fight, but not your hart to malice; since true valure needes no other whetstone, then desire of honour.

6   Having writte and sealed his letter, he delivered it to the Heraulde, and withall tooke a faire chaine from off his owne necke, and gave it him. And so with safe convoy sent him away from out his Citie: and he being gone, *Amphialus* shewed unto his mother, and some other of his chiefe Counsailours, what he had receyved, and howe he had aunswered: telling them withall, that he was determined to aunswere the chalenge in his owne person. His mother with prayers authorized by motherly commaundement; his olde governour with perswasions mingled with reprehensions, (that he would rather affect the glorie of a private fighter, then of a wise Generall) *Clinias* with falling downe at his feete, and beseeching him to remember, that all their lives depended uppon his safetie, sought all to dissuade him. But *Amphialus* (whose hart was enflamed with courage, and courage enflamed with affection) made an imperious resolution cutte off the tediousnesse of replyes, giving them in charge, what they shoulde doo uppon all occasions, and particularly to deliver the Ladies, if otherwise then well happened unto him: onely desiring his mother, that she woulde bring *Philoclea* to a window, where she might with ease perfectly discerne the combat. And so, as soone as the morning beganne to draw dewe from the fairest greenes, to wash her face withall, against the approach of the burning Sunne, he went to his stable, where himselfe chose out a horse, whom (though he was neere twentie yeere olde) he preferred for a peece of sure service, before a great nūber of yonger. His colour was of a browne bay, dapled thick with black spots; his forhead marked with a white starre; to which, in all his bodie

there was no part sutable, but the left foote before; his mane
and taile black, and thick, of goodly, and well proportioned
greatnes. He caused him to be trimmed with a sumptuous
saddle of tawnie, and golde ennamell, enriched with pretious
stones: his furniture was made into the fashiõ of the branches
of a tree, from which the leaves were falling: and so artificiallie
were the leaves made, that as the horse moved, it seemed indeed
that the leaves wagged, as when the winde plaies with them;
and being made of a pale cloath of gold, they did beare the
straw-coloured liverie of ruine. His armour was also of tawnie
and golde, but formed into the figure of flames darckened, as
when they newelie breake the prison of a smoakie furnace. In
his shielde he had painted the *Torpedo* fish. And so appointed,
he caused himselfe, with his trumpet and squire (whom he had
taken since the death of *Ismenus*) to be ferried over into the
Iland: a place well chosen for such a purpose. For, it was so
plaine, as there was scarcely any bush, or hillock, either to
unlevell, or shadowe it: of length and breadth enough, to trie
the uttermost both of launce and sword, and the one end of it
facing of the castle, the other extending it selfe toward the
campe, and no accesse to it, but by water: there coulde no
secreate trecherie be wrought, and for manifest violence, ether
side might have time inough to succour their party.

But there he found *Phalantus*, alredy waiting for him upon 7
a horse, milke white, but that upon his shoulder and withers,
he was fretned with red staines, as when a few strawberies are
scattered into a dish of creame. He had caused his mane and
taile to be died in carnation; his reines were vine branches,
which ingendring one with the other, at the end, when it came
to the bitte, there, for the bosse, brought foorth a cluster of
grapes, by the workeman made so lively, that it seemed, as the
horse champed on his bitte, he chopped for them, and that it
did make his mouth water, to see the grapes so neere him. His
furniture behind was of vines, so artificially made, as it semed
the horse stood in the shadow of the vine, so pretily were
clusters of rubie grapes dispersed among the trappers which
embraced his sides. His armour was blew, like the heaven,
which a Sun did with his rayes (proportionately delivered)
guilde in most places. His shield was beautified with this
device; A greyhound, which overrunning his fellow, and taking

the hare, yet hurts it not whẽ it takes it. The word was, *The glorie, not the pray.*

8   But as soone as *Amphialus* landed, he sent his squire to *Phalantus*, to tel him, that there was the Knight, redy to know whether he had any thing to him. *Phalantus* answered, that his answere now must be in the lãguage of launces; & so each attended the warning of the trũpets, which were to sound at the appointment of foure judges, who with consideration of the same, had devided the ground. *Phalantus*-his horse young, and feeling the youth of his master, stoode corvetting; which being wel governed by *Phalãtus*, gave such a glittering grace, as when the Sunne shines upon a waving water. *Amphialus*-horse stood panting upon the ground, with his further foot before, as if he would for his masters cause begin to make himselfe angry: till the trumpet sounded together. Together they set spurres to their horses, together took their launces from their thighes, conveied them up into their restes together, together let them sinke downward; so as it was a deleƈtable sight, in a dangerous effeƈt; and a pleasant consideration, that there was so perfeƈt agreement, in so mortall disagreement: like a musick, made of cunning discords. But their horses keeping an even line their masters had skilfully allotted unto them, passed one by another without encountring, although either might feel the angry breath of other. But the staves being come to a just descent, but even when the mark was ready to meet them, *Amphialus* was runne through the vamplate, and under the arme: so as the staffe appearing behind him, it semed to the beholders he had bene in danger. But he strake *Phalantus* just upon the gorget, so as he battred the lamms therof, and made his head almost touch the back of his horse. But either side having staied the spur, & used the bit to stop their horses fury, casting away the trõcheons of their staves, & drawing their swords, they attended the second summons of the death-threatning trumpet, which quickly folowed; and they assoone making their horses answer their hãds, with a gẽtle galop, set the one toward the other; til being come in the neernes of litle more then a staves length. *Amphialus* trusting more to the strength, then to the nimblenes of his horse, put him foorth with speedie violence, and making his head joyne to the others flanke, guiding his blow with discretion, and strengthning it

with the course of his horse, strake *Phalantus* upon the head, in such sort, that his feeling sense did both dazell his sight, and astonish his hearing. But *Phalantus* (not accustomed to be ungratefull to such benefites) strake him upon the side of his face, with such a force, that he thought his jawe had bene cut asunder: though the faithfulnes of his armour indeede garded him from further damage. And so remayned they awhile, rather angry with fighting, then fighting for anger, till *Amphialus*-his horse, leaning harde upon the other, and winning ground, the other horse feeling himselfe prest, began to rise a little before, as he was woont to doo in his corvette: which advantage *Amphialus* taking, set forward his own horse with the further spurre, so as *Phalantus*-his horse came over with his master under him. Which *Amphialus* seeing, lighted, with intention to help *Phalantus*. But his horse that had faulted, rather with untimely arte, then want of force, gatte up from burdning his burden, so as *Phalantus* (in the fall having gotten his feete free of & the stirrop) could (though something bruised) arise, seeing *Amphialus* neere him, he asked him, Whether he had givẽ him any help in removing his horse. *Amphialus* said No. Truely sayd *Phalantus*, I asked it, because I would not willingly have fought with him, that had had my life in his mercie. But now (said *Phalantus*) before we proceed further, let me know who you are, because never yet did any man bring me to the like fortune. *Amphialus* listing to keepe him selfe unknowne, told him he was a Gentlemã, to whom *Amphialus* that day had given armour and horse to trie his valour, having never before bene in any combat worthy remembrance. Ah, (said *Phalantus* in a rage) And must I be the exercise of your prentis-age? & with that, choler tooke away either the bruse, or the feeling of the bruse, so as he entred a fresh into the cõbat, & boiling in his armes the disdaine of his harte, strake so thicke upon *Amphialus*, as if every blow would faine have bene foremost. But *Amphialus* (that many like trials had taught, great spending to leave small remnants) let passe the storme with strong wardes, and nimble avoidings: till seeing his time fit, both for distaunce and nakednes, he strake him so cruell a blow on the knee, that the poore Gentleman fell downe withall in a sowne.

But *Amphialus*, pittying approved valoure, made pretious by 9 naturall curtesie, went to him; & taking of his head-piece to give him aire, the young Knight (disdained to buy life with yeelding) bad him use his fortune: for he was resolved never to yeeld. No more you shall (said *Amphialus*) if it be not to my request, that you will account your self to have great interest in me. *Phalantus* more overcome by his kindnes, thẽ by his fortune, desired yet once againe to know his name, who in his first beginning had shewed such furie in his force, and yet such stay in his furie. *Amphialus*, then named himselfe, telling him withall, he would think his name much bettred, if it might be honored by the title of his friẽd. But no Baulme could be more comfortable to his wound, then the knowledge thereof was to his mind, when he knew his mishap should be excused by the renowmed valour of the other. And so promising each to other assurednes of good will, *Phalantus*, (of whom *Amphialus* would have no other raunsome, but his word of friẽdship) was conveyed into the campe, where he would but litle remaine among the enimies of *Amphialus*: but went to seeke his adventures other-where.

CHAP. 12.

[1] Philocleas *il-taking* Amphialus *wel-meaning.* [2] *His challenge and conquests continued for Love, & his love.* [3] Argalus *sent for to this challenge.* [4] *The conjugall happines of him and his wife.* [5] *The passions stirred by this message.* [6] *Their sorrow-sounding farewell.* [7] Argalusis *defie.* [8] Amphialusis *answere.* [9] Argalusis *furniture.* [10] *Their combat, bloudy to both, deadly to* Argalus. [11] Parthenia *comes to the end of it, and him.* [12] *Her* [13] *and his lamentations.* [14] *The funerals.*

[1] AS for *Amphialus* he was receaved with triumph into the castle; although one might see by his eyes (humbly lifted up to the window where *Philoclea* stood) that he was rather suppliaunt, then victorious: whiche occasion *Cecropia* taking, (who as then stoode by *Philoclea*, and had lately lefte *Pamela* in another roome, whence also she might see the combate) Sweet Lady (said she) now you may see, whether you

have cause to love my sonne, who then lies under your feete, when he standes upon the necke of his bravest enemies. Alas said *Philoclea*, a simple service to me, me thinkes it is, to have those, who come to succour me, destroied: If it be my dutie to call it love, be it so: but the effects it brings foorth I confesse I account hatefull. *Cecropia* grew so angry with this unkind answere, that she could not abstayne from telling her, that she was like them that could not sleepe, when they were softly layed: but that if her sonne would follow her counsell, he should take another course with her: and so flange away from her.

Yet (knowing the desperate melancholy of *Amphialus* in ² like cases) framed to him a very thankefull message, poudring it with some hope-giving phrases; which were of such joy to *Amphialus*, that he (though against publike respect, & importunity of dissuaders) presently caused it to be made knowne to the campe, that whatsoever Knight would trie the like fortune as *Phalantus* did, he should in like sorte be answered: so as divers of the valiantest, partly of themselves, partly at the instigation of *Basilius*, attempted the combat with him: and according to every ones humour, so were the causes of the challēge groūded: one laying treason to his charge; another preferring himselfe in the worthines to serve *Philoclea*; a third, exalting some Ladies beautie beyond ether of the sisters; a fourth, laying disgraces to Love it selfe, naming it the bewitcher of the witt, the rebell to Reason, the betrayer of resolution, the defiler of thoughts, the underminer of magnanimitie, the flatterer of vice, the slave to weakenesse, the infection of youth, the madnesse of age; the curse of life, and reproch of deathe; a fifth, disdayning to caste at lesse then at all, woulde make the cause of his quarrell the causers of love, and proclayme his blasphemies against womankinde; that namely that sex was the oversight of Nature, the disgrace of reasonablenes, the obstinate cowards, the slave-borne tyrants, the shops of vanities, the guilded wethercocks; in whō conscience is but peevishnes, chastitie waywardnes, & gratefulnes a miracle. But all these challenges (how wel so ever endited) were so well answered, that some by death taught others, though past learning themselves; & some by yeelding gave themselves the lie for having blasphemed; to the great griefe of *Basilius*, so to see his Rebell prevaile, and in his own sight to crowne himselfe with deserved honour.

3 Wherupon thirsting for revenge, & else not hoping to prevaile, the best of his campe being already overthrowne; he sent a messenger to *Argalus*, in whose approved courage and force, he had (and had cause) to have great confidence, with a letter; requiring him, to take this quarrell in hand, from which he had hetherto spared him in respect of his late mariage. But now his honour, and (as he esteemed it) felicitie standing upon it, he could no longer forbeare to chalenge of him his faithfull service.

4 The messenger made speede, and found *Argalus* at a castle of his owne, sitting in a parler with the faire *Parthenia*, he reading in a booke the stories of *Hercules*, she by him, as to heare him reade; but while his eyes looked on the booke, she looked on his eies, & sometimes staying him with some prety question, not so much to be resolved of the doubte; as to give him occasion to looke upon her. A happy couple, he joying in her, she joying in her selfe, but in her selfe, because she enjoyed him: both encreasing their riches by giving to each other; each making one life double, because they made a double life; one, where desire never wanted satisfactiö, nor satisfaction never bred sacietie; he ruling, because she would obey: or rather because she would obey, she therein ruling.

5 But when the messenger came in with letters in his hand, & hast in his countenance, though she knew not what to feare, yet she feared, because she knew not; but she rose, and went aside, while he delivered his letters and message; yet a far of she looked, now at the messenger, & then at her husband: the same feare, which made her loth to have cause of feare, yet making her seeke cause to nourish her feare. And wel she foũd there was some serious matter; for her husbands countenance figured some resolution betweene lothnesse and necessitie: and once his eie cast upon her, & finding hers upon him, he blushed; & she blushed, because he blushed; and yet streight grew paler, because she knew not why he had blushed. But when he had read, & heard, & dispatched away the messenger (like a man in whom Honour could not be rocked on sleepe by Affection) with promise quickly to follow; he came to *Parthenia*, and as sorie as might be for parting, and yet more sorie for her sorrow, he gave her the letter to reade. She with

fearful slownes tooke it, and with fearefull quicknesse read it; and having read it, *Ah* my *Argalus* (said she) and have you made such hast to answere? and are you so soone resolved to leave me? But he discoursing unto her, how much it imparted his honour (which since it was deare to him, he knew it would be deare unto her) her reason overclowded with sorow, suffered her not presently to replie, but left the charge thereof to teares, and sighes; which he not able to beare, left her alone, and went to give order for his present departure.

By that time he was armde, and readie to go, she had 6 recovered a little strength of spirite againe, & cõming out, & seing him armed, & wanting nothing for his departure but her farewell, she ran to him, tooke him by the arme, and kneeling downe without regard, who either heard her speach, or saw her demeanour, My *Argalus*, my *Argalus* (said she) doo not thus forsake me. Remember, alas, Remember that I have interest in you, which I will never yeeld shalbe thus adventured. Your valour is already sufficiently knowne: sufficiently have you already done for your country: ennow, ennow there are besides you to loose lesse worthie lives. Woe is me, what shall become of me, if you thus abandon me? Then was it time for you to follow these adventures, when you adventured no body but your selfe, and were no bodies but your owne. But now pardon me, that now, or never, I claime mine owne; mine you are, & without me you can undertake no dãger: & will you endãger *Parthenia*? *Parthenia* shalbe in the battle of your fight: *Parthenia* shall smart in your paine, & your blood must be bled by *Parthenia*. Deare *Parthenia* (said he) this is the first time, that ever you resisted my will: I thanke you for it; but persever not in it; & let not the teares of those most beloved eies be a presage unto me of that, which you would not should happen. I shal live, doubte not: for so great a blessing, as you are, was not given unto me, so soone to be deprived of it. Looke for me therefore shortly, and victorious; and prepare a joyfull welcome, and I will wish for no other triumph. She answered not, but stood as it were thunder-striken with amazement: for true Love made obedience stande up against all other passions. But when he tooke her in his armes, and sought to printe his harte in her sweete lippes, she fell in a sounde, so as he was faine to leave her to her Gentlewomen:

and caried away by the tyrannie of Honour, though with manie a backe-cast looke, and hartie grone, went to the campe. When understanding the notable victories of *Amphialus*, he thought to give him some dayes respite of rest, because he woulde not have his victorie disgraced by the others wearinesse. In which dayes, he sought by all meanes (having leave to parley with him) to dissuade him from his enterprise: and then imparting his mind to *Basilius*, because he found *Amphialus* was inflexible, wrote his defie unto him in this maner.

7   RIght famous *Amphialus*, if my persuasion in reason, or praier in good wil, might prevaile with you, you should by better meanes be like to obteine your desire. You shoulde make many brave enemies become your faithful servãts, & make your honor flie up to the heavẽ, being caried up by both the wings of valure & justice; whereof now it wants the latter. But since my suite, nor counsel can get no place in you, disdaine not to receive a mortall chalenge, from a man so farre inferiour unto you in vertue, as that I do not so much mislike of the deed, as I have the doer in admiration. Prepare therfore your self, according to the noble maner you have used, and think not lightly of never so weake an arme, which strikes with the sword of justice.

To this quickely he received this answere.

8   MUch more famous *Argalus*, I, whom never threatnings could make afraid, am now terrified by your noble curtesie. For wel I knowe, from what height of vertue it doth proceed, and what cause I have to doubt such vertue bent to my ruine: but Love, which justifieth the unjustice you lay unto me, dooth also animate me against all daungers, since I come full of him by whom your selfe have beene (if I be not deceived) sometimes conquered. I will therfore attend your appearaunce in the Ile, carying this advantage with me, that as it shal be a singular honour if I get the victorie, so there can be no dishonour in being overcome by *Argalus*.

9   The chalenge thus denounced, and accepted, *Argalus* was armed in a white armour, which was guilded over with knots of womans haire, which came downe from the crest of his head-peece, and spred it selfe in rich quãtitie over all his armour: his furniture was cut out into the fashion of an Eagle, whereof the beake (made into a rich jewell) was fastened to the saddle,

the taile covered the crooper of the horse, and the wings served
for trappers; which falling of ech side, as the horse stirred, the
bird seemed to flie. His pettrell and reines, were embrodered
with feathers sutable unto it: upon his right arme he ware a
sleeve, which his deare *Parthenia* had made for him, to be
worne in a justes, in the time that successe was ungratefull to
their well-deserved love: It was full of bleeding hartes, though
never intended to any blooddie enterprise. In this shield (as
his owne device) he had two Palme trees, neere one another,
with a worde signifying, *In that sort flourishing*. His horse was
of a firie sorrell, with blacke feete, and blacke list on his back,
who with open nostrels breathed warre, before he could see an
enemy: and now up with one legge, and then with another,
seemed to complain of Nature, that she had made him any
whit earthie.

But he had scarcely viewed the grounde of the Ilande, and 10
considered the advauntages (if any were) therof, before the
Castel boat had delivered *Amphialus*, in al points provided to
give a hard entertainmẽt. And then sending ech to other
their Squires in honourable maner, to knowe whether they
should attende any further ceremony; the trumpets sounding,
the horses with smooth running, their staves with unshaked
motion, obediently performed their cholericke cõmandements.
But when they drew nere, *Argalus*-his horse being hot, prest
in with his head: which *Amphialus* perceiving, knowing if he
gave him his side, it should be to his disadvauntage, prest in also
with him, so as both the horses & men met shoulder to shoulder,
so as the horses (hurt as much with the striking, as being
striken) tumbled downe to the earth, daungerously to their
maister, but that they by strength nimble, and by use skilfull,
in the falling shunned the harme of the fall, and without more
respite, drewe out their swordes with a gallant braverie, eche
striving to shewe himselfe the lesse endamaged, and to make
knowne that they were glad, they had nowe nothing else to
trust to, but their owne vertue. True it is, that *Amphialus*
was the sooner up; but *Argalus* had his sworde out the sooner:
and then fell they to the cruellest combate, that any present
eye had seene. Their swordes first, like Canons, battering
downe the walles of their armour, making breaches almost in
everie place for troupes of woundes to enter. Among the rest,

Argalus gave a great wound to *Amphialus*-his disarmed face;
though part of the force of it *Amphialus* warded upon his
shielde, and with-all (first casting his eye up to *Philocleas*
Window, as if he had fetched his courage thence) feyning to
entend the same sort of blowes, turned his sword, and with
a mightie reverse, gave a cruell wounde to the right arme
of *Argalus*, the unfaythfull armour yeelding to the swoordes
strong-guided sharpenesse. But though the blood accused the
hurt of *Argalus*, yet woulde he in no action of his confesse it:
but keeping himselfe in a lower warde, stoode watching with
timely thrustes to repaire his losse; which quickly he did.
For *Amphialus* (following his fawning fortune) laid on so thicke
upon *Argalus*, that his shield had almost fallen peece-meale to
the earth, when *Argalus* comming in with his right foote, and
something stowping to come under his armour, thrust him into
the belly daungerously, and mortally it would have beene, but
that with the blowe before, *Amphialus* had overthrowne himselfe so, as he fell side-warde downe, and with falling saved
himselfe from ruine. The sworde by that meanes slipping
aside, and not pearcing more deeply, *Argalus* seeing him fall,
threatning with voyce and sworde, bad him yeelde. But he
striving without aunswere to rise, *Argalus* strake with all
his might upon his head. But his hurte arme not able to
maister so sounde a force, let the swoorde fall so, as *Amphialus*,
though astonished with the blowe, could arise: which *Argalus*
considering, ranne in to graspe with him, and so closed
together; falling so to the grounde, nowe one getting above,
and then the other; at length, both wearie of so unlovely
embracements, with a dissenting consent gate up, and went to
their swordes: but happened eche of his enemies: where
Argalus finding his foes sworde garnished in his blood, his hart
rase with the same swoorde to revenge it, and on that blade to
allie their bloods together. But his minde was evill wayted-on
by his lamed force, so as he receyved still more and more
woundes, which made all his armour seeme to blush, that it
had defended his master no better. But *Amphialus* perceiving
it, & waying the small hatefulnesse of their quarrell, with the
worthinesse of the Knight, desired him to take pitie of himselfe.
But *Argalus*, the more repining, the more he founde himselfe
in disadvauntage, filling his veynes with spite in steade of blood,

and making courage arise agaynst faintnesse, (like a Candle, which a little before it goes out, gives then the greatest blaze) so did he unite all his force, that casting away the little remnaunt of his shielde, and taking his swoorde in both handes, he stroke such a notable blowe, that he cleft his shielde, armour, and arme almost to the bone.

But then *Amphialus* forgat all ceremonies, and with cruell 11 blowes made more of his blood succeed the rest; til his hand being staied by his eare, his eare filled with a pitifull crie, the crie guided his sight to an excellent faire Ladie, who came running as fast as she could, and yet because she coulde not as fast as she would, she sent her lamentable voyce before her: and being come, and being knowne to them both, to be the beautifull *Parthenia*, (who had that night dreamed shee sawe her husbande in such estate, as she then founde him, which made her make such haste thither) they both marvailed. But *Parthenia* ranne betweene them (feare of love making her forget the feare of Nature) and then fell downe at their feete, determining so to part them, till she coulde get breathe to sigh out her doolefull speeches: and when her breath (which running had spent, and dismayednesse made slowe to returne) had by sobbes gotten into her sorow-closed breast, for a while she coulde say nothing, but, O wretched eyes of mine, O wailefull sight, O day of darkenesse: at length turning her eyes (wherein sorrowe swamme) to *Amphialus*, My Lorde (saide she) it is saide you love; in the power of that love, I beseech you to leave of this combate, as even your harte may finde comfort in his affection, even for her sake, I crave it: or if you be mortally determined, be so pitifull unto me, as first to kill me, that I may not see the death of *Argalus*. *Amphialus* was aboute to have aunswered, when *Argalus*, vexed with his Fortune, but most vexed that she shoulde see him in that fortune, Ah *Parthenia* (saide he) never till nowe unwelcome unto me, do you come to get my life by request? And can not *Argalus* live but by request? Is it a life? With that he went aside, for feare of hurting her, and woulde have begunne the combate afresh. But *Amphialus* not onely conjured by that which helde the Monarchie of his mind, but even in his noble hart melting with compassion at so passionate a sight, desired him to withholde his handes, for that he shoulde strike one, who sought his favour, and woulde not make resistaunce. A notable example of the woonderfull effectes of Vertue, where the conquerour, sought for friendship of the conquered, and the conquered woulde not pardon the conquerour: both indeede being of that minde to love eche other for accepting, but not for giving mercie, and neyther affected to over-live a dishonour: so that *Argalus* not so much striving with *Amphialus* (for if he had had him in the like sorte, in like sort he would have dealt with him) as labouring against his owne power (which he chiefly despised) set himselfe forward, stretching his strength to the uttermost. But the fire of that strife, blowen with his inward rage, boyled out his bloud in such aboundance, that he was driven to rest him upon the pommel of his sword: and then each thing beginning to turne rounde in the daunce of Death before his eyes, his sight both dazled, and dimmed, till (thinking to sit downe) he fell in a sowne. *Parthenia*, and *Amphialus* both hastely went unto him : *Amphialus* tooke of his helmet, and *Parthenia* laid his head in her lap, tearing of her linnen sleeves & partlet, to serve about his wounds; to bind which, she tooke of her hair-lace, and would have cut of her faire haire herselfe, but that the squires and judges came in with fitter things for the purpose : while she bewayled her selfe with so lamentable sweetnes, as was inough to have taught sorrow to the gladdest thoughts, and have engraved it in the mindes of hardest mettall.

12   O *Parthenia*, no more *Parthenia* (said she) What art thou? what seest thou? how is thy blisse in a moment fallen? how art thou, even-now before all ladies the example of perfect happines, and now the gasing-stock of endles miserie? O God, what hath bene my desert to be thus punished? or if such have bene my desert, why was I not in my selfe punished? O wandring life, to what wildernes wouldst thou lead one? But Sorow, I hope thou art sharp inough to save my labour from other remedies. *Argalus*, *Argalus*, I will folow thee, I wil folow thee.

13   But with that *Argalus* came out of his sowne, and lifting up his languishing eyes (which a painefull rest, and iron sleepe did seeke to lock up) seeing her, in whŏ (even dying) he lived, and him selfe seated in so beloved a place, it seemed a little cheerefull bloud came up to his cheekes, like a burning cole, almost dead, if some breath a little revive it: & forcing up (the

best he could) his feeble voice, My deare, my deare, my better halfe (said he) I finde I must now leave thee: and by that sweet hand, and faire eyes of thine I sweare, that Death bringes nothing with it to grieve me, but that I must leave thee, and cannot remaine to answere part of thy infinit deserts, with being some comfort unto thee. But since so it pleaseth him, whose wisdome and goodnesse guideth all, put thy confidence in him, and one day we shall blessedly meet againe, never to depart: meane while live happily, deare *Parthenia*, and I perswade my selfe, it will increase the blessednes of my soule, so to see thee. Love well the remembrance of thy loving, and truely loving, *Argalus:* and let not (with that worde he sighed) this disgrace of mine, make thee one day thinke, thou hadst an unwoorthie husband. They could scarcely understand the last wordes: for Death began to seaze him selfe of his harte, neither coulde *Parthenia* make answere, so full was her breast of anguish. But while the other sought to stanch his remediles wounds, she with her kisses made him happie: for his last breath was delivered into her mouth.

But when indeede she found his ghost was gone, then 14 Sorrowe lost the witte of utterance, and grewe ragefull, and madde, so that she tare her beautifull face, and rent her haire, as though they could serve for nothing, since *Argalus* was gone; till *Amphialus* (so moved with pittie of that sight, as that he honoured his adversaries death with teares) caused her (with the helpe of her women that came with her) partelie by force, to be conveyed into boate, with the dead body of *Argalus*, from which she could not depart. And being come of the other side, there she was receaved by *Basilius* him selfe, with all the funerall pompe of militarie discipline, trayling all their Ensignes upon the ground, making his warlike instruments sound dolefull notes, and *Basilius* (with comfort in his mouth, and woe in his face) sought to perswade some ease into *Parthenias* minde: but all was as easefull to her, as the handling of sore woundes: all the honour done, being to her but the triumph of her ruine, she finding no comfort, but in desperate yeelding to Sorrow: and rather determined to hate her selfe, if ever she should finde ease thereof. And well might she heare as she past through the Campe, the great prayses spoken of her husbande, which all were recordes of her losse. But the more excellent he was

(being indeede accounted seconde to none in all Greece) the
more did the breath of those praises, beare up the winges of
Amphialus-his fame: to whom yet (such was his case) that
Trophe upon Trophe, still did but builde up the monumēt of
his thraldome; he ever finding himselfe in such favour of
Philoclea, that she was most absent, when he was present with
her; and ever sorriest, when he had best successe: which would
have made him renounce all comfort, but that his mother, with
diversity of devises, kept up his hart.

But while he allayed thus his outward glorie, with inward
discomfort, he was like to have bene overtaken with a notable
treason, the beginning wherof (though meerely ridiculous) had
like to have brought forth unto him a weeping effeĉt.

CHAP. 13.

[1]Dametas *put in harte* [2]*to defie* Clinias. [3]Clinias *out of harte to
see the vie.* [4]Dametas *braverie, adoubements, and imprese.*
[5]Clinias *drawne* [6]*to answere him.* [7]*Their passions in comming
to the field.* [8]*Their aĉtions in it, not so doubty, as their fortune
doubtfull.* [9]Clinias *yeelding to triumphant* Dametas.

[1] AMong other that attended *Basilius* in this expedition, *Dametas*
was one; whether to be present with him, or absent from
Miso: once, certaine it was without any minde to make his
sworde cursed by any widow. Nowe, being in the campe,
while each talke seemed injurious, which did not acknowledge
some duety to the fame of *Amphialus*, it fell out sometimes in
communication, that as the speech of heaven doth often beget
the mention of hell, so the admirable prowes of *Amphialus* (by a
cōtrarie) brought forth the remembrance of the cowardise of
Clinias: in so much, as it grew almost to a proverb, *As very a
cowarde, as* Clinias. Describing him in such sort, that in the
end, *Dametas* began to thinke with himselfe, that if he made a
chalenge unto him, he would never answere it; and that then
he should greatly encrease the favourable conceite of *Basilius*.
This fancie of his he uttered to a young Gentleman, that
waited upon *Philanax*, in whose friendship he had especiall

cõfidence, because he haunted his company, laughing often merely at his speeches, and not a little extolling the goodly *dotes* of *Mopsa*. The young Gentleman as glad, as if he had found a Hare sitting, egd him on, breaking the matter with *Philanax*, and then (for feare the humour should quayle in him) wrote a challenge him selfe for *Damætas*, and brought it to him. But when *Damætas* read it, putting his head on his shoulder, and somewhat smiling; he said, it was prettie indeed; but that it had not a loftie stile enough: and so would needes indite it in this sort.

O Clinias, *thou* Clinias, *the wickedest worme that ever went* 2 *upon two legges; the very fritter of fraude, and seething pot of iniquitie: I* Damætas, *chiefe governour of all the royall cattell, and also of* Pamela (*whom thy Maister most perniciously hath suggested out of my dominion*) *doo defie thee, in a mortall affray from the bodkin to the pike upwarde. Which if thou doost presume to take in hande, I will out of that superfluous bodie of thine make thy soule to be evacuated.*

The young Gentleman seemed dumbe-striken with admira- 3 tion, and presently tooke upon him to be the bearer thereof, while the heate of the fit lasted: and having gotten leave of *Basilius* (every one helping on, to ease his minde overcharged with melancholy) he went into the towne according to the manner before time used, and in the presence of *Amphialus* delivered this letter to *Clinias*; desiring to have an answere, which might be fit for his reputation. *Clinias* opened it, and read it; and in the reading, his bloud not daring to be in so daungerous a place, went out of his face, and hid it selfe more inwardly: and his very wordes (as if they were afraid of blowes) came very slowly out of his mouth: but, aswell as his painting breath would utter it, he bad him tell the lowte that sent him, that he disdained to have any thing to doo with him. But *Amphialus*, perceaving the matter, tooke him aside, and very earnestly dealt with him not to shame himselfe; *Amphialus* not onely desirous to bring it to passe to make some sport to *Philoclea*, but not being able to perswade with him, *Amphialus* licenced the Gentleman, telling him, by the next morning he should have answere.

The yong Gentlemã (sory he had sped no better) returned 4

to *Damætas*, who had fetched many a sower-breathed sigh, for fear *Clinias* would accept the chalēge. But whē he perceived by his trusty messenger, that this delay was in effeêt a denial, there being no dispositiō in him to accept it; then lo, *Damætas* began to speake his lowd voice, to looke big, to march up & down, & in his march to lift his legs higher thē he was wont, swearing by no meane devotiōs, that the wals should not keepe the coward frō him, but he would fetch him out of his connie-berrie: & then was hotter then ever to provide himselfe of horse & armour, saying, he would go to the Iland bravely addoubed, & shew himself to his charge *Pamela*. To this purpose many willing hāds were about him, letting him have reynes, pettrell, with the rest of the furniture, and very brave bases; but all comming from divers houses, nether in coulour or fashion, shewing any kinred one with another; but that liked *Damætas* the better: for that he thought would argue, that he was maister of many brave furnitures. Then gave he order to a painter for his device; which was, a plowe with the oxen lewsed from it, a sword with a great many armes and legges cut of; and lastly a great armie of pen and inke-hornes, and bookes. Nether did he sticke to tell the secrete of his intent, which was, that he had lefte of the plowe, to doo such bloudy deedes with his swoorde, as many inkehornes and bookes should be employed about the historifying of them: and being asked, why he set no worde unto it, he said, that was indeede like the painter, that sayeth in his piêture, Here is the dog, and here is the Hare: & with that he laughed so perfeêtly, as was great consolation to the beholders. Yet remembring, that *Miso* would not take it well at his returne, if he forgat his dutie to her, he caused about in a border to be written:

Miso *mine own pigsnie, thou shalt heare news o'* Damætas.

Thus all things being condignely ordered, with an ill favoured impatiencie he waited, until the next morning, that he might make a muster of him selfe in the Iland; often asking them that very diligently wayted upon him, whether it were not pittie, that such a coward, as *Clinias*, should set his runaway feete upon the face of the earth?

5 But as he was by divers principal yong Gentlemen, to his no small glory, lifted up on horsebacke, comes me a page of

Amphialus, who with humble smiling reverence delivered a
letter unto him from *Clinias*: whom *Amphialus* had brought to
this, first with perswasions (that for certaine, if he did accept
the combat, *Damætas* would never dare to appeare, and that
then the honour should be his) but principally threatning him,
that if he refused it, he would turne him out of the towne to
be put to death for a traitour by *Basilius*: so as the present
feare (ever to a coward most terrible) of being turned out of the
towne, made him, though full unwillingly, undertake the other
feare, wherein he had some shewe of hope, that *Damætas* might
hap either to be sick, or not to have the courage to performe
the matter. But when *Damætas* heard the name of *Clinias*,
very aptly suspecting what the matter might be, he bad the
page carry backe his letter, like a naughty boy as he was: for
he was in no humour, he tolde him, of reading letters. But
Damætas-his friĕd, first persuading him, that for certaine it was
some submission, tooke upon him so much boldnesse, as to open
his letter, and to reade it alowd in this sort.

F*Ilthy drivell, unworthy to have thy name set in any letter by a* 6
*souldiers hande written: could thy wretched harte thinke it
was timorousnesse, that made* Clinias *suspende a while his answere?
No caitiffe, no: it was but as a Ramme, which goes backe to returne
with the greater force. Know therefore that thou shalt no sooner
appeare (appeare now if thou darest) I say thou shalt no sooner
appeare in the Ilande (O happy thou, if thou doo not appeare) but
that I will come upon thee withall my force; and cut thee in pieces
(marke, what I saie) joynte after joynte, to the eternall terrour of all
presumptuous villaynes. Therefore looke what thou doost: for I tell
thee, horrible smarte, and paine shalbe thy lot, if thou wilt needes be
so foolish (I having given thee no such cause) as to meete with me.*

These terrible wordes *Clinias* used, hoping they would give 7
a cooling to the heate of *Dametas*-his courage: and so indeede
they did, that he did grone to heare the thundring of those
threatnings. And when the Gentleman had ended the reading
of them, *Damætas* tolde them, that in his opinion he thought
his answere came too late, and that therefore he might very
well go, and disarme him selfe: especially considering, the other
had in curteous maner warned him not to come. But they

(having him now on horsebacke) led him unto the ferrie, and so into the Iland; the clashing of his owne armour striking miserable feare into him, and in his minde thinking great unkindnesse in his friende, that he had brought him to a matter so contrarie to his complexion. There stayed he but a little (the Gentlemen that came with him teaching him how to use his sworde and launce, while he cast his eye about, to see which way he might runne away, cursing all Ilands in being evill scituated) when *Clinias* with a brave sounde of trumpets landed at the other ende: who came all the way debating with himselfe, what he had deserved of *Amphialus* to drive him to those inconveniences. Sometimes his witte made him bethinke him selfe what was beste to be done: but feare did so corrupt his witt, that whatsoever he thought was best, he still found daunger therein; fearefulnesse (contrarie to all other vices) making him thinke the better of another, the worse he found him selfe; rather imagining in him selfe, what wordes he would use (if he were overcome) to get his life of *Damætas*, then how to overcome, whereof he could thinke with no patience. But oftentimes looking to the Earth pittifully complayning, that a man of such sufficiencie (as he thought him selfe) shoulde in his best yeares be swallowed up by so base an element. Faine he would have prayed, but he had not harte inough to have confidence in praier; the glittering of the armour, and sounding of the trumpets giving such an assault to the weake-breache of his false senses, that he grewe from the degree of feare to an amazement, not almost to know what he did; till two judges (chosen for the purpose) making the trumpets cease, and taking the oth of those champions, that they came without guile or witchcraft, set them at wonted distaunce; one from the other.

8   Then the trumpets sounding, *Damætas*-his horse (used to such causes) when he thought lest of the matter, started out so lustely, that *Damætas* was jogde back with head, and bodie, and pulling withall his bridle-hande, the horse (that was tender of mouth) made halfe a stop, and fell to bounding, so that *Damætas* threw away his launce, and with both his hands held by the pummell: the horse, halfe running, halfe leaping, till he met with *Clinias*: who fearing he should misse his reste, had put his staffe therein before he began his careere: neither would he then have begun, but that at the trumpets warning, one (that

stood behinde) strake on his horse, who running swiftly, the winde tooke such holde of his staffe, that it crost quite over his breast, and in that sorte gave a flat bastonado to *Damætas:* who, halfe out of his sadle, went neere to his olde occupation of digging the earth, but with the creste of his helmet. *Clinias* when he was paste him, not knowing what he had done, but fearing lest *Damætas* were at his backe, turned with a wide turne; & seeing him on the ground, he thought then was his time, or never, to treade him under his horses feete; & withall (if he could) hurt him with his launce, which had not broken, the encounter was so easie. But putting forth his horse, what with the falling of the staffe to low before the legs of the horse, & the cõming upon *Damætas*, who was then scrãbling up, the horse fell over & over, and lay upon *Clinias*. Which *Damætas* (who was gotten up) perceiving, drew out his sword, prying which way he might best come to kil *Clinias* behind. But the horse that lay upon him, kept such a pawing with his feet, that *Damætas* durst not approch, but verie leysurely; so as the horse (being lustie) gat up, and withall fell to strike, and leape, that *Damætas* started up a good way, and gave *Clinias* time to rise, but so bruised in bodie, and broken in hart, that he meant to yeeld himselfe to mercie: and with that intent drew out his sworde, entending when he came nearer, to present the pommell of it to *Damætas*. But *Damætas*, when he sawe him come with his sword drawne, nothing conceiving of any such intent, went backe as fast as his backe and heeles woulde leade him. But as *Clinias* founde that, he beganne to thinke a possibilitie in the victorie, and therefore followed with the cruell haste of a prevailing cowarde; laying upon *Damætas*, who did nothing but crie out to him to holde his hand: sometimes that he was dead, sometimes that he woulde complaine to *Basilius:* but still bare the blowes ungratefully, going backe, till at length he came into the water with one of his feete.

But then a new feare of drowning tooke him, so that not daring to go back, nor to deliberat (the blows stil so lighted on him) nor to yeelde (because of the cruell threatnings of *Clinias*) feare being come to the extremitie, fell to a madnesse of despaire: so that (winking as hard as ever he could) he began to deale some blowes, and his arme (being used to a flaile in his youth) laid thẽ on so thick, that *Clinias* now began with lamẽt-

9

able eies to see his owne blood come out in many places, and before he had lost halfe an ounce, finding in himselfe that he fainted, cried out aloud to *Damætas*, that he yeelded. Throw away thy sword then (said *Damætas*) and I will save thee; but still laying on, as fast as he could. *Clinias* straight obeyed, and humbly craved mercie, telling him, his sworde was gone. Then *Damætas* first opened his eyes, and seeing him indeed unweaponed, made him stande a good way of from it; and then willed him to lie downe upon the earth as flat as he could. *Clinias* obeyed; and *Damætas* (who never could thinke himselfe safe, till *Clinias* were deade) began to thinke with himselfe, that if he strake at him with his sworde, if he did not kill him at the first blowe, that then *Clinias* might happe to arise, and revenge himselfe. Therefore he thought best to kneele downe upon him, and with a great whittle he had (having disarmed his heade) to cut his throate, which he had used so with Calves, as he had no small dexteritie in it. But while he sought for his Knife, which under his armour he coulde not well finde out, and that *Clinias* lay with so sheepish a countenaunce, as if he would have beene glad to have his throate cut for feare of more paine, the Judges came in, and tooke *Damætas* from off him, telling him he did against the lawe of Armes, having promised life, if he threwe away his sworde. *Damætas* was loath to consent, till they sware, they woulde not suffer him to fight any more, when he was up: and then more forced, then perswaded, he let him rise, crowing over him, and warning him to take heede how he dealt any more with any that came of his fathers kinred. But thus this *combate of cowardes* being finished, *Damætas* was with much mirth and melodie received into the campe as victorious, never a Page there failing to waite upon this Triumph.

CHAP. 14.

[1]Clinias *a slie traitour.* [2]Artesia *his malcontent accomplice.* [3]Zelmanes *passions.* [4]*Her practise with* Artesia. [5]*The complot revealed to the disliking sisters,* [6]*bewrayed by* Pamela.

[1] BUT *Clinias*, though he wanted hart to prevent shame, yet he wanted not witte to feele shame; not so much repining at it for the abhorring of shame, as for the discommodities,

that to them that are shamed, ensue. For well he deemed, it would be a great barre to practize, and a pulling on of injuries, when men needed not care, how they used him. Insomuch, that *Clinias* (finding himselfe the scorning-stocke of every companie) fell with repining to hate the cause thereof; & hate in a cowards hart, could set it selfe no other limites, but death. Which purpose was well egged on by representing unto himselfe, what daunger he lately was in; which still kept no lesse ougly figure in his minde, then when it was present: and quickly (even in his dissembling countenance) might be discerned a concealed grudge. For though he forced in himselfe a farre more diligent officiousnesse towarde *Amphialus*, then ever before, yet a leering eye upon the one side at him, a countenance still framed to smiling before him (how little cause soever there was of smiling) and grombling behind him, at any of his commaundements, with an uncertaine manner of behaviour: his words comming out, though full of flatterie, yet slowly, and hoarcely pronounced, might well have blazed, what armes his false hart bare. But despised, because of his cowardlinesse, and not marked, because despised, he had the freer scope of practize. Which he did the more desperately enter into, because the dayly dangers *Amphialus* did submit himselfe into, made *Clinias* assuredly looke for his overthrow, and for his owne consequently, if he did not redeme his former treason to *Basilius*, with a more treasonable falshood toward *Amphialus*.

His chiefe care therefore was, to find out among all sorts of 2 *Amphialus*, whom either like feare, tediousnes of the siege, or discõtentment of some unsatisfied ambitiõ would make apt to dig in the same mine that he did: & some alredy of welthy weary folks, & unconstãt youths (who had not found such sudden successe as they had promised thẽselves) he had made stoupe to the lure. But of none he made so good account as of *Artesia*, sister to the late slain *Ismenus*, & the chiefe of six maids, who had trained out the Princesses to their banket of miserie: so much did the sharpnes of her wit countervaile (as he thought) any other defects of her sex: for she had undertaken that dangerous practise by the persuasion of *Cecropia*; who assured her that the two princesses should be made away; & thẽ *Amphialus* wold marry her: which she was the apter to beleve, by some false persuasiõ her glas had givẽ her of her own incõparable excellencies, & by the great favor she knew he bare to her brother *Ismenus*, which (like a self-flattering womã) she conceived was done for her sake. But when she had atchieved her attempt, & that she found the Princesses were so far frõ their intended death, as that the one of them was like to be her sovereigne, & that neither her service had woon of *Amphialus* much more thẽ ordinary favor, nor her over-large offring herself to a mind otherwise owed, had obteined a loked-for acceptatiõ; disdain to be disdained spite of a frustrate hope, & perchance unquenched lust-growne rage, made her unquiet thoughts find no other rest, but malice: which was increased by the death of her brother, whõ she judged neither succoured against *Philanax*, nor revẽged upon *Philanax*. But all these coles were wel blowne by the cõpany she especially kept with *Zelmane*, all this time of her imprisonment. For finding her presence uncheerfull to the mourning *Philoclea*, and contemned of the hie harted *Pamela*, she spent her time most with *Zelmane*. Who though at the first hardly broking the instrument of their miserie, learning cunning in the schoole of adversitie, in time framed her selfe to yeeld her acceptable intertainment.

3   For *Zelmane*, when she had by that unexpected mischief her bodie imprisoned, her valure overmastred, her wit beguiled, her desires barred, her love eclipsed; assured of evill, fearing worse, able to knowe *Philocleas* misfortune, and not able to succour her, she was a great while, before the greatnes of her hart could descend to sorow, but rather rose boyling up in spight and disdain; Reason hardly making Courage beleeve, that it was distressed: but as if the walles would be afraid of her, so woulde her lookes shoote out threatning upon them. But the fetters of servitude (growing heavier with wearing) made her feele her case, and the little prevailing of repining: and then griefe gat seate in her softned minde, making sweetenesse of passed comfortes by due title claime teares of present discomfort: and since her fortune made her able to helpe as litle as any bodie, yet to be able to waile as much as any bodie; solitarie Sorrowe, with a continuall circle in her selfe, going out at her owne mouth, to come in againe at her owne eares. Then was the name of *Philoclea* graved in the glas windowes, and by the foolish idolatrie of affection, no sooner written, thẽ adored; & no sooner adored, thẽ pitied: al the wõted praises (she was wont

to give unto her) being now but figures of rethorick to amplifie the injuries of misfortune; against which being alone, she woulde often make invective declamations, methodized onely by raging sorow.

But whē *Artesia* did insinuat herself into her acquaintance, 4 she gave the government of her courage to wit, & was cōtent to familiarize herselfe with her: so much the rather, as that she perceived in her certaine flawes of il-cōcealed discontentmēt. Insomuch that whē *Zelmane* would sweetē her mouth with the praises of the sisters, especially setting forth their noble grate-fulnes, in never forgetting wel-intended services, & invoking the justice of the gods, not to suffer such treasures to be wrōg-fully hiddē, & somtimes with a kind unkindnes, charging *Artesia* that she had ben abused to abuse so worthy persōs: *Artesia* (though falsly) wold protest, that she had bin beguiled in it, never meaning other matter thē recreatiō: & yet withall (by alleaging how ungratefully she was dealt with) it was easie to be seene, it was the unrewarding, & not the evil employing her service, which grieved her. But *Zelmane* (using her own bias to bowle neer the mistresse of her owne thoughtes) was content to lende her beleefe, and withall, to magnifie her desert, if willingly she would deliver, whom unwillingly she had imprisoned; leaving no argument which might tickle ambition, or flatter revenge. So that *Artesia*, (pusht forward by *Clinias*, and drawne onward by *Zelmane*) bound her selfe to that practise; wherin *Zelmane* (for her part) desired no more, but to have armour and weapons brought into her chamber, not doubting, therewith to perfourm any thing, how impossible soever, which longing Love can perswade, and invincible Valour dare promise.

But *Clinias* (whose faith could never comprehende the 5 misteries of Courage) perswaded *Artesia*, while he by corruptiō had drawn the guard of one gate, to open it (when he would appoint the time) to the enemie: that she should impoyson *Amphialus*, which she might the easier do, because she her selfe had used to make the broaths, when *Amphialus* (either wearied or wounded) did use such diet. And al things alredy were ready to be put in executiō, when they thought best to breake the matter with the two excellent sisters, not doubting of their cōsent in a thing so behoofefull to thēselves: their reasons

being, that the Princesses knowing their service, might be
sure to preserve them from the fury of the entring souldiers:
whereof *Clinias* (even so) could scarcely be sufficiently certaine:
and withall, making them privie to their action, to binde them
afterwardes to acknowledg gratefulnes towards them. They
went therefore at one time, when they knewe them to be
alone, *Clinias* to *Philoclea*, and *Artesia* to *Pamela*: and *Clinias*,
with no fewe words, did set forth what an exploite was intended
for her service. But *Philoclea* (in whose cleere minde treason
could finde no hiding place) told him, that she would be glad,
if he could perswade her cosin to deliver her, and that she
would never forgett his service therin: but that she desired
him to lay down any such way of mischiefe, for that (for her
part) she would rather yeeld to perpetuall imprisonment, then
consent to the destroying her cosin, who (she knewe) loved her,
though wronged her. This unlooked-for answere amazed
Clinias, so that he had no other remedie in his minde, but
to kneele downe to *Philoclea*, and beseech her to keep it secrete,
considering that the intention was for her service: and vowing
(since she misliked it) to proceed no further therin. She
comforted him with promise of silence, which she perfourmed.

6   But that little avayled: for *Artesia* having in like sort
opened this device to *Pamela*, she (in whose mind Vertue
governed with the scepter of Knowledge) hating so horrible a
wickednes, and streight judging what was fitte to doo, Wicked
woman (said she) whose unrepenting harte can find no way to
amend treason, but by treason: nowe the time is come, that
thy wicked wiles have caught thy selfe in thine owne nette: as
for me, let the Gods dispose of me as shall please them; but
sure it shall be no such way, nor way-leader, by which I will
come to libertie. This she spake something with a lowder
voice then she was woont to use, so as *Cecropia* heard the
noise; who was (sooner then *Artesia* imagined she would) come
up, to bring *Pamela* to a window, where she might see a
notable skirmish happened in the Campe, as she thought,
among themselves: and being a cunning fisher in troubled
waters, streight found by their voices and gestures, there was
some matter of consequence, which she desired *Pamela* to tell
her. Aske of her (said *Pamela*) & learne to know, that who
do falshoode to their superiours, teach falshoode to their

inferiours. More she would not say. But *Cecropia* taking
away the each-way guiltie *Artesia*, with feare of torture, gat
of her the whole practise: so as *Zelmane* was the more closely
imprisoned, and *Clinias* (with the rest of his corrupted mates,
according to their merites) executed: For, as for *Artesia*, she
was but lockt up in her chamber, *Amphialus* not consenting
(for the love he bare *Ismenus*) that further punishment should
be laide upon her.

CHAP. 15.

¹ *Proude* Anaxius *breaketh through the besiegers.* ² *His welcome*
by Amphialus. ³ *The Musicke,* ⁴ *and lovesong made to*
Philoclea. ⁵ *The sallie of* Anaxius *and his on the* Basilians,
⁶ *backt by* Amphialus, ⁷ *beaten backe by three unknowen*
Knightes. ⁸ *The Retraite of both sides.*

BUt the noyse they hearde in the campe, was occasioned by the ¹
famous Prince *Anaxius*, nephewe to the Giant *Euardes*
whom *Pyrocles* slew: A Prince, of body excedingly strong; in
armes so skilfull and fortunate, as no man was thought to excel
him; of courage that knew not how to feare: partes worthie
praise, if they had not bene guyded by pride, and followed by
unjustice. For, by a strange composition of minde, there was
no man more tenderly sensible in any thing offred to himselfe,
which in the farthest-fette construction, might be wrested to
the name of wrõg; no man, that in his own actions could
worse distinguish betwene Valour and Violence: So proud, as
he could not abstaine from a *Thraso*-like boasting, and yet (so
unluckie a lodging his vertues had gotten) he would never boast
more then he would accomplish: falsly accounting an unflexible
anger, a couragious constancie: esteeming feare, and astonishment, righter causes of admiration, then Love and Honour.
This man had foure sundrie times fought with *Amphialus*, but
Mars had bene so unpartiall an arbiter, that neither side gate
advauntage of the other. But in the end it hapned, that
Anaxius found *Amphialus* (unknowen) in a great danger, and
saved his life: wherupon (loving his owne benefite) began to

439

favour him, so much the more, as, thinking so well of himselfe, he coulde not choose but like him, whom he founde a match for himselfe : which at last grewe to as much friendship towardes him, as could by a proud harte be conceived. So as in this travaile (seeking *Pyrocles* to be revenged of his uncles death) hearing of this siege, never taking paines to examine the quarrell (like a man whose will was his God, and his hand his lawe) taking with him his two brothers (men accounted little inferiour to him selfe in martiall matters) and two hundred chosen horsemen (with whome he thought him selfe able to conquere the world) yet commaunding the rest of his forces to follow, he him selfe upon such an unexpected suddainenesse entred in upon the backe of *Basilius,* that many with great unkindnesse tooke their death, not knowing why, nor how they were so murdred. There, if ever, did he make knowne the wonderfulnes of his force. But the valiant, & faithfull *Philanax,* with wel governed speed made such head against him, as would have
„ shewed, how soone Courage falles in the ditch which hath not the eie of Wisdome: but that *Amphialus* at the same time issued out, & winning with an abondaunce of courage one of the sconses, which *Basilius* had builded, made waie for his friend *Anaxius* with great losse of both sides, but especially of the *Basilians*; such notable monuments had those two swords especially lefte of their Maisters redoubted worthynesse.

2 There with the respect fit to his estate, the honour dewe to his worthinesse, and the kindnesse which accompanies friendship (made fast by enterchaunged benefites) did *Amphialus* enforce him selfe (as much as in a besieged towne he could) to make *Anaxius* know, that his succour was not so needefull, as his presence gratefull. For causing the streates and houses of the towne to witnes his welcome (making both souldiers and Magistrates in their countenaunces to shewe their gladnesse of him) he led him to his mother, whom he besought to entertain him with no lesse love and kindnesse, then as one, who once had saved her sonnes life, and now came to save both life and honour. Tush (said *Anaxius,* speaking alowde, looking upon his brothers) I am onely sorie there are not halfe a dozen Kinges more about you: that what *Anaxius* can doo, might be the better manifested. His brothers smiled, as though he had over-modestly spoken farre underneath the pitch of his

power. Then was he disarmed at the earnest request of
Amphialus: for *Anaxius* boiled with desire to issue out uppon
the enemies, perswading himselfe, that the Sunne shoulde not be
sette, before he had overthrowne them. And having reposed
himselfe, *Amphialus* asked him, whether he woulde visite the
yong Princesses. But *Anaxius* whispered him in the eare: In
trueth (saide he) deare friende *Amphialus*, though I am none of
those, that love to speake of themselves, I never came yet in
companie of Ladies, but that they fell in love with me. And
I that in my hart scorne them as a peevish paltrie sexe, not
woorthie to communicate with my vertues, would not do you
the wrong: since (as I heare) you doo debase your selfe so much
as to affect them. The curteous *Amphialus* could have beene
angrie with him for those wordes; but knowing his humour,
suffered him to daunce to his owne musicke : and gave himselfe
to entertaine both him and his brothers, with as cheerefull a
maner, as coulde issue from a minde whome unluckie love had
filled with melancholie. For to *Anaxius* he yeelded the direction
of all. He gave the watchwoorde, and if any grace were
graunted, the meanes were to be made to *Anaxius*. And that
night when supper was ended, wherein *Amphialus* woulde
needes himselfe waite upon him, he caused in Boates upon the
Lake an excellent musicke to be ordered : which, though
Anaxius might conceive was for his honour, yet indeede he was
but the Bricke-wall to convey it to the eares of the beloved
Philoclea.

The musicke was of Cornets, whereof one aunswering the 3
other, with a sweete emulation, striving for the glorie of
musicke, and striking upon the smooth face of the quiet Lake,
was then delivered up to the castell walles, which with a
proude reverberation, spreading it into the aire; it seemed
before the harmonie came to the eare, that it had enriched it
selfe in travaile, the nature of those places adding melodie to
that melodious instrument. And when a while that instrument
had made a brave proclamation to all unpossessed mindes of
attention, an excellent consort streight followed of five Violles,
and as manie voyces; which all being but Oratours of their
maisters passions, bestowed this song uppon her, that thought
uppon another matter.

4
THe Fire to see my woes for anger burneth:
    The Aire in raine for my affliction weepeth:
The Sea to ebbe for griefe his flowing turneth:
The Earth with pitie dull his center turneth.
    Fame is with wonder blazed:
    Time runnes away for sorrow:
    Place standeth still amazed,
To see my night of ils, which hath no morrowe.
    Alas all onely she no pitie taketh
To know my miseries, but chaste and cruell
    My fall her glory maketh;
Yet still her eyes give to my flames their fuell.

Fire, burne me quite till sense of burning leave me:
Aire, let me drawe thy breath no more in anguish:
Sea, drown'd in thee of tedious life bereave me:
Earth, take this earth wherein my spirits languish.
    Fame, say I was not borne:
    Time, hast my dying hower:
    Place, see my grave uptorne:
Fire, aire, sea, earth, fame, time, place show your power.
    Alas from all their helpe I am exiled:
For hers am I, and Death feares her displeasure.
    Fie Death thou art beguiled:
Though I be hers, she sets by me no treasure.

5   But *Anaxius* (seeming a weary before it was ended) told *Amphialus*, that for his part he liked no musick, but the neighing of horses, the sound of trumpets, and the cries of yeelding persons: and therefore desired, that the next morning they shoulde issue upon the same place, where they had entred that day, not doubting to make them quickly a wearie of being the besiegers of *Anaxius*. *Amphialus*, who had no whit lesse courage, though nothing blowne up with pride, willingly condiscended: and so the next morning (giving false alarum to the other side of the campe) *Amphialus* at *Anaxius* earnest request, staying within the towne to see it garded, *Anaxius* and his brethren, *Lycurgus*, and *Zoilus*, sallied out with the best chosen men. But *Basilius* (having bene the last day somewhat unprovided) now had better fortified the overthrowne sconse;

and so well had prepared every thing for defence, that it was impossible for any valour from within, to prevaile. Yet things were perfourmed by *Anaxius* beyonde the credite of the credulous. For thrise (valiantly followed by his brothers) did he set up his banner upon the rampire of the enemie: though thrise againe by the multitude, and advauntage of the place, but especially by the comming of three valiant Knights, he were driven downe againe. Nübers there were that day, whose deathes and overthrowes were executed by the well knowen sworde of *Anaxius*: but the rest, by the length of time and injurie of Historians, have bene wrapped up in darke forgetfulnesse: onely *Tressennius* is spoken of, because when all abandoned the place, hee onely made head to *Anaxius*; till having lost one of his legs, yet not lost the harte of fighting, *Lycurgus* (second brother to *Anaxius*) cruellie murthered him; *Anaxius* him selfe disdayning any further to deale with him.

But so farre had *Anaxius* at the thirde time prevayled, that 6 now the *Basilians* began to let their courage descende to their feete, *Basilius,* and *Philanax* in vaine striving, with reverence of authoritie to bridle the flight of astonishment, and to teach Feare discretion: so that *Amphialus,* seeing Victorie shew such a flattering countenaunce to him, came out with all his force; hoping that day to end the siege.

But that fancie altered quicklie by the suddaine comming 7 to the other side of three Knights, whereof the one was in white armour, the other in greene, and the thirde by his blacke armour, and device streight knowne to be the notable Knight, who the first day had given Fortune so short a stoppe with his notable deedes, and fighting hand to hand with the deemed invincible *Amphialus.* For the very cowardes no sooner saw him, but as borrowing some of his spirit, they went like yong Eagles to the pray, under the wing of their damme. For the three adventurers, not content to keepe them from their rampier, leapt downe among them, and entered into a brave combate with the three valiaunt brothers. But to whether side Fortune woulde have beene partiall, could not be determined. For the *Basilians,* lightened with the beames of these straungers valure; followed so thicke, that the *Amphialians* were glad with some haste to retire to the walles warde: though *Anaxius* neither reason, feare, nor example, coulde make him asswage the furie of his fight: untill one of the *Basilians* (unwoorthie to have his name registred, since he did it cowardly, sidewarde, when he least looked that way) almost cut off one of his legges: so as he fell downe, blaspheming heaven, that all the influences thereof had power to overthrow him; and there death would have seazed of his proude hart, but that *Amphialus* tooke in hand the blacke knight, while some of his souldiers conveied away *Anaxius*, so requiting life for life unto him.

8 And for the love and example of *Amphialus*, the fight began to enter into a new fitte of heate: when *Basilius* (that thought inough to be done for that day) caused retraite to be sounded; fearing least his men following over-hastily, might bee the losse of those excellent Knights whom he desired to knowe. The Knights as soone as they heard the retraite (though they were „ eagerly set, knowing that courage without discipline is nearer „ beastlinesse then manhood) drew backe their swords, though hungrie of more blood: especially the blacke Knight, who, knowing *Amphialus*, could not refraine to tell him, that this was the second time he escaped out of his hands, but that he would shortly bring him a bill of all the former accounts. *Amphialus* seing it fit to retire also (most of his people being hurt, both in bodies and harts) withdrew himselfe, with so well seated a resolution, that it was as farre from anger, as from dismayednesse; answering no other to the blacke Knights threats, but that when he brought him his account, he should finde a good pay-master.

CHAP. 16.

[1] *The unknowne Knights will not be knowne.* [2] *The Knight of the Tombes shew,* [3] *and challenge accepted by* Amphialus. [4] *Their fight, with the death of the Tombe-knight.* [5] *Who that Knight was.* [6] *The dying speeches, and* [7] *the lamentable funerals.*

THe fight being ceased, and ech side withdrawne within their strengthes, *Basilius* sent *Philanax* to entertaine the straunge Knights, and to bring them unto him, that he might acknowledge what honour was due to their vertue. But they excused themselves, desiring to be knowne first by their deedes, before their names should accuse their unworthinesse: and though the other replied according as they deserved, yet (finding that unwelcome curtesie is a degree of injury) he „ suffered them to retire themselves to a tent of their owne without the campe, where they kept themselves secrete: *Philanax* himselfe being called away to another straunge Knight; straunge not onely by the unlookedfornesse of his comming, but by the straunge maner of his comming.

For he had before him foure damosels, and so many behind 2 him, all upon palfreys, & all appareled in mourning weedes; ech of them servants of ech side, with like liveries of sorrow. Himselfe in an armour, all painted over with such a cunning of shadow, that it represented a gaping sepulchre, the furniture of his horse was all of Cypresse braunches; wherwith in olde time they were woont to dresse graves. His Bases (which he ware so long, as they came almost to his ankle) were imbrodered onely with blacke wormes, which seemed to crawle up and downe, as readie alreadie to devoure him. In his shielde for *Impresa*, he had a beautifull childe, but having two heades; whereof the one shewed, that it was alreadie dead: the other alive, but in that case, necessarily looking for death. The word was, *No way to be rid from death, but by death.*

This Knight of the tombe (for so the souldiours termed him) 3 sent to *Basilius*, to demaund leave to send in a damosel into the towne, to cal out *Amphialus*, according as before time some others had done. Which being grãted (as glad any would undertake the charge, which no bodie else in that campe was knowne willing to do) the damosell went in, and having with tears sobbed out a brave chalenge to *Amphialus*, from the Knight of the Tombe, *Amphialus*, honourably enterteining the gentlewoman, & desiring to know the Knights name (which the doolefull Gentlewoman would not discover) accepted the chalenge, onely desiring the Gentlewoman to say thus much to the strange Knight, from him; that if his minde were like to his title, there were more cause of affinitie, then enmitie betweene them. And therefore presently (according as he was woont) as soone as he perceyved the Knight of the Tombe, with his Damosels and Judge, was come into the Iland, he also went over in accustomed maner: and yet for the curtesie of his nature, desired to speake with him.

4   But the Knight of the Tombe, with silence, and drawing his horse backe, shewed no will to heare, nor speake: but with Launce on thigh, made him knowe, it was fitte for him to go to the other ende of the Career, whence wayting the starte of the unknowne Knight, he likewise made his spurres claime haste of his horse. But when his staffe was in his rest, comming downe to meete with the Knight, nowe verie neere him, he perceyved the Knight had mist his rest: wherefore the curteous *Amphialus* woulde not let his Launce descende, but with a gallant grace, ranne over the heade of his there-in friended enemie: and having stopped his horse, and with the turning of him, blessed his sight with the Windowe where he thought *Philoclea* might stand, he perceyved the Knight had lighted from his horse, and throwne away his staffe, angrie with his misfortune, as having mist his rest, and drawne his sworde to make that supply his fellowes fault. He also lighted, and
„ drew his sworde, esteeming victorie by advantage, rather robbed then purchased: and so the other comming eagerly toward him, he with his shield out, and sword aloft, with more braverie then anger, drew unto him; and straight made their swords speake for them a pretie-while with equall fearcenes. But *Amphialus* (to whom the earth brought forth few matches) having both much more skill to choose the places, and more force to worke upon the chosen, had already made many windowes in his armour for death to come in at; whẽ (the noblenes of his nature abhorring to make the punishment overgoe the offence) he stept a little backe, and withal, Sir Knight (said he) you may easely see, that it pleaseth God to favour my cause; employ your valour against them that wish you hurte: for my part, I have not deserved hate of you. Thou lyest false traytor, saide the other, with an angrie, but weake voyce. But *Amphialus*, in whome abused kindnesse became spitefull rage, Ah barbarous wretch (said hee) onely couragious in discourtesie; thou shalt soone see whether thy toonge hath betrayed thy harte, or no: and with that, re-doubling his blowes, gave him, a great wounde upon his necke, and closing with him overthrew him, and with the fall thrust him mortally into the bodie: and with that went to pull off his

helmet, with intention to make him give himselfe the lye, for having so saide, or to cut off his head.

But the head-peece was no sooner off, but that there fell 5 about the shoulders of the overcome Knight the treasure of faire golden haire, which with the face (soone knowne by the badge of excellencie) witnessed that it was *Parthenia*, the unfortunatelie vertuous wife of *Argalus*: her beautie then even in despight of the passed sorrow, or comming death, assuring all beholders, that it was nothing short of perfection. For her exceeding faire eyes, having with continuall weeping gotten a little rednesse about them; her roundy sweetly swelling lippes a little trembling, as though they kissed their neighbour death; in her cheekes the whitenesse striving by little and little to get upon the rosinesse of them; her necke, a necke indeed of Alablaster, displaying the wounde, which with most daintie blood laboured to drowne his owne beauties; so as here was a river of purest redde, there an Iland of perfittest white, each giving lustre to the other; with the sweete countenãce (God-knowes) full of an unaffected languishing: though these thinges to a grosly conceaving sense might seeme disgraces; yet indeed were they but apparailing beautie in a new fashion, which all looked-upon thorough the spectacles of pittie, did evẽ encrease the lynes of her naturall fairenes, so as *Amphialus* was astonished with griefe, compassion, & shame, detesting his fortune, that made him unfortunate in victory.

Therfore, putting off his headpeece & gauntlet; kneeling 6 down unto her, & with teares testifying his sorow, he offred his (by himselfe accursed) hands to helpe her: protesting his life and power to be readie to doo her honour. But *Parthenia* (who had inward messingers of the desired deathes approch) looking upon him, and streight turning away her feeble sight, as from a delightlesse object, drawing out her wordes, which her breath (loath to parte from so sweete a bodie) did faintly deliver, Sir (saide she) I pray you (if prayers have place in enemies) to let my maides take my body untouched by you: the onely honour I now desire by your meanes, is, that I have no honour of you. *Argalus* made no such bargaine with you, that the hands which killed him, shoulde helpe me. I have of them (and I doo not onely pardon you, but thanke you for it) the service which I desired. There rests nothing now, but that I go live with him, since whose death I have done nothing but die. Then pawsing, and a little fainting, and againe comming to herselfe, O sweete life, welcome (saide she) nowe feele I the bandes untied of the cruell death, which so long hath helde me. And O life, O death, aunswere for me, that my thoughts have not so much as in a dreame tasted any comfort; since they were deprived of *Argalus*. I come, my *Argalus*, I come: And, O God hide my faultes in thy mercies, and graunt (as I feele thou doost graunt) that in thy eternall love, we may love eche other eternally. And this O Lorde: But there *Atropos* cut off her sentence: for with that, casting up both eyes and hands to the skies, the noble soule departed (one might well assure himselfe) to heaven, which left the bodie in so heavenly a demeanure.

7   But *Amphialus* (with a hart oppressed with griefe, because of her request) withdrewe himselfe, but the Judges, as full of pitie, had bene al this while disarming her, and her gentle-women with lamentable cries, laboring to stanch the remediles wounds: & a while she was dead before they perceived it; death being able to divide the soul, but not the beauty frō that body. But whē the infallible tokens of death assured thē of their losse, one of the women would have killed her selfe, but that the squire of *Amphialus* perceaving it, by force held her. Others that had as strong passions, though weaker resolution, fell to cast dust upon their heads, to teare their garments: all falling upon, and crying upon their sweet mistres; as if their cries could perswade the soul to leave the celestiall happines, to come again into the elemēts of sorrow: one time calling to remembrance her vertue, chastnes, sweetnes, goodnes to them: another time accursing themselves, that they had obeyed her, they having bene deceaved by her words, who assured thē, that it was revealed unto her, that she should have her harts desire in the battaile against *Amphialus*, which they wrongly understood. Then kissing her cold hands and feet, wearie of the world, since she was gone, who was their world. The very heavens semed, with a cloudie countenance, to loure at the losse, and Fame it selfe (though by nature glad to tell rare accidents, yet) could not choose but deliver it in lamentable accents, & in such sort went it quickly all over the Campe: &, as if the aire had bene infected with sorow, no hart was so

hard, but was subject to that contagion; the rarenes of the accident, matching together (the rarely matched together) pittie with admiration, *Basilius* himselfe came foorth, and brought foorth the faire *Gynecia* with him, who was gone into the campe under colour of visiting her husband, and hearing of her daughters: but indeed *Zelmane* was the Sainct, to which her pilgrimage was entended: cursing, envying, blessing, and in her harte kissing the walles which imprisoned her. But both they with *Philanax*, and the rest of the principall Nobilitie, went out, to make Honour triumph over Death, conveying that excellent body (wherto *Basilius* himself would needes bend his shoulder) to a church a mile from the campe, where the valiant *Argalus* lay intombed; recommending to that sepulchre, the blessed reliques of faithfull and vertuous Love: giving order for the making of marble images, to represent them, & each way enriching the tombe. Upon which, *Basilius* himself caused this Epitaphe to be written.

CHAP. 17.

[1] *The remorse of* Amphialus *for his last deede, and lasting destinie.*
[2] *His reverent respect in love.* [3] *His mothers ghosty counsell to a rape.*

[1] THen with eyes full of teares, and mouthes full of her prayses, returned they to the campe, with more and more hate against *Amphialus*: who (poore Gentleman) had therfore greater portion of woe, then any of them. For that courteous harte, which would have grieved but to have heard the like adventure, was rent with remembring himselfe to be the author: so that his wisdome could not so farre temper his passion, but that he tooke his sword, counted the best in the world (which with much bloud he had once conquered of a mightie Giant) and brake it into many peeces (which afterwardes he had good cause to repent) saying, that neither it was worthie to serve the noble exercise of chivalrie, nor any other worthie to feel that sword, which had stroken so excellent a Ladie: & withall, banishing all cheerfulnes of his countenance, he returned home. Where he gate him to his bed, not so much to rest his restles minde, as to avoyd all companie, the sight whereof was tedious unto him. And then melancholie (onely riche in unfortunate remembrances) brought before him all the mishappes, with which his life had wrestled: taking this, not onely as a confirming of the former, but a presage of following miserie; and to his harte (alredie overcome by sorrowfulnes) even trifling misfortunes came, to fill up the rolle of a grieved memorie, labouring onely his wittes to pearce farther and farther into his owne wretchednes. So all that night (in despite of darkenes) he held his eyes open; and the morning when the light began to restore to each body his colour, then with curtaines barde he himselfe from the enjoying of it: neither willing to feele the comfort of the day, nor the ease of the night: untill his mother (who never knew what love meant, but onely to himward) came to his bed side, and beginning with loving earnestnes to lay a kinde chiding upon him, because he would suffer the weakenesse of sorow, to conquere the strength of his vertues; he did with a broaken peecemeale speach (as if the tempest of passion unorderly

blewe out his words) remember the mishappes of his youth, the evils he had bene cause of, his rebelling with Shame, and that shame increased with shamefull accidents, the deaths of *Philoxenus* and *Parthenia*, wherein he found himselfe hated of the ever-ruling powers, but especially (and so especially, as the rest seemed nothing when he came to that) his fatall love to *Philoclea*: to whom he had so governed himselfe, as one that could neither conquere, nor yeeld; being of the one side a slave, and of the other a jaylor: and with all, almost up-brayding unto his mother the little successe of her large hoping promises, he in effect finding *Philoclea* nothing mollified, and now himselfe so cast downe, as he thought him unworthy of better.

But his mother (as she had plentifull cause) making him 2 see, that of his other griefes there was little or no faulte in him selfe, and therefore there ought to be little or no griefe in him; when she came to the head of the sore, indeed seeing that she could not patch up her former promises (he taking a desperate deafnesse to all delaying hopes) she confest plainly, that she could prevaile nothing: but the faulte was his owne, who had marred the yong Girle by seeking to have that by praier, which he should have taken by authoritie. That as it were an absurd cunning to make hie ladders to go in a plaine way; so was it an untimely and foolish flattery, there to beseech, where one might commaund, puffing thē up by being besought, with such a selfe-pride of superioritie, that it was not (forsooth) to be held out, but by a denial. O God (said *Amphialus*) how wel I thought my fortune would bring forth this end of your labors? assure your self, mother, I will sooner pull out these eies then they shal looke upon the heavenly *Philoclea*, but as upõ a heavē, whence they have their light, & to which they are subject, if they will power down any influēces of cõfort, O happy I: but if by the sacrifice of a faithfull hart, they will not be called unto me, let me languish, & wither with languishing, & grieve with withering, but never so much as repine with never so much grieving. Mother, ô Mother, lust may well be „ a tyrant, but true-love where it is indeed, it is a servant. „ Accursed more then I am, may I be, if ever I did approch her, but that I friezed as much in a fearefull reverence, as I burned in a vehement desire. Did ever mans eye looke thorough love upõ the majesty of vertue, shining through beauty, but that he became (as it wel became him) a captive? & is it the stile of a captive, to write, *Our will and pleasure?*

3   Tush, tush sonne (said *Cecropia*) if you say you love, but withall you feare; you feare lest you should offend; offend? & how know you, that you should offend? because she doth denie: denie? Now by my truth; if your sadnes would let me laugh, I could laugh hartily, to see that yet you are ignorant, that No, is no negative in a womans mouth. My „sonne, beleeve me, a womã, speaking of women: a lovers modesty among us is much more praised, then liked: or if we like it, so well we like it, that for marring of his modestie, he shall never proceed further. Each vertue hath his time: if you cõmand your souldier to march formost, & he for curtesie put others before him, would you praise his modesty? love is your Generall: he bids you dare: & will *Amphialus* be a dastard? Let examples serve: doo you thinke *Theseus* should ever have gotten *Antiope* with sighing, and crossing his armes? he ravished her, and ravished her that was an *Amazon*, and therefore had gotten a habite of stoutnes above the nature of a woman; but having ravished her, he got a child of her. And I say no more, but that (they say) is not gotten without consent of both sides. *Iole* had her owne father killed by *Hercules*, & her selfe ravished, by force ravished, & yet ere long this ravished, and unfathered Lady could sportfully put on the Lions skin upon her owne faire shoulders, & play with the clubbe with her owne delicate hands: so easily had she pardoned the ravisher, that she could not but delight in those weapõs of ravishing. But above all, mark *Helen* daughter to *Jupiter*, who could never brooke her manerly-wooing *Menelaus*, but disdained his humblenes, & lothed his softnes. But so well she could like the force of enforcing *Paris*, that for him she could abide what might be abidden. But what? *Menelaus* takes hart; he recovers her by force; by force carries her home; by force injoies her; and she, who could never like him for serviceablenesse, ever after loved him for violence. For what can be more agreable, then upon force to lay the fault of desire, and in one instant to joyne a deare delight with a just excuse? or rather the true cause is (pardon me ô woman-kinde for revealing to mine owne sonne the truth of this mystery) we

thinke there wants fire, where we find no sparkles at lest of furie. Truly I have knowen a great Lady, long sought by most great, most wise, most beautifull, most valiant persons; never wonne; because they did over-suspiciously sollicite her: the same Ladie brought under by an other, inferiour to all them in all those qualities, onely because he could use that imperious maisterfulnesse, which nature gives to men above women. For indeede (sonne, I confesse unto you) in our very creatiõ we are servants: and who prayseth his servaunts shall never be well obeyed: but as a ready horse streight yeeldes, when he findes one that will have him yeelde; the same fals to boundes when he feeles a fearefull horseman. Awake thy spirits (good *Amphialus*) and assure thy selfe, that though she refuseth, she refuseth but to endeere the obtaining. If she weepe, and chide, and protest, before it be gotten, she can but weepe, and chide, and protest, when it is gottẽ. Thinke, she would not strive, but that she meanes to trie thy force: and my *Amphialus*, know thy selfe a man, and shew thy selfe a man: and (beleeve me upon my word) a woman is a woman.

CHAP. 18.

[1] *The forsaken Knights defie.* [2] Amphialus *answere.* [4] *The one* [3] *and others armour and imprese.* [5] *The issue of their quarrell.* [6] *Their heroicall monomachy on horse,* [7] *and foot.* [8] *Their breathings,* [9] *& reencounters.* [10] Amphialus *rescued by An-* axius *brethren, the Blacke Knight by the greene and white.* [11] *The supply of both sides to cary away the breathles Knights.* [12] *The Blackknights grieves.*

AMphialus was aboute to answere her, when a Gentlemã of his made him understande, that there was a messenger come, who had brought a letter unto him from out of the campe: whom he presently calling for, tooke, opened, and read the letter, importing this.

TO thee Amphialus *of* Arcadia, *the forsaken Knight wisheth* [1] *health, and courage, that by my hand thou maiest receyve punishment for thy treason, according to thine owne offer, which wickedly occasioned, thou haste proudly begun, and accursedly main-*

teyned. I will presently (if thy minde faint thee not for his owne guiltinesse) meete thee in thy Iland, in such order, as hath by the former beene used : or if thou likest not the time, place, or weapon, I am ready to take thine owne reasonable choise in any of them; so as thou do perfourme the substaunce. Make me such answere as may shew that thou hast some taste of honour : and so I leave thee, to live till I meete thee.

Amphialus read it, and with a deepe sigh (according to the humour of inward affection) seemed even to cõdemne him selfe, as though indeed his reproches were true. But howsoever the dulnes of Melancholy would have languishingly yeelded thereunto, his Courage (unused to such injuries) desired helpe of Anger to make him this answere.

2 *F Orsaken Knight, though your namelesse challenge might carry in it selfe excuse for a man of my birth and estate, yet herein set your harte at rest, you shall not be forsaken. I will without stay answere you in the woonted manner, and come both armed in your foolish threatnings, and yet the more fearelesse, expecting weake blowes, where I finde so strong wordes. You shall not therefore long attende me in the Ilande, before proofe teache you, that of my life you have made your selfe too large a promise. In the meane time, Farewell.*

3 This being written, and delivered, the messenger tolde him, that his Lord would (if he liked the same) bring two Knights with him to be his *Patrons*. Which *Amphialus* accepted, and withall shaking of (with resolution) his mothers importunate disswasions, he furnished him selfe for the fight : but not in his wonted furniture. For now (as if he would turne his inside outwarde) he would needes appeare all in blacke; his decking both for him selfe, and horse, being cut out into the fashion of very ragges : yet all so dainty, joyned together with pretious stones, as it was a brave raggednesse, and a riche povertie : and so cunningly had a workeman followed his humour in his armour, that he had given it a rustie shewe, and yet so, as any man might perceive was by arte, and not negligence; carying at one instant a disgraced handsomnesse, and a new oldnes. In his shield he bare for his devise, a Night, by an excellently painter, with a Sunne with a shadow, and upon the shadow

with a speech signifying, that it *onely* was *barrd from injoying that, whereof it had his life*: or, *From whose I am bannished.* In his creste he caried *Philocleas* knives, the onely token of her forwarde favour.

So past he over into the Iland, taking with him the two 4 brothers of *Anaxius*; where he founde the forsaken Knight, attired in his owne liverie, as blacke, as sorrowe it selfe could see it selfe in the blackest glasse: his ornaments of the same hew, but formed in the figure of Ravens, which seemed to gape for carrion: onely his raynes were snakes, which finely wrapping themselves one within the other, their heads came together to the cheekes and bosses of the bit, where they might seeme to bite at the horse, and the horse (as he champte the bit) to bite at them; and that the white foame was ingendred by the poysonous furie of the combatt. His *Impresa* was a *Catoblepta* which so long lies dead, as the Moone (whereto it hath so naturall a sympathie) wants her light. The worde signified that *The Moone wanted not the light, but the poore beast wanted the Moones light.* He had in his headpiece, a whippe, to witnesse a selfe-punishing repentaunce. Their very horses were cole-blacke too, not having so much as one starre to give light to their night of blackenesse: so as one would have thought they had bene the two sonnes of Sorrow, and were come thether to fight for their birth-right in that sorie inheritance.

Which aliance of passions so moved *Amphialus* (alredy 5 tender-minded by the afflictions of Love) that without staffe or sword drawne, he trotted fairely to the forsakē Knight, willing to have put off his combat, to which his melancholy hart did (more then ever in like occasion) misgive him: and therefore saluting him, Good Knight (said he) because we are men, and should knowe reason why we doo things; tell me the cause, that makes you thus eager to fight with me. Because I affirme (answered the forsaken Knight) that thou dost most rebellious injurie to those Ladies, to whome all men owe service. You shall not fight with me (saide *Amphialus*) upon that quarrell: for I confesse the same too: but it proceeds from their owne beauty, to inforce Love to offer this force. I maintaine then (said the forsaken Knight) that thou art not worthy so to love. And that confesse I too (saide *Amphialus*) since the world is not so richly blessed, as to bring forth any thing worthy thereof.

But no more unworthy then any other, since in none can be a more worthy love. Yes, more unworthy then my self (said the forsaken Knight) for though I deserve contempt, thou deservest both contempt, and hatred.

6 But *Amphialus* by that thinking (though wrongly, each indeede mistaking other) that he was his rivall, forgat all minde of reconciliation, and having all his thoughts boũd up in choler, never staying either judge, trũpet, or his owne laũce, drew out his sword, & saying, Thou lyest false villaine, unto him; his words & blowes came so quick togither, as the one seemed a lightning of the others thũder. But he foũd no barrẽ groũd of such seede: for it yeelded him his owne with such encrease, that though Reason and Amazement go rarely togither, yet the most reasonable eies that saw it, founde reason to be amazed at the fury of their combat. Never game of death better plaid; never fury set it self forth in greater braverie. The curteous *Vulcan*, whẽ he wrought at his nowe more curteous wives request, *Æneas* an armour, made not his hammer beget a greater sounde; then the swordes of those noble Knights did; they needed no fire to their forge; for they made the fire to shine at the meeting of their swords, & armours; ech side fetching new spirit from the castle window, and careful of keeping their sight, it was a matter of greater consideration in their combat, then either the advantage of Sun or winde: which Sunne and wind (if the astonished eies of the beholders were not by the astonishment deceived) did both stand still to be beholders of this rare match. For neither could their amazed eies discerne motion in the Sunne, and no breath of wind stirred, as if either for feare it would not come amõg such blows, or with delight had his eies so busie, as it had forgot to open his mouth. This fight being the more cruell, since both Love and Hatred conspired to sharpen their humours, that hard it was to say, whether Love with one trumpet, or Hatred with another, gave the lowder alarum to their courages. Spite, rage, disdaine, shame, revenge, came waighting upon Hatred: of the other side came with love-longing Desire, both invincible Hope, and fearelesse Despaire, with rivallike Jealousie, which (although brought up within doores in the schoole of *Cupid*) woulde shewe themselves no lesse forwarde, then the other dustie bande of *Mars*, to make themselves notable in the

notablenes of this combat. Of eyther side Confidence, un-acquainted with Losse, but assured trust to overcome, and good experience howe to overcome: nowe seconding their terrible blowes with cunning labouring the horses, to winne ground of the enimie; now unlooked-for parting one from the other, to win advantage by an advantageous retourne. But force against force, skill against skill, so enterchangeably encountred, that it was not easie to determine, whether enterprising, or preventing came former: both, sometimes at one instant, doing and suffring wrong, and choller no lesse rising of the doing, then of the suffring. But as the fire, the more fuell is put to it, the more hungrie still it is to devoure more: so the more they strake, the more unsatisfied they were with striking. Their verie armour by piecemeale fell away from them: and yet their flesh abode the wounds constantly, as though it were lesse sensible of smarte, then the senselesse armour: their blood in most places stayning the blacke, as if it would give a more lively coulour of mourning, then blacke can doo. And so a long space they fought, while neither vertue, nor fortune seemed partiall of either side: which so tormented the unquiet hart of *Amphialus*, that he resolved to see a quicke ende: and therefore with the violence of courage, adding strength to his blow, he strake in such wise upon the side of the others heade, that his remembrance left that battered lodging: so as he was quite from himselfe, casting his armes abroade, and redie to fall downe; his sword likewise went out of his hande; but that being fast by a chaine to his arme, he could not loose. And *Amphialus* used the favour of occasion, redoubling his blowes: but the horse (weary to be beaten, as well as the master) carried his master away, till he came unto himselfe: But then who could have seene him, might wel have discerned shame in his cheekes, and revenge in his eyes: so as setting his teeth togither with rage, he came running upon *Amphialus*, reaching out his arme, which had gathered up the sword, meaning with that blow to have cleaved *Amphialus* in two. But *Amphialus* seeing the blow comming, shunned it with nimble turning his horse aside; wherwith the forsaken Knight over-strake himself so, as almost he came downe with his owne strength. But the more hungrie he was of his purpose, the more he was bard the food of it: disdaining the resistance, both of force, and fortune, he returned upon the spurre againe, and ranne with such violence upon *Amphialus*, that his horse with the force of the shocke rose up before, almost overturned: which *Amphialus* perceaving, with rayne and spurre put forth his horse; and withall gave a mightie blow in the descent of his horse, upon the shoulder of the forsaken Knight; from whence sliding, it fell upon the necke of his horse, so as horse and man fell to the ground: but he was scarce downe before he was up on his feete againe, with brave gesture shewing rising of corage, in the falling of fortune.

7   But the curteous *Amphialus* excused himselfe, for having (against his will) kild his horse. Excuse thy selfe for viler faults (answered the forsaken Knight) and use this poore advantage the best thou canst; for thou shalt quickely finde thou hast neede of more. Thy folly (said *Amphialus*) shall not make me forget my selfe: and therewith (trotting a little aside) alighted from his horse, because he would not have fortune come to claime any part of the victory. Which curteous act would have mollified the noble harte of the forsaken Knight, if any other had done it, besides the Jaylor of his mistres: but that was a sufficient defeazaunce for the firmest bonde of good nature; and therfore he was no sooner alighted, but that he ranne unto him, re-entring into as cruel a fight, as eye did ever see, or thought could reasonably imagine; farre beyond the reach of weak words to be able to expresse it. For what they had done on horsebacke, was but as a morsell to keep their stomakes in appetite, in comparison of that, which now (being themselves) they did. Nor ever glutton by the châge of daintie diet could be brought to fetch feeding (when he might have bene satisfied before) with more earnestnes, then those (by the change of their maner of fight) fell cleane to a new fight, though any else would have thought they had had their fill alredy. *Amphialus* being the taller man, for the most part stood with his right legge before; his shield at the uttermost length of his arme; his sword hie, but with the point toward his enemy. But whê he strake, which came so thick, as if every blow would strive to be foremost, his arme seemed still a postillion of death. The forsaken Knight shewed with like skil, unlike gesture, keeping himselfe in continual motion, proportioning the distance betweene thê to any thing that *Amphialus*

attempted: his eye guided his foote, and his foote conveighed his hand; and since nature had made him something the lower of the two, he made art follow, and not strive with nature: shunning rather thẽ warding his blowes; like a cũning mastiffe, who knowes the sharpnes of the horne, and strẽgth of the Bul; fights low to get his proper advãtage; answering mightines with nimblenes, and yet at times imploying his wonderfull force, wherein he was seconde to none. In summe, the blowes were stronge, the thrusts thicke, and the avoydings cunning. But the forsaken Knight (that thought it a degree of being cõquered to be long in conquering) strake so mightie a blow, that he made *Amphialus* put knee to the ground, without any humblenes. But when he felt himselfe striken downe, and saw himselfe striken downe by his rivall, then shame seemed one arme, and disdaine another; fury in his eyes, and revenge in his hart; skill and force gave place, & they tooke the place of skil & force: with so unweariable a manner, that the forsaken Knight was also driven to leave the streame ot cunning, and give himselfe wholly to be guided by the storme of fury: there being in both (because hate would not suffer admiration) extreame disdaine to finde themselves so matched.

What (said *Amphialus* to himselfe) am I *Amphialus*, before 8 whom so many monsters & Gyants have falne dead, when I onely sought causelesse adventures? and can one Knight now withstand me in the presence of *Philoclea*, and fighting for *Philoclea*? or since I lost my liberty, have I lost my courage? have I gotten the hart of a slave, as well as the fortune? If an armie were against me in the sight of *Philoclea*, could it resist me? O beast, one man resistes thee; thy ryvall resistes thee: or am I indeed *Amphialus*? have not passions kild him, and wretched I (I know not how) succeeded into his place? Of the other side the forsaken Knight with no lesse spite, fel out with himself; Hast thou brokẽ (said he to himselfe) the cõmãdemẽt of thy only Princesse to come now into her presẽce, & in her presẽce to prove thy self a coward? Doth *Asia* and *Ægypt* set up Trophes unto thee, to be matched here by a traytor? O noble *Barsanes*, how shamed will thy soule be, that he that slew thee, should be resisted by this one man? O incomparable *Pyrocles*, more grieved wilt thou be with thy friends shame, thẽ with thine owne imprisonment, when thou shalt know how little I have bene able to doo for the deliverie of thee, and those heavenlie Princesses. Am I worthie to be friend to the most valourous Prince that ever was entituled valourous, and shewe my selfe so weake a wretch? No, shamed *Musidorus*, worthie for nothing, but to keepe sheepe, get thee a sheephooke againe, since thou canst use a sword no better.

9   Thus at times did they, now with one thought, then with another, sharpen their over-sharpe humors; like the Lion, that beates himselfe with his owne taile, to make himselfe the more angrie. These thoughtes indeede not staying, but whetting their angrie swordes, which now had put on the apparraile of Crueltie: they bleeding so aboundantly, that every bodie that sawe them, fainted for them, & yet they fainted not in themselves: their smart being more sensible to others eyes, then to their owne feeling: Wrath and Courage barring the common sense from bringing any message of their case to the minde: Paine, Wearines, and Weakenes, not daring to make knowen their case (though already in the limits of death) in the presence of so violent furie: which filling the veines with rage, in stead of bloud, and making the minde minister spirites to the bodie, a great while held out their fight, like an arrowe shotte upward by the force of the bowe, though by his owne nature he would goe downward. The forsaken Knight had the more wounds, but *Amphialus* had the soarer; which the other (watchinge time and place) had cõningly geven unto him. Who ever saw a well-mand Galley fight with a tall ship, might make unto himselfe some kind of comparison of the difference of these two Knights; a better couple then which, the world could not bragge of. *Amphialus* seemed to excell in strength, the forsaken Knight in nimblenes; and yet did the ones strength excel in nimblenes, and the others nimblenes excell in strength: but now, strength and nimblenes were both gone, and excesse of courage only maintayned the fight. Three times had *Amphialus* with his mightie blowes driven the forsaken Knight to go staggering backwarde, but every one of those times he requited pain with smarte, and shame with repulse. And now, whether he had cause, or that over-much confidence (an over-forward scholer of unconquered Courage) made him think he had cause, he begã to persuade himself he had the advãtage of the combat, though the advantage he toke himselfe

to have, was onely that he should be the later to die: which hopes, Hate (as unsecrete as Love) could not conceale, but drawing himself a little back frõ him, brake out in these maner of words.

Ah *Amphialus* (said the forsakẽ knight) this third time thou 8 shalt not escape me, but thy death shall satisfie thy injury, & my malice; and pay for the cruelty thou shewedst in killing the noble *Argalus*, & the fair *Parthenia*. In troth (said *Amphialus*) thou art the best knight that ever I fought withal, which would make me willing to graũt thee thy life, if thy wit were as good as thy corage; that (besides other follies) layest that to my charge, which most against my will was committed. But whether my death be in thy power, or no, let this tel thee; And upon the worde wayted a blow, which parted his shield into two peeces; & despising the weak resistance of his alredie brokẽ armor, made a great breach into his hart side, as if he would make a passage for his love to get out at.

But paine rather seemed to increase life, then to weaken life 9 in those champions. For, the forsaken Knight comming in with his right leg, and making it guide the force of the blow, strake *Amphialus* upon the bellie, so horrible a woũd, that his guts came out withall. Which *Amphialus* perceaving (fearing death, onely because it should come with overthrow) he seemed to conjure all his strength for one moments service; and so, lifting up his sword with both hands, hit the forsaken knight upõ the head, a blow, wherewith his sword brake. But (as if it would do a notable service before it died) it prevayled so, even in the instant of breaking, that the forsaken Knight fell to the ground, quite for that instant forgetting both love and hatred: and *Amphialus* (finding him self also in such weaknes, as he loked for speedy death) glad of the victorie, though little hoping to enjoy it, puld up his visar, meaning with his dagger to give him death; but in stead of death, he gave him life: for, the aire so revived his spirits, that comming to himself, and seeing his present danger, with a life conquering death, he tooke *Amphialus* by the thigh, & together rose himselfe, and overturned him. But *Amphialus* scrambled up againe, both now so weake indeede, as their motions rather seemed the afterdrops to a storme, then any matter of great furie.

But *Amphialus* might repent himselfe of his wilfull breaking

his good sword : for, the forsaken Knight (having with the extremitie of justly-conceived hate, and the unpitifulnes of his
owne neere-threatning death, blotted out all complements of
courtesie) let flie at him so cruelly, that though the blowes
were weake, yet weaknes upon a weakned subject, proved such
strĕgth, that *Amphialus* having attempted in vaine, once or twise
to close with him, receaving wound upõ wound, sent his whole
burden to strike the earth with falling, since he could strike his foe
no better in standing: geving no other tokens of himself, then as
of a man even ready to take his oath to be Deathes true servant.

10   Which when the hardie brothers of *Anaxius* perceaved, not
recking law of armes, nor use of chivalrie, they flew in to
defende their friende, or revenge their losse of him.   But they
were foorthwith encountred with the two brave cõpanions of
the forsaken Knight; whereof the one being all in greene, both
armour and furniture, it seemed a pleasant garden, wherein
grewe orange trees, which with their golden fruites, cunningly
beaten in, & embrodered, greatly enriched the eye-pleasing
colour of greene.   In his shield was a sheep, feeding in a pleasant
field, with this word, *Without feare, or envie.* And therfore was
called the Knight of the sheep.   The other Knight was all in
milke white, his attiring els, all cutte in starres, which made of
cloath of silver, and silver spangles, each way seemed to cast
many aspects.   His device was the very Pole it selfe, about
which many starres stirring, but the place it selfe lefte voide.
The word was, *The best place yet reserved.* But these foure
Knights, inheriting the hate of their friends, began a fierce
combat: the forsaken Knight himselfe not able to helpe his
side, but was driven to sit him downe, with the extreame faintnesse of his more & more fainting body.   But those valiant
couples seeking honour by dishonouring, and to build safety
upon ruine, gave new appetites, to the almost glutted eies of
the beholders: and now bloud began to put sweat from the full
possession of their outsides, no advantage being yet to be seene;
onely the Knight of the sheepe seeming most deliver, and
affecting most all that viewed him, when a company of souldiers
sent by *Cecropia*, came out in boates to the Ilande: and all
came running to the destruction of the three Knights, whereof
the one was utterly unable to defend himselfe.

11   But then did the other two Knights shewe their wonderfull

462

courage, and fidelitie. For turning backe to backe, and bothe bestriding the blacke forsaken Knight (who had fainted so long till he had lost the feeling of faintnesse) they helde playe against the rest, though the two brothers unknightly helped them; till *Philanax* (who watchfully attended such traiterous practises) sent likewise over, both by boate and swimming, so choise a number as did put most of the other to the sworde. Onely the two Brothers, with some of the bravest of them, carrying away the body of *Amphialus*, which they would rather have died, then have left behind them.

So was the forsaken Knight (layed upon clokes) carried home 12 to the campe. But his two friends knowing his earnest desire not to be knowen, covering him from any bodies eyes, conveyed him to their owne tente: *Basilius* himselfe conquering his earnest desire to see him, with feare to displease him, who had fought so notably in his quarrell. But Fame set the honour upon his backe, which he would not suffer to shine in his face: no mans mouth being barrein of prayses to the noble Knight, that had bettered the most esteemed Knight in the world: every bodie praying for his life, and thinking that therein they prayed for themselves. But he him selfe, when by the diligent care of friends, and well applied cunning of surgeons, he came to renewe againe the league betweene his minde and body, then fell he to a freshe warre with his owne thoughts, wrongfully condemning his manhood, laying cowardise to him selfe, whome the impudentest backbiter would not so have wrōged. For his courage (used to use victory as an inheritaunce) could brooke no resistance at any time: but now that he had promised him selfe, not onely the conquest of him, but the scaling of the walles, and delivery of *Pamela*, though he had done beyond al others expectation, yet so short was he of his owne; that he hated to looke upon the Sunne, that had seene him do so weakely: and so much abhorred all visitation or honour, whereof he thought him selfe unworthy, that he besought his two noble friends to carrie him away to a castle not far of, where he might cure his wounds, and never be knowne till he made successe excuse this (as he thought) want in him. They lovingly obeyed him, leaving *Basilius* and all the campe very sorrie for the parting of these three unknowne Knights, in whose prowesse they had reposed greatest trust of victory.

CHAP. 19.

[1]*The state of the leaguer, and beleaguered.* [2]*The agonies of* Amphialus. [3]*The wit-craft of* Cecropia, *to threaten* Basilius *with the three Ladies death.* [4]Kalanders *compassion.* [5]Philanax-*his counter-counsell.* [6]*The breaking up the siege.*

[1] BUt they being gone, *Basilius* and *Philanax* gave good order to the strengthning of the siege, fortifying themselves, so as they feared no more any such suddaine onset, as that of *Anaxius.* And they within (by reasõ of *Anaxius* hurt, but especially of *Amphialus*-his) gave themselves onely to diligent watch & ward, making no sallies out, but committing the principall trust to *Zoilus* and *Lycurgus.* For *Anaxius* was yet forced to keepe his chamber. And as for *Amphialus,* his body had such wounds, and gave such wounds to his mind, as easily it coulde not be determined, whether death or he made the greater hast one to the other: for when the diligent care of cunning surgeons, had brought life to the possession of his owne right, Sorrowe and Shame (like two corrupted servaunts) came waiting of it, perswading nothing but the giving over of it selfe to destruction. They laide before his eyes his present case, painting every piece of it in moste ougly colours: they shewed him his love wrapped in despaire, his fame blotted by overthrow; so that if before he languished, because he could not obtaine his desiring, he now lamented because he durst not desire the obtaining. Recreant *Amphialus,* (would he say to him selfe) how darest thou intitle thy selfe the lover of *Philoclea,* that hast neither shewed thy self a faithfull coward, nor a valiant rebell, but both rebellious and cowardly, which no law cã quite, nor grace have pitie of ? Alas life, what little pleasure thou doost me, to give me nothing but sense of reproach, and exercise of ruine? I would sweete *Philoclea,* I had died, before thy eies had seene my weaknes: & then perchaunce with some sigh thou wouldest have cõfessed, thou hadst lost a worthy servaunt. But now, caitife that I am, what ever I have done, serves but to builde up my rivals glory. To these speeches he would couple such gestures of vexation, & would fortifie the gestures with such effects of furie, as sometimes offring to teare

up his woũds, sometimes to refuse the sustenance of meat, &
counsell of phisitions, that his perplexed mother was driven to
make him by force to be tended, with extreame corsey to her
selfe, & annoiance to him: till in the end he was contented to
promise her, he would attempt no violence upon himself, upon
condition he might be troubled by no body, but onely his
Phisitions: his melancholy detesting all cõpany, so as not the
very surgeons nor servants durst speak unto him in doing him
service: only he had praied his mother, as she tendered his life,
she would procure him grace; and that without that, she would
never come at him more.

His mother, who had cõfined all her love only unto him, 3
set only such about him, as were absolutely at her cõmandement, whom she forbad to let him know any thing that passed
in the castle, till his wounds were cured, but as she from time
to time should instruct them: she (for her selfe) being resolved,
now she had the government of al things in her owne hands, to
satisfie her sonnes love, by their yeelding, or satisfie her owne
revenge in their punishment. Yet first, because he should be the
freer frõ outward force, she sent a messenger to the campe, to
denounce unto *Basilius*, that if he did not presently raise his
siege, she would cause the heads of the three Ladies, prisoners,
to be cut of before his eies. And to make him the more feare
a present performance, she caused his two daughters & *Zelmane*
to be led unto the wals, where she had made a scaffold, easie to
be seene by *Basilius*: and there caused thẽ to be kept, as ready
for the slaughter, til answere came from *Basilius*. A sight full
of pittie it was, to see those three (all excelling in all those
excellencies, wherwith Nature can beautifie any body: *Pamela*
giving sweetnes to majesty, *Philoclea* enriching noblenes with
humblenes, *Zelmane* setting in womanly beautie manlike valour)
to be thus subjected to the basest injury of unjust Fortune.
One might see in *Pamela* a willingnesse to die, rather then to
have life at others discretion, though sometimes a princely
disdaine would sparkle out of her Princely eies, that it should
be in others power to force her to die. In *Philoclea* a prety
feare came up, to endamaske her rosie cheekes: but it was
such a feare, as rather seemed a kindly childe to her innate
humblenes, then any other dismaiednes: or if she were
dismaied, it was more for *Zelmane*, then for her selfe; or if

more for her selfe, it was because *Zelmane* should loose her. As for *Zelmane*, as she went with her hands bound (for they durst not adventure on her well knowne valour, especially amõg people which perchãce might be moved by such a spectacle to some revolte) she was the true image of over-maistred courage, & of spite, that sees no remedie. For her breast swelled withall, the bloud burst out at her nose, and she looked paler then accustomed, with her eies cast on the ground, with such a grace, as if she were fallen out with the heavens, for suffering such an injury. The lookers on were so moved withal, as they misliked what themselves did, and yet still did what themselves misliked. For some, glad to rid themselves of the dangerous annoyaunce of this siege, some willing to shorten the way to *Amphialus*-his succession (whereon they were dependents) some, & the greatest some, doing because others did, and suffring because none durst begin to hinder, did in this sort set their hands to this (in their owne conscience) wicked enterprise.

4   But whẽ this message was brought to *Basilius*, & that this pittifull preparation was a sufficient letter of credit for him to beleeve it, he called unto him his chief coũcelors: amõg which, those he chiefly trusted were *Philanax* and *Kalander* (lately come to the campe at *Basilius* cõmandement, & in him selfe wery of his solitary life, wanting his sons presence, & never having heard him his beloved guestes since they parted from him). Now in this doubt what he should do, he willed *Kalander* to give him his advise: who spake much to this purpose. You cõmaund me Sir (said he) to speake, rather because you will keepe your wonted grave, & noble manner, to do nothing of importãce without coũcell, then that in this cause (which indeed hath but one way) your mind needs to have any counsell: so as my speech shall rather be to cõfirme what you have alredy determined, thẽ to argue against any possibilitie of other determination. For what sophistical scholler can finde any question in this, whether you will have your incomparable daughters live, or dye? whether since you be here to cause their deliverance, you will make your being here the cause of their destruction? for nothing can be more unsensible, „then to thinke what one doth, & to forget the end why it is done, Do therfore as I am sure you meane to doo, remove the

siege, and after seeke by practise, or other gĕtle meanes, to
recover that which by force you cãnot: & therof is indeed
(whĕ it please you) more coũsel to be takĕ. Once, in extremi- „
ties the winning of time is the purchase of life, & worse by no
meanes then their deaths cã befal unto you. A mã might use
more words, if it were to any purpose to guild gold, or that I
had any cause to doubt of your mind: But you are wise, & are
a father. He said no more, for he durst not attempt to perswade the marrying of his daughter to *Amphialus*, but left that
to bring in at another consultation. But *Basilius* made signe
to *Philanax*, who stãding a while in a maze as inwardly
perplexed, at last thus delivered his opiniõ.

If ever I could wish my faith untried, & my counsell un- 5
trusted, it should be at this time, whĕ in truth I must cõfesse
I would be cõtent to purchase silĕce with discredit. But since
you cõmand, I obey: onely let me say thus much, that I obey
not to these excellent Ladies father, but to my Prince: & a
Prince it is to whõ I give coũsel. Therefore as to a Prince I
say, that the grave and (I well know) true-minded counsell of
my Lord *Kalander* had come in good time whĕ you first tooke
armes, before al your subjects gate notice of your intention,
before so much blood was spĕt, & before they were drivĕ to
seek this shift for their last remedy. But if now, this force
you away, why did you take armes? since you might be sure
when ever they were in extremitie they would have recourse to
this threatning? and for a wise man to take in hand that which
his enimie may with a word overthrow, hath in my conceit
great incongruity, & as great not to forethink what his enemy
in reason wil doo. But they threaten they wil kil your
daughters. What if they promised you if you removed your
siege, they would honorably send home your daughters? would
you be angled by their promises? truly no more ought you be
terrified by their threatnings. For yet of the two, promise „
binds faith more then threatning. But indeede a Prince of „
judgemĕt ought not to consider what his enimies promise, or „
threaten, but what the promisers and threatners in reasõ wil „
do: & the neerest cõjecture therunto, is what is best for their „
own behoofe to do. They threatĕ if you remove not, they wil
kil your daughters, and if you doo remove, what surety have
you, but that they will kil thĕ, since if the purpose be to cut off

al impediments of *Amphialus*-his ambitiõ, the same cause wil continue when you are away; & so much the more encoraged, as the revenging power is absent, & they have the more oportunitie to draw their faƈtious friends about them: but if it be for their security onely, the same cause wil bring forth the same effeƈt: & for their security they wil preserve thẽ. But it may be said, no man knows what desperate folkes will do: it is true, and as true that no reason nor policie can prevent what ,, desperate folks wil do: & therfore they are amõg those dangers, ,, which wisdome is not to reckẽ. Only let it suffice to take away their despaire, which may be by granting pardon for what is past; so as the Ladies may be freely delivered. And let them that are your subjeƈts, trust you that are their Prince: doo not you subjeƈt your selfe to trust them, who are so untrusty as to be manifest traitors. For if they finde you so base-minded, as by their th[r]eatning to remove your force, what indignitie is it, that they would not bring you unto, still by the same threatning? since then if Love stir them, love will keep them from murthering what they love; and if Ambition provoke them, ambitious they will be, when you are away, as well as while you are here: take not away your force, which bars not the one, & bridels the other. For as for their shewes and words they are but to feare babes, not worthy once to move a worthy mans conceit; which must still cõsider what in reasõ they are like to do. Their despaire I grant you shall do wel to prevent, which as it is the last of all resolutions, so no man ,, fals into it, while so good a way as you may offer, is open unto ,, thẽ. In sũ, you are a Prince, & a father of people, who ought ,, with the eye of wisdome, the hand of fortitude, and the hart of ,, justice to set downe all private conceits, in comparison of what ,, for the publike is profitable.

6   He would have proceeded on, whẽ *Gynecia* came rũning in amazed for her daughter *Pamela*, but mad for *Zelmane*; & falling at *Basilius* feet, besought him to make no delay: using such gestures of cõpassiõ instead of stopped words, that *Basilius*, otherwise enough tender minded, easily granted to raise the siege, which he saw dangerous to his daughters: but indeed more carefull for *Zelmane*, by whose besieged person, the poore old man was streightly besieged: so as to rid him of the famine of his minde, he went in speed away; discharging his soul-

diors: only leaving the authority, as before, in *Philanax* his hands, he himselfe went with *Gynecia* to a strong Castle of his, where he took coūsell how first to deliver *Zelmane*, whom he called the poore stranger, as though onely Law of hospitalitie moved him; and for that purpose sent divers messengers to trafficke with *Cecropia*.

CHAP. 20.

[2] *The sweete resistance of the true sisters* [1] *to the sower assaultes of their false Aunt. The whipping of* [3] Philoclea [5] *and* Pamela. [4] *The patience of both* [6] *and passions for their lovers.*

CEcropia by this meanes rid of the present daunger of the [1] siege (desiring *Zoilus* and *Lycurgus* to take the care, till their brother recovered, of revictualling, and furnishing the Citie, both with men and what els wanted, against any new occasion should urge them, she her selfe disdaining to harken to *Basilius*, without he would grant his daughter in mariage to her son, which by no means he would be brought unto) bent all the sharpenesse of her malicious wit, how to bring a comfortable graunt to her sonne; whereupon she well found no lesse then his life depended. Therfore for a while she attēpted all meanes of eloquent praying, and flattering perswasion, mingling sometimes gifts, somtimes threatnings, as she had cause to hope, that either open force, or undermining, would best winn the castle of their Resolution. And ever as much as she did to *Philoclea*, so much did she to *Pamela*, though in manner sometimes differing, as she found fit to levell at the ones noble height, and the others sweet lowlinesse. For though she knew her sonnes harte had wholly given it selfe to *Philoclea*, yet seeing the equall gifts in *Pamela*, she hoped, a faire grant would recover the sorrow of a faire refusal: cruelly entēding the present impoysoning the one, as soone as the others affection were purchased.

But in vaine was all her vaine oratory employed. *Pamelaes* [2] determination was built upõ so brave a Rock, that no shot of hers could reach unto it: and *Philoclea* (though humbly seated) was so invironed with sweete rivers of cleere vertue, as could neither be battred, nor undermined : her witty perswasions had wise answeres; her eloquence recompenced with sweetnes; her threatnings repelled with disdaine in the one, & patience in the other; her gifts either not accepted, or accepted to obey, but not to bind. So as *Cecropia* in nature violent; cruel, because ambitious; hateful, for old rooted grudge to their mother, & now spitefull because she could not prevaile with girles, as she counted them; lastly, drawne on by her love to her son, & held up by a tyrannical authoritie, forthwith followed the byas of her own crooked disposition, & doubling and redoubling her threatnings, fel to cōfirme some of her threatned effeᶜts: first withdrawing al cōfort, both of servāts, & service from thē. But that those excellēt Ladies had bene used unto, evē at home, & thē foūd in thēselves how much good the hardnes of educatiō doth to the resistāce of misery. Then dishonorably using them both in dyet, and lodging, by a contempt to pull downe their thoughts to yeelding. But as before, the consideration of a prison had disgraced al ornamēts, so now the same cōsideratiō made thē attend al diseasefulnes. Then stil, as she found those not prevaile, would she go forward with giving them terrors, sometimes with noices of horror, sometimes with suddaine frightings in the night, when the solitary darkenesse thereof might easier astonish the disarmed senses. But to all Vertue, and Love resisted, strengthned one by the other, when each found it selfe over-vehemently assaulted. *Cecropia* still sweetning her fiercenesses with faire promises, if they would promise faire; that feeling evill, and seing a way far better, their minds might the sooner be mollified. But they that could not taste her behaviour, when it was pleasing, indeed could worse now, when they had lost al taste by her injuries.

3   She resolving all extremities, rather then faile of cōquest, pursued on her rugged way : letting no day passe, without new and new perplexing the poore Ladies minds, and troubling their bodies : and still swelling, the more she was stopped, and growing hot with her owne doings, at length, abhominable rage carried her to absolute tyrānies, so that taking with her certaine olde women (of wicked dispositions, and apt for envie-sake to be cruel to youth and beautie) with a countenāce impoysoned with malice, flew to the sweet *Philoclea*, as if so many Kites

should come about a white Dove, & matching violent gestures with mischievous threatnings, she having a rod in her hãd (like a fury that should carry wood to the burning of *Dianas* temple) fel to scourge that most beautifull body: Love in vaine holding the shield of Beautie against her blind cruelty. The Son drew clouds up to hide his face from so pitiful a sight; & the very stone wals did yeeld drops of sweate for agonie of such a mischiefe: each senselesse thing had sense of pittie; onely they that had sense, were senseles. Vertue rarely found her worldly weakenes more, then by the oppression of that day: and weeping *Cupid* told his weeping mother, that he was sorie he was not deaf, as well as blind, that he might never know so lamentable a worke. *Philoclea*, with tearefull eyes, and sobbing breast (as soon as her wearines rather then compassion, gave her respite) kneeled dow[n]e to *Cecropia*, and making pittie in her face honourable, and torment delightfull, besought her, since she hated her (for what cause she tooke God to witnesse she knew not) that she would at once take away her life, and not please her self with the tormenting of a poore Gentlewoman. If (said she) the common course of humanitie cannot move you, nor the having me in your owne walles, cannot claime pittie: nor womanly mercie, nor neere alliance, nor remẽbrance (how miserable so ever now) that I am a Princes daughter; yet let the love (you have often tolde me) your sonne beares me, so much procure, that for his sake, one death may be thought inough for me; I have not lived so many yeares, but that one death may be able to conclude them: neither have my faults, I hope, bene so many, but that one death may satisfie them. It is no great suite to an enemie, when but death is desired. I crave but that, and as for the graunting your request, know for certaine you lose your labours, being every day furtherof-minded from becõming his wife, who useth me like a slave. But that in stead of getting grace renued againe *Cecropias*, fury: so that (excellent creature) she was newly again tormented by those hellish monsters: *Cecropia* using no other words, but that she was a proud and ungratefull wench: and that she would teach her to know her owne good, since of her selfe she would not conceave it.

So with silence and patience (like a faire gorgeous armour, 4 hammered upon by an ilfavoured Smith) she abode their pittiles dealing with her: till, rather reserving her for more, then meaning to end, they left her to an uncomfortable leysure, to consider with her selfe her fortune; both helplesse her selfe, being a prisoner, and hopeles, since *Zelmane* was a prisoner: who therein onely was short of the bottome of miserie, that she knew not how unworthilie her Angell, by these devils was abused: but wanted (God wot) no stings of griefe, when those words did but strike upon her hart, that *Philoclea* was a captive, and she not able to succour her. For well she knew the confidence *Philoclea* had in her, and well she knew, *Philoclea* had cause to have confidence: and all troden under foot by the wheele of 6 senselesse Fortune. Yet if there be that imperious power in the soule, as it can deliver knowledge to another, without bodilie organs; so vehement were the workings of their spirites, as one mette with other, though themselves perceaved it not, but only thought it to be the doubling of their owne loving fancies. And that was the onely wordly thing, whereon *Philoclea* rested her minde, that she knewe she should die beloved of *Zelmane*, and shoulde die, rather then be false to *Zelmane*. And so this most daintie Nimphe, easing the paine of her minde with thinking of anothers paine; and almost forgetting the paine of her bodie, through the paine of her minde, she wasted, even longing for the conclusion of her tedious tragedie.

5 But for a while she was unvisited, *Cecropia* employing her time in using the like crueltie upon *Pamela*, her harte growing not onely to desire the fruite of punishing them, but even to delight in the punishing them. But if ever the beames of perfection shined through the clowdes of affliction, if ever Vertue tooke a bodie to shewe his (els unconceaveable) beautie, it was in *Pamela*. For when Reason taught her there was no resistance, (for to just resistance first her harte was enclined) then with so heavenly a quietnes, and so gracefull a calmenes, did she suffer the divers kindes of torments they used to her, that while they vexed her faire bodie, it seemed, that she rather directed, then obeyed the vexation. And when *Cecropia* ended, and asked whether her harte woulde yeelde: she a little smiled, but such a smiling as shewed no love, and yet coulde not but be lovelie. And then, Beastly woman (saide she) followe on, doo what thou wilt, and canst upon me: for I know thy power is not unlimited. Thou maist well wracke this sillie bodie, but me thou canst never overthrowe. For my part, I will not doo thee the

pleasure to desire death of thee: but assure thy self, both my life and death, shall triumph with honour, laying shame upon thy detestable tyranny.

And so, in effect, conquering their doing with her suffering, 4 while *Cecropia* tried as many sorts of paines, as might rather vexe them, then spoyle them (for that she would not do while she were in any hope to winne either of them for her sonne) *Pamela* remained almost as much content with triall in her selfe, what vertue could doo, as grieved with the miserie wherein she found her selfe plunged: only sometimes her thoughts softned in her, when with open wings they flew to *Musidorus*. For then she would thinke with her selfe, how grievously *Musidorus* would take this her miserie; and she, that wept not for her selfe, wept yet *Musidorus*-his teares, which he would weep for her. For gentle Love did easlier yeeld to lamentation, then the constancy of vertue would els admitte. Then would she re-member the case wherein she had left her poore shepheard, and she that wished death for her self, feared death for him; and she that condemned in her selfe the feeblenes of sorrow, yet thought it great reason to be sory for his sorow: & she that long had prayed for the vertuous joyning themselves together, now thinking to die herself, hartely prayed, that long time their fortunes might be seperated. Live long my *Musidorus* (would she say) and let my name live in thy mouth; in thy harte my memorie. Live long, that thou mayst love long the chast love of thy dead *Pamela*. Then would she wish to her selfe, that no other woman might ever possesse his harte: and yet scarcely the wish was made a wish, when her selfe would finde fault with it, as being too unjust, that so excellent a man should be banished from the comfort of life. Then would she fortifie her resolution, with bethinking the worste, taking the counsell of vertue, and comfort of love.

CHAP. 21.

[1]Cecropias *indurate tyrannies.* [2]*Her devise with the death of one to threaten another.* [3]Philoclea *threatned, persisteth.* [4]*The execution done in sight of* Philoclea & Zelmane. [5]Philocleas *sorrow for her sister.*

1 SO these diamonds of the worlde whom Nature had made to be preciously set in the eyes of her creatures, to be the chiefe workes of her workemanship, the chiefe ornaments of the worlde, and Princesses of felicitie, by rebellious injury were brought to the uttermost distres that an enemies hart could wish, or a womans spite invent: *Cecropia* dayly in one or other sorte punishing thẽ, still with her evill torments giving them feare of worse, making the feare it selfe the sorriest torment of all; that in the end wearie of their bodies they should be content to bestow them at her appointmẽt. But as in labour, the more one doth exercise it, the more by the doing one is enhabled to doo; strength growing upõ the worke, so as what at first would have seemed impossible, after growes easie: so these Princesses second to none, and far from any second, only to be matched by thẽselves, with the use of suffering their minds gat the habit of suffring so, as all feares & terrors were to them but summons to a battaile, whereof they knew before hãd they would be victorious, & which in the suffering was painfull, being suffered, was a trophe to it self: whereby *Cecropia* found her self still farder of: for where at first she might perchance have perswaded them to have visited her sonne, and have given him some comforte in his sicknesse, drawing neere to the cõfines of Deaths kingdome, now they protested, that they would never otherwise speake to him, then as to the enemy, of most unjust cruelty towards them, that any time or place could ever make them know.

2 This made the poison swell in her cankred brest, perceiving that (as in water) the more she grasped the lesse she held: but yet now having run so long the way of rigour, it was too late in reason, and too contrary to her passion, to returne to a course of meekenesse. And therefore (taking counsell of one of her olde associates who so far excelled in wickednesse as that she had not only lost all feeling of conscience, but had gotten a very

glory in evill) in the ende they determined, that beating, and
other such sharp dealing did not so much pull downe a womans
harte, as it bred anger, and that nothing was more enemy to
yeelding, then anger; making their tẽder harts take on the
armour of obstinacy: (for thus did their wicked mindes blind
to the light of vertue, & owly eied in the night of wickednes
interpret of it) & that therfore that was no more to be tried.
And for feare of death (which no question would doo most with
them) they had bene so often threatened, as they began to be
familiarly acquainted with it, and learned to esteeme threatning
wordes to be but words. Therefore the last, but best way now
was, that the one seing indeede the others death, should perceive,
there was no dallying meant: and then there was no doubt,
that a womans soule would do much, rather then leave so
beautifull a body.

This being concluded, *Cecropia* went to *Philoclea*, and tolde 3
her, that now she was to come to the last parte of the play: for
her part, though she found her hard harted obstinacie such, that
neither the sweetnesse of loving meanes, nor the force of harde
meanes could prevaile with her, yet before she would passe to a
further degree of extremity; she had sought to win her sister;
in hope, that her sonne might be with time satisfied with the
love of so faire a Lady: but finding her also rather more then
lesse wilful, she was now minded that one of their deathes
should serve for an example to the other, that despising worthy „
folks was more hurtfull to the despiser, then the despised: that
yet because her sonne especially affected her, & that in her owne
selfe she was more inclinable to pittie her, thẽ she had deserved,
she would begin with her sister; who that afternoone should
have her head cut of before her face; if in the mean time one
of them, did not pull out their il-wrought stiches of unkindnes,
she bad her looke for no other, nor lõger time thẽ she told her.
There was no assault givẽ to the sweet *Philocleas* mind, that
entered so far, as this: for where to all paines and daungers of
her selfe, foresight with (his Lieutenant Resolution) had made
ready defence; now with the love she bare her sister, she was
driven to a stay, before she determined: but long she staied not,
before this reason did shine unto her, that since in her selfe she
preferred death before such a base servitude, love did teach her
to wish the same to her sister. Therefore crossing her armes,

& looking sideward upon the groũd, Do what you wil (said she) with us: for my part, heaven shall melt before I be removed. But if you will follow my counsell, for your owne sake (for as for praiers for my sake I have felt how little they prevaile) let my death first serve for example to win her, who perchaunce is not so resolved against *Amphialus*, and so shall you not onely justly punish me (who indeede doo hate both you and your sonne) but, if that may moove you, you shall doo more vertuously in preserving one most worthy of life, and killing an other most desirous of death: lastly in winning her, in steed of a peevish unhappie creature, that I am, you shall blesse your sonne with the most excellent woman in all praise-worthy thinges, that the worlde holdeth. But *Cecropia*, (who had already set downe to her selfe what she would do) with bitter both termes, & countenaunce, told her, that she should not neede to woo death over-egerly: for if her sister going before her did not teach her witt, herselfe should quickly follow. For since they were not to be gotten, there was no way for her sonnes quiet, but to know, that they were past getting. And so since no intreating, nor threatning might prevayle, she bad her prepare her eies for a new play, which she should see within fewe houres in the hall of that castle.

4   A place indeed overfit for so unfit a matter: for being so stately made that the bottome of it being even with the grounde, the roofe reached as hie as any part of the castle, at either ende it had convenient lodgeings. In the one end was (one storie from the ground) *Philocleas* abode, in the other of even height, *Pamelas*, and *Zelmanes* in a chamber above her: but all so vaulted of strong, and thickly built stone, as one could no way heare the other: each of these chambers had a litle windowe to looke into the hall, but because the sisters should not have so much comforte, as to looke out to one another, there was (of the outsides) curtaynes drawne, which they could not reach with their hands, so barring the reach of their sight. But when the houre came that the Tragedie should beginne, the curtaynes were withdrawen from before the windowes of *Zelmane*, and of *Philoclea*: a sufficient challenge to call their eyes to defende themselves in such an incounter. And by and by came in at one ende of the hall, with about a dozen armed souldiers a Ladie, led by a couple, with her handes bounde before her: from above her eyes to her

lippes muffled with a faire kerchiefe, but from her mouth to the shoulders all bare: and so was led on to a scaffold raised a good deale from the floore, and all covered with crimsin velvet. But neither *Zelmane*, nor *Philoclea* needed to be tolde, who she was: for the apparell she ware made them too well assured, that it was the admirable *Pamela*. Whereunto the rare whitenesse of her naked necke gave sufficient testimonie to their astonnished senses. But the fayre Ladie being come to the scaffold, and then made to kneele downe, and so lefte by her unkinde supporters, as it seemed that she was about to speake somewhat (whereunto *Philoclea*, poore soule, earnestly listned, according to her speach even minded to frame her minde, her harte never till then almost wavering to save her sisters life) before the unfortunate Ladie could pronounce three wordes, the executioner cutt of the ones speech, and the others attention, with making his sworde doo his cruell office upon that beautifull necke. Yet the pittilesse sworde had such pittie of so pretious an object, that at first it did but hitte flat long. But little availed that, since the Ladie falling downe astonnished withall, the cruell villayne forced the sworde with another blowe to divorce the faire marriage of the head and body.

And this was done so in an instant, that the very act did overrun *Philocleas* sorrow (sorrow not being able so quickly to thunderbolte her harte thorough her senses, but first onely opprest her with a storme of amazement) but when her eies saw that they did see, as condemning themselves to have seene it, they became weary of their owne power of seing: & her soule then drinking up woe with great draughts, she fel downe to deadly traûces: but her waiting jaylors with cruell pitty brought lothed life unto her; which yet many times tooke his leave as though he would indeed depart: but when he was staied by force, he kept with him deadly Sorrow, which thus exercised her mourning speech. *Pamela* my sister, my sister *Pamela*, woe is me for thee, I would I had died for thee. *Pamela* never more shall I see thee: never more shall I enjoy thy sweet companie, and wise counsell. Alas, thou arte gone to beautifie heaven, and haste thou lefte me here, who have nothing good in me, but that I did ever love thee, and ever will lament thee? Let this day be noted of all vertuous folkes for most unfortunate: let it never be mentioned, but among curses; and cursed be they that did this mischiefe, and most accursed be mine eyes that behelde it. Sweete *Pamela*; that head is striken of, where onely wisedome might be spoken withall; that bodie is destroied, which was the living booke of vertue. Deare *Pamela*, how haste thou lefte me to all wretchednesse, and miserie? Yet while thou livedst, in thee I breathed, of thee I hoped. O *Pamela*, how much did I for thy excellencie honour thee, more then my mother, and love thee more then my selfe? Never more shall I lie with thee: never more shall we bathe in the pleasant river together: never more shall I see thee in thy shephearde apparell. But thou arte gone, and where am I? *Pamela* is dead; and live I? My God, And with that she fell againe in a soune, so as it was a great while before they could bring her to her selfe againe; but being come to her-selfe, Alas (said she) unkind women, since you have given me so many deathes, torment me not now with life: for Gods sake let me goe, and excuse your hands of more blood. Let me follow my *Pamela*, whom ever I sought to follow. Alas *Pamela*, they will not let me come to thee. But if they keepe promise, I shall treade thine owne steppes after thee. For to what am I borne (miserable soule) but to be most unhappie in my selfe, and yet more unhappie in others? But ô that a thousand more miseries had happened unto me, so thou haddest not dyed: *Pamela*, my sister *Pamela*. And so, like lamentable *Philomela*, complained she the horrible wrong done to her sister, which if it stird not in the wickedly closed minds of her tormentors, a pittie of her sorrow, yet bredde it a wearinesse of her sorrow: so as onely leaving one to prevent any harme she should doo her selfe, the rest went away, consulting againe with *Cecropia*, how to make profite of this their late bloodie act.

CHAP. 22.

¹Cecropias *pollicie to use* Zelmanes *intercession.* ²Zelmanes *selfe-conflict.* ³*Her motion to* Philoclea *rather to dissemble then dye.* ⁴Philocleas *resolution rather to dye then dissemble.* ⁵*At sight of* Philocleas *head* Zelmanes *extasies,* ⁷*desperate deseignes,* ⁸*and comfortlesse complaints.*

IN the ende, that woman that used most to keep company 1 with *Zelmane,* told *Cecropia,* that she founde by many most sensible proofes in *Zelmane,* that there was never woman so loved another, as she loved *Philoclea :* which was the cause that she (further then the commandement of *Cecropia*) had caused *Zelmanes* curtaines to be also drawne : because having the same spectacle that *Philoclea* had, she might stand in the greater feare for her, whom she loved so wel : and that indeed she had hit the needle in that devise : for never saw she creature so astonished as *Zelmane,* exceedingly sory for *Pamela,* but exceedingly exceeding that exceedingnes in feare for *Philoclea.* Therefore her advice was, she should cause *Zelmane* to come and speake with *Philoclea.* For there being such vehemencie of friendship between them, it was both likely to move *Zelmane* to perswade, and *Philoclea* to be perswaded. *Cecropia* liked wel of the counsell, and gave order to the same woman to go deale therein with *Zelmane,* and to assure her with othe, that *Cecropia* was determined *Philoclea* should passe the same way that *Pamela* had done, without she did yeeld to satisfie the extremitie of her sonnes affection : which the woman did, adding therunto many (as she thought) good reasons to make *Zelmane* thinke *Amphialus* a fit match for *Philoclea.*

But *Zelmane* (who had from time to time understood the 2 cruell dealing they had used to the sisters, & now had her own eies wounded with the sight of ones death) was so confused withall (her courage still rebelling against her wit, desiring still with force to doo impossible matters) that as her desire was stopped with power, so her côceit was darkned with a mist of desire. For blind Love, & invincible valure stil would cry out, that it could not be, *Philoclea* should be in so miserable estate, and she not relieve her : and so while she haled her wit to her courage,

479

she drew it from his owne limits. But now *Philocleas* death (a word able to marshall al his thoughts in order) being come to so short a point either with smal delay to be suffred, or by the giving her selfe to another to be prevented, she was drivē to think, and to desire some leasure of thinking: which the woman granted for that night unto her. A night that was not halfe so blacke, as her mind; not halfe so silent, as was fit for her musing thoughts. At last, he that would faine have desperatly lost a thousand lives for her sake, could not finde in his harte, that she should loose any life for her owne sake; and he that despised his owne death in respect of honour, yet could well nye dispense with honor it self in respect of *Philocleas* death: for once the thought could not enter into his harte, nor the breath issue out of his mouth, which could consent to *Philocleas* death for any bargaine. Then how to prevent the next degree to death (which was her being possest by another) was the point of his minds labour: and in that he found no other way, but that *Philoclea* should pretend a yeelding unto *Cecropias* request; & so by speaking with *Amphialus*, and making faire (but delaying) promises, procure libertie for *Zelmane*; who onely wisht but to come by a sword, not doubting then to destroy them all, and deliver *Philoclea*: so little did both the mē, and their forces seeme in her eyes, looking downe upon them from the hye toppe of affections tower.

3   With that minde therefore (but first wel bound) she was brought to *Philoclea*, having alredy plotted out in her cōceite, how she would deale with her: & so came she with hart and eyes, which did each sacrifice either to Love upon the aultar of Sorrow: and there had she the pleasing displeasing sight of *Philoclea*: *Philoclea*, whō alredie the extreame sense of sorrow had brought to a dulnesse therin, her face not without tokens that beautie had bene by many miseries cruelly battered, & yet shewed it most the perfection of the beautie, which could remaine unoverthrowne by such enimies. But whē *Zelmane* was set downe by her, & the womē gone away (because she might be the better perswaded whē no body was by, that had heard her say she would not be perswaded) then began first the eyes to speake, and the harts to crie out: Sorrow a while would needes speake his owne language without using their tongues to be his interpreters. At last *Zelmane* brake silence, but spake with the

onely eloquence of amazement: for all her long methodized oration was inherited onely by such kinde of speeches. Deare Ladie, in extreame necessities we must not. But alas unfortunate wretch that I am, that I live to see this day. And I take heaven and earth to witnesse, that nothing: and with that her brest swelled so with spite and griefe, that her breath had not leasure to turne her selfe into words. But the sweet *Philoclea* that had alredie dyed in *Pamela*, and of the other side had the heavines of her hart somthing quickned in the most beloved sight of *Zelmane*, ghessed somewhat at *Zelmanes* minde; and therefore spake unto her in this sort. My *Pyrocles* (said she) I know this exceeding comfort of your presence, is not brought unto me for any good-will that is owed unto me: but (as I suppose) to make you perswade me to save my life with the ransome of mine honour: although no bodie should be so unfit a pleader in that cause, as your selfe, yet perchance you would have me live. Your honour? God forbid (said *Zelmane*) that ever, for any cause, I should yeeld to any touch of it. But a while to pretend some affection, til time, or my libertie might worke somthing for your service: this, if my astonished senses would give me leave, I would faine have perswaded you.

To what purpose my *Pyrocles?* (said *Philoclea*) of a miserable 4 time what gaine is there? hath *Pamelaes* example wrought no more in me? is a captive life so much worth? cã ever it goe out of these lips, that I love any other but *Pyrocles?* shal my tongue be so false a traitor to my hart, as to say I love any other but *Pyrocles?* And why should I do all this? to live? O *Pamela*, sister *Pamela*, why should I live? onely for thy sake *Pyrocles* I would live: but to thee I know too well I shal not live; and if not to thee, hath thy love so base allay, my *Pyrocles*, as to wish me to live? for dissimulation, my *Pyrocles*, my simplicitie is such, that I have hardly bene able to keepe a straight way; what shall I doo in a crooked? But in this case there is no meane of dissimulation, not for the cunningest: present answere is required, and present performance upon the answere. Art thou so terrible, ô Death? No my *Pyrocles*; and for that I doo thanke thee, and in my soule thanke thee; for I confesse the love of thee is heerein my chiefest vertue. Trouble me not therefore, deare *Pyrocles*, nor double not my death by tormenting my resolution: since I cannot live with thee, I wil dye for thee. Onely remember me deare *Pyrocles*; and love the remembrance of me: and if I may crave so much of thee, let me be thy last love, for though I be not worthy of thee (who indeed art the worthiest creature living) yet remember that my love was a worthy love. But *Pyrocles* was so overcome with sorrow (which wisdome & vertue made just in so excellent a Ladies case, ful of so excellēt kindnes) that words were ashamed to come forth knowing how weake they were to expresse his mind, & her merit: and therfore so stayed in a deadly silence, forsaken of hope, & forsaking comfort: till the appointed gardians came in, to see the fruits of *Zelmanes* labour: & then *Zelmane* warned by their presence, fel againe to perswade, though scarcely her selfe could tell what; but in sum, desirous of delayes. But *Philoclea* sweetly continuing cōstant, & in the end punishing her importunity with silence, *Zelmane* was faine to ende. Yet craving an other times cōference, she obtained it, & divers others; till at the last *Cecropia* found it was to no purpose, and therfore determined to follow her owne way. *Zelmane* yet stil desirous to win (by any meanes) respit, even wasted with sorrow, & uncertaine, whether in worse case in her presēce, or absence, being able to do nothing for *Philocleas* succour, but by submitting the greatest corage of the earth to fall at the feete of *Cecropia*, and crave stay of their sentence till the uttermost was seene, what her perswasions might doo.

5   *Cecropia* seemed much to be moved by her importunitie, so as divers dayes were wonne of painefull life to the excellent *Philoclea*: while *Zelmane* suffred some hope to cherish her mind, especially trusting upon the helpe of *Musidorus*, who (she knew) would not be idle in this matter, till one morning a noise awaked *Zelmane*, from whose over-watchfull mind, the tired body had stolne a little sleep: and streight with the first opening of her eyes, Care taking the woonted place, she ranne to the window which looked into the hall (for that way the noise guided her,) and there might she see (the curtaine being left open ever since the last execution) seven or eight persons in a cluster upon the scaffold: who by & by retiring themselves, nothing was to be seene thereupon, but a bason of golde, pitifully enameled with bloud, and in the midst of it, the head of the most beautifull *Philoclea*. The horriblenes of the mischiefe was such, as *Pyrocles* could not at first beleeve his own senses,

but bent his woful eyes to discerne it better: where too well he might see it was *Philocleas* selfe, having no veile, but beautie, over the face, which still appeared to be alive: so did those eyes shine, even as they were wont, and they were woont more then any other: and sometimes as they moved, it might well make the beholder think, that death therin had borowed their beutie, and not they any way disgraced by death: so sweet and pearsing a grace they caried with them.

It was not a pitie, it was not an amazement, it was not a 6 sorow which then laid holde on *Pyrocles*, but a wilde furie of desperate agonie, so that he cried out, O tyraunt heaven, traytor earth, blinde providence; no justice, how is this done? how is this suffered? hath this world a government? If it have, let it poure out all his mischiefes upon me, and see whether it have power to make me more wretched then I am. Did she excell for this? have I prayed for this? abhominable hande that did it; detestable devil that commaunded it; cursed light that beheld it: and if the light be cursed, what are then mine eyes that have seene it? And have I seen *Philoclea* dead, and doo I live? and have I lived, not to help her, but to talke of her? and stande I still talking? And with that (caried with the madnes of anguish, not having a redier way to kill himselfe) he ranne as hard as ever he could, with his head against the wall, with intention to braine himself: but the haste to doo it, made the doing the slower. For, as he came to give the blow, his foot tript, so as it came not with the full force: yet forcible inough to strike him downe, and withall, to deprive him of his sense, so that he lay a while, comforted by the hurt, in that he felte not his discomfort.

And when he came againe to himselfe, he heard, or he 7 thought he heard a voice, which cried, Revĕge, Revenge; whether indeed it were his good Angell, which used that voice to stay him from unnaturall murdering of him selfe ; or that his wandering spirites lighted upon that conceite, and by their weakenes (subjeĉt to apprehensions) supposed they heard it. But that indeed, helped with Vertue, and her valiant servant Anger, stopped him from present destroying him selfe: yeelding, in reason and manhoode, first to destroy, man, woman, and childe, that were any way of kinne to them that were accessarie to this crueltie; then to raze the Castle, and to builde a sumptuous monument for her sister, and a most sumptuous for her selfe; and then, himselfe to die upon her tomb. This determining in himselfe to do, and to seeke all meanes how (for that purpose) to get out of prison: he was content a while to beare the thirst of death: and yet went he againe to the windowe, to kisse the beloved head with his eies, but there saw he nothing but the scaffold, all covered over with skarlet, and nothing but solitarie silence, to mourn this mischiefe. But then, Sorrow having disperste it selfe from his harte, in all his noble partes, it proclaimed his authoritie, in cries, and teares, and with a more gentle dolefulnes, could poure out his inward evill.

8   Alas (said he) and is that head taken away too, so soone from mine eyes? What, mine eyes, perhappes they envie the excellencie of your sorrow? Indeede, there is nothing now left to become the eyes of all mãkind, but teares: and wo be to me, if any exceede me in wofulnes. I do conjure you all, my senses, to accept no object, but of Sorow: be ashamed, nay, abhor to thinke of comfort. Unhappie eyes, you have seene too much, that ever the light should be welcome to you: unhappie eares, you shall never heare the musicke of Musicke in her voice: unhappie harte, that hast lived to feel these pangues. Thou hast done thy worst, World, & cursed be thou, and cursed art thou, since to thine owne selfe thou hast done the worst thou couldest doo. Exiled Beautie, let onely now thy beautie be blubbered faces. Widowed Musick, let now thy tunes be rorings, and lamentations. Orphane Vertue, get thee winges, and flie after her into heaven; here is no dwelling place for thee. Why lived I, alas? Alas why loved I? to die wretched, and to be the example of the heavens hate? And hate, & spare not, for your worst blow is striken. Sweet *Philoclea*, thou art gone, and hast caried with thee my love; & hast thy love in me, & I wretched mã do live; I live, to die cõtinually, till thy revenge do give me leave to dy: & then dy I will, my *Philoclea*, my hart willinglie makes this promise to it selfe. Surely he did not looke upon thee, that gave the cruell blow: for no eye coulde have abidden to see such beautie overthrowen by such mischiefe. Alas, why should they divide such a head from such a bodie? no other bodye is worthy of that head; no other head is woorthie of that body: O yet, if I had taken my last leave, if I might have taken a holie kisse from that dying mouth. Where art

thou Hope which promisest never to leave a mã while he liveth?
Tell me, what canst thow hope for? nay tel me, what is there
which I would willingly hope after? Wishing power (which is
accounted infinite) what now is left to wish for? She is gone,
and gone with her all my hope, all my wishing. Love, be
ashamed to be called Love: cruell Hate, unspeakable Hate is
victorious over thee. Who is there now left, that can justifie
thy tyrannie, and give reason to thy passion? O cruell divorce
of the sweetest mariage that ever was in Nature: *Philoclea* is
dead, and dead is with her all goodnesse, all sweetnesse, all excellencie. *Philoclea* is dead, and yet Life is not ashamed to
cõtinue upon the earth. *Philoclea* is dead: O deadly word;
which containeth in it selfe the uttermost of all misfortunes.
But happie worde when thou shalt be said of me, and long it
shall not be, before it be said.

CHAP. 23.

[1]*A Ladies kinde comforts to* Pyrocles *comfortlesse unkindnesse.* [2]*His
hardly knowing her.* [3]*Her unmasking of* Cecropias *fruitlesse
sophistrie.* [4]*Their medley of solace and sorowe.*

THen stopping his woordes with sighes, drowning his sighes [1]
in teares, & drying againe his teares in rage, he would
sitte a while in a wandring muse, which represented nothing
but vexations unto him: then throwing himselfe somtimes
upon the floore, and sometimes upon the bedde: then up
againe, till walking was wearisome, and rest loathsome: and
so neither suffering foode, nor sleepe to helpe his afflicted nature,
all that day and night he did nothing, but weepe *Philoclea*, sigh
Philoclea, and crie out *Philoclea*: till as it happened (at that time
upon his bed) towarde the dawning of the day, he heard one
stirre in his chamber, by the motion of garmẽts; and he with an
angry voice asked, Who was there? A poore Gentlewoman
(answered the partie) that wish long life unto you. And I
soone death to you (said he) for the horrible curse you have
given me. Certainely (said she) an unkinde answere, and far

unworthy the excellencie of your mind; but not unsutable to the rest of your behaviour. For most parte of this night I have hearde you (being let into your chamber, you never perceiving it, so was your minde estraunged from your senses) and have hearde nothing of *Zelmane,* in *Zelmane,* nothing but weake waylings, fitter for some nurse of a village, then so famous a creature as you are. O God (cried out *Pyrocles*) that thou wert a man that usest these wordes uɴto me. I tell thee I am sory: I tell thee I will be sory in despite of thee, and all them that would have me joyfull. And yet (replied she) perchaunce *Philoclea* is not dead, whom you so much bemone. I would we were both dead of that condition, said *Pyrocles.* See the folly of your passion (said she) as though you should be neerer to her, you being dead, and she alive; then she being dead, & you alive: & if she be dead, was she not borne to die? what then do you crie out for? not for her, who must have died one time or other; but for some fewe yeares: so as it is time, & this world that seeme so lovely things, and not *Philoclea* untu you. O noble Sisters (cried *Pyrocles*) now you be gone (who were the onely exalters of all womankind) what is left in that sex, but babling, and businesse? And truly (said she) I will yet a little longer trouble you. Nay, I pray you doo (said *Pyrocles*) for I wishe for nothing in my shorte life, but mischiefes, and combers: and I am content you shall be one of them. In truth (said she) you would thinke your selfe a greatly priviledged person, if since the strongest buildings, and lastingest monarchies are subject to end, onely your *Philoclea* (because she is yours) should be exempted. But indeede you bemone your selfe, who have lost a friende: you cannot her, who hath in one act both preserved her honour, and lefte the miseries of this worlde. O womans philosophie, childish follie (said *Pyrocles*) as though if I do bemone my selfe, I have not reason to doo so, having lost more then any Monarchie, nay then my life can be woorth unto me. Alas (said she) comforte your selfe, Nature did not forget her skill, when she had made them: you shall find many their superiors, and perchaunce such, as (when your eyes shall looke abroad) your selfe will like better.

2   But that speech put all good mãners out of the conceit of *Pyrocles*; in so much, that leaping out of his bed, he ran to have striken her: but comming neere her (the morning then winning

the field of darkenesse) he saw, or he thought he sawe, indeede, the
very face of *Philoclea*; the same sweetenesse, the same grace, the
same beautie: with which carried into a divine astonishment, he
fell downe at her feete. Most blessed Angell (said he) well
haste thou done to take that shape, since thou wouldest submit
thy selfe to mortall sense ; for a more Angelicall forme could
not have bene created for thee. Alas, even by that excellent
beautie, so beloved of me, let it be lawfull for me to aske of thee,
what is the cause, that she, that heavenly creature, whose forme
you have taken, should by the heavens be destined to so unripe
an ende? Why should unjustice so prevaile? Why was she
seene to the world, so soone to be ravished from us? Why was
she not suffered to live, to teach the world perfection? Doo not
deceive thy selfe (answered she) I am no Angell; I am *Philoclea*,
the same *Philoclea*, so truely loving you, so truly beloved of
you. If it be so (said he) that you are indeede the soule
of *Philoclea*, you have done well to keepe your owne figure:
for no heaven could have given you a better. Then alas, why
have you taken the paines to leave your blisfull seat to come to
this place most wretched, to me, who am wretchednes it selfe,
& not rather obtain for me, that I might come where you are,
there eternally to behold, & eternally to love your beauties? you
know (I know) that I desire nothing but death, which I only
stay, to be justly revenged of your unjust murtherers. Deare
Pyrocles (said she) I am thy *Philoclea*, and as yet living: not
murdred, as you supposed, and therefore to be comforted. And
with that gave him her hand. But the sweet touch of that
hande, seemed to his astraied powers so heavenly a thing, that
it rather for a while confirmed him in his former beliefe: till
she, with vehement protestations (and desire that it might be
so, helping to perswade that it was so) brought him to yeeld;
yet doubtfully to yeelde to this height of al comfort, that
Philoclea lived: which witnessing with the teares of joy, Alas
(said he) how shall I beleeve mine eies any more? or doo you yet
but appeare thus unto me, to stay me from some desperate end?
For alas I sawe the excellent *Pamela* beheaded: I saw your
head (the head indeede, and chiefe parte of all natures workes)
standing in a dishe of golde, too meane a shrine (God wote) for
such a relike. How can this be, my onely deare, and you live?
or if this be not so, how can I beleeve mine owne senses? and

if I can not beleeve thē, why should I now beleeve these blessed
tidings they bring me?

3   The truth is (said she) my *Pyrocles*, that nether I (as you
finde) nor yet my deare sister is dead: although the mischievously
suttle *Cecropia* used slightes to make either of us thinke so of
other. For, having in vaine attempted the fardest of her wicked
eloquence, to make eyther of us yeeld to her sonne, and seeing
that neither it, accompanied with great flatteries, and riche
presents, could get any grounde of us, nor yet the violent way
she fell into of crueltie, tormenting our bodies, could prevayle
with us; at last, she made either of us thinke the other dead,
and so hoped to have wrested our mindes to the forgetting of
vertue: and first she gave to mine eyes the miserable speċtacle
of my sisters (as I thought) death: but indeede not my sister: it
was onely *Artesia*, she who so cunningly brought us to this
misery. Truly I am sory for the poore Gentlewoman, though
justly she be punished for her double falshood: but *Artesia*
muffled so, as you could not easily discerne her; and in my
sisters apparell (which they had taken from her under colour of
giving her other) did they execute: And when I (for thy sake
especially deare *Pyrocles*) could by no force, nor feare be won,
they assayed the like with my sister, by bringing me downe
under the scaffolde, and (making me thrust my head up through
a hole they had made therin) they did put about my poore necke
a dishe of gold, whereout they had beaten the bottome, so as
having set bloud in it, you sawe how I played the parte of death
(God knowes even willing to have done it in earnest) and so had
they set me, that I reached but on tiptoes to the grounde, so as
scarcely I could breathe, much lesse speake: And truely if they
had kepte me there any whit longer, they had strangled me, in
steed of beheading me: but then they tooke me away, and
seeking to see their issue of this praċtise, they found my noble
sister (for the deare love she vouchsafeth to beare me) so grieved
withall, that she willed them to doo their uttermost crueltie
unto her: for she vowed, never to receive sustenaunce of them,
that had bene the causers of my murther: and finding both of
us, even given over, not like to live many houres longer, and my
sister *Pamela*, rather worse then my selfe, (the strength of her
harte worse bearing those indignities) the good woman *Cecropia*
(with the same pittie as folkes keepe foule, when they are not

fatte inough for their eating) made us know her deceipt, & let us come one to another; with what joye you can well imagine, who I know feele the like; saving that we only thought our selves reserved to miseries, and therefore fitter for condoling, then congratulating. For my parte, I am fully perswaded, it is but with a little respite, to have a more feeling sense of the tormentes she prepares for us. True it is, that one of my guardians would have me to beleeve, that this proceedes of my gentle cousin *Amphialus:* who having hearde some inckling that we were evill entreated, had called his mother to his bedside, from whence he never rose since his last combat, and besought, & charged her upon all the love she bare him, to use us with all kindnesse: vowing, with all the imprecations he could imagine, that if ever he understood for his sake, that I received further hurt then the want of my libertie, he woulde not live an houre longer. And the good woman sware to me that he would kill his mother, if he knewe how I had bene dealte with; but that *Cecropia* keepes him from understanding thinges how they passe, onely having heard a whispering, and my selfe named, he had (of aboundaunce, forsooth, of honorable love) given this charge for us. Whereupon this enlargement of mine was growne: for my parte I know too well their cunning (who leave no mony unoffered that may buy mine honour) to beleeve any worde they say, but (my deare *Pyrocles*) even looke for the worste, and prepare my selfe for the same. Yet I must confesse, I was content to robbe from death, and borrowe of my misery the sweet comfort of seeing my sweet sister, and moste sweete comforte of thee my *Pyrocles*. And so having leave, I came stealing into your chamber: where (O Lord) what a joy it was unto me, to heare you solemnise the funerals of the poore *Philoclea?* That I my selfe might live to heare my death bewailed? and by whom? by my deere *Pyrocles*. That I saw death was not strong enough to divide thy love from me? O my *Pyrocles*, I am too well paide for my paines I have suffred: joyfull is my woe for so noble a cause; and welcome be all miseries, since to thee I am so welcome. Alas how I pittied to heare thy pittie of me; and yet a great while I could not finde in my hart to interrupt thee, but often had even pleasure to weepe with thee: and so kindly came forth thy lamentations, that they inforced me to lament to, as if indeed I had beene a looker on, to see poore *Philoclea* dye. Til at last I spake with you, to try whether I could remove thee frō sorrow, till I had almost procured my selfe a beating.

4   And with that she pretily smiled, which, mingled with her teares, one could not tell whether it were a mourning pleasure, or a delightful sorrow: but like whē a few Aprill drops are scattered by a gentle *Zephyrus* among fine coloured flowers. But *Pyrocles*, who had felt (with so smal distāce of time) in himself the overthrow both of hope and despaire, knew not to what key he should tune his mind, either of joy, or sorrow. But finding perfite reason in neither, suffred himselfe to be caried by the tide of his imagination, & his imaginations to be raised even by the sway, which hearing or seing, might give unto thē: he saw her alive, he was glad to see her alive: he saw her weep, he was sory to see her weep: he heard her cōfortable speeches, nothing more gladsome: he hard her prognosticating her own destructiō, nothing more dolefull. But when he had a little taken breath from the panting motion of such contrarietie in passions, he fell to consider with her of her present estate, both comforting her, that certainely the worst of this storme was past, since alreadie they had done the worst, which mans wit could imagine: and that if they had determined to have killed her, they would have now done it: and also earnestly counselling her, and inhabling his counsels with vehement prayers, that she would so far second the hopes of *Amphialus*, as that she might but procure him liberty; promising then as much to her, as the liberalitie of loving corage durst promise to himselfe.

CHAP. 24.

[1]Amphialus *excuseth*. [2]*The Princesses accuse*. [3]Cecropia *seeking their death* [4]*findeth her owne*. [5]Amphialus-*his death-panges and selfe-killing*. [6]*The wofull knowledge of it*.

1 BUt who would lively describe the manner of these speeches, should paint out the lightsome coulours of affection, shaded with the deepest shadowes of sorrow, finding them betweene hope and feare, a kind of sweetenes in teares: til *Philoclea* content to receave a kisse, and but a kisse of *Pyrocles*, sealed up with

moving lippes, and closed them up in comfort: and her-selfe (for the passage was left betweene them open) went to her sister: with whom she had stayed but a while, fortifying one another (while *Philoclea* tempered *Pamelas* just disdaine, and *Pamela* ennobled *Philocleas* sweete humblenesse) when *Amphialus* came unto them: who never since he had heard *Philoclea* named, coulde bee quiet in himselfe, although none of them about him (fearing more his mothers violence thē his power) would discover what had passed: and many messages he sent to know her estate, which brought answere backe, according as it pleased *Cecropia* to indite them, till his hart full of unfortunate affliction, more and more misgiving him, having impatiently borne the delay of the nights unfitnesse, this morning he gat up, and though full of wounds (which not without daunger could suffer such exercise) he apparelled himselfe, and with a countenance, that shewed strength in nothing but in griefe, he came where the sisters were; and weakely kneeling downe, he besought them to pardon him, if they had not bene used in that castle according to their worthines, and his duetie; beginning to excuse small matters, poore Gentleman, not knowing in what sort they had bene handled.

But *Pamelaes* hye hart (having conceived mortall hate for the injurie offred to her and her sister) coulde scarcely abide his sight, much lesse heare out his excuses; but interrupted him with these words. Traitor (said she) to thine owne blood, and false to the profession of so much love as thou hast vowed, doo not defile our eares with thy excuses; but pursue on thy crueltie, that thou and thy godly mother have used towards us: for my part, assure thy self, and so do I answere for my sister (whose mind I know) I do not more desire mine owne safetie then thy destruction. Amazed with this speech, he turned his eye, ful of humble sorrowfulnesse, to *Philoclea*. And is this (most excellent Ladie) your doome of me also? She, sweete Ladie, sate weeping: for as her most noble kinsman she had ever favoured him, & loved his love, though she could not be in love with his person; and now partly unkindnes of his wrong, partly pittie of his case, made her sweete minde yeelde some teares, before she could answere; and her answere was no other, but that she had the same cause as her sister had. He replyed no further, but delivering from his hart two or three (untaught) sighes, rose, and with most low reverence went out of their chamber: and streight by threatning torture, learned of one of the women, in what terrible manner those Princesses had bene used. But when he heard it, crying out, O God; and then not able to say any more (for his speech went backe to rebounde woe upon his hart) he needed no judge to goe upon him: for no man could ever thinke any otherworthy of greater punishmẽt, thẽ he thought himselfe.

3   Ful therefore of the horriblest despaire, which a most guiltie conscience could breed, with wild lookes promising some terrible issue, understanding his mother was on the toppe of the leades, he caught one of his servants swords from him, and none of them daring to stay him, he went up, carried by furie, in steede of strength; where she was at that time, musing how to goe thorough with this matter, and resolving to make much of her Neeces in shew, and secreatly to impoison them; thinking since they were not to be wonne, her sonnes love woulde no otherwise be mitigated.

4   But when she sawe him come in with a sworde drawne, and a looke more terrible then the sworde, she streight was strickẽ with the guiltines of her own conscience: yet the wel known humblenes of her son somwhat animated her, till he, comming nearer her, and crying to her, Thou damnable creature, onely fit to bring forth such a monster of unhappines as I am; she fearing he would have stricken her (though indeed he meant it not, but onely intended to kill himselfe in her presence) went backe so far, til ere she were aware, she overthrew her selfe from over the Leades, to receave her deathes kisse at the ground: and yet was she not so happie as presently to dye, but that she had time with hellish agonie to see her sonnes mischiefe (whom she loved so well) before her end; when she confest (with most desperate, but not repẽting mind) the purpose she had to im-poison the princesses, & would then have had them murthred. But everie bodie seing, and glad to see her end, had left obedience to her tyranny.

5   And (if it could be) her ruine increased woe in the noble hart of *Amphialus*, who when he saw her fal, had his owne rage stayed a little with the soddennes of her destruction. And was I not enough miserable before (said he) but that before my end I must be the death of my mother? who how wicked so ever,

yet I would she had receaved her punishmēt by some other. O *Amphialus*, wretched *Amphialus*; thou hast lived to be the death of thy most deere cōpanion & friend *Philoxenus*, and of his father, thy most carefull fosterfather. Thou hast lived to kill a Ladie with thine owne handes, and so excellent, and vertuous a Lady, as the faire *Parthenia* was: thou hast lived to see thy faithfull *Ismenus* slaine in succouring thee, and thou not able to defende him: thou hast lived to shew thy selfe such a coward, as that one unknowne Knight could overcome thee in thy Ladies presence: thou hast lived to beare armes against thy rightfull Prince, thine owne unckle: Thou hast lived to be accounted, and justly accounted, a traitor, by the most excellent persons, that this world holdeth: Thou hast lived to bee the death of her, that gave thee life. But ah wretched *Amphialus*, thou hast lived for thy sake, and by thy authoritie, to have *Philoclea* tormented: O heavens, in *Amphialus* castle, where *Amphialus* commaunded; tormented, tormented? torment of my soule, *Philoclea* tormented: and thou hast had such comfort in thy life, as to live all this while. Perchance this hande (used onely to mischievous actes) thinkes it were too good a deede to kill me; or else filthy hande, onely woorthy to kill women, thou art afraide to strike a man. Feare not cowardly hand, for thou shalt kill but a cowardly traitor: and doo it gladlie; for thou shalt kill him, whome *Philoclea* hateth. With that, furiously he tare open his doublet, and setting the pommell of the sworde to the grounde, and the point to his brest, hee fell upon it. But the sworde more mercifull then hee to him-selfe, with the slipping of the pommell, the point swarved, and razed him but upon the side: yet with the fall, his other wounds opened so, as hee bledde in such extremitie, that *Charons* boate might verie well be carried in that flood: which yet he sought to hasten by this meanes. As he opened his dublet, and fell, there fell out *Philocleas* knives, which *Cecropia* at the first had taken from her, and delivered to her sonne; and he had ever worne them next his hart, as the only relique he had of his Saint: now seeing them by him, (his sword being so, as weakenes could not well draw it out from his doublette) he tooke the knives, and pulling one of them out, and many times kissing it, and then, first with the passions of kindnes, and unkindnes, melting in teares, O deare knives, you are come in a good time, to revenge the wrong I have done you all this while, in keeping you from her blessed side, and wearing you without your mistresse leave. Alas, be witnes with me, yet before I die, (and well you may, for you have layn next my hart) that by my consent, your excellent mistresse should have had as much honour, as this poore place could have brought foorth, for so high an excellencie; and now I am condemned to die by her mouth. Alas, other, far other hope would my desire often have given me: but other event it hath pleased her to lay upon me. Ah *Philoclea* (with that his teares gushed out, as though they would strive to overflow his bloud) I would yet thou knewest how I love thee. Unworthie I am, unhappie I am, false I am; but to thee, alas, I am not false. But what a traitor am I, any way to excuse him, whom she condemneth? Since there is nothing left me, wherein I may do her service, but in punishing him, who hath so offended her. Deare knife, then doo your noble mistresses commaundement. With that, he stabbed himselfe into divers places of his breast, and throte, untill those wounds (with the old, freshly bleeding) brought him to the senselesse gate of Death.

6   By which time, his servants having (with feare of his furie) abstained a while from comming unto him, one of them (preferring duetifull affection before fearfull duetie) came in, and there found him swimming in his owne bloud, there giving a pittiful spectacle, where the conquest was the conquerors overthrow, and self-ruine the onely triumph of a battaile, fought betweene him, and himselfe. The time full of danger, the person full of worthines, the maner full of horror, did greatlie astonish all the beholders; so as by and by, all the town was full of it, and then of all ages came running up to see the beloved body; every body thinking, their safetie bledde in his woundes, and their honor died in his destruction.

CHAP. 25.

[1]Anaxius-*his rages for the death*[2], Queen Helens *comming for the cure of* Amphialus. [3]*Her complaints over him.* [4]*Her passport and safeconduct, to carrie him to her Chirurgion.* [5]*The peoples sorow,* [6]*set downe in a song.*

BUt when it came, (and quickly it came) to the eares of his **1** proude friende *Anaxius,* (who by that time was growẽ well of his woũd, but never had come abroad, disdayning to abase himselfe to the companie of any other but of *Amphialus*) he was exceedingly vexed, either with kindnes, or (if a proud hart be not capable therof) with disdaine, that he, who had the honor to be called the frend of *Anaxius,* should come to such an unexpected ruine. Therfore, then comming abroad, with a face red in anger, and engrained in pride, with liddes raysed up, and eyes levelling from toppe to the toe of them that met him, treading, as though he thought to make the earth shake under him, with his hande upon his sword; short speeches, and disdainfull answeres, giving streight order to his two brothers, to goe take the oath of obedience, in his name, of all the souldiers, and Citizens in the towne: and withall, to sweare them to revenge the death of *Amphialus,* upon *Basilius.* He himself went to see him, calling for all the surgeons & physicions there; spending some time in vewing the body, and threatning them all to be hanged, if they did not heale him. But they (taking view of his woundes, and falling down at *Anaxius* feete) assured him, that they were mortall, & no possible meanes to keep him above two dayes alive: and he stood partly in doubt, to kil, or save them, betweene his own furie, and their humblenes. But vowing, with his owne hands to kill the two sisters, as causers of his friends death: when his brothers came to him, & told him they had done his commaundement, in having receaved the oath of allegeance, with no great difficultie: the most part terrified by their valure, & force of their servants, & many that had bene forward actors in the rebellion, willing to do any thing, rather then come under the subjection of *Basilius* againe; and such fewe as durst gainesay, being cut of by present slaughter.

But withall (as the chiefe matter of their comming to him) **2** they told *Anaxius*, that the faire Queen *Helen* was come, with an honorable retinue, to the towne: hūblie desiring leave to see *Amphialus*, whõ she had sought in many places of the world; & lastly, being returned into her owne countrie, she heard together of the late siege and of his combat with the strange Knight, who had dangerously hurt him. Wherupon, full of loving care (which she was content even to publish to the world, how ungratefully soever he dealt with her) she had gotten leave of *Basilius*, to come by his frontiers, to cary away *Amphialus* with her, to the excellentest surgeon then knowen, whom she had in her Countrey, but so olde, as not able to travaile: but had given her soveraigne annointments, to preserve his body withal, till he might be brought unto him: and that *Basilius* had graunted leave: either naturall kindnes prevailing over all the offences done, or rather glad to make any passage, which might leade him out of his countrie, and from his daughters. This discourse *Lycurgus* understanding of *Helene*, delivered to his brother, with her vehement desire to see the body, and take her last farewell of him. *Anaxius*, though he were fallen out with all woman-kind (in respeƈt of the hate he bare the sisters, whom he accounted murtherers of *Amphialus*) yet at his brothers request, graunted her leave. And she (poore Lady) with grievous expeƈtation, and languishing desire, caried her faint legs to the place where he lay, ether not breathing, or in all appearance breathing but death.

3   In which pittious plight when she saw him, though Sorow had set before her minde the pittifullest conceit thereof that it could paint, yet the present sight went beyonde all former apprehensions: so that beginning to kneele by the bodie, her sight ranne from her service, rather then abide such a sight; and she fell in a soune upon him, as if she could not choose but die of his wounds. But when her breath (aweary to be closed up in woe) broke the prison of her faire lippes, and brought memorie (with his servaunt senses) to his naturall office, she yet made the breath convey these dolefull wordes with it. Alas (said she) *Amphialus*, what strange diseases be these, that having sought thee so long, I should be now sorie to finde thee? that these eyes should looke upon *Amphialus*, and be grieved withall? that I should have thee in my power without glory, and embrace thee without comfort? How often have I blest the means that

might bring me neer thee? Now, woe worth the cause that brings me so neer thee. Often, alas, often hast thou disdained my teares: but now, my deare *Amphialus*, receive them: these eies can serve for nothing else, but weepe for thee; since thou wouldest never vouchsafe them thy comforte, yet disdaine not them thy sorrowe. I would they had bene more deare unto thee; for then hadst thou lived. Woe is me that thy noble harte could love who hated thee, and hate who loved thee. Alas, why should not my faith to thee cover my other defects, who only sought to make my Crowne thy foote-stoole, my selfe thy servaunt? that was all my ambition; and alas thou disdainedst it to serve them, by whom thy incomparable selfe were disdained. Yet (ô *Philoclea*) wheresoever you are, pardon me, if I speake in the bitternes of my soule, excellent may you be in all other things (and excellent sure you are since he loved you) your want of pittie, where the fault onely was infinitenesse of desert, cannot be excused. I would, O God, I would that you had graunted his deserved suite of marrying you, and that I had bene your serving-maide, to have made my estate the foile of your felicitie, so he had lived. How many weary steps have I trodden after thee, while my onely complaint was, that thou werte unkinde? Alas I would now thou werte, to be unkind. Alas why wouldest thou not cõmaund my service, in persuading *Philoclea* to love thee? who could, or (if every one could) who would have re-counted thy perfections so well, as I? who with such kindly passions could have stirred pittie for thee as I? who should have delivered not onely the wordes but the teares I had of thee? and so shouldest thou have exercised thy disdaine in me, and yet used my service for thee.

With that the body moving somewhat, and giving a grone 4 full of deaths musicke, she fell upon his face, & kist him, and with all cried out. O miserable I, that have onely favour by miserie: and then, would she have returned to a fresh careere of complaints, when an aged and wise Gentleman came to her, and besought her, to remember what was fit for her greatnesse, wisdome, & honour: and with al, that it was fitter to shew her love, in carying the body to her excellent Surgeon, first applying such excellent medicines as she had received of him for that purpose, rather then onely shew her selfe a woman-lover in fruitles lamẽtations. She was streight warned with the obedi-

ence of an overthrowen mind, and therefore leaving some
surgeons of her owne to dresse the body, went her selfe to
Anaxius, & humbling her selfe to him, as lowe as his owne
pride could wish, besought him, that since the surgeons there
had utterly given him over, that he would let her carrie him
away in her litter with her, since the worst he could have should
be to die, and to die in her armes that loved him above al things;
& where he should have such monuments erected over him,
as were fit for her love, & his worthines: beseeching him withall,
since she was in a country of enemies (where she trusted
more to *Anaxius* valour, then *Basilius* promise) that he would
convey them safely out of those territories.   Her reasons
something moved him, but nothing thoroughly perswaded him,
but the last request of his helpe: which he streight promised,
warrāting all securitie, as long as that sword had his master
alive.   She as happy therein as unhappines could be (having
received as small cōfort of her owne surgeons as of the others)
caused yet the body to be easily conveyed into the litter: all the
people then beginning to roare and crie, as though never till
then they had lost their Lorde.   And if the terrour of *Anaxius*
had not kept them under, they would have mutinied, rather then
suffered his bodie to be caried away.

5   But *Anaxius* him selfe riding before the litter, with the
choyce men of that place, they were affraid even to crie, though
they were readie to crie for feare: but (because that they might
doo) every bodie forced (even with harming themselves) to doo
honour to him: some throwing themselves upon the grounde;
some tearing their clothes, and casting duste upon their heades,
and some even wounding themselves, and sprinkling their owne
bloud in the aire.   Among the rest, one accounted good in that
kinde, and made the better by the true feeling of sorrowe, roared
out a song of Lamentation, which (as well as might be) was
gathered up in this forme.

6   *S*Ince *that to death is gone the shepheard hie,*
            Whom most the silly shepheards pipe did pryse,
         Your dolefull tunes sweete Muses *now applie.*

         And you ô trees (if any life there 'lies
            In trees) now through your porous barkes receave
         The straunge resounde of these my causefull cries:

And let my breath upon your braunches leave,
  My breath distinguish'd into wordes of woe,
  That so I may signes of my sorrowe leave.
But if among yourselves some one tree growe,
  That aptest is to figure miserie,
  Let it embassage beare your grieves to showe.
The weeping Myrrhe I thinke will not denie
  Her helpe to this, this justest cause of plaint.
  Your dolefull tunes sweet Muses *now applie.*

And thou poore Earth, whom fortune doth attaint
  In Natures name to suffer such a harme,
  As for to loose thy gemme, and such a Sainɛt,
Upon thy face let coaly Ravens swarme :
  Let all the Sea thy teares accounted be :
  Thy bowels with all killing mettals arme.
Let golde now rust, let Diamonds waste in thee :
  Let pearls be wan with woe their damme doth beare :
  Thy selfe henceforth the light doo never see.
And you, ô flowers, which sometimes Princes were,
  Till these straunge altrings you did hap to trie,
  Of Princes losse your selves for tokens reare.
Lilly in mourning blacke thy whitenes die :
  O Hiacinthe *let* Ai *be on thee still.*
  Your dolefull tunes sweet Muses *now applie.*

O Echo, *all these woods with roaring fill,*
  And doo not onely marke the accents last,
  But all, for all reach out my wailefull will :
One Echo *to another* Echo *cast*
  Sounde of my griefes, and let it never ende,
  Till that it hath all woods and waters past.
Nay to the heav'ns your just complaining sende,
  And stay the starrs inconstant constant race,
  Till that they doo unto our dolours bende :
And aske the reason of that speciall grace,
  That they, which have no lives, should live so long,
  And vertuous soules so soone should loose their place?
Aske, if in great men good men doo so thronge,
  That he for want of elbowe roome must die?
  Or if that they be skante, if this be wronge?

499

THE COUNTESSE OF PEMBROKES

Did Wisedome this our wretched time espie
In one true chest to rob all Vertues treasure?
Your dolefull tunes sweete Muses *now applie.*

And if that any counsell you to measure
Your dolefull tunes, to them still playning say,
To well felte griefe, plainte is the onely pleasure.
O light of Sunne, which is entit'led day,
O well thou doost that thou no longer bidest;
For mourning light her blacke weedes may display.
O Phœbus *with good cause thy face thou hidest,*
Rather then have thy all-beholding eye
Fould with this sight, while thou thy chariot guidest.
And well (me thinks) becomes this vaultie skie
A stately tombe to cover him deceased.
Your dolefull tunes sweet Muses *now applie.*

O Philomela *with thy brest oppressed*
By shame and griefe, helpe, helpe me to lament
Such cursed harmes as cannot be redressed.
Or if thy mourning notes be fully spent,
Then give a quiet eare unto my playning:
For I to teach the world complainte am bent.
You dimmy clowdes, which well employ your stayning
This cheerefull aire with your obscured cheere,
Witnesse your wofull teares with daily rayning.
And if, ô Sunne, thou ever didst appeare,
In shape, which by mans eye might be perceived;
Vertue is dead, now set thy triumph here.
Now set thy triumph in this world, bereaved
Of what was good, where now no good doth lie;
And by thy pompe our losse will be conceaved.
O notes of mine your selves together tie:
With too much griefe me thinkes you are dissolved.
Your dolefull tunes sweete Muses *now applie.*

Time ever old, and yonge is still revolved
Within it selfe, and never tasteth ende:
But mankind is for aye to nought resolved.
The filthy snake her aged coate can mende,
And getting youth againe, in youth doth flourish:
But unto Man, *age ever death doth sende.*

The very trees with grafting we can cherish,
  So that we can long time produce their time :
  But Man which helpeth them, helplesse must perish.
Thus, thus the mindes, which over all doo clime,
  When they by yeares experience get best graces,
  Must finish then by deaths detested crime.
We last short while, and build long lasting places :
  Ah let us all against foule Nature crie :
  We Natures workes doo helpe, she us defaces.
For how can Nature unto this reply ?
  That she her child, I say, her best child kilieth ?
  Your dolefull tunes sweete Muses now apply.

Alas, me thinkes, my weakned voice but spilleth,
  The vehement course of this just lamentation :
  Me thinkes, my sound no place with sorrow filleth.
I know not I, but once in detestation
  I have my selfe, and all what life · containeth,
  Since Death on Vertues fort hath made invasion.
One word of woe another after traineth :
  Ne doo I care how rude be my invention,
  So it be seene what sorrow in me raigneth.
O Elements, by whose (men say) contention,
  Our bodies be in living power maintained,
  Was this mans death the fruite of your dissention ?
O Phisickes power, which (some say) hath restrained
  Approch of death, alas thou helpest meagerly,
  When once one is for Atropos *distrained.*
Great be Physitions brags, but aid is beggerly,
  When rooted moisture failes, or groweth drie,
  They leave off al, and say, death comes too eagerlie.
They are but words therefore that men do buy,
  Of any since God AEsculapius *cecsed.*
  Your dolefull tunes sweete Muses now applie.

Justice, justice is now (alas) oppressed :
  Bountifulnes hath made his last conclusion :
  Goodnes for best attire in dust is dressed.
Shepheards bewaile your uttermost confusion ;
  And see by this picture to you presented,
  Death is our home, life is but a delusion.

For see alas, who is from you absented?
  Absented? nay I say for ever banished
  From such as were to dye for him contented?
Out of our sight in turne of hand is vanished
  Shepherd of shepherds, whose well setled order
  Private with welth, publike with quiet garnished.
While he did live, farre, farre was all disorder;
  Example more prevailing then direction,
  Far was homestrife, and far was foe from border.
His life a law, his looke a full correction:
  As in his health we healthfull were preserved,
  So in his sicknesse grew our sure infection.
His death our death.   But ah; my Muse hath swarved,
  From such deepe plaint as should such woes descrie,
  Which he of us for ever hath deserved.
The stile of heavie hart can never flie
  So high, as should make such a paine notorious:
  Cease Muse therfore: thy dart ô Death applie;
And farewell Prince, whom goodnesse hath made glorious.

CHAP. 26.

[1] *The publike griefe amplified.*   [2] Anaxius *death-threatning to the* Princesses.   [3] *Their resolutenes in it.*   [4] *His returne, and stop.* [5] Zelmanes *brave challenge unto him* [6] *scorned by him.*   [7] *His love to* Pamela *scorned by her.*   [8] *His brothers brave loves have as meane successe.*

[1] THe general consort of al such numbers mourning, perfourmed so the naturall times of sorrow; that even to them (if any such were) that felt not the losse, yet others grief taught them griefe; having before their compassionate sense so passionate a spectacle, of a young man, of great beautie, beautified with great honour, honored by great valure, made of inestimable valure, by the noble using of it, to lye there languishing, under the arrest of death, and a death, where the manner could be no comfort to the discomfortablenes of the matter.   But when the bodie was carried thorough the gate, and the people (saving such

as were appointed) not suffred to goe further, then was such an universal crie, as if they had all had but one life, and all receaved but one blow.

Which so moved *Anaxius* to consider the losse of his friend, 2 that (his minde apter to revenge, then tendernesse) he presently giving order to his brother to keepe the prisoners safe, and unvisited, till his retourne from cŏveying *Helen*, he sent a messenger to the sisters, to tel them this curteous message: that at his retourne, with his owne hands, he would cut off their heads, and send them for tokens to their father.

This message was brought unto the sisters, as they sate at 3 that time together with *Zelmane*, conferring how to carrie themselves, having heard of the death of *Amphialus*. And as no ,, expectation of death is so painfull, as where the resolution is ,, hindred by the intermixing of hopes, so did this new alarum, though not remove, yet move somwhat the cŏstancy of their minds, which were so unconstantly dealt with. But within a while, the excellent *Pamela* had brought her minde againe to his old acquaintance: and then, as carefull for her sister (whom most deerely she loved) Sister (said she) you see how many acts our Tragedy hath: Fortune is not yet a wearie of vexing us: but what? A shippe is not counted strong for byding one storme? It is but the same trumpet of death, which now perhaps gives the last sounde: and let us make that profite of our former miseries, that in them we learned to dye willingly. Truely said *Philoclea*, deare sister, I was so beaten with the evils of life, that though I had not vertue enough to despise the sweetnesse of it, yet my weaknesse bredde that strength, to be wearie of the paines of it: onely I must confesse, that little hope, which by these late accidents was awaked in me, was at the first angrie withall. But even in the darkenesse of that horrour, I see a light of comfort appeare; and how can I treade amisse, that see *Pamelas* steppes? I would onely (O that my wish might take place) that my schoole-Mistres might live, to see me say my lesson truely. Were that a life, my *Philoclea*? said *Pamela*. No, no, (said she) let it come, and put on his worst face: for at the worst it is but a bug-beare. Joy is it to me to see you so well resolved; and since the world will not have us, let it lose us. Onely (with that she stayed a little, and sight) onely my *Philoclea*, (then she bowed downe, and whispered in her eare) onely *Musidorus*, my shepheard, comes betweene me and death, and makes me thinke I should not dye, because I know he would not I should dye. With that *Philoclea* sighed also, saying no more, but looking upon *Zelmane*: who was walking up & downe the chamber, having heard this message from *Anaxius*, and having in times past heard of his nature, thought him like enough to performe it, which •winded her againe into the former maze of perplexitie. Yet debating with her selfe of the manner how to prevent it, she continued her musing humour, little saying, or indeed, little finding in her hart to say, in a case of such extremitie, where peremptorily death was threatned: and so stayed they; having yet that comfort, that they might tarrie togither. *Pamela* nobly, *Philoclea* sweetly, and *Zelmane* sadly, and desperately none of them entertaining sleepe, which they thought should shortly begin, never to awake.

4   But *Anaxius* came home, having safely conducted *Helen*: and safely he might wel do it: For though many of *Basilius* Knights would have attempted something upon *Anaxius*, by that meanes to deliver the Ladies, yet *Philanax*, having received his masters commãdement, & knowing his word was givẽ, would not cõsent unto it. And the black-Knight (who by thẽ was able to carie abroad his woũds) did not know therof; but was bringing forces, by force to deliver his Lady. So as *Anaxius*, interpreting it rather feare, then faith, and making even chance an argument of his vertue, returned: and as soone as he was returned, with a felon hart calling his brothers up with him, he went into the chamber, where they were all three togither; with full intention to kill the sisters with his owne hands, and send their heads for tokens to their father: Though his brothers (who were otherwise inclined) disswaded him: but his reverence stayed their perswasions. But when he was come into the chamber, with the very words of cholerike threatning climing up his throate, his eies first lighted upon *Pamela*; who hearing he was comming, and looking for death, thought she would keepe her owne majestie in welcomming it; but the beames thereof so strake his eyes, with such a counterbuffe unto his pride, that if his anger could not so quickly love, nor his pride so easily honor, yet both were forced to finde a worthinesse.

5   Which while it bred a pause in him, *Zelmane* (who had

ready in her mind both what and how to say) stept out unto him, & with a resolute stayednes (void either of anger, kindnes, disdaine, or humblenesse) spake in this sort. *Anaxius* (said she) if *Fame* have not bene overpartiall to thee, thou art a man of exceeding valour. Therefore I doo call thee even before that vertue, and will make it the judge betweene us. And now I doo affirme, that to the eternall blot of all the faire actes that thou hast done, thou doest weakly, in seeking without daunger to revenge his death, whose life with daunger thou mightst perhaps have preserved: thou doost cowardly, in going about by the death of these excellent Ladies, to prevent the just punishmēt, that hereafter they by the powers, which they better then their father, or any other could make, might lay upon thee; and doost most basely, in once presenting thy selfe as an executioner; a vile office upon men, and in a just cause: beyond the degree of any vile worde, in so unjust a cause, and upon Ladies, and such Ladies. And therefore, as a hangman, I say, thou art unworthy to be counted a Knight, or to be admitted into the companie of Knights. Neither for what, I say, will I alleadge other reasons, of wisdome, or justice, to proove my speech, because I know thou doost disdaine to be tied to their rules: but even in thine owne vertue (whereof thou so much gloriest) I will make my triall: and therefore defie thee, by the death of one of us two, to prove, or disprove these reproaches. Choose thee what armes thou likest, I onely demaund, that these Ladies (whom I defend) may in liberty see the combat.

When *Zelmane* began her speech, the excellency of her beautie, and grace, made him a little content to heare. Besides that, a new lesson he had read in *Pamela*, had already taught him some regard. But when she entered into braverie of speech, he thought at first, a mad, and railing humor possest her; till, finding the speeches hold well together, and at length come to flatte challenge of combat; he stood leaning back with his bodie and head, sometimes with bent browes looking upon the one side of her, sometimes of the other, beyonde marvell marvailing, that he, who had never heard such speeches from any Knight, should be thus rebuffed by a woman; and that marvell made him heare out her speech: which ended, he turned his head to his brother *Zoilus*, and said nothing, but onely lifting up his eyes, smiled. But *Zelmane* finding his minde, *Anaxius* (said she) perchaunce thou disdaynest to answere me, because, as a woman, thou thinkest me not fitte to be fought withall. But I tell thee, that I have bene trayned up in martial matters, with so good successe, that I have many times overcome better Knightes then thy selfe: and am well knowen to be equall in feates of armes, to the famous *Pyrocles*, who slewe thy valiaunt Uncle, the Giant *Euardes*. The remembraunce of his Uncles death something netled him, so as he answered thus.

Indeed (saide he) any woman may be as valiaunt as that coward, and traytorly boy, who slewe my Uncle trayterouslie, and after ranne from me in the plaine field. Five thousand such could not have overcome *Euardes*, but by falshood. But I sought him all over *Asia*, following him still from one of his cony-holes to another: till, comming into this Countrie, I heard of my friendes being besieged, and so came to blowe away the wretches that troubled him. But wheresoever the miserable boy flie, heaven, nor hell, shall keep his harte from being torne by these handes. Thou lyest in thy throate (said *Zelmane*) that boye, where ever he went, did so noble actes, as thy harte (as proude as it is) dares not thinke of, much lesse perfourme. But to please thee the better with my presence, I tell thee, no creature can be neerer of kinne to him, then my selfe: and so well we love, that he woulde not be sorrier for his owne death, then for mine: I being begotten by his father, of an Amazon Ladie. And therefore, thou canst not devise to revenge thy selfe more upon him, then by killing me: which, if thou darest doo manfullie, doo it; otherwise, if thou harme these incomparable Ladies, or my selfe, without daring to fight with me, I protest before these Knightes, and before heaven, and earth, (that will reveale thy shame) that thou art the beggerliest dastardly villaine, that dishonoureth the earth with his steppes: and if thou lettest me over-live them, so will I blaze thee. But all this could not move *Anaxius*, but that he onely said, Evill should it become the terror of the world, to fight, much lesse to skolde with thee.

7 But (said he) for the death of these same (pointing to the Princesses) of my grace, I give them life. And withall, going to *Pamela*, and offring to take her by the chin, And as for you,

Minion (said he) yeeld but gently to my will, and you shall not only live, but live so happely, He would have said further, whē *Pamela*, displeased both with words, matter, and maner, putting him away with her faire hand, Proud beast (said she) yet thou plaiest worse thy Comedy, then thy Tragedy. For my part, assure thy selfe, since my destiny is such, that at ech moment my life & death stand in equall balance, I had rather have thee, & think thee far fitter to be my hangman, then my husband. Pride & anger, would faine have cruelly revēged so bitter an answer, but alredy *Cupid* had begun to make it his sport, to pull his plumes: so that, unused to a way of courtesie, and put out of his byas of pride, he hastily went away, grumbling to himselfe, betwene threatning & wishing; leaving his brothers with thē: the elder of whom, *Lycurgus*, liked *Philoclea*, & *Zoilus* would nedes love *Zelmane*; or at lest, entertain themselves with making thē beleve so. *Lycurgus* more braggard, & nere his brothers humor, begā, with setting foorth their bloud, their deedes, how many they had despised, of most excellent womē; how much they were boūd to them, that would seek that of them. In summe, in all his speeches, more like the bestower, then the desirer of felicitie. Whom it was an excellent pastime (to those that would delight in the play of vertue) to see, with what a wittie ignorance she would not understand: and how, acknowledging his perfections, she would make, that one of his perfections, not to be injurious to Ladies. But when he knew not how to replie, then would he fall to touching and toying, still vewing his graces in no glasse but self-liking. To which, *Philocleas* shamefastnes, and humblenes, were as strong resisters, as choller, and disdaine. For though she yeelded not, he thought she was to be overcome: and that thought a while stayed him from further violence. But *Zelmane* had eye to his behaviour, and set in her memorie, upon the score of Revenge, while she her selfe was no lesse attempted by *Zoilus*; who lesse full of bragges, was forwardest in offering (indeed) dishonourable violence.

CHAP. 27.

[1] Zelmanes *perswasions to temporize, and referre them to* Basilius. [2] Anaxius-*his embassage to treate the mariage.* [3] Basilius *recourse to a newe Oracle,* [4] *and his negative thereon.* [5] *The flattering relation of his* Mercurie. [6] *The brothers course to resist force without, and use force within.*

[1] BUt when after their fruitlesse labours they had gone away, called by their brother, (who began to be perplexed betweene new conceaved desires, and disdaine, to be disdained) *Zelmane* (who with most assured quietnesse of judgement looked into their present estate) earnestly perswaded the two sisters, that to avoide the mischiefes of prowde outrage, they would onely so farre sute their behaviour to their estates, as they might winne time; which as it could not bring them to worse case then they were, so it might bring forth inexpected relief. And why (said *Pamela*) shal we any longer flatter adversity? Why should we delight to make our selves any longer balls to injurious *Fortune,* since our owne kinne are content traitorously to abuse us? Certainely, in mishap it may be some comforte to us, that we are lighted in these fellowes handes, who yet will keepe us from having cause of being miserable by our friends meanes. Nothing grieves me more, then that you, noble Ladie *Zelmane* (to whome the worlde might have made us able to doo honour) shoulde receave onely hurte by the contagion of our miserie. As for me, and my sister, undoubtedly it becomes our birth to thinke of dying nobly, while we have done, or suffered nothing, which might make our soule ashamed ,, at the parture from these bodies. Hope is the fawning traitour ,, of the minde, while under colour of friendship, it robbes it of his chiefe force of resolution. Vertuous and faire Ladie (said *Zelmane*) what you say is true; and that truth may well make up a part in the harmonie of your noble thoughts. But yet the time (which ought alwaies to be one) is not tuned for it; while that may bring foorth any good, doo not barre your selfe thereof: ,, for then would be the time to die nobly, when you cã not live nobly. Then so earnestly she persuaded with them both, to referre themselves to their fathers consent (in obtayning whereof

they knewe some while would be spent) and by that meanes to temper the mindes of their prowde woers; that in the ende *Pamela* yeelded to her, because she spake reason; and *Philoclea* yeelded to her reason, because she spake it.

And so when they were againe sollicited in that little 2 pleasing petition, *Pamela* forced her selfe to make answere to *Anaxius*, that if her father gave his consent she would make her selfe believe, that such was the heavenly determination, since she had no meanes to avoide it. *Anaxius* (who was the most franke promiser to him selfe of successe) nothing doubted of *Basilius* consent, but rather assured him selfe, he would be his oratour in that matter: And therefore he chose out an officious servaunt (whome he esteemed very wise, because he never found him but just of his opinion) and willed him to be his embassadour to *Basilius*, and to make him knowe, that if he meant to have his daughter both safe and happie, and desired him selfe to have such a sonne in lawe, as would not onely protect him in his quiet course, but (if he listed to accept it) would give him the monarchy of the worlde, that then he should receave *Anaxius*, who never before knewe what it was to pray any thing. That if he did not, he would make him know, that the power of *Anaxius* was in every thing beyonde his will, and yet his will not to be resisted by any other power. His servaunt with smiling and caste-up looke, desired God to make his memorie able to containe the treasure of that wise speach: and therefore besought him to repeate it againe, that by the oftener hearing it, his mind might be the better acquainted with the divinenesse therof, and that being gratiously granted, he then doubted not by carying with him in his conceit, the grace wherewith *Anaxius* spake it, to persuade rocky minds to their owne harme: so little doubted he to win *Basilius* to that, which he thought would make him thinke the heavens opened, when he harde but the proffer thereof. *Anaxius* gravely allowed the probabilitie of his conjecture, and therefore sent him away, promising him he should have the bringing up of his second sonne by *Pamela*.

The messenger with speede perfourmed his Lords com- 3 maundement to *Basilius*, who by nature quiet, and by super-stition made doubtfull, was lothe to take any matter of armes in hand, wherin already he had found so slowe successe; though

Philanax vehemently urged him therunto, making him see that
his retiring back did encourage injuries. But *Basilius* betwixt
the feare of *Anaxius* might, the passiŏ of his love, & jealousie of
his estate, was so perplexed, that not able to determine, he tooke
the cŏmon course of mē, to flie only thē to devotiŏ, whē they
want resolutiŏ: so detaining the messēger with delaies, he
deferred the directing of his course to the coūsell of *Apollo*,
which because himself at that time could not well go to require,
he entrusted the matter to his best trusted *Philanax*: who (as
one in whom obedience was a sufficient reason unto him)
wente with diligence to *Delphos*, where being entred into the
secrete place of the temple, and having performed the sacrifices
usuall, the spirite that possest the pro[p]hesying woman, with a
sacred fury, attended not his demaund, but as if it would argue
him of incredulitie, tolde him, not in darke wonted speeches,
but plainely to be understood, what he came for, and that he
should returne to *Basilius*, and will him to denie his daughters
to *Anaxius* and his brothers, for that they were reserved for
such as were better beloved of the gods. That he should not
doubte, for they should returne unto him safely and speedily.
And that he should keepe on his solitary course, till bothe
Philanax and *Basilius* fully agreed in the understanding of the
„ former prophecie: withall, commaunding *Philanax* from thence
forward to give tribute, but not oblation, to humane wisedome.

4 *Philanax* then finding that reason cannot shewe it self more
„ reasonable, then to leave reasoning in things above reason,
returnes to his Lorde, and like one that preferred truth before
the maintaining of an opinion, hidde nothing from him, nor
from thence foorth durste any more disswade him, from that
which he founde by the celestiall providence directed; but he
him selfe looking to repayre the government as much as in so
broken an estate by civill dissention he might, and fortifying
with notable arte, bothe the lodges, so as they were almost
made unaprochable, he lefte *Basilius* to bemone the absence of
his daughters, and to bewayle the imprisonment of *Zelmane*:
yet wholy given holily to obey the Oracle, he gave a resolute
negative unto the messenger of *Anaxius*, who all this while had
waited for it, yet in good termes desiring him to shewe him
selfe, in respect of his birth and profession, so Princely a
Knight, as without forcing him to seeke the way of force,

to deliver in noble sorte those Ladies unto him, and so should the injurie have bene in *Amphialus*, and the benefite in him.

The messenger went backe with this answere, yet having 5 ever used to sugre any thing which his Maister was to receave, he tolde him, that when *Basilius* first understood his desires, he did overreach so farre all his most hopefull expectations, that he thought it were too great a boldnesse to harken to such a man, in whome the heavens had such interest, without asking the Gods counsell, and therefore had sent his principall counsailour to *Delphos*, who although he kepte the matter never so secrete, yet his diligence, inspired by *Anaxius* his priviledge over all worldly thinges, had founde out the secrete, which was, that he should not presume to marrie his daughters, to one who already was enrolled among the demie-Gods, and yet much lesse he should dare the attempting to take them out of his hands.

Anaxius, who till then had made Fortune his creator, and 6 Force his God, nowe beganne to finde an other wisedome to be above, that judged so rightly of him: and where in this time of his servauntes wayting for *Basilius* resolution, he and his brothers had courted their Ladies, as whome they vouchsafed to have for their wives, he resolved now to dally no longer in delayes, but to make violence his Oratour, since he had found persuasions had gotten nothing but answeres. Which intention he opened to his brothers, who having all this while wanted nothing to take that way, but his authoritie, gave spurres to his running, and, unworthy men, neither feeling vertue in themselves, nor tendring it in others, they were headlong to make that evill consorte of love and force, when *Anaxius* had worde, that from the Tower there were descried some companies of armed men, marching towardes the towne; wherefore he gave presente order to his servauntes, and souldiers, to goe to the gates and walles, leaving none within but himselfe, and his brothers: his thoughts then so full of their intended pray, that *Mars*-his lowdest trumpet could scarcely have awaked him.

CHAP. 28.

[1] Zoilus *the messenger,* [2] *and first offerer of force,* [3] *is forced to flie, and die.* [4] Lycurgus *pointed to kill,* [5] *is fought withal,* [6] *foiled,* [7] *& killed.* [8] Anaxius *the* Revenger *with* Pyrocles *the* Punisher *brave, and bravely combatted.*

[1] BUt while he was directing what he would have done, his yongest brother *Zoilus,* glad that he had the commission, went in the name of *Anaxius,* to tel the sisters, that since he had answere from their father, that he and his brother *Licurgus,* should have them in what sort it pleased them, that they would now graunt them no longer time, but presently to determine, whether they thought it more honorable comfort to be compelled, or perswaded. *Pamela* made him answere, that in a matter whereon the whole state of her life depended, and wherin she had ever answered, she would not lead, but follow her parents pleasure; she thought it reason she should, either by letter, or particular messẽger understãd somthing from thẽselves, & not have her beleef bound to the report of their partiall servants, & therefore, as to their words, she & her sister, had ever a simple & true resolution, so against their unjust force, God, they hoped, would either arme their lives, or take away their lives.

[2] Wel Ladies (said he) I wil leave my brothers, who by & by wil come unto you, to be their own embassadors, for my parte, I must now do my self service. And with that turning up his mustachoes, and marching as if he would begin a paven, he went toward *Zelmane.* But *Zelmane* (having had all this while of the messengers being with *Basilius,* much to do to keepe those excellent Ladies from seeking by the pasport of death, to escape those base dangers whereunto they found themselves subject) still hoping that *Musidorus* would finde some meanes to deliver them; and therefore had often both by her owne example, & comfortable reasons, perswaded thẽ to overpasse many insolent indignities of their proud suters, who thought it was a sufficient favour not to doo the uttermost injurie, now come againe to the streight she most feared for them, either of death or dishonor, if heroicall courage would have let her, she

512

had beene beyonde herselfe amazed: but that yet held up her wit, to attend the uttermost occasion, which evē then brought his hairie forehead unto her: for *Zoilus* smacking his lippes, as for the Prologue of a kisse, and something advancing himselfe, Darling (said he) let thy hart be full of joy, and let thy faire eies be of counsel with it, for this day thou shalt have *Zoilus*, whō many have lōged for; but none shall have him, but *Zelmane*. And oh, how much glory I have to think what a race will be betwene us. The world, by the heavens, the world will be too litle for them: And with that, he would have put his arme about her necke, but she, withdrawing her selfe from him, My Lord (said she) much good may your thoughts do you, but that I may not dissemble with you, my nativitie being cast by one that never failed in any of his prognostications, I have bene assured, that I should never be apt to beare children. But since you wil honor me with so hie favor, I must onely desire that I may performe a vow which I made among my coūtriwomen, the famous *Amazons*, that I would never marrie none, but such one as was able to withstand me in Armes: therfore, before I make mine own desire serviceable to yours, you must vouchsafe to lend me armor and weapons, that at least, with a blow or two of the sword, I may not finde my selfe perjured to my selfe. But *Zoilus* (but laughing with a hartie lowdnes) went by force to embrace her; making no other answere, but since she had a minde to trie his Knighthood, she should quickly know what a man of armes he was: and so, without reverence to the Ladies, began to struggle with her.

But in *Zelmane* then Disdaine became wisdome, & Anger 3 gave occasion. For abiding no longer aboad in the matter, she that had not put off, though she had disguised, *Pyrocles*, being farre fuller of strong nimblenes, tript up his feete, so that he fel down at hers. And withall (meaning to pursue what she had begun) puld out his sword, which he ware about him: but before she could strike him withall, he gat up, and ranne to a faire chamber, where he had left his two brethrē, preparing themselves to come downe to their mistresses. But she followed at his heeles, & evē as he came to throw himself into their arms for succor, she hit him with his own sword, such a blow upō the wast, that she almost cut him a sūder: once, she sundred

his soule frõ his body, sēding it to *Proserpina*, an angry Goddesse against ravishers.

4   But *Anaxius*, seing before his eyes the miserable end of his
brother, fuller of despite thē wrath, & yet fuller of wrath
then sorow, looking with a wofull eye upon his brother
Lycurgus, Brother, said he, chastice this vile creature, while I
go down, & take order lest further mischief arise: & so went
down to the Ladies, whom he visited, doubting there had bene
some further practise thē yet he conceived. But finding thē
only strong in pacience, he went & lockt a great Iron gate, by
which onely any body might mounte to that part of the Castle,
rather to conceale the shame of his brother, slaine by a woman,
then for doubt of any other anoyance, and thē went up to
receave some comfort of the execution, he was sure his brother
had done of *Zelmane*.

5   But *Zelmane* no sooner saw those brothers, of whom Reasõ
assured her she was to expect revēge, but that she lept to a
„ target, as one that well knew the first marke of valure to be
defence. And thē accepting the oportunitie of *Anaxius* going
away, she waited not the pleasure of *Lycurgus*, but without any
words (which she ever thought vaine, whē resolutiõ tooke the
place of perswasion) gave her owne hart the contentment to be
the assailer. *Lycurgus*, who was in the dispositiõ of his nature
hazardouse, & by the luckie passing through many dangers,
growne confident in himselfe, went toward her, rather as to
spoile, then to fight, so farre from feare, that his assurednesse
disdained to hope. But whē her sword made demonstrations
above al flattery of argumēts, & that he found she prest so upon
him, as shewed that her courage sprang not from blind despair,
but was garded both with cunning & strength: self-love thē
first in him divided it selfe frõ vain-glory, & made him find
that the world of worthines had not his whole globe cõprised
in his brest, but that it was necessary to have strong resistãce
against so strong assailing. And so between thē, for a few
blowes, *Mars* himself might have bin delighted to looke on.
But *Zelmane*, who knew that in her case, slownesse of victory
was little better thē ruine, with the bellowes of hate, blew the
fire of courage, and he striking a maine blow at her head, she
warded it with the shield, but so warded, that the shield was
cut in two pieces, while it protected her, & withall she ran in

to him, and thrusting at his brest, which he put by with his target, as he was lifting up his sword to strike again, she let fall the piece of her shield, and with her left hand catching his sword of the inside of the pōmel, with nimble & strong sleight, she had gottē his sword out of his hand before his sence could cōvey to his imaginatiō, what was to be doubted. And having 6 now two swords against one shield, meaning not foolishly to be ungratefull to good fortune, while he was no more amazed with his being unweapned, then with the suddainnes therof, she gave him such a woūd upō his head, in despite of the shields over-weak resistāce, that withal he fel to the groūd, astonished with the paine, & agast with feare. But seing *Zelmane* ready to cōclude her victory in his death, bowing up his head to her, with a countenance that had forgotten al pride, Enough excellent Lady, said he, the honor is yours: Wherof you shall want the best witnes, if you kil me. As you have takē frō men the glory of māhood, returne so now againe to your owne sex, for mercy. I wil redeeme my life of you with no smal services, for I will undertake to make my brother obey all your commādements. Grant life I beseech you, for your own honor, and for the persons sake that you love best.

Zelmane represt a while her great hart, either disdaining to 7 be cruell, or pitiful, & therfore not cruell: & now the image of humane condition, begā to be an Orator unto her of compassiō, whē she saw, as he lifted up his armes with a suppliāts grace, about one of thē, unhappily, tied a garter with a Jewel, which (givē to *Pyrocles* by his aunt of *Thessalia*, & greatly esteemed by him) he had presēted to *Philoclea*, & with inward rage promising extream hatred, had seene *Lycurgus* with a proud force, & not with out some hurt unto her, pull away frō *Philoclea*, because at entreatie she would not give it him. But the sight of that was like a cyphar, signifying all the injuries which *Philoclea* had of him suffred, & that remēbrance feeding upō wrath, trod down al cōceits of mercy. And therfore saying no more, but, No villaine, dye: It is *Philoclea* that sēds thee this tokē for thy love. With that she made her sword drink the blood of his hart, though he wresting his body, & with a coūtenāce prepared to excuse, wold fain have delaied the receiving of deaths embassadors.

8   But neither that staied *Zelmanes* hand, nor yet *Anaxius* crie
unto her, who having made fast the Iron gate, even then came
to the top of the staires, when, contrarie to all his imaginations,
he saw his brother lie at *Zelmanes* mercie. Therefore crying,
promising, and threatning to her to hold her hand: the last
grone of his brother was the onely answere he could get to
his unrespected eloquence. But then Pittie would faine have
drawne teares, which Furie in their spring dried; and Anger
would faine have spoken, but that Disdaine sealed up his lippes;
but in his hart he blasphemed heaven, that it could have such a
power over him; no lesse ashamed of the victorie he should have
of her, then of his brothers overthrow: and no more spited, that
it was yet unrevenged, then that the revenge should be no
greater, then a womans destruction. Therefore with no speach,
but such a groning crie, as often is the language of sorowfull
anger, he came running at *Zelmane*, use of fighting then serving
in steed of patient cõsideration what to doo. Guided wherewith, though he did not with knowledge, yet did he according
to knowledge, pressing upon *Zelmane* in such a wel defended
manner, that in all the combats that ever she had fought, she
had never more need of quicke senses, & ready vertue. For
being one of the greatest men of stature then living, as he did
fully answere that stature in greatnesse of might, so did he
exceed both in greatnes of courage, which with a coũtenãce
formed by the nature both of his mind & body, to an almost
horrible fiercenes, was able to have carried feare to any mind,
that was not privie to it selfe of a true & cõstant worthines.
But *Pyrocles*, whose soule might well be separated frõ his body,
but never alienated frõ the remembring what was comely, if
at the first he did a little apprehend the dangerousnes of his
adversarie, whom once before he had something tried, & now
perfectly saw, as the very picture of forcible furie: yet was that
apprehension quickly stayed in him, rather strengthning, then
weakning his vertue by that wrestling; like wine, growing the
strõger by being moved. So that they both, prepared in harts,
and able in hands, did honor solitarines there with such a combat, as might have demaunded, as a right of fortune, whole
armies of beholders. But no beholders needed there, where
manhood blew the trumpet, & satisfaction did whette, as much
as glorie. There was strength against nimblenes; rage, against

resolution, fury, against vertue; confidence, against courage; pride, against noblenesse: love, in both, breeding mutual hatred, & desire of reveging the injurie of his brothers slaughter, to *Anaxius*, being like *Philocleas* captivity to *Pyrocles*. Who had seen the one, would have thought nothing could have resisted; who had marked the other, would have marveiled that the other had so long resisted. But like two contrarie tides, either of which are able to carry worldes of shippes, and men upon them, with such swiftnes, as nothing seemes able to withstand them: yet meeting one another, with mingling their watrie forces, and strugling together, it is long to say whether streame gets the victorie: So betweene these, if *Pallas* had bene there, she could scarcely have tolde, whether she had nurced better in the feates of armes. The Irish greyhound, against the English mastiffe; the sword-fish, against the whale; the Rhinoceros, against the elephãt, might be models, & but models of this côbat. *Anaxius* was better armed defensively: for (beside a strong caske bravely covered, wherwith he coverd his head) he had a huge shield, such perchance, as *Achilles* shewed to the pale walles of Troy, wherewithall that body was covered. But *Pyrocles*, utterly unarmed for defence, to offend had the advantage: for, in either hand he had a sword, & with both hands nimbly performed that office. And according as they were diversly furnished, so did they differ in the manner of fighting. For *Anaxius* most by warding, and *Pyrocles* oftnest by avoyding, resisted the adversaries assault. Both hastie to end, yet both often staying for advantage. Time, distance, & motiõ custom made them so perfect in, that as if they had bene felow Counsellers, and not enemies, each knewe the others minde, and knew how to prevent it. So as their strêgth fayled them sooner then their skill, and yet their breath fayled them sooner then their strength. And breathles indeed they grew, before either could complaine of any losse of bloud.

CHAP. 29.

[1]*The Combattants first breathing,* [2]*reencounter, and*

1 **S**O consenting by the mediation of necessitie, to a breathing
time of truce, being withdrawen a little one from the
other; *Anaxius* stood leaning upon his sworde, with his grym
eye, so setled upon *Zelmane*, as is wont to be the look of an
earnest thought. Which *Zelmane* marking, &, according to
the *Pyroclean* nature, fuller of gay braverie in the midst, then in
the beginning of däger; What is it (said she) *Anaxius*, that thou
so deeply musest on? Dooth thy brothers exäple make thee
thinke of thy fault past, or of thy cöming punishmët? I think
(said he) what spiteful God it should be, who, envying my
glory, hath brought me to such a waywarde case, that neither
thy death can be a revenge, nor thy overthrow a victorie.
Thou doost well indeede (saide *Zelmane*) to impute thy case to
the heavenly providence, which will have thy pride find it selfe
(even in that whereof thou art most proud) punished by the
weake sex, which thou most contemnest.

2 But then, having sufficiently rested themselves, they renewed
againe their combatte, farre more terribly then before: like
nimble vaulters, who at the first and second leape, doo but
stirre, and (as it were) awake the fierie and aërie partes, which
after in the other leapes, they doo with more excellencie exercise.
For in this pausing, ech had brought to his thoughts the maner or
the others fighting, and the advantages, which by that, and by the
qualitie of their weapons, they might work themselves; and so
againe repeated the lesson they had said before, more perfectly,
by the using of it. *Anaxius* oftner used blowes, his huge force
(as it were) more delighting therein, and the large protection of
his shield, animating him unto it. *Pyrocles*, of a more fine, and
deliver strength, watching his time when to give fitte thrustes;
as, with the quick obeying of his bodie, to his eyes quicke commaundement, he shunned any harme *Anaxius* could do to him:
so would he soon have made an end of *Anaxius*, if he had not
foûd him a mä of wonderful, & almost matchlesse excellëcy in
matters of armes. *Pyrocles* used divers faynings, to bring *Anaxius*
on, into some inconvenience. But *Anaxius* keeping a sound

518

maner of fighting, never offered, but seeing faire cause, & then followed it with wel-governed violence. Thus spent they a great time, striving to doo, and with striving to doo, wearying themselves, more then with the very doing. *Anaxius* finding *Zelmane* so neere unto him, that with little motion he might reach her, knitting all his strength together, at that time mainly foyned at her face. But *Zelmane* strongly putting it by with her right hande sword, comming in with her left foote, and hande, woulde have given him a sharpe visitation to his right side, but that he was faine to leape away. Whereat ashamed, (as having never done so much before in his life)

A LIST OF MISPRINTS IN THE QUARTO, WHICH HAVE BEEN CORRECTED.

51.	4.	*Reversed* t *in* then
57.	3.	sufficienr 29. perceivcd
58.	1.	soohest
73.	9.	Geutleman
78.	13.	applie [*correction supplied by catchword*]
79.	24.	ininjury
90.	34.	the the *before* Princesse
96.	35.	*Baſilius*
100.	9.	wenr
101.	13.	peatle
114.	2.	*Maſidorus*
116.	10.	shephadrs 19. constancic
118.	16.	*Menelcas*
120.	38.	from hec
122.	21.	youug
127.	2.	couclude
134.	8.	otbers
141.	24.	tbe
153.	10.	ot like
154.	39.	nothiug
167.	11.	lirtle
183.	16.	woule
186.	24.	*Enarchus*
215.	33.	*turned parenthesis before* delighted
220.	5.	*Tbe*
229.	19.	*shc*
233.	22.	thē cries
238.	26.	*turned* u *in* though
269.	4.	afterwarwardes
285.	27.	*LElius*
318.	33.	judgement
322.	16.	minlegd
336.	16.	*But*
360.	33.	of of them
386.	18.	of of that
401.	19.	forcibie
436.	9.	*turned* n *in* perchance
444.	9.	Q *misprints* 3 *for* 8
448.	30.	themselvcs
452.	17.	servc

520

A LIST OF MISPRINTS

471.　20.　hunanitie
485.　16.　Q *misprints* 17 *for* 23
487.　6.　a a more　　40.　beleeeve
489.　25.　samc
505.　9.　wfth
507.　25.　injurions
509.　8.　rhat
511.　13.　presnme

NOTES

In the following references to the text the lines are numbered from the top of the page, including titles, but not, of course, the headline. The page numbers are in heavier type.

The folio editions are as follows:

(**A**) The | Countesse | of Pembrokes | Arcadia. | Written by Sir | Philip Sidney Knight. | Now since the first edi- | tion augmented and ended. | London. | Printed for William Ponsonbie. | Anno Domini. 1593.

(**B**) The | Countesse | of Pembrokes | Arcadia. | Written by Sir | Philip Sidney | Knight. | Now the third time | published, with sundry new additions | of the same Author. | London | Imprinted for William Ponsonbie. | Anno Domini. 1598.

(**C**) The | Countesse | of Pembrokes | Arcadia. | Written by Sir | Philip Sidney | Knight. | Now the third time published, with sundry new | additions of the same Author. | Edinburgh. | Printed by Robert | walde-grave, Printer to the | Kings Majestie. | Cum privilegio Regio. 1599.

(**D**) The | Countesse | of Pembrokes | Arcadia. | Written by Sir | Philip Sidney | Knight. | Now the fourth time | Published, With Sundry | New Additions Of The | same Author. | London | Imprinted for Mathew Lownes | Anno Domini. | 1605. [*Some copies have* "Imprinted for Simon Waterson"]

(**E**) The | Countesse | of Pembrokes | Arcadia. | Written by Sir | Philip Sidney ⸶ Knight. | Now the fourth time | published, with some new | Addi-tions. | London | Imprinted by H. L. for Simon | Waterson 1613. [*Some copies have* "Imprinted by H. L. for Mathew Lownes"]

(**F**) The | Countesse | of Pembrokes | Arcadia. | Written by Sir | Philip Sidney | Knight. | Now the fift time published, | with some new Additions. | Also a supplement of a defect in | the third part of this | History. | By Sir W. Alexander. | Dublin, | Printed by the Societie of | Stationers. 1621. | Cum Privilegio.

(**F'**) The | Countesse | of | Pembrokes | Arcadia. | Written by Sir | Philip Sidney, | Knight. | Now the sixt time pub- | lished. | London | Imprinted by H. L. for Matthew | Lownes. 1623.
[*The same edition as* **F** *with a new title-page.*]

(**G**) The | Countesse | Of | Pembrokes | Arcadia. | Written by Sir Philip Sidney | Knight. | Now the sixt time published, | with some new Additions. | Also a supplement of a defect in | the third part of this Historie, | By Sir W. Alexander. | London, | Printed by W. S. for Simon | Waterson. | 1627.

NOTES

(**G'**) The | Countesse | of Pembrokes | Arcadia. | Written by Sir | Philip Sidney | Knight. | Now the seventh time published, | with some new Additions. | With the supplement of a Defect in the third | part of this History, by Sir W. A. Knight. | Whereunto is now added a sixth Booke, | By R. B. of Lincolnes Inne, Esq. | London printed by H. L. and R. Y. and are | sold by S. Waterson in S. Pauls Church- | yard, 1629.

[*The same edition as* **G** *with a new title-page.*]

(**H**) The | Countesse | of Pembrokes | Arcadia. | Written by Sir Philip Sidney | Knight. | Now the eighth time published, | with some new Additions. | With the supplement of a Defect in the third | part of this History, by Sir W. A. Knight. | Whereunto is now added a sixth Booke, | By R. B. of Lincolnes Inne, Esq. | London, | Printed for Simon Waterson and | R. Young, Anno 1633.

(**I**) The | Countesse | of Pembrokes | Arcadia, | Written by Sir Philip Sidney | Knight. | Now the ninth time published, with a | twofold supplement of a defect in the third | Book : the one by Sr W. A. Knight ; the | other, by M^r Ja. Johnstoun Scoto-Brit. | dedicated to K. James, and now | annexed to this work, for | the Readers be- | nefit. | Whereunto is also added a sixth Booke, | By R. B. of Lincolnes Inne, Esq. | London, | Printed for J. Waterson and R. Young, 1638.

(**K**) The | Countess | of | Pembroke's | Arcadia | Written by | Sr Philip Sidney | Knight. | The tenth Edition. | With his Life and Death ; a brief Table of the principal | heads, and som other new Additions. | London, | Printed by William Du-Gard : and are to bee sold by | George Calvert, at the half Moon in the new buildings in Paul's | Church-yard ; and Thomas Pierrepont, at the Sun in | Paul's Church-yard, M. DC. LV.

(**L**) The | Countess | of | Pembroke's | Arcadia | Written by | Sir Philip Sidney | Knight. | The eleventh Edition | With his Life and Death ; a brief Table of the principal | Heads, and som other new Additions. | London, | Printed by Henry Lloyd, for William Du-Gard : and | are to bee sold by George Calvert, at the half Moon in the new | buildings ; and Thomas Pierrepont, at the Sun in St. Paul's | Church-yard, MDCLXII.

(**M**) The | Countess | of | Pembroke's | Arcadia | Written by | Sir Philip Sidney | Knight. | The Thirteenth Edition. | With his Life and Death ; a brief Table of the principal | Heads, and some other new Additions. | London, | Printed for George Calvert, at the Golden-Ball in | Little-Britain, MDCLXXIV.

In the following notes each of these folios is referred to by the capital letter prefixed to it in the above list. Q = 1590.

3. 26. D *having many fancies* 29. LM *this chief*

4. 3. F—M *if much good* 10. A—M *in a* 12—13. M *and most heartily* 14. C *ornament of* 17. *This notice, as well as the division into chapters, and the summaries preceding them, are omitted in all the folio editions.*

NOTES

After the epistle, To My Deare Ladie and Sister, etc., *the folios, with the exception of* E, *insert the following preface:*

To the Reader.

THE *disfigured face, gentle Reader, wherewith this worke not long since appeared to the common view, moved that noble Lady, to whose Honour* [H—M *insert* "*it was*"] *consecrated, to whose protection it was committed, to take in hand the wiping away those spottes wherewith the beauties therof were unworthely blemished. But as often in* [DF—M *omit* "*in*"] *repairing a ruinous house, the mending of some olde part occasioneth the making of some new: so here her honourable labour begonne in correcting the faults, ended in supplying the defectes; by the view of what was ill done guided to the consideration of what was not done. Which part with what advise entred into, with what successe* [DF—M *accesse*] *it hath* [F—M *had*] *beene passed through, most by her doing, all by her directing, if they may be entreated not to define, which are unfurnisht of meanes to discerne, the rest (it is hoped) will favourably censure. But this they shall, for theyr better satisfaction, understand, that though they finde not here what might be expected, they may finde neverthelesse as much as was intended, the conclusion, not the perfection of* Arcadia: *and that no further then the Authours own writings, or knowen determinations could direct. Whereof who sees not the reason, must consider there may be reason which hee sees not. Albeit I dare affirme hee either sees, or from wiser judgements then his owne may heare, that* Sir Philip Sidneies *writings can no more be perfected without* Sir Philip Sidney, *then* Apelles *pictures without* Apelles. *There are that thinke the contrary: and no wonder. Never was* Arcadia *free from the comber of such* Cattell. *To us, say they, the pastures are not pleasaunt: and as for the flowers, such as we light on we take no delight in, but the greater part growe not within our reach. Poore soules! what talke they of flowers? They are* Roses, *not flowers, must doe them good, which if they finde not here, they shall doe well to go* [F—M *omit* "*go*"] *feed elswhere: Any place will better like them: For without* Arcadia *nothing growes in more plenty, then* Lettuce *sutable to their* Lippes, *If it be true that likenes is a great cause of liking, and that contraries, inferre contrary consequences: then is it true, that the wortheles Reader can never worthely esteeme of so worthye a writing: and as true, that the noble, the wise, the vertuous, the curteous, as many as have had any acquaintaunce with true learning and knowledge, will with all love and dearenesse entertaine it, as well for affinity with themselves, as being child to such a father. Whom albeit it do not exactly and in every lineament represent; yet considering the fathers untimely death prevented the timely birth of the childe, it may happily seeme a thanke-woorthy labour, that the defects being so few, so small, and in no principall part, yet the greatest unlikenes is rather in defect then in deformity. But howsoever it is, it is now by* [KLM *omit* "*by*"] *more then one interest* The Countesse of Pembrokes Arcadia: *done, as it was, for her: as it is, by her. Neither shall these pains be the last (if no unexpected accident cut off her determination) which the everlasting love of her excellent brother, will make her consecrate to his memory.*

H. S.

[*After the above* KLM *insert thirteen leaves containing* The Life and Death of Sir Philip Sidney *and many epigrams and epitaphs.*]

524

NOTES

5. 26. FGH shore

6. 3. ABDEF graze G—M grace 27. A—M to us E cherries
31. HI others 35. I minde how 38. L sweetness fairness

7. 2. BD—M the sight 32. A—M then by

8. 1. A other HI of the 3. G—M others A we two
19. M of a goodly 24. A—M water come 36—37. A—M *Pyrocles*
destruction? therewithall hee offered wilfully to cast himselfe againe

9. 13. A *omits* any 18. DF—M precious food 26. A men

10. 8. KLM do condemn 11. A—M of the water 13. KLM
her mate 20. BD—GK—M man 30. A—M such superstition
36. A—M corde

11. 3. H—M paines 5. C discribed 14. M to fight
15. A—M nothing wherewith to 16. F—I not to KLM nought to
20. HI *omits* well 30. GKLM fisherman 34. LM so full

12. 4—11. C find thē, now sir 16—17. A—M confines there
dwelleth 19. HI stirs FGK come 27. AC is sweet
31. A—M *omit* but in that respect,

13. 3. D *Loconia* 5. A sorowful-mind B—M *print two words*
12. BD—GK—M misfortune 17. E the length 30. F—M the
refreshing 33. ACF—M disposition 39. G voice musick H—M
voice-musick

15. 6—7. KLM *print* provision is...of magnificence *in Italics* 19. C
countenance 20—21. E aswell care of them that did serve, as to be
served. 35. A—M was thus

16. 2. M he had had 6. A—M that they were 12. HI
respectively 13. C sight 20. KLM *Laconian* Pirats 29. G—M
Missenia

17. 14. M delighted in. The 21. A—M a thicket, and behinde
35. A—M follie, meane while

18. 9. C ane other 10. DG—M were only 22. KLM bestowed nothing on 23. H—M skil on the

19. 2. D which extraordinary 5. C treasures 28. A did
serve 29. G—M as the zealous

20. 21. I proceedings 37. C lodgings

21. 6. AC daughter of 21. A—M The verses 24. KLM
When virtues HI *beautie* HI *may them know* 25. BD—M
then C *them*

22. 4. BD—M smoothed 6. BDFG on time 11. D in-
tempered 17. G—M *omit* his *before* bluntnesse 23. I she
33. F—M with grosse

23. 11. M *prints throughout* "*Clitiphon*" 12—13. E *omits*
preparing...celebrated 26. G—M his countrey 32. C ane
33. LM fancied

24. 5—26. 14. KLM *print this letter in Italics, with the exception of*
wisdom...to follow [**24.** 12—13] *and* hee cannot...is good [**26.** 3] *which
lines are in Roman type.*

24. 14. C to leade 16. A weakenes 19. KLM *omit* not
21. A—M kindes of soothsayings 22. F—M *omit* to 26. G—M
stretched 31. LM your obedience 38. BD—M example

NOTES

25. 5. I be not to be   28. *After* then C *repeats* straightning...
unpleasant, then   29. BD—M whether a   33. I measures
34. ABD—M to each mans C to catch mans   36. ABD—M then
had

26. 2. M ill ground   15. I But the contents   25. A—M
having left   29. BD—M envying the   35. I keeps

27. 13. B—M as to your   23—24. G—M discourse   37. C
omits (saie they)   39. KLM are given

28. 8. KLM *print* ease, the Nurse of Poetrie *in Italics*   17—18.
A—M have they   18. B—M prise   36. E forbid, that where

29. 3—4. BD—M but being   12. E were throughly   28. A—
M *omit* and attend

30. 1. E this   3—4. *Instead of* before...marriage, E *has* not
long since   15. HI that, as if   37. BD—H or worse   I—M
alike or worse

31. 35. C *Chlitophon*

32. 14. C affection   31. A had guilded

33. 24. C ane   36. A—M in the meane while

34. 13. HI *omit* the   22. KLM *omit* they   28. H—M power

35. 3. HI *insert* him *after* assured   12. BD celeration   19.
BD—M example   27. F—M it is

36. 5. KLM from whom   13. BD—M now to thinke   18. HI
to take   27. F—M it is

37. 1. I his succour   5. LM inroades   8. GH where

38. 34. G—M braver

39. 3. ABC incamping   14. G or the cause   22. A—M
made them   32. BDF—L his generall   37. HI *omit* to be

40. 13. BDF—I was captaine   25. M against the   33. F—M
omit ever   40. E raunsome

41. 2. E the Captaine   13. GH grates   20. AC gave
27. BD—M example   33. BDFGKL master

42. 1. AC gave HI giveth   15. FG left wind   26. HI
omit as M *prints* at

43. 2. KLM objections ABDF—M lightning   3. I beginne
10. LM *omit* that   16. D misdoubted   19. E forgot

44. 6. KLM valor   29. K *Palladians*

45. 5. L here is here   6. LM now begotten   7. F—M
who alreadie   8—9. HI his onely benefite   31. GHI all readie

46. 7. I & cure   14. A—M had they not   23. A—M *omit*
out   27. E Now I have

47. 3. BDF—L names of priviledges   4. A—M the *Spartane*
6. KLM *print* fellowes *and* servaunts *in Italics*   7—8. BD—M contention   10. KLM *print* forgetfulnes *in Italics*   16. HI *omit*
the   21. I *omits* that   24. DF—M then lose E thou to lose
28. KLM *omit* yet   29. C *omits* any   31. A—M setting
32. HI bad them

526

NOTES

48. *From p.* 48 *to p.* 49 *l.* 14 C *prints "Parthenea"*   **5.** F *Kalandet:* There   **10.** BD—M on his face   **13.** KLM the sight
13—14. F—I continuances   **24.** KLM *omit* then   **29.** GHI desire   **32.** M his company   **35.** G the saw   **39.** A—M that this

49. **4.** A—M *omit* in *after* came   **6.** KLM change   **7.** I telling him   **11.** A—M disfigured   **32.** C ane   **33.** C ane
38. F—M *no parenthesis before* first   F—M doing   FGHKLM *parenthesis before* doing   **40.** A—M am I bound

50. **1.** F—M much bound   **12.** I beene to love   **16.** C receive such disgrace, (said she)   **28.** A—F lonely   **30.** F—M sent to her a   **32.** A—M saw he had perfourmed   **39.** E dearest
40. G—M guest

51. **10.** A btahbādõed C btahbandonned *instead of* both abãdoned
11. KLM taking   **17.** BD *omit* to   **24.** A—I *Messena* KLM *Messina*

52. **8.** F—M returned   **9.** AELM *omit* the   **14.** A—M *omit* it *after* by   **24.** C other-waies   **35.** C the vaile

53. **2.** BC with in few D—M within few   **3.** A—M so much the   **9.** A—M also   **12.** AC and they by   **24.** FG desiring   **32.** G—M their marriage   **34.** DF—M decking
39. A—M though

54. **5.** C bare she was if the voward failed, yet that woulde conquer *Daiphantus* marking I bare she was, if   **6.** AC to *Jupiter* DFGHKLM saith he I quoth he   **33.** FGKLM whereof he

55. **4.** KL its self of its own M it self of its own   **20.** KLM leav off at her secreter   **23.** M come   **39.** BD—M points KLM without any

56. **7.** M love hath   **10.** M through I have ever though weakness   **27.** KLM thought   KLM *omit* in   **28.** I as thinke
29. C of the these

57. **24.** G deepe sight   **27.** HI *Pyrocles* his countenance KLM *Pyrocles*'s countenance   C attentation   **36.** HI burden
38. HI praise

58. **7.** F—M which had   **20.** L known   **27.** A—M either se many

59. **2.** I lifted   **10.** C spake   **20.** A—M left sealed in a letter   **31.** C journey ever   **35.** I your selfe

60. **12.** G graving   **19—20.** A—M trust to the   **24.** KLM advertisement   **38.** A—M at a bay

61. **2.** CKL into   **11.** C for that he met   **19.** A—M candles begin   **23.** I *Tyrocles*   **26—31.** KLM *print this letter in Italics*   **28.** I than you me   **29.** A—M in the respect
34. HI banished out of   **38.** BD—M thy selfe frõ me

62. **6.** DFG objectiõ   **26.** G for is charge   **27.** G—M would not other   **40.** D *Daipantus*

63. **16.** HI of her   **17.** DF—M *Phineus*   **19.** BD—M tongues   **20.** L enquire   **21.** HI she was   **23.** E uncertaine   **29.** F—M pulled   **38.** A—IL *Clitophon*

527

NOTES

64. 3. C unto me   4. A—DF—M and cause of doubte   E and cause of his doubt   20. CF—IL black-a-more boye   K black-a-Moor-boy   M Block-a-Moor Boy   24. C about a dosen   30. LM overpast   36. KLM in the

65. 1. E *omits* but   6. GHI his cŏflict   16. HI cãnot F accomplished   18. KLM into tears   37. LM *omit* selfe

66. 24. CE possessor of G—M possessed of   31. F—M estate   33. KLM heart

67. 25. BD—M besought for   29. F—M unto you   31. A—M monuments   34. ILM wert   37. M Then you must

68. 2. BDF—M their true   5. KLM *omit* a   8. KLM of an   KLM *parenthesis after* " Argos "   10. ·HI *parenthesis after* " Basilius "   FG *parenthesis after* " Timotheus "   11. F—I *no parenthesis before* betwene   12. CEKLM *parenthesis after* hospitality 18. B—M *no parenthesis after* " Timotheus "   21. C *omits* so 27. C to bespoken off   28. A—M conquests   36. LM stretcht 38. BD—M mine

69. 7. KLM *omit* a   16. KLM waited on   18. KLM this letter   KLM shall   20. KLM my   38. BD—M not yet   A—M to discover so much   40. KLM affections

70. 18. A will knew   20. LM *omit* I feare   33. KLM with thus

71. 1. ABCE injury   3. BD—I thine   7. BD—M withall so to   13. AC and unhappye   20. DF—M stage of   26. F meeding   38. ABCE *omit* the *before* thickest

72. 10. KLM caus, if at   37. LM of this

73. 36. B—M rose

74. 2. E he had   24. A—F monuments engraved G—M monuments engraven   25. A—M durably   30. AC louelinesse 34. A—M were possible   38. A—M a freshe searche

75. 1. A—M which resembling   6. A. flat-tryng   DF—I makes   6—7. KLM *print* that discreet...journies *in Italics*   20. C for paterne a   21. A—M the more   29. A—M part   BD—M *omit* so   34. DF—M wore   35. A—M under her   36. BD—M fastening on   39. LM an *Hercules*   40. A—M but set with a distaffe in his hand

76. 27. KLM *Since that*

77. 2. FGKLM which was   HI cause   28. D she are 33—34. KLM *print* to say...womanish *in Italics*   37—38. KLM *print* your behaviour...unto it *in Italics*   40. A—M imperfections A—M to soften

78. 3. KLM *print this line in Italics*   A—M either excellentlie 10. A—M all of them generallie   11. A—M *omit* right   12. *After* bastarde KLM *print* Love *in Italics*   13—14. KLM *print* engendred... idelness *in Italics*   18. G—M yeelding   23. E this much 31. A—F these kinde of loves G—M these kinds of loves   35. A—M womanize   36. B a distaffe spinner D a distaffe a spiner F—M a distaffe, a spinner

NOTES

79. 12. LM of his own   14. KLM had been   15. DF—M this I must   23. A—M *omit* to   28. FGKLM doe well   29. A—M disposition   34—35. KLM *print* Kite...Hauk *in Italics*   36. F—M who is so   39. A—M to them

80. 2—4. KLM *print* like's mee...dunghill *in Italics*   7. KLM it were excusable   11. A—FM your now handling G—L your now-handling   12. BD—M to confirme my former   15. E *omits* then   18. KLM content to   24. KLM manner and form   25. HI am a good   26. C witnesses KLM my own   28. E *omits* for   29. BD—M mine own   37. A—M a weake braine   38. A—M the best

81. 3. F made readie   11. C *omits* and   15. A—M that possesseth   16. C *omits* Lord   18. E me sharp-witted   21. E *omits* all   21—22. KLM *print* each...knowledges *in Italics*   27. E excellent, said *Musidorus*, I would   28. KLM *print* Enjoying *in Italics* A—M deepe sigh   31. G—M speake

82. 8. G *omits* in   18. HI not establisht   19. A—M impatient   20. A—M this last   21. AC soule for thinking BDF—M soule. For thinking E soule : For thinking   23. C hew of HI shewes of   26. A—DF—M the triumph   35. A—M *omit* a   A—M is there any   36. BD—M am a slave   A—M *omit* to (*last word in line*)

83. 2. A—M was unable   4—5. A—M *omit* as if...burthen   9. C if he had   10. KLM *omit* a   15. HI the more to melt   21. KLM upon the other HI well point out   36. A—M with the two   38. AC at his

84. 1. A—M are farre fitter   13. HI no nothing   18—19. KLM *print* between friends...tedious *in Italics*   23. C if I by chance   24. K Queen of *Amazons* LM Queen of *Amazon*   36. A—M whom so well

85. 16. BD—M *print* Architecture *in Roman type*   21. A—M those wishes   24. A—M part   27. A—M the sounde of   35. A—M call to   37. A—M *omit* needs

86. 3—4. KLM *print* a heart...lothsom *in Italics*   5—6. KLM *print* nothing...friend *in Italics*   7—8. KLM *print* less...will *in Italics*   14. F—M from my   16. A—L taken   18. A—M unmarked by any, to   BD—M escape   21. KLM *Philanax's* letter   33. A—M me to be found   34. DF—M mine own   39. AC cope

87. 3. EHI pantofle   9. F—M unto me   10. KLM not to name   13. KLM *omit* any   17. A—M as if he would have had a   37. E *omits* backe

88. 14—15. KLM *print* They are...thoughts *in Italics*   19. HI mine own   20. A—M pleasure   23. A—M *omit* a   25—26. KLM *print* open...themselves *in Italics*   28. KLM *print* generall goodness *in Italics*   29—30. KLM *print* everie one...themselves *in Italics*   40. A—M hath alreadie brought

89. 7. G—M *omit* it   16. A—M tast of that   E—M he had   17. H well tell   18. KLM should use   24. E forth his   25. BD—M *omit* all   30. C *omits* a   34. A—M *omit* a C *omits* of   38. I more sumptuous   39. A—M to shew how

529

NOTES

90. 1. BD—M rose up 2. A—M vale 3. HI have seene read 7. A—M the life of beauty 8. A—M the Queene of 13. A—M able to have caught 20. A—M miracle with her selfe 26. A—M more freely 31. I stepped 35. A—M Princesse 39. ABD—M princesses

91. 4. A—M much mistaken 6. A—M to whom 15. A—M so to do 16—17. KLM *print* great.. prais-worthie *in Italics* 31—32. A—M cleere, an other more 39. BD—M *print* Comet *in Roman type*

92. 8. A—M where, in a 10. A branches The C bran-ches : The EH—M branches, the 14. DFGKLM sensible 30. BD—M stole 36. A—M liddes

93. 14. LM being a familiar 16. A—M· private 38. AC showers

94. 2. A—M are even miserable 9. A—M such vehement suits 24. C unfortuate 27. A—M And therewith 34. L counsel*r* 38. KLM *print* a noble...case *in Italics* 39. E vexeth me so much

95. 4. B—M *comma at end of line* 13. HI close till that 15. F—M bewray him 16. G *omits* a

96. 6. DF—M not ceremonies 7. A—M before 15. KLM upon the roots of flourishing 17. HI *Pamelia* 23. E brought him HI a silly 26. A—M caused all 28—29. KLM *print* opinion...dangerous *in Italics* 30. E of a more 32. G—M conquest

97. 4. FHI *Philantus* 5. KLM the better 7. HI to that 11. E tents 15. HI *Philantus* 18. A—M report of his good justing 19. KLM *print* The fair man of arms *in Italics* 30. LM matter 33. A—M winning cherefulnes 39. G *Arthesia*

98. 3. KLM at their first 7. A—M leave upon 9. G *Arthesia* 10. BDF—M thinketh 14. BD—M worthinesses 19. A—M *omit* and A—M had taught 20. A—M both heaven 23. ABD—HKLM good a disciple she C good (a Disciple shee...her,) 39—40. A—G must say truly courteous HI must say truely, courteous KLM must say, truly courteous

99. 6—7. I *Philantus* 15. C nor affection 17. BD—M on the other 18—19. KLM *print* a foolish...think's *in Italics* 19. K witness LM foolish-witness 21. A—M of his profession BD—M services 27. CLM that hath 29. F—M praising 31. G out of her

100. 2. A—M he must 14. G *Arthesia's* 15. G *Arthesia* 16. KLM preheminencie 19. A—M pictures C Lades 20. G *Arthesia's* 27. KLM *omit* is

101. 11. G—M *omit* "*it*" *after* "*gave*" 13. F—M purple 19. I every place 19—20. KLM turn'd 28. G *Arthesia* 31. E assemblies

101. 35—**102.** 1. KLM *print* liking is...beauty *in Italics*

102. 1. KLM *print* whatsoëver...beautifull *in Italics* 4. G *Arthesia* 5. DF—M as a true 8. A—M her most delightfull 21. E *omits* a 22. E her part 30. A—M a made

NOTES

32. A—M idlenes, and with   33. A—M disswaded   34. A—M overrunne   39. A—M obeyed to that   40. A—M markte

103. 5. A—M possessioners   A—M nor absolute   11. A—M but intercurled   12. A—M pearle   13. A—M fast and loose   14. A—M richnes   17. A—M thē the conterſaiting   23. A—M in pleasure   24. HI not with admiration   34. HI have sate   36. HI Ensigne-bearer   37. A—M the humblenes   38. A—M beautie

104. 5. E *omits* a   13. HI eyes   16. F—M which he   17. A—M of that coupled   17—18. A—M their mouthes   20. E attentive unto it   38. G *Arthesia*

105. 2. F—M some other harts   7. G *Arthesias*   19. EILM gentlewoman   24. AC all ready

106. 4. I remedilesse   12. G *Arthesia's*   13. EM reckoned   16. G—M *Thelamon*   G—K *Polexena* LM *Pelexena*   AC *Eurileon* BD—M *Eurilion*   29. A—M pretie a grace   38. E it is not   40. LM matcht

107. 13. KLM their companion's   17. A—M beginning   26. F—M worthinesse   34. BDF—M was for a   36. BD—M scape

108. 13. K *Philantus*   22. HI could not   30. KLM *Ermelin*   37. HI who had   38. F—M the triall

109. 11. HI *omit* by   20. E sith   25. KLM ill apparelled   31. DF—M *omit* his   38. A—I two adversaries KLM but two adversaries   40. A—M himselfe came to   FG stickler

110. 9. A—M but even in   20. A abickering   23. F—M he sent him   35. A—M all the other heavenly

111. 3. F—M readily he   16. AC ill by apparelled   17. A—M cŏfort of   25. HI with some great   33. K keep him   39. HIM out of the Princes

112. 12. E *omits* or   22. A—M come, on which   24. KLM before   35. A—M sometimes cast up   36. HI strove

113. 1. A—M burthen   4. C *has no division into stanzas*   5. A—M [*and* England's Helicon]*change*   6. D *Nor he*   12. England's Helicon *plaints*   13. LM *is plaint*   19. M these Woods   24—25. LM *print* all is...experience *in Italics*   36. A—M in the Pulpit

114. 5. M compassion on me   6. HI pardoning of them   14. A—M secret flames   17. M light unto thee   20. HI so throughly   29. F—M sight of a   39. HI names had the   40. A—M of the Goddesse

115. 6. F—M of mind   7. F—M me such a thraldome   8. E I think, I had spoken   18. HI not to the   23. F—M *omit* again   25—26. KLM *print* Love...tyrant *in Italics*

116. 3. F—M everie evening   9. A—M persecutors   17. E his rayment   KLM *omit* the   31. DF—M *omit* thus   32. F—K *note of interrogation instead of semicolon after* Shepheard   34—36. KLM *print* highest...miserable *in Italics*

117. 3—4. KLM *print* the most...capacitie *in Italics*   5. F—M greater   6. A—M wit to discerne   9—10. G—M *omit* and his

531

NOTES

senses...reward him   17—18. KLM *print* though...honorable *in Italics*
30. A—M   well provided

118. 5. F—M   his tale   6. LM   brother to the   18. A—M
manners   19. E   maner   22. A—M   that sued to be   29. KLM
omit so

119. 8. BD--M   *print* Theatre *in Roman type*   A—M   *omit* a
after such   E   sorts   12. A—M   *omit* tree to tree   13. A—M
insert tree to tree *after* from   17. A—M   inquiring diverse questions
20. E   sport for the   27. E   sith   39. LM   like a

120. 3—4. A—M   composition   7. DF—M   *omit* upon
17. A—M   was presented to   18. E   *omits* the *before* twise
34. A—M   she neither   37. DF—M   *omit* to   39. A—D
presenting

121. 1. A—M   his   12. DF—M   grace and pity   19. BD—M
Chirurgerie   21. A—M   ever with the contempt of cowardes
24. A—M   *omit* great   28. E   was returning   33. A—M   her witt

122. 4. A—M   *bloodie strife*   7. A—M   *eie*   15. HI   meanes
18. BD—M   a horrible fowle   22. LM   *omit* I   25. BD--M
on my   26. A—M   this yong shepheard with a wonderfull courage having
29. A—M   already neare   35. E   *omits* up   37. G—M   blessing

123. 1. KL   not *instead of* nor   8. A—M   easily discipher
20. A—M   head and breast   23. HI   on himselfe   ILM   fully
25. A—M   great while   33. A—DF—M   *omit* us   35. KLM
not *instead of* nor   40. A—M   construction

124. 4. A—M   the very face   12. A—M   given him a   20. M
others   26. HI   meanes   37. HI   first was curious   40. BD—M
desired   A—M   the Pastorals

125. 7. KLM   *omit* of   11. G—M   beast   16. E   cause then
18. F—M   those words   20. A—M   mistrusting greatly *Cecropia*

126. 1. G—M   Eclogue   4—6. A—M   And because many of the
shepheardes were but newlie come, hee did in a gentle manner chastise their
negligence with making   7—8. A—M   *omit* later come   16. KLM
according   18. KLM   *omit* chiefe   20. M   bawl   22—23. A
answere. as the one halfe saying. C   answer: as the one halfe saying.
D   answere as the one halfe; saying: BEFG   answer as the one halfe,
saying: HI   answere: as the one halfe, saying: KLM   answer at the
one half, saying;   24. England's Helicon *has* " We love, etc." *but
omits ll.* 25, 27, 29, 31, 33   25. HI   other   29. A—M   in a quire
30. G   *despaire full*   34. H   *And in who*

127. 1. F—M   Then joyning all their   England's Helicon *omits
ll.* 1 *and* 2   5. F—M   song   7. A—M   *have* " Thyrsis" *instead
of* " Lalus "   10. A—M   troubled mind   13. A—M   Thyrsis and
Dorus   14. A—M   Thyrsis   24. G   *most, deep deep silent*
H   *most deep deep silent*   25. D—M   *true-love*   BE   *comma
after* "true love loves"   DF—M   *put a comma after* "true-love" *and omit*
"loves"   A—M   *have* "his" *instead of* "those"   G—M   *his love
with others*   26. A—M   Thyrsis

128. 4. A—M   Thyrsis   5. A—E   *omit* " is "   7. KLM
sweet   18. FG   *tittle*   25. E   *worlds*   BD—M   *shall yeeld*
26. FGK   *decke your* LM   *deck you*   BDE   *wish your comparison*
28. A—M   Thyrsis

129. 5. FGI—M *from the* 6. HI *love with lovers hurt is*
11. A—I *hope fayling* BD—M *lifes pleasure* 13. A—M
Thyrsis 16. M *if so mean* 18. M *seeds* 22. A—M
she did beare

130. 6. E *charmes* ·7. A—M *case* KLM *Muse my, my*
sorrow 9. BD—M *one point* 11. A—M *can foile* 15. A—M
thrall 16. A—M *Thyrsis* 27. L *we well the* 31—32. DE
have no space between l. 31 and l. 32 32. E *omits* Dorus
34. DFGKLM *Here plaints*

131. 1. G—M *lamenting* 2. C *wares* 6. KLM *dolor*
10. A—M *Thyrsis* A—M *thus my* 12. A—M *which too*
much sawe. 13. *Instead of this line* A—I *have the following:*

      If shee still hate loves lawe,

KLM :

      If shee did hate love's law,

14. CF—M *earthly* A—M *doth melt* 15. CF—M *earthly*
17. KLM *heart fire* 19. A—M *Thus doth* 20. A—M *Thyrsis*
A—M *Thus doth* 21—22. *Instead of these lines* A—M *have the*
following:

      That I growe like the beaste,
      Which beares the bytt a weaker force doth guide,

23. *Instead of this line* A—I *have the following:*

      Yet patient must abide.

KLM :

      Yet patience must abide.

24—26. *Instead of these lines* A—M *have the following:*

      Such weight it hath which once is full possest.
   Dorus. *Such weight it hath which once is full possest*
      That I become a vision.

27. *Instead of this line* A—I *have the following:*

      Which hath in others head his only being

KLM :

      Which hath in others held his only being,

28. *Instead of this line* A—M *have the following:*

      And lives in fancie seing.

29. *Instead of this line* A—I *have the following:*

      O wretched state of man in selfe division!

KL :

      O wretched state of man in self-divisions!

30—32. *Instead of these lines* A—M *have the following:*

   Thyrsis. *O wretched state of man in selfe division*
      O well thou saiest! a feeling declaration
      Thy toong hath made of Cupids *deepe incision.*

33. A—M *But now hoarse voyce, doth* 35. A—M *singing thou hast*
got the

132. 1. A—M *singing thou hast got the* 2. A—M *have* " *Good*
Thyrsis mine," instead of " *New friend of mine ;"* 3. A—FH—M

My hart doth G *My hearth doth*   4.   A—M *hadst facilitie*   5.   E *thy goddesse*   8—9. This Eclogue...commendations. *This sentence is not in the folio editions*   10—19.   *Cf.* Appendix *p.* 565 *ll.* 4, 32, 37

132.   19—140.   30. *this songe...vaine annoy. In all the folio editions this passage is to be found in the third Eclogues*

132.   20.   A—M   had ever subjected   23.   A—D *the couthe* 33.   G—M *eye*   D *chipping notes*

133.   9.   LM *shepherds*   14.   E—M *our wits*   21—22.   E *has no space between l. 21 and l. 22*   24.   E—M *because I loved* 27.   F—M *recounted be*   29.   LM *omit* "*was*"   35.   DE *into hem*

134.   2.   I *where n' order is*   6.   BDE *beast*   28.   LM *with you love*   30.   LM *cloathed*   33.   I *song*

135.   4.   HI *her eyes faire*   30.   M *omits* "*not*"

136.   7.   C *omits* "*he*"   8.   E—M *murther*   13.   M *common* 20.   E—M *may*   21.   C *When fall on they*   23.   HKLM *be us'd* 30.   A—M *glorie*   M *swelly in*   35.   C *you strengths*

137.   1.   E—M *will I sing*   4.   FG *domewards*   11.   L *what shee*   17.   C *omits* be   17—19.   KLM *print* this is...them-selvs *in Italics*   20.   KLM *melancholy*   32.   D *pray you*

138.   20.   C *Pulling* KLM *Puling*   G—M *have* "*or*" *instead of* "*and*"   19.   *Cf.* Appendix *p.* 565 *l.* 48   21.   D *cars*

139.   4.   KLM *their servants*   9.   D *live alone*   11.   F—M *this life*   13.   L *good good haps*   25.   FGKLM *The father* 28.   HI *The common-wealth*   39.   F—M *fault*

140.   5.   HI *content*   7.   E—M *these are your*   11.   D *wonders*   31.   *Cf.* Appendix *p.* 565 *l.* 29   32—33. easilie...his person. *In all the folio editions this sentence occurs in the third Eclogues*

140.   33—141.   2.   But *Basilius* to...performed in.   *This passage is not in the folio editions, but cf.* Appendix *p.* 564 *l.* 30

141.   2—143.   9.   this doble Sestine...*song at evening. In all the folio editions this passage is to be found in the second Eclogues*

141.   8.   A—M *give*   20.   M *affliction*

142.   19.   BD—I *all those*   29.   A—M *I hate my selfe* 30.   KLM *my ears*   31.   HI *maintaine*

143.   3.   C *whose reproche*   4.   KLM *mourning*   8.   A—M *transfer* Klaius *to l.* 9   10—13. *Zelmane* seing...*Philoclea* eares. *Cf.* Appendix *p.* 566 *l.* 1   13—14. laying fast...Hope. *Cf.* Appendix *p.* 563 *l.* 23   24.   G—M *becomes*   KLM *monument*   HI *our praise*   28.   DF—M *but as death*   31.   LM *humane lives*

144.   5.   G—M *omit* "*doo*"   6.   BD—M *doth hap.*   7.   KLM *deceived*   9—14. What exclaiming...unto it.   *Cf.* Appendix *p.* 564 *l.* 1   14—16. Yea, he fel...body. *Cf.* Appendix *p.* 566 *l.* 7   16—18. But the...time waste. *Cf.* Appendix *p.* 564 *l.* 16   18—20. and therefore...one side. *This sentence does not occur in the folio editions*   20—23. and considering...death. *Cf.* Appendix *p.* 564 *ll.* 17, 22

145.   8.   F—M *pastorall times*   10.   F—M *of the*   13.   A—M *angry*   18.   LM *whose deserts*   22.   ABCE—M *terrors*   24.   I *his vice*   29.   A—M *to be witnesse*

NOTES

146. 5. A—M *omit* or   7. C *and on essentiall*   8. KLM *have* now *instead of* most   21. KLM *omit* were   27. K *omits* it *before* is *at end of line*   31. KLM desire   A—M *no inverted commas in margin*   31—32. KLM *print* in shame there...of shame *in Italics*   37. A—M *no inverted commas in margin*   LM *print* a lamentable...mind *in Italics*   38. E drew thitherwards, in hope 39. A—M paced

147. 7. C *has no division into stanzas*   G *your labour* 9. BDF—M *you did so send*   12. KL sights   27. C much thou art   28. H—M thou wast   32. I *omits* like. 34—36. A—M *omit* and the more I...hoping.

148. 3. A—M spoke   E *omits* a   8. LM to miserie 11. A—M morning early of   13. F—M looked   25. I *has* my *instead of* me

149. 8. C his complaining   10. C *has no division into stanzas* 11. KLM *transpose* "soule" *and* "shape"   17. A—M *doo homage unto*   27. A—M gotten some leasure   28. M he did her 35. A—M able to discerne

150. 3. F most lonely   12. D intents   29. LM *omit* up 35. HI minde, as will with the humblest   36. HI *omit* to *before* receive   37. HI speake of any

151. 9. G—M want of what   10. I my behalfe   34. H—M Tired therewith

152. 2. H—M Flannell   6. A—M and how with the same 8. A—M *Dametas* holding   KLM hands   12. A—M unfeatie   25. LM languishing   26. BD—M *omit* us   BD—M yet I am   38. DF—M in her owne

153. 2. M power   7. C desire

154. 2. A—M voyd of counsell   6. A—M that it could 15. A—M grudge not at their   C bodes   16. C enjoyning 18. HI I have   22. E burdens   24—25. LM *print* nothing is...attempted *in Italics*   25—26. LM *print* Lying still...forward *in Italics*   28. BD—M one after another

155. 1. I eyes   9. KLM to *Mopsa*   12. A—M Princesse the better   14. BDFG baggage not to winne   23. LM *omit* in 25. C *has no division into stanzas*   34. D *worthies*   37. BD—M mine eye

156. 1. A—M setling   3. A—M fortune must be the measure 19. A—M *omit* of   20. L as in his soul devoted M as in his Soul is devoted   22. KLM hands   25. A—M wrieng her waste 31. L *omits* in *before* Fortune   40. FG vertues shines KLM virtues shine

157. 6. D mortall would   20. KL most confess   24. H—M Lover   26. C tender   27. E *omits* a   30. BD—M produced thus   33. M she should   40. M my eye

158. 4. G—M engraven   15. KLM and that my   20. C judgement   28. F—M inclosed   30—31. KLM *print* that as well...onset *in Italics*

159. 2. I discern my desires   F—M *omit* I   3. F—M honourable Ladie   4. F—M doted you   8. B—M *omit commas*

535

NOTES

in margin 19. I matters of HI tragedie 26. I lost duties 27. E *omits his before* friends

160. 7. A—M occasions 11. HI widdowhood LM widowed 15. DFH—M much must I say G much I say 16. E make me 33. HI *omit* a 34. D say was

161. 7. A—I *omit* his KLM *Musidorus's* infortunes HI misfortunes 8. A—M infirmities 10. F—M *omit* the 15. F—M beautie had 26. BDF—M cause 27. BDF—I at last EKLM at least

162. 2. A—M are too monstrous 5. HI his tale 11. BD—M mine owne 21. A—M your being here 24. A—M either 28. HI *omit* as 37. E *omits* his mariage

163. 5. A—M was thus to 18. E *omits* (said he) 27. A—M their Prince 30. I Historiographers 31. I Astrologe 34. KLM *insert* is *before* to shew 38. E *has:*

On barren sweetes they feeding sterve:

164. 2. England's Helicon *desires* 9. A—M her noble hart 20. I speake 23. KLM *Menalcas's* brother 23—24. C brother; & here I know 28. A—M *omit* highe

165. 13. G—M just as we 28. A—M will spurre 35. A—M *omit* a

166. 9. G—M *omit* his LM *omit* in 13. KLM of a rebound 34. A—M though but in

167. 1. A—M imbracing 11. HI of himselfe

167. 40—**168.** 1. F—M flie out quite another

168. 11. A—M wine-press 15. H *prints* part *in Italics* 16. HILM burden 32. F—M she to lie

169. 9. LM the sweet 14. A—M whose tender 16. C force chosing 17. F—M to a point 24. DE lovely place 28. D we made LM of a most

170. 1. F—M her selfe to that 8. E—M *omit* by 29. KLM ere she was A—M the badge 35. BD—M hath an

171. 12. E—M Waking did 24. A—M descended 33. BD—M lockes

172. 7. A—M banished 17. ILM *omit* as 20. C *has no division into stanzas*

173. 16. LM she had present 17. DF—M retraction 19. C *has no division into stanzas* BD—M *a* stedfast 21. KLM *defile my fancies* FHI *no comma after "defaste"* 22. A—M shames

174. 16. M extremity 17. H hath oppressed

175. 7. F—M most excellent 19. A—M she ravingly have

176. 8. A—M sorow 13. M Law of the 24. LM and their 35. KLM whether did you 36. M Pastorals sports

177. 11. A—M pretend 16—17. A—M constancy 28. C *omits* so 33. KLM whatéver hee

178. 12. I *omits* but 13. BD—M slow of beliefe 36. A—M dancer 40. F—M *omit* is

536

NOTES

179. 8. A—M change did   34. E all but one   39. A—M fine cleenes

180. 4. LM strength of mine   5. A—M confesse, that as

181. 1. E shall   8. C shill shine   11. A—M and too late   16—17. A—M you, the onely honour   22. A—M so ever he be   30. I *omits* since   38. KLM delivered how

182. 20. E my sister   34. F—M their walking

183. 3. A—M *omit* But   4. A encreased, But cãe C encreased But came (*There is a dot after* encreased *which looks like a broken comma*) BDF—M increased, but came   6. C condition 8—9. A—FI time a day GHKLM time aday   13. DF—M of the agony

184. 4. ABD—M for victories C as victories   38. A—ILM latter

185. 7. E not want   21. M now I wear   24. A—M to the age

186. 1. E—M taxation   3. G—M place of the   4. A—M as the abiding   10. E—M they shining   14. I were faultfinding F—M & so given to   17. E—M *omit* a   40. A—M *insert* and his lawes *before* as it were   A—M his axioms

187. 10. A—M *omit* can   E—M *omit* if   20. A—M delight in their   26. AC by an accasion BD—I by an occasion KLM by occasion   32. A—M was come   34. A—M betweene their

188. 5. KLM folks   33. I *omits* his   39. E—M requiring A—M of life

189. 9. A—M time so set   KLM *omit* of   14. A—M of *Musidorus*   23. D cruell heart   F—M ill   31. D uttermost heart

190. 11. KLM an habit   15. A—M nothing I so much 38. I yeares of war

191. 10. LM bound in his   12. A—M till now being both sent for by *Euarchus*, & finding *Pyrocles* able

192. 28. M others   30. LM where the

193. 2. KLM thunder   5. A—M floting kingdomes   6. L natural   7. A—M the desolation   A—HKLM far-being I far being   10. F—M *omit* a   12. A—M striken   16. I accused   D on point   19. A—M *omit* not   24. H—M daies cleerenesse   EM so blindly

194. 1. A—M roaring voices   3. KLM passion   6. I for his   9. KLM in the huge   17. KLM *Musidorus*'s infancie 25. G—M of a great   32. A—M they mente to

195. 9. A—M Navie they lately had, they had left but one little peece 5. A—M exceeding   33. F—M on him, and

196. 14. BDE *print* Phrigia *in Roman type*   16. LM wicked say, ever   36. BDE *print* Thessalia *in Roman type*   37. A—K unsuccesse LM success

197. 3. A—M no humour   3—4. LM *print* there is no...serviceable *in Italics*   4. M whom impudent   5. A—M those of desparate

ambition   7. F—M as a servitude   11. KLM stirred up a
16. E—M their faces   21. L determining   27. A—M he
thought   A—M take him away   A—M from being   28. F—M
things prepared   34. I destroyed vertue   39. BD *print* Pontus
in Roman type   E—M *have "Bithynia" instead of "Pontus"*

198. 8. A—M he ever profest   18. F—M the Tyrant
21. A—M the worke   28. I that notable   30. E—M of the
conquerour   31. A—M welcome praie   31—32. A—M *omit*
that wisht...worste of all :

199. 1. KLM causeth   25. HIM murder   32. D this
case   34. KLM *Pamela* smiling

200. 1. A—M making it a   KLM *omit* in   3. KLM they
slew   34. M Art or some   35. F—M by some chaunce
37. E—M with a loud

201. 5. A—M wiser   11. G—M grow to a   22—23. I
to deliver them   27. BD—M fostered up in

202. 1. I hand   5. I for of good   6. KLM incline
14. I the magnificence   17. A—M and *instead of* or   18. I
avenge   24. KLM bearing up   E—M land of *Bithinia*
27. G—M of the countrey   28—29. A—M revengefulnes
30. A—M inconstant in his

203. 9. M burden   25. A—M *insert* death of the *after* late
BD—H *print* Phrigia *in Roman type*   38. A—M bubble blowne up

204. 1. A—M foresaw their   12. ABCE—M enclining
17. A—KM to their dead carcasses L to their death carcasses   22. KL
mariage to to the   33. M on the top

205. 6. E—M worthy   21. A—M pleased   33. A—M
hands : and so they were

206. 1. E—M *omit* ever   A—M make one occasion   5. G—M
valour

207. 4. A—M which a certaine   A—M *omit* it   14. A—M
there *instead of* these   17. E—M griefe, and my

208. 11. HI have had mee   14. KLM ingrafted   23. C
yeares *instead of* eares   30. A—M prove some ominous   36. A—M
such a one   39. I no farther   40. F *omits* a *before* bastarde

209. 3. A—M or to doo   5. ABD be used E—M she
used   9. A—M remembraunce, of naughtinesse delightes   10. A—M
his trappes   27. EFGKLM my sea   29. KLM *omit* my
34. KLM murtherers   38. A—M felt a pitty   39. A—M
unslaine duety

210. 6. F—M reckoning   7. A—M of doing himselfe
11. A—M well deserving   25. HI filiall pitie   28. BD—M
agonie   29. BD—M so you shal   32. CKLM to take
38. CF—KM his brother

211. 2. CF—M but of two   7. A—M assayled   29. BD—M
it in others   31. A—M *omit* their   32. G—M valour

212. 18. G—M once united by   28. E—I this access of
KLM his access of   29. HI bale no longer   A—M vitall spirites
32. F—M *omit* for   35. A—M *omit* men

NOTES

213. 1´. A—M turningnes   A of of sleights   C off of sleightes
3. M grow of good   7. M denyal will but   8. M make the
the fault   10. D alive into hands   26. M Minister   28. A—M
had more come   30. KLM *omit* his   32. L *Plexirtos*   34. C
leave   35. G—M enjoy some benefite

214. 1. BD—I *print* Lycia *and* Armenia *in Roman type*   4. BD—I
print Armenia *in Roman type*   10. E—HKLM *Euardus* I *Evardus*
12. A—M *omit* two   13. M commendation   14. A—M *omit*
yong   16. BD—I *print* Lycia *in Roman type*

215. 6. E—M I kneeled   7. A—D hardy earnestnes   E—M
my graces   E—M said I   16. M power   22. M farther
30. E—M as I   31. E—M my selfe

216. 4. G—M stole   11. KLM and speaking   12. M
River side   13. M in Greece   M the praise   22. A—M
still would slippe   31. D thought it was   32. A as on bodie
C as no one bodie

217. 8. C *omits* it   25. M of a shrugging.   27. C *omits* so

218. 3. C make warres   8. E—K plaid then   12. KLM
omit he   16. C countenance   30. M whereunto   32. E—M
perfection   33. M *tongues may*

219. 2. KLM *angels*   5. HIM *two heavenly*   30. M *to
kiss*

220. 6. D *wantons nests*   16. F—M *Indians*   25. D *doth
untie*   29. BD—L *their glad* M *there glad*   37—38. E—M
omit commas in margin   40. A—M *Hir thighes*

221. 2. E—M *her stately*   3. G—M *cliffes*   28. A—M
hate-spott   F—M *Emerlin*   38. *Warn Snow*

222. 12. E—M *dwell therein*   17. HI *perfection*   27. KLM
rayment   29. M *of instead of* upon   30. M bearing it away
G—M But when *Zelmane*   36. F—M in her selfe shee had

223. 6. KLM of themselvs   12. E—M sith   13. M my
self to part   22. C his two   24 E—M sith   29. G—M
bastinado   33. KL bearing [*catchword, instead of* harkening] M hearing
[*catchword*]   36. D kill courtesie

224. 26. M *omits* yet   29. BD—M *print* Macedon *in Roman type*

225. 1. I *prints* Arcadian *in Roman type*   11. E solitarie paces
16. D left the smart   28. M hate to *Zelmane*

226. 16. BD—M *omit* the   20. M *omits* and   26. D *omits*
had   27. KLM he was forced   31. D at the first   34. F
omits if

227. 2. F—M *omit* "*long*"   11. CDF—M spirites   16. C
life is helpe   21. F—M *Which cries*   32. HI *judgements*
35. F—M *mournefull*

228. 12. M *then dip so*   17. A—M *have* :
        (*Though in despaire*) *for Love so forceth me;*

18. A—L *shall* Erona M *shall* Erona's   25. KLM *dost move*
26. A—M *causefull*   35. KLM *omit* "*that*"   36. A—M
beate us on to blisse

NOTES

229. 2. A—M *Of windes* 7. BD *enflame* 14. HI *the spoyles* 17. C *What mynd* 21. LM *heavens* 32. A—M *flames* 36. E—M *omit commas in margin* 37. M *his face* 39. HI *onely lace*

230. 1. LM *touch* A—M *we did* 2. A—M *that hand* M *spent* 6. M *be spent* 12. D *must prone* 20. A—M *these childish* 23. C *lamentation* 31. BD—M *knew* 32. A—M *From any joy* 33. KLM *In mortall* 35. M *Which swelling* 36. M *help* 37. B—M *painfulnesse* 39. A—M *this ougly*

231. 15. A—M *outward* A—M *that most* 30. M *farther* 32. A—M *this Dialogue*

232. 2. M *omits* a 3. A—M *omit* unto him *after* fully 17. A—M *Lydia* 21. A—M *Lydia* 23. M *omits* that 24. G—M *it could be no* 26. M *all them statues* 28. ACF—M *Lydians* BDE *Lydians* 35. C *omits* of *after* king BD—I *print* Armenia *in Roman type*

233. 3. KLM *by perswasions* KLM *by threatnings* 9. A—M *omit* by *before* knife 14. M *to to the holy* 19. F—M *no man* CKLM *nor child* 35. M *praise her self* 36. C *tow* 39. BD—I *print* Lycians *in Roman type*

234. 3. M *on both* 6. I *Evardes* M *Euardus* 22. E—M *were of farre greater* 23. M *Pyracles* H *Evardes* M *Euardus* 24. BD—I *print* Bithinia *and* Hircania *in Roman type* 28. M *Pyracles* H *Evardes* 29. M *these Princes*

235. 1. M *omits* as 5. A—M *her to preserve* 6. CG—K *united* 14. A—M *shalbe still gnawing* 23. M *omits* in 25. A—M *partie*

236. 3. A—M *fruits of denying* A—M *omit* As 6. M *Amphilus's* F—L *further* M *farther* 8. KLM *for his death* 11. A—M *conditions* 15. KLM *omit* yet to 17. LM *know* 19. M *constancy* 24. E—M *or weapon* HI *or by* 30. M *lamentation* 31. LM *unto the world* 32. F—M *by all meanes* 35. M *reward* 38. LM *omit* all

237. 8. C *your years*

238. 3. A—M *full in your* A—M *tattlings* 6. KLM *omit* it *after* have 9. F—M *omit* a *before* seven 13. M *in my neck* 17. HI *old instead of* wold 18. HI *old instead of* wold 19. M *omits* as 34. C *a long lace* M *omits* of *before* a man 37. M *skirked*

239. 2. HI *of faire* 3. BD—M *parenthesis after* priest, *not before* GKLM *put the concluding parenthesis after* had EF *no concluding parenthesis* 5. D *we said* BD—M *ballads* 19. M *deceit* 21. AC *blinde young, with* BD—G *blind, young with* HIKLM *blind, young, with* 26. M *arrows too* 35. M *of such* 37. M *did breed* 38. *Instead of this line* A—M *have the following:*

To lye, to steale, to pry, and to accuse,

540

240. 2. A—M *feete*   11. F—M *omit "stil"*   H   *be deckt*
I *bedeckt*   17. *Instead of this line* A—L *have the following:*

     But for that Love is worst which rules the eyes,

M *has:*

     But for that Love is worst that rules the eyes,

18. A—M *Thereon*   19. M *rivel'd* Cupid   25. A—M The
Ladies   28. M should   30. M with the beautifying her   35. D
would be

241. 4. C prehemencie   8. BDEFH—L that did ever M
omits did   12. M *omits* of   19. KL *print* And so...rejoice *in
Roman type* M *prints* in May...rejoyce *in Roman type*   HIM they
stole   25. F—M blessing, never to aske him   31. KLM *such
instead of* as   32. M Skrich-owl   40. M to the second

242. 4. F—M of that bargaine   8. M the *instead of* this
26. BD his King   30. KLM beeing at first married

243. 3. KLM *omit* in *before* himselfe   E—M *omit* a *after* and
14. A—M onely outside   16. M the point   27. M one to
the other   34. E—M make them   38. M Father into a

244. 3. A—M attempt   11. M *omits* a *before* less   M
omits of before three   12. M behaved himself   16. M *omits* all
24. A—M so greedily   25. *After* mourning A—M *insert* garments
32. M fall to dispair   38. BD—GKLM *omit* I *before* repeat

245. 7. A thinking on other B—M thinking on no other   8.
BD—M at first   E—M measures   12. M victorious over
the   17. EFGKLM besides was HI besides that she was   25. A
harm form   31. F—M *print* Sycophants *in Italics*

246. 12. I putting off objection   15. F—M many like
16—17. KLM *print* Ambition...lingring *in Italics*   17—18. KLM
print ever urgeth...successes *in Italics*

247. 12. BD—M affection   24. A—M made hideous
27. A—M hill where upon his   36. HI strove, strove to be M
starve, starve to be   37. GHKLM bolled I boeled

248. 6. C who though they   14. M *omits* he   18. BD—M
brought thus to   19. F—M the same   27. LM *omit* him *after*
give   29. M farther   34. M bring him to a   35. BD she
should

249. 5. HI out of every   7. BD husbands mother   11. E—M
to put to her   17. A—M with a sword   20. F—M naked, yet
standing   40. HI engraven

250. 3. A—M did even   5. F—M in his Court   10: HI
tortures   14. F—M *omit* it   18. G—M hatred on   31. M
his Sons councel   35. A—M whose cause   36. F—M *omit* that
M *omits* it

251. 4. M in valor   20. I sometimes use   23. M is
sacrificed

252. 1. AC were not only   6. KLM of the divels   15. F
the could be   17. G—M sleep in their   20. M comforts
21. M *omits* up   23. DM chasted   26. G—M changling?
happy, be they   KLM that bee not   27. M *omits* thy   D to

this respect   28. HI a great part   31. M comly argument
32. KLM the head   D with so wicked   E—M only desire

253. 3. A kept form   5. C *omits* more *before* his   9. KLM
mishap   10. B—M blesse   15. DM too ill matched   19. LM
over to the   20. HI of good old   31. LM is the work
37. F—M from beyond   F—M trees   38. I she hand fully

254. 5. HI (said she)   20. HI asswaging   21. I my
heart   24. G—M bent to   27. KLM no *instead of* to *after* yield
29. BD he should

255. 11. D words with Desire   15. BD over-burthened
23. I to disdain   24. I name of Father   33. M farther   36. M
import

256. 8. F—M *omit* so   30. E—L streame

257. 2. M duty   9. C *has no division into stanzas*   M *wine*
eyes   11. M *face even wherein*   15. KLM *thought*   16. E—M
breath   17. F—M *sound of this*   18. C he doth   20. A—M
griefe   28. M feet   30. A—M whose delight   32. M
omits a   F—M lighting   E—M *omit* of *before* beauty

258. 20. F—I consisted   27. A—M passe by the   KLM
respect   32. KLM hath com   36. M *omits* all

259. 11. A—M me into a   27. BD let it be   E—M let it not
be   33. M decree   37. C how he should

260. 7. BD surfet joy   28. F—M should I doe

261. 2. E—M to be loved   10. H *Evarchus*   M had
almost   15—18. E—M mouthes did, they passed the promise of mariage:
which faine *Pyrocles* would have sealed with the chiefe armes of his desire; but
Philoclea commanded the contrary.   33. BD—M my eares   M so
sweetly be fed   38. M farther

262. 5. A—M that entertainement   9. A—M might   13. E—M
sith   14. A—M give it the hearing   22. F hold his   23. KLM
omit so   25. G pottomelesse

263. 6. A—M deeds   8. BD—M *print* Giants *in Roman type*
13. BDE. chosen *Tiridates*   22. A—M challenge unto me
27. KLM *omit* had   28. D had *instead of* hath   29. E—M
borne universally the   34. M and would needs go alone   38. D
then any thing in   39. G—M what ever before   K I had do
40. G what ever theres, or

264. 3. ILM such a mist   K a such mist   5. A—M heaven
G—M requite to him   8. GKLM stayed   10. HI strove
16. LM I after knew   19. G sore feeling   22. A—M advĕture,
which (though   33. DLM making my   E—M eares
39—40. BD—M *transpose* they *and* continually

265. 10. G—M to get away   20. A—M ran all away   29. D
she should   A—M the sharpe remembrance   34—35. C Gentlemen

266. 3. M *omits* is   8. HI words full of   9. KLM such
an one   11. A—M the delight   A to thers   13. KLM such
an one   23. KLM gave way   30. HIM what he had   31. KLM
was the Prince   35. LM we would not   37. C *transposes* use *and* his

NOTES

267. 6. ABD—H in end   9. AC by her owne   20. M *omits* a *before* triumph   21. KLM to him   25. HI greatest occasion   34. A—M joyne in fellowshipp

268. 18. M whatsoever   23. BD lowlinesse   27. I *omits* in *before* my selfe   37. ABC villanie

269. 3. M with that trifling   17. I injures   29. A—E in ende   33. M till he were

270. 15. B rad upon me   17. A—M *omit* but   22. F—M astonied   29. A—M *omit* it   30. E—M say true   32. E—M *omit* to

271. 3. M beholden to   5. LM the *instead of* that   12. M sight to me   22. A in in mine   33. HI railed   36. I *omits* as

272. 3. M as it were   11. M *transposes* with *and* only 13—14. KLM *print* amongst...unpunished *in Italics*

273. 16. A—M *omit* a   19. D *omits* of   23. A—M mischances   28. M she had deserved   32. A—GKLM should finde want HI should finde wants

274. 2. M had so lately   3. A—M *omit* rather   4. F—M *omit* a   12. A—M for what I had   23. A—M talke of nothing 30. HI grieved   33. F—M with that he had

275. 5. BD—M *omit* tyed   10. EFGKL of a   11. M her hand   18. KLM to the Captain   A—M Garrison neere by   FG which thought   24. ABD—HK *omit* in   27—28. KLM *print* a churle's courtesie...falshood *in Italics*   28. A—L rarely M seldome   29. F—M maners   32. C *omits* I   36. A—M And so we

276. 6. M *omits* I had   9. A—M *omit commas in margin* G—M guiltines   11. E—M *omit* yet   17. A—M he found 23. M to farther   27. BD—M *transposes* before *and* I   39. A—M of the worthy

277. 17. A—M alas poore

278. 1. I for *Anaxius*   2. A learne thing   A gone no out   4. I with the   11. A—M raines of affection   18. M to march   19. M *transposes* neither *and* guided   35—36. A—M *omit inverted commas in margin*

279. 2. A—M with his reproch   4. M decree   6. M as abused   12. M to stay   16. E—M her, as now   17. A—M yet a while she   M *omits* so   18. A—D tempted   22. A—M *omit* that   KLM not to be   28. E—M but *instead of* how   M wandring   33. A—M one request   38. A—M because *instead of* that

280. 6. E—M state   7. A—M we had had   C *parenthesis before* in   E—M *omit parenthesis after* " Galatia "   11. A—M our armes   17. M *omits* a   18. C restraint to so   23. BD—M in a captivity   25. A—M *insert* had *before* saved   29. M would express   35. M him to send   38. A—M pleasures were directed to the

NOTES

281. 8. AC hath a spot   13. E—M his Queene   18. A—M most noble *Plangus*   22. E—M *omit* not   40. M their being

282. 1. M farther   5. I alas more the   10. HI follow this   15. KLM *print* what *in Italics*   16. KLM *print* why *in Italics*   25. KLM *omit* fit *before* time

283. 1. A—M did *instead of* indeede   A—M proclaime   2. A—M that people   7. A—M *omit* and   21. H drawne: could shee I drawne, could shee   24. A—M countries about her were   26. G—M the threatned   34. A—M *omit* by   38. C *transposes* I *and* have

284. 11. LM as that time   19. KLM servant   20. LM *Andronama*   24. M farther   A—M sonne, nor ever to   27. F—M insert an *before* eye   LM Wee are   31. LM run a Tilt   32. KLM stranger

285. 3. C neere the moone   7. FG wood   9. F—M of that time   10. HI Ladies departure   A—M among whom   12—13. M *PHILISIDIS*   19. HI *omit* so   22. A—DF—ILM a crosse   26. KLM *transpose* I *and* have   27. QA *LElius* C *L. Elius*   30. M *omits* the   31. M *omits* but   34. KLM *omit* close

286. 10. G—M wildernesse   13. M *omit* in   30. A—M farre into   34. A—M the partie   35. C otherwaies   39. A—M night on the

287. 1. LM fit time   A—M the deliverie   4. M commanded   7. M farther   21. G—M *omit* a   25. HI not fearing   M esteemed a few words   26. A—M many unjust   27. M both we   30. E—M now had we the   32. M their assailers

288. 8. I *omits* the   9. A—M her fault   10. KLM had com   15. A—M would have   19. KLM *omit* the   22. M *omits* I *after* wherein   23. M not only   A—D praiers   C are from   35. KLM *omit* a   36. A—M goe on in his   37. KLM *omit* how

289. 11. M sand   24. KLM *omit* and   30. A—M a wethercocke

290. 12. M impudent   24. CD kindnesse   25. A—M of his cruell handling *Dido*   26. KLM it would   27. F—L for him

291. 14. A—M her into my   17. M particulars   23—24. KLM *print* there is...becaus hee love's *in Italics*   28. M apprentice, no bond-slave   34. A—M mervailed   36. M *transposes* I *and* then   37. A—M a childish inexperience   38. A—M more cleere unto

292. 1. A—M But in such sort   5. M our selves into either   10. F—M called *instead of* towarde the most martiall   D *omits* a   17. M do give   22. A—M rare beautie   23. A—M bewondred   E—M   27. C the time   40. FGHKLM into a stray I into a strange

293. 3. E—L would he   4. M not he suffer   9. M *omits* it   17. A—M vertue to rule it   24. KLM that gracious

544

294. 10. C thought not   14. A—M even *instead of* ever
15. KLM each other, from delivering   18. FGH *omit* as   21. E—M
each promised   25. D no more then those   28. A—M those
two worthie   30. M in their pitiful   34. M than dying in himself   37. M having believing

295. 3. M *transposes* us *and* to   A—M care of him   12. M
we learned   13. A—M story   25. E—M *omit* but   27. A—M
the case   M farther   M *transposes* I *and* did

296. 1. C and the excellencie   5. M school than Love
7. A—M *Otanes*   8. M of six   16. D—M *print* Giants *in
Roman type*   20. A—M with all speede   26. M went to seek
Tydeus   31. M we enquiring   32. M farther   39. M fell
presently   40. HIM swounings   KL swoundings

297. 6. A—M harbingers   11. A—M *transpose* it *and* is
12. A—M gives me   22. A—M the modestie   LM are amazed
25. BD—M *transpose* we *and* forthwith   31. A—M shortly would
oppresse   33. A—M with that word she wept   38. A—M thinke
that I was

298. 2. G doe, because   8. A—M your well placed
11. A—M manner   12. A—M *omit* I   14. KLM enfeebled
24. I justly received   28. A—M come once into   32. F—M
that I may do   33. A—M *transpose* may *and* yet   37. M when
you were   40. M petions

299. 3. M her of her lightness   6. M and *instead of* that
11. A—M was of her selfe   26. A—M *Otanes*   BD—M *print*
Giants *in Roman type*   27. M that *instead of* as   28—29. A—M
so far engaged   39. A—M auncient Lord   40. C good Castle

300. 2. M *Plexirtua*   8. C that one child-birth   10. A—M
cunning to winne   15. M by *Trebisond*   18. C forget
19. A—M private   20. M giving himself   21. M their thought
28. F—M to a death   33. K *omits* a *before* Tygre   37. A—L
his beast   39. M there *instead of* they   A—M had in that   G—M
monstrous strength

301. 4. F—M to perish   7. BD—M *omit inverted commas in
margin*   7—8. KLM *print* the journey...ways *in Italics*   11. A—M
not to trouble   24. D hast bene   25. M great friends
30. A—M *Otanes*   38. A—M *Otanes*

302. 30. CDG—M renowned   32. CDG—M renowned
36. KLM of the comparison

303. 1. M judges to speak   6. A—M longer from *Erona*
7. A—M who had made   9. KLM who, seemed a   10. KLM
omit parenthesis   24. KLM *omit* so   M our selves unto   31. K
hath been   LM have been   33. A—M And so having

304. 11. G—M while I live   17. I—M upon an old   19. F—M
into my mind   25. AC *commas in margin*   30. A—M shore, so
that they sawe   31. HI *insert* he *after* Then   32. GHI came
to the captain   33. HI it would seeme   G—M disswaded

305. 7. LM knew in time   16. G—M of the swords   19. L—M
drave us two   21. LM *print* less evill...a friend *in Italics*   29. A—M
evill auditours   30. A—M but by being last alive   33. M were

reduced   M *omits* when   34. M weary, weary of those   35. M was fast tied   39. KLM *omit* a *before* fire

306. 6. LM *print* a common...war *in Italics*   7. G—M all we are   E—M by some man   13. M till truly   17. M as it might   22. LM to abide it   25. M *omits* owne   28. CF—M to abide   40. KLM such manner

307. 11. A—M knew   17. I tell your meeting : for   24. A—M desired him that   31. H—M *transpose* so *and* be

308. 2. KLM and spake   22. A—M And so went   24. KLM so much molested   28. E—M with such anguish

309. 3. M had been an   11. KLM smiling   34. A—M fault   37. D though wise

310. 2. M *omits* and   7. E—M *other of Jealousie*   8. E—I *transpose* "*finde*" *and* "*I*"   9. M *strength*   11. I *Love makes* A *wakes the the jealous*   15. HI *doe doleful*   16. I *my prayers prostrate*   19. M *jewel small*

311. 10. KLM cried *save*   21. F—M trembling   23. F—M *omit* a *after* such   24. E—M *omit* such   HI *omit* an   25. A *omits* for   38. A—M made him runne among

312. 1. KLM him for ever   5. FGKLM they verie killing 6. KLM by conquering   10. G—M he had   12. E—M and his eyes   21. G—M being suter to   23. M he stoopedd 30. A—M upon the side

313. 5. A—M that he should   9. A—M skirmish   14. A—M stood stock still   24. E—M more outragious   26. M mixt 28. A—M hindering the succour   32. F—M *transpose* onely *and* the 34. M opening

314. 3. KLM go up to   4. M guess of that   A—M the court gate   9. G—M daring approch   12. KLM his kindness 31. M to their   32. M crueltys   33. K *omits* the *before* principal   38. E—M I am sent

315. 18. G—M looked to   M he would never   22. F—M the farmers   24. A—M al the Gentlemẽ   30. HI mislikings 35. LM the riches   39. LM to dividing

316. 6. LM willing   7. E—M *omit* the   13. M pretence 23. A—M this zealous rage   M bent to these   24. A—M there be *instead of* are   26. C new feared   C Here he nether   30. F It I is then   G It is I then   31. M *omits* it   34. C a strangers 37. HI on me   38. M farther   39. LM *omit* it

317. 5. M *omits* or   KLM *omit* not   12. KLM to make 13. E—M meannesse   16—17. M andetermined   19. A—M with much labour   26. A—GKLM example a lesson to you   HI example a lesson unto you   31. LM *omit* with

318. 7. I *transposes* you *and* now   19. A—M such an admirable 38. KLM bent again such   40. M did guide

319. 2. A—M fault on his   20. BDEF shamefastnesse, in nature, GH shamefastnesse in nature, I shamefac'tnesse in nature : KLM shamefastness in nature ;   30. M in the peoples

NOTES

320. 4. M he had a prologue   5. M *omits* a   9. HI happy men   12. C your good Prince   BD—HKLM or good *Basilius* 20. A—M never stay   23. HI most upon the   27. KLM scambling   31. M as the blow   39. M None were

321. 1. EF taught then   8. M to heart   11. A—M feeding wildly   13. A—M in the chase   19. M hereafter   20. A—M sharp marks   23. BD know this frenzie   32. E—M ushers of his   34. E—M miles   35. I—M *omit* a   37. M dancing 38. I boughs

322. 8. G nigh   25. KLM *omit* a *before* greatness   28. A—M God wott thought   31. E—M dislike   34. M if your arms

323. 4. BD live or go   18. A—M glorious name of liberty 25. HI *omit* man   FGLM speake to other   31. M funeral 40. KLM *omit* to *before* your health

324. 5. M thither   13. KLM murthering   18. D what he did   A—M reached not to thé   E—M hundreth   28. M farther   37. C then *instead of* them   M in readiness

325. 13. A—M *omit commas in margin*   15. A—M undiscreete 18. GHKLM safety wrought   21. G—M *omit* the *before* ranke 23. M Cittern   25. A *omits* of *after* spite   27. C *has no division into stanzas*   L *to hel* M *to hell*   30. A—M be bob'd   33. A—L *others*   34. AC *omit* "*brave*"   38. I *Who have*

326. 4. A—M of the cave   5. KLM was it is his   7. A—L fall   8. A—M *omit inverted commas in margin*   21. BD—M come with an   30. A—M this solitarie   39. FGKLM hold in (in my conceit) one   H hold (in my conceit) in one

327. 2. M *transposes* not *and* good   9. ABC. *And uncouth* 11. C *they beer*   13. BD—M *In thine*   15. GHI *shalt* 19. F—M unto me   23. A—M chaunceable   24. F—M the authority

328. 8. HI in that seat   13—14. A—M keeping them (while he lived) unmaried   21. M *earthy*   22. M *do ever shine*   23. A—M *spoile*   24. A—M *omit inverted commas in margin*   A—M *snakish sinne*   25. BD Latonus   27. A—M *omit inverted commas in margin*   28. I *While brittle*   C *painting*   30. M the knowledge   31. M *fruite*   34. A—M *omit inverted commas in margin*   35. LM priviledg   39. KLM in the best

329. 7. M farther   13. E—M *omit* a   19. C *Blangus* 38. M *omits* more

330. 3. C bad so pulled   12. LM *transpose* "*Pyrocles*" *and* already 13. LM those too   14. E—M *insert* like *before* good   30. A—M bounds   36. L other

331. 2. F—M measure to their false musick   3. F—M wisest and worthiest   4. E—M *omit* a *before* royall   5. H—M found our unblushing   6. A—M *insert* though *before* unjustly   8. C not in it self   15. A—M messages   18. A—M shee purposed 26. A—M yong- mastered   29. F—M *concluding parenthesis instead of comma after* ground   30. M flatters   32. M farther   35. A—M would be   40. I can excuse

547

NOTES

332. 1. HI way for her   11. BD—M murther   29. M in the two   31. M then taken   32. A—M begging of life   40. F—M guiltinesse

333. 2. I Princesse   3. A—M women both more   16. B—E which he had not   30. BD he should yeeld   32. M love of her   38. A—M could give

334. 4. M an year   22. C be the aucthoritie   33. A—M this practise   37. KLM will to escape   39. F—M should lay

335. 9. A—M from her malice   14. A—M at the humble 16. F—M hated   18. BD—M *print* Pyramis *in Roman type* 33. LM of a far

336. 3. F—M by oath   E—M *omit* that   22. A—M any conditions   24. E—M *omit* not

337. 9. M and *instead of* that   19. C Noble-men   21. C of the time   24. B would not do   40. C *omits* & brother BD—M recovering of his

338. 1. C *omits* before   6. H *Evarchus*   11. KLM murdered   21. I accōmodated him   22. H *Evarchus*   27. C *omits* well   32. H *Evarchus*   35. M farther   36. A—M saw allready ready for

339. 4. KLM a skirmish   13. A—M the Reasonable 14. BD—M *Reason. Thou*   16. BD—M *Passion. No*   17. BD—M *R. Can*   18. BD—M *P. If*   27. KLM *doth ensure*   31. A—M side   34. A—M *dimme*   37. C *your strength*   38. C *your weaknes*   KLM *weakned*

340. 2. C Reason   3. KLM *abode*   10. E—M *Who to be weake*   BD—M *do faine*   13. A—M *Passions yeeld at* 21. A—M *R. Then let*   22. A—M *P. Which*   A—M *Passions kill*   32. HI entred speech

341. 6. I *vertues*   7. A—D *mettals*   9. E—M *soone change*   22. C *sheepe*   24. M *my slavery*   32. M *be gets*

342. 3. A—M *his booke*   BD *lover*   4. C *waild*   16. D *thy name*   28. KLM *no parenthesis after "say"*   E—M *me mischiefs*   29. K *has a comma after "reflection"*   LM *a parenthesis* 31. BD *fam'd*

343. 3. I *then thou mine*   KLM *ear*   4. LM *do breed* 5. L *omits "a"*   7. A—M *others woe*   8. KLM *omit "so"* 23. A—M *omit commas in margin*   25. A—M *omit commas in margin* 26. BD—M *it is zeale*   A—M *omit commas in margin*   27. HI hates   34. A—L *blow* M *blows*   A—M *no asterisk in margin*

344. 12—19. the more...requited. *This passage is not in the folio editions*

344. 20—**348.** 27. *This dialogue is not in the folio editions*

348. 28—**349.** 2. Some speech...persons. *This passage is not in the folio editions, but cf.* Appendix *p.* 564 *ll.* 11, 12, 30

349. 2—3. *See* Appendix *p.* 564 *l.* 40   6. ABD—M *delight am tyr'd* 12. M *darkness in my sight*   13. A—M *Dwell in my ruines, feede with*   A—M *no comma at end of line*   21. A—M *conquerd harte* 22. KLM *no other*   37. BD—M *of sight a*

548

350. 3. KLM *root* 8. HK Klaius *instead of* Strephon 9. B *But cause* 13. M *from anchors Hope* 23. M *the years is* 24. A—M *no comma at end of line* 25. BDG—M *Hatefully growne* BDEF *sprong* G—M *sprung* 37. A—M *Thus, Thus alas, I had my*

351. 1. A—M *Thus, Thus alas, I had my* 16. I *transposes* "I" *and* "now" ACM *shall fall* 17. ABDEF *soule have hent* CG—M *soule have bent* 20. KL *earthy* 21. L *earthy* 23. A—E *heavens sell* 27. A—M *desastres to me* 28. KLM *thou from, O mee!* 30. M *and to dedest* 31. M *and to detest* 32. A—M *But now* I *and end* (O Klaius) *now and end* 33. A—M *hatefull musique*

351. 35—**352.** 1. So wel...own troubles. *Cf.* Appendix *p.* 564 *l.* 45

352. 1—5. And...unto them. *This passage is not in the folio editions* 6—11. Which he in parte to satisfie...uttered. *Cf.* Appendix *p.* 565 *l.* 40 12. A—M *have:*

Philisides.   Echo.

14. A—M *what barrs me* KLM *who is that* 16. A—M *Oh! I* A—M *I have mett* 17. A—M *aproche: then tell me* 19. A—M *for a griefe* 25. A—M *Oh! what* 27. A—M *which for to enjoy* 29. K *will no give* F—M *give me leave* 30. A—M *thy physick* 31. KLM *say they again* A—M *thy advise for th' ev'lls* 32. A—M *of his harme* 35. A—L *that leanes* M *that learns* BD—I *to fancie* KLM *to fantasie* 37. KLM *made on mee these torments on mee to* 38. A—GKLM *go die? Yea*

353. 1. KLM *from them from mee fal's* 3. KLM *can that art bee* A—HKLM *have* "that" *instead of* "which" I *omits* "which" KLM *by speech* 5. HI *these words* KLM *transpose* "more" *and* "me" C *to blisse* 7. A—M *omit* "bad" A—M *but how* 8. FGHM *what I doe gaine* KL *what I do again* KLM *since under her* 10. *Instead of this line* A—M *have the following:*

Silly rewarde! yet among women hath she of vertu the most, Most.

13. LM *desire bliss* A—M *the course. Curse.* 14. I *Curs'd by* 15. A—M *be not heard?* 16. A—M *omit this line* 17. A—M *What makes them be unkind?* KLM *speak forth ha'st* 18. A—M *Whence can pride come* BD *beautie he thence* 22. AC *is their* 23. *Instead of this line* A—E *have the following:*

Tell yet againe me the names of these faire form'd to do ev'lls. Dev'lls.

F—I :

Tell yet againe me the names of those faire form'd to do evills? Devills.

KLM :

Tell yet again met the names of those fair form'd to doe evills? Devills.

24. AC *Dev'lls? if in hell such dev'lls do a bide, to the hells I* BD *Devils? if in hell such devils do abide, to the hells I* E *Devils? if in hell such devil do abide, to the hells I* F—L *if in hell such devill doe abide, to the hells I* M *if hell such devil do abide, to the hells I* 25. A—M *omit* "After this well placed *Echo,*" *but cf.* Appendix *p.* 565 *l.* 48 25—35. the other...private desires. *See* Appendix *p.* 566 *l.* 19 36. A—E *second Eclogues* F—I *second Eclogues*

NOTES

354. 11. A—M from looking out　15. KLM *omit* a　19. A—M beames to thawe awaye　25. A—M *omit commas in margin*　28. I—M unexpected　34. M *omits* that *after* but

355. 5—6. KLM *omit* his cheere...Hope encouraging (*exactly one line in* F—I)　8. C *omits* away　15. A—M first up to heaven 16. D mazed　KLM *omit* the　20. KLM *omit* for　25. I—M *omit* so　26. BD—M *omit* It was not an amazement　32. F—M into lamentation　38. M other but *Pamela*　39. M despising it, greedily

356. 7. A—M that image　18. KLM thought good to　19. M *omits* to *after* and　21—22. A—M never pen did more quakingly 24. LM *omit* the *before* Muses　BD—M *print* Muses *in Roman type* 34. M *omits* he　M *omits* & *before* being　A—M ended, was diverse 35. D til this reason

357. 13. A—M not now to grow　22. C *craftie wretch* 24. KLM *last moment*　28. I *omits* " *of* "　34. KLM *cannot bee hope*　37. KLM *tears of man*

358. 1. E—M *that do I not conceive*　3. ACE—M *that do I not conceive*　C *mouse clime*　7. A—M *an inly relenting*　11. D love he reserved　12. A—M. he thence must　A—M *only he liv'd* 13. F—M *the triumphes*　14. A—M *must I be*　A—M *such monument*　20. A—M *Plannets tend*　26. KLM *omit* " *me* " *after* " *had* "　32. KLM *veil*　37. D *hand- nayls*

359. 3. A—M *doo so excessive*　5. A—M *O not*　HKLM *had afforded*　6. C *leane*　D *omits* " *a* "　7. A—M *Love be so*　8. KL *boy should bee a*　M *Boy, should he a*　11. A—M such faith be abolisht　13. KLM *not yet thus refresh*　19. KLM *I worthy then such*　21. F—M *omit* " *more* "　22. BD—M *I well should find*

360. 14. G flame of fewel　LM flame or farewell　22. KLM *transpose* in *and* of　34. A—M beautifull might have bene　36. LM full of graceful　38. F—M *omit* and

361. 7. G—M to them　L who excellencies　14. BD—M stirred up　17. KLM *omit* and　25. F—M *omit* yet

362. 8. BD—M burthened　10. G—M deliver to them 11. GHKLM smelling grapes　12. KLM childe with *Bacchus* 15. M cold wine　20. F—M on *Zelmane*　23. HI *transpose* in vaine *and* crying　25. D *omits* the *before* injury　26. I—M *omit* a *before* foure　28. BD—M *omit* that *after* time　30. A—M *omit* of *after* mile　38. C Princesse

363. 35. C all speaches　36. A—M this country　37. A—M but younger

364. 2. IKL obtaining　6. KLM of a subjection　8. KLM of the Ladies　14. M seems　16. G—M my delight　23. I—M *omit* on *after* troden　26. M have need to　28. L stop　29. M nor *instead of* or　38. A—M *omit commas in margin*

365. 2. BDE it were faine　5. A—M two daughters　17. A—M then an ordinary　18—19. A—M *omit commas in margin*　KLM *print* in all miseries...folks *in Italics*, all *excepted, which is in Roman type*

550

33. I fine-wittie   34. A—M these goodly   38. KLM *omit* you   39. A—M *omit commas in margin*

366. 9. E—M *transpose* are *and* ever   11. M may once by 13. A—L under these base M under those base   15. A—M happie my policy' hath brought matters   38. GHKL lovelinesse 38—39. A—M *omit commas in margin*

367. 9. IKLM was not dainty   13. I into *instead of* unto 16. I tuftes   17. M black lustre   31. KLM murder

368. 2. G—M hapned   22. I motion of her   24. M *transposes* her *and* hear   28. M thy *instead of* the *at end of line* 32. H—M degree of death   33. AC *omit* am

370. 10—11. A—M degenerate to such a deadly palenesse   24. A—M assuring him   40. I *omits* a little

371. 5. LM So that calling   7. I letters to those   9. KLM motion   10. E or *instead of* of   20. E—M he was then   22. I humours do blow   27. E—M *transpose* hide *and* indeede

372. 21. E—M as it were   26. A—M *omit commas in margin* KLM *print* new...remedies *in Italics*   I required   I *omits* there 28. I states   32. I states   A—M he should be assailed

373. 14. A—M bent both his   17. LM rockly   19. LM if not not impossible   35. D peaceably   36. A—M would serve 37. E—M yeares   40. A—M wittes *instead of* wills

374. 13. M allotteth   23. BD—M things   40. C standerds F—M himselfe to talke

375. 1. A—M to do some thing   3. A—E hand   5. KLM about where   31. A—M more beautifull   32. F—M *transpose* is *and* it   35. C when hee

376. 5. A—M She seing her   6. A—M of a desirer   12. F—M *Philoclea* to receive   21. A—M teares, they hoong upon   23. C bedewed   24. KLM Art of carefulness   25. I to an neglected 28. C *omits* no

377. 10. M my eyes   14. G—M misconstrue   18. KLM say unto you   21. M female inquisitive of   23. BD—HKLM to burthen   25. HI *omit* the *before* very

378. 8. A—M reason & wit   12. M or *instead of* not   13. LM *omit* of *before* Ewe   20. E *omits* it   27. A—M with neernesse 36. F—M farre it is

379. 13. A—M with an unspeakable   15. F *omits* the *before* sweet   19. I *omits* like   23. A—M must come   27. A—M offend for sullennes   29. F is but a burdenous   33. I *omits* to *before* draw   39. A—M is for ever

380. 7. M lose of his former   10. M comfort   21. M make a just   35. A—M was resolved   37. D reasonably 38. F & constraints must

381. 7. M or those   8. B eloquent with passions through 9. E—M *omit* no   12. EF being besirers G—M being desirers 18. F Musicke   C especiall   31. C as of authoritie 34. ABD—M *colon instead of full stop after* knots C *prints* knots. but in E—M but she in hart   35. A—D *full stop instead of comma after* one

NOTES

382. 3. CF—M exprobate   4. M estate : but even   6. B right better servitude   7. KLM carried away   9. M *Amphialus* effectually   L lauguishing M languishing   14. E—M *omit* beautie   17. A—M Therefore   21. A—M of subtile   24. K intend   34. A—M even where she stood

382. 35—**383.** 22. O all-seeing Light...vertuous *Musidorus.* KLM *print this prayer in Italics* M *prints* And pausing a while (**383.** 20) said she (**383.** 21) Musidorus (**383.** 22) *in Roman type*

383. 1. A—M hande   4. A—M unexcuseable   11. LM that I and thy creature   12. M *omits* so   13. E—M confidently on   17. I if so seeme   21. KLM *becom's of mee*   30. D they hap begun

384. 9. A—M fortune, which shoulde not onely have   14. LM matcht   22. A—M at lest   36. LM rise

385. 20. HI amated mind   23. H burthen   25. KLM *omit* as   27. K of this unassailed   37. A—M scarcely   40. A—M he would hide

386. 4. M *omits* the *after* more   18. A—M the country   24. I farther   25. E—M but to view   37. BD—M not knowing

387. 4. F—M rekning   6. HI into his   13. A—M vampalt   24. I whether the pity   A—M revenge against the other   26. ABD and his hinde to his   34. BDE weapon   36. D flew in peeces

388. 5. FGHKLM and the grones   11. M accident   13. I burdens   25. A—M common reason   A—GI—M burden   30. CG—M valoure   31. A—M *transpose* hatred *and* choller   33. F—M hand   35. A—M exercises

389. 8. A—M in the never   16. KLM went to battel   18. A—M mistrusting those verie guards lest they   24. KLM only his face for   27. KLM upon his enemy   35. A—M away from himselfe   37. F—M *omit* when

390. 2. BD escaping valiant hand   ABD by base   10. A—M But thus with   G—M valour   15. E—M thrust just into   19. M side of the   22. HI *Philanax*'s KLM *Philanax*   25. A—HKLM Deaths   28. F—M see their   I murderers   29—30. E—I *Philanax* sword KLM *Philanax*'s sword   31. E—M squire   34. E—I *omit* his KLM *Amphialus*'s   G—M valour   35. E—M to a most shamefull

391. 1—2. E—M asking advise of no other thought   6. A under the the hande   10. M towards to him   11. BD—M meaning to take   15. F—M espied   23. ABC bewaile and untimely   25. E—M falling feete   33. LM the caus of   36. A—M where being   39. E—I *Philanax* men KLM *Philanax*'s men

392. 5. KLM black as darkness   7. LM made him know   13. F—M ofter   17. A—M his sword   26. A—M *omit commas in margin*   35. I scarcely   36. BD—HKLM armour

393. 5. E—M house   22. F—M right let backeward   30. KLM Fortune and Valor   35. I cryed unto him

NOTES

394. 1. C *retreitie*   3. KLM *of the sluce*   6. F—M returned himselfe   10. A—M gotten a horse   16. D as I could 18. BD subject   19. KLM insert yet *after* not   30. KLM seen in the   31. B accord the pretty

395. 6. KLM *of her death*   9. KLM *brains boyl*   11. I *thought*   12. I *pompe*   C *bast desire*   14. BD *defile the muddy*   E—M *defile with muddie*   18. A—M *transpose "doth" and "downeward"*   20. HI *omit "how"*   22. M *lid*   24. E—M *omit this line*   32. M Somothea

396. 2. BD—I *do stow*   6. M care   12. D falcone 13. KLM *a fair Chariot*   26. C *glaring shoe*   30. M *brought for a mouse*   35. KLM *As thus I*   36. KLM *The writing Nymph*

397. 5. E—M *humble eyes*   HI *O eye*   E—HKLM *Summe of sight*   8. KLM *I in whom all my*   14. C *I admire*   21. C estate   24. I *off-springs spoil'd*   A—M *priests*   31. CD breed   32. D *feed*   36. LM *weaking work*   38. M *heavens*

398. 24. G—M *otherwise*   36. E—M *all that I*

399. 12. M *gift*   17. C *made far to be*   19. I Cupids 20. A—G *unwarn'd to take*   H—M *unarm'd to take*   22. E—M *omit mark of ellipsis*   24. ABD—L *but as a pleasant*   CM *but as pleasant*   37. A—M *worthy, then they to be loved*

400. 1. F—M to the knowledge   8. F—M receive judgement 22. M and *instead of* as   24. D of the bloud   28. K word 30. A—EG—M what a maze   A—DI *of a mazemēt*   39. KLM insert *the before* knowledg   A—M by *instead of* with   KL Amphialus's his

401. 1. M of the Town   16. BE *catchword is* seene *but should be* curtesie   25. A—M not visitinge the Princesses   27. A—M by force to be reskued   30. A—M their songs   33. A—M owne resolutions   38. A—M humours to prepare   39. F—M *omit* used

402. 8. A—M rugged race   15. A—M sorow that then owed 21. A—M thitherward   26. A—M hands   28. A wherof the 29. A—E therby   31. F—M unawares   34. M *omits* an

403. 3. A—M as if it had   6. KLM *transpose* one *and* might 10. A—M sorrowe to dresse   13. M *omits* to   16. E—M therewith   17. LM fully   28. F—M outward glosse   30. M *omits* is   31. M farther   38. F—M is beyond   KLM is a great

404. 12. KLM which is not most notable   AC lawe   A *colon after* lawe   13. A—M become lawes themselves   15. A—EKLM Feare or Love   F—I Feare of Love   18. A—M her onely lippes 30. A—M speake   32. KLM the whole battels   40. G—M never to suffer

405. 7. KLM honouring it   15. I then she   21. E—M that would not be   26. G of of *Autumn*   27. I *prints "april of your age" in Italics*   34. A—M hidden   38. KLM imperfection

406. 14. KLM *omit* that   39. A—M chafe at the

553

NOTES

407. 5. A—M when *instead of* but 13. HI miserable foolish 34. A—M might have not 35. A—M so if chaunceable 35—36. A—M *omit* as now being, thē not being 38. KLM *omit* if

408. 3. KLM changeable effects 14. ABD his goodly F—M *omit* a *before* earth 15. BD—M height of the ring E—M or *instead of* nor 18—19. A—M *omit* or...of these 20—21. A—M *omit* and eternitie...inconstancie 28. F—M absolutly 30. C unexpresseable F—K unexpressible 31. E—M *omit* a *after* without 32—33. I unpossible 33. KLM unless that you will

409. 2. BD name of the sea 4. A—M superscribed 10. H—M regard any 17. M of the contrarieties 20. I up to so high 22. A—M of a base 25. KL yiel'd M yield 27. KLM directed to an end of preservation 35. A—M this beastly absurditie

410. 1. A—M *omit* so 2. KLM *print* Books...defects *in Italics* 4. KLM need 21. M be known F—M if there were 23. F—M if his knowledge 30. M dissembling thoughts 38—39. A—M ougly shamefulnes

411. 9. F—M so fowle 12. A—M amazement of a M self-excusing 33. LM both by any more

412. 14. C sailles 16. BD—M of the place 19. E—M then to 20. M equital 21. I *omits* side 27. A—M who refrained 32. C obeience A—M and so had 33. A—M knowledges

413. 4. M both safe by 7. KLM consider he was A—M and *instead of* but 15. M matter E—M dislike 21. ABE—M will armed KLM *comma before* armed 22. A—M *omit* will 23. M be prisoner 33. A—M *omit* much 37. I *Philantus*

414. 7. A—M from any 10. G—M valour 10—11. KLM *print* true...of honor *in Italics* 21. KLM reprehension 22. M effect the glory 28. LM them a charge 31. A—M whence she might 32. KLM And so soon as

415. 2. KLM and goodly 10. H of a tawnie 11. BD—M figures 20. A—M facing the castle 25. KLM an hors 26. A—E freckned F—M freckled M stain 29. KLM when he came

416. 1. E yet hunts it 5. A—M any thing to say to him 12. A—M Sunne in a cleare day shines 13. BD—M pawing upon the M farther foot 15. G—M trumpets A—M sounding ABD—HK together, Together they ILM together, together they 17. E—M into the rest 19. M *omits* a *before* pleasant 24. F—M breath of the other 25. E—M *omit* but 36. A—M *omit* the *before* one D *prints* on *instead of* one F—M till they being E—M come to the 40. M guided his blow

417. 3. KLM customed 5. A—M such force 7. M farther 9. E—I *Amphialus* horse KLM *Amphialus's* hors 13. M farther E—I *Phalantus* horse KLM *Phalantus's* hors 17. I burthening 18. A—M *omit* & 19. A—M *insert* and *before* seeing 23. M farther 24. M *omits* yet 25. F—I bring to me the 32. A—M boiling into his 35. KLM *print* great spending...remnants *in Italics*

554

NOTES

418. **2.** A—M disdaining **14.** DG—M renowned

419. **9.** LM shee *instead of* he **16.** K *transposes to and* bee
28. KLM slave of weakness

420. **7.** G—M his quarrel **19.** BD—M encreased their
21. A—M *omit semi-colon after* life A—GKLM *semi-colon instead
of comma after* one HI *colon* **22.** A—M ever bred **32.** F—M
lothsomnesse **35.** A—M grew pale **37.** ABC rocked a sleepe·
D—M rocked asleepe

421. **4—5.** A—M imported **10.** A—M · But by that time
22. LM adventurers

422. **3.** A—M Where understanding **10—22.** M *prints this
passage in Italics,* Amphialus *excepted, which is in Roman type* **13—14.** A
and and make **14.** A—M to heaven **15.** F—M *omit* the *before*
wings G—M valor **18.** E—M *omit* as **23.** F—L *print
this line in Italics* KLM *To his* A—M *transpose* quickely *and* he
24—34. M *prints this passage in Italics,* Argalus *excepted, which is in Roman
type* **24.** D wore *instead of* more **36.** A—M was al guilded
D guided *instead of* guilded **37.** HI womens **38.** F—M and
so spred **39.** M out in the

423. **6.** M worn in the Just, in time that **8.** A—M In his shield
11. KLM of fierie BD backe list **21.** M farther **22.** A—M
the staves HIM unshaken **24.** A—M *Argalus* horse **28.** I
with striking **30.** A—M maisters

424. **1.** A—I *Amphialus* disarmed KLM *Amphialus 's* disarmed
2. KLM force of *Amphialus* **5.** I—M extend A—M blow
16. HI and mortall **17.** A—M had over striken **25.** AC
arispe *instead of* arise **29.** AC dissending BD descending **30.** I
each on his **31.** F—M garnished in bloud **32.** HI rose with

425. **8.** A—M of his best blood **11.** KLM so *instead of* as *after*
not **21.** AC *semi-colon after* sobbes **27.** A—M as ever your
harte **29.** M I might **33.** D unwelcome to me **34.** A—M
Is that

426. **1.** D effect **2—3.** M friendship of the codquerer **7.** M
if he had him **12.** M to rest himself **26.** F—M fallen? how
wert **30.** LM *omit* in **31.** A—M thou lead me

427. **1.** A—M *omit second* my deare **26.** CE—HKLM her
woman **27.** A—M into the boat **28.** A—M she would not
depart KLM com on the other **31.** A—D these warlike E—M
their warlike **34.** LM all was easful

428. **3.** E—I *Amphialus* fame KLM *Amphialus 's* fame EF
such was was his **4.** M till did but **13.** M forth to him **20.** I
others

429. **1.** BDEF merily G—M merrily **6.** BD—M *print
throughout* "Dametas" **10.** K *that every went* **21.** A—M
every body helping on **25.** A—M *omit* and **29.** A—M panting
33. A—M *omit* not *after* "Amphialus" **36.** A—M him, that by
next morning

430. **10.** LM *omit* to **14.** HI from divers horses A—M
coulour nor ¡fashion **19.** A—M with a great number of armes

555

NOTES

26. **A—M** dog, and there is   **30.** A—M caused in a border about to **33.** E—M impatience   **34.** F in the land   **35.** I waited on him

431. 16. A—D *Damætas*-is friend   18. G—M the Letter **22.** KLM *omit "as"*   26. A—M *with all my*   29. E—M *paines*   30. HI *omit "I"*   C *omits "such"*   31. B The terrible words   32. A—D *Damætas*-is courage   E—I *Dametas* courage KL *Dameta*'s courage M *Dametas*'s courage   33. E thundrings   36. ABD—M this answere

432. 1. C *omits* (having...horsebacke)   E—M into the   5—8. C *omits* (the Gentlemen...scituated) *and puts a semi-colon after* little   5. F—M Gentleman   8. ABD—M for being   11. K inconveniencies 15. C *omits* (contrarie...vices)   17. C *omits* (if he were overcome) *and puts a semi-colon after* use   27. C *omits* (chosen for the purpose) *and puts a comma after* judges   31. A—M *Damætas* horse   33. BC jogd blacke with   34. C *omits* that

433. 6. C when we was   19. M withal began to strike   20. A—M started back a good way   25. E—M *omit* of   26. A—L could leade him   28. M followed him with   39. KLM used to the flail

434. 13. F—M to rise   19. BD sleepish   A—M quietnes *instead of* countenaunce   30. F—M upon his

435. 2. A—M to his practize   11. F—M forced himselfe 14. F framed no smiling   20. C free scope   22. BD—M himselfe unto   26—27. A—EG—M sorts of the *Amphialians* F sorts of the *Amphilians*   28. E—M discontent   32. A—M to his lure 33. A—M of the six

436. 5. M that one of them   6. KLM *omit* had   7. M than an ordinary   16. BD—M condemned   C hie hatred *Pamela* 31. M got   32. A—M a seate   33. D comfort   A—M discomforts

437. 10. D praise   16. D then creation   36—37. I *transposes* wearied *and* wounded

438. 5. A—M afterwardes to a promised gratefulnes towards   15. L destroying of her M destruction of her   20. C farther   28. A—DF—M thy wretched wiles E they wretched wiles   31. I spake somewhat with

438. 39—**439.** 1. LM *print* who do...inferiors *in Italics*

439. 5. M according to Merits   7. A—M bare to *Ismenus* 15. A—D was occasiõ of the   E—M was by occasiõ of the   16. HI Evardes   17. HI exceeding strong   19. F—M of parts worthy 23. M farthest-fetcht   28. HI inflexible   32. C side-gate

440. 15. F—M murthered   I *transposes* he *and* did   18. A—M *omit commas in margin*   35. I *transposes* once *and* had

441. 9. F—M *insert* any *before* company   30. E walles, which was a   35. D all possessed mindes

442. 1. B—M *omit division into stanzas*   A—M *to see my wrongs for*   4. A—M *his center keepeth*   8. A—M *night of evils*   9. E

556

NOTES

Alas alonly F—M *Alas alonely* 21. ABCE—M *helpes* 22. I *hers I am* 24. A—M *she makes of me no treasure* 25. I *seeming weary* 36. CD sayled out with

443. 7. KLM he was 9. A—M were excused by the 29. E—M *omit* and ABCEF *omit* with 33. C three adventures 37. I lighted GHKLM beames of their 38. G—M valour 40. D examples

444. 1. KLM of this fight 12. A—M following over-earnestly 15—16. A—M *omit commas in margin* KLM *print* courage...manhood *in Italics*

445. 5. AM *omit commas in margin* KLM *print* unwelcom... injury *in Italics* M *misprints* unwtleome 9. M not only for the anlookedforness 13. A—M them a servant of 20. D *omits* alreadie 22. A—M whereon the one KLM was ready dead 26. M send a Damosel 28. F—M have done KLM as glad as any 32. M entertained 37. B then enemie

446. 13. I befriended enemy F—M *omit the after* with 14. F—M running of him 17. A—M as of having 19. A—M *omit commas in margin* BD—M victorie with advantage 27. A—M whē in the 29. A—M *omit parenthesis* 37. B betrayed the hart 39. A—L & in the fall

447. 22. H looking upon 33. A—M loath to departe

448. 4. CKLM bands united 12. D up her eyes and 13. BD which lift the 20. CKLM beauty from the 21. C when that infallible 23. BD—M *omit it after* perceiving 24. A—M passion 26. A—M falling upon the earth & crying 31. E—M being *instead of* they having bene 34. C could handes 37. A—M tell such rare

449. 1. BD was as subject to 4. A—M *omit* foorth A—M who was come into 11. A—M needes lende his 14. E—M of a faithfull 15. BD making of the marble E—M making of two marble 16. M *Basilius* caused himself A—M *add the following epitaph:*

The Epitaph.

H*IS being was in her alone:*
And he not being, she was none. [M *gone*]
They joi'd one joy, one griefe they griev'd,
One love they lov'd, one life they liv'd.
The hand was one, one was the sword
That did his death, hir death afford.

As all the rest, so now the stone
That tombes the two, is justly one.

ARGALUS & PARTHENIA.

C *omits division into stanzas*

450. 5. G—M full of their 23. D all his mishaps 28. A—M So as all that 29. D—M and in the 30. BD the delight began to restore to each boy his

451. 18. A—M could no lōger patch up 21. G maried the yong 27. M but by denyal 30. E—M then they should look 36—37. A—M *omit commas in margin* KLM *print* lust may...servant *in Italics* 37. HI indeed, is a servant

NOTES

452. 4. E—M *omit* if   9. KLM *print* No is no...mouth *in Italics*
10. B—M *omit commas in margin*   C speaking of a womã   10—11.
KLM *print* a lover's...liked *in Italics*   17. F—M example   20. D
gotten an habite   23. M on both sides   30. C *Jubiter*   I the
manerly-wooing   35. BD—M who wold never like

453. 4. ABCEG—M over-superstitiously   DF over-superstiously
5. C same Ladies   9. E--M who prayeth   9—10. LM *print*
who...obeyed *in Italics*   28. M a Gentlewoman of

454. 3. G *if thou liked not*   5. M such an answer   6. I
transposes thou *and* hast   9. A—M inward affliction   31. D yet
also   A—M daintely joyned   37—38. A—M by an excellent
painter excellently painted, with

455. 1. E—M *omit* with   M *prints* was *in Italics*   4. A—M
forced favour   9. ABD—M formed into   C formed in to   15. KLM
Catoblepas   18. M *beasts*   28. A—M this combat   35. BD—M
upon the quarrell   39. F—M that I confesse

456. 8. KLM neither staying   16. M *omits* set   17. A—M
omit nowe   HI most curteous   20. D not fire   22. A—M
fetching still new spirit   23. A—M keeping their sight that way as a
matter of   28. E—M motion of the Sunne   30. F—M *omit* his
31. E—M that *instead of* both

457. 2. BD—M assuring trust   4. F—M their horses   6. KLM
advantages   17. A—M stayning their blacke couler, as if   18—19.
M so along a space   29. HI as well as his   30. F—M came
to himselfe   34. E—M his sword   39. A—M *omit* he was

458. 9. M was upon on his   26. CD but a morsel   29. A—M
brought to fresh feeding   31. F—M of this manner of fight

459. 11. A—M strake him so mightie   16. M force give place
18. ABCE—M also was driven   D was driven also   A—M the
sterne of cunning   23—24. M when only I   24. E—M fought
causelesse   31. F—M into this place   37. M ashamed   E
my soule   40. D with thy owne

460. 26. C tale ship   26—27. KLM *print* make unto...com-
parison *in Italics*   34. M blow   35. M one of these

461. 1. FGI the latter   2. A—M hope   3. F—M brake
out into these   38. I seemed after-drops   KLM of a storm

462. 8. BD—M burthen   LM for *instead of* foe   23. C
silver sprangles   27. A—M began a most fierce   35. LM most
to deliver   36. E—HKLM most of all that   I almost all that
39. F—M *omit* the *before* one

463. 10. HI *omit* them   13—14. M conveying him   19. B
that hast   BD—M battered the most   26. M would not have so

464. 10. ABCEF *Amphialus*-is   D *Amphilalus*-is   E—M to
a diligent   11. C no sailes   14. A—M and he gave   16. H—M
one to another   17. BD—GK Chirurgians   HLM Chirurgions   I
Chirurgious   19. I—M waiting on it   27. GHKLM or *instead
of* nor

465. 8. BD—GK Chirurgians   HILM Chirurgions   12. D
only to him   19. A—M because she would be the   31. HI in
a womanly

558

NOTES

466. 4. A—M among a people 7. D out of her nose 14.
E—I *Amphialus* succession KLM *Amphialus's* succession 25. A—M
heard from his beloved M departed from 39. A—M *omit
commas in margin*

467. 2. LM and therefore is 3. A—M *omit commas in margin*
F—M it pleaseth 3—4. KLM *print* in extremities...of life *in Italics*
11. FGHKLM in amaze 28. F—M great, so ω forethinke
33—34. KLM *print* promiss...threatning *in Italics* 33—37. A—M
omit commas in margin

468. 1. E—I *Amphialus* ambition KLM *Amphialus* 's ambition
9—10. CDF—M *omit commas in margin* 11—13. ABE *commas in
margin* 23. A—M are but feare-babes 27—31. CDF—M *omit
commas in margin* 28. A—E of a people

469. 1—2. A—F *Philanaxis* hands 11. A—M But she by this
meanes 21. KLM perswasions 27. D sweete holinesse

470. 19. D *omits* same 22. E—M noise of

471. 7. KLM wall 29. G—M *full stop instead of comma after*
that F—M *omit* and 30. E—M for a certaine G—M labour
33. A—M *omit comma after* "Cecropias" 38. A—M So that with
silence 39. G—M hammered on by G—M abode her pitilesse

472. 13. F—M working 18. E—M would die F—M
then to bee false 27. K though the clouds affliction 28. M self
instead of els 32. KLM shee used to her 39. F—M but thou canst

473. 4. I her doing with their suffering 7. KLM she was in
11. D when in open 14. A—I *Musidorus* teares KLM *Musidorus* 's
tears

474. 7. A—M set in the eyes of men, to be 13. A—M sorest
torment 22. I wherin they knew E—M they should be
25. BD—M further off 29. F—M to their enemie

475. 6. I owle-eyed 7. F—M interprete it 11. KLM
but the best way 14. E—M do so much 22. E—M bee in
time 23. K of so a fair Lady 25. B—M *omit commas in
margin* 37. KLM driven to stay

476. 1. D aside ward 10. E—I of peevish 14. G—M
both with bitter termes 28. KLM also vaulted 32. ABCE—M
looke one to another D looke one to an other 34. E—K But then
the houre 35. BD—GKLM beginne, and curtaynes HI begin, and
the curtains

477. 1. KLM mouth to her 12. A—M even minding to
18. I at the first 30. I life into her 31. D when it was
36. E—M gone to a beautified heaven 37. ABD—M hast left me
C hath left me 38. D ever did lament

478. 1. KLM most cursed 10. DKLM shepeheards apparell
12. A—M O my God 20. M what I am born 21. D happie
in my selfe 22. A—M had chanced unto me 24. E—M *insert* a
before lamentable 25. KLM if stir'd

479. 9. KLM more sensible 10. G *Philiclea* 20. A—M
was most likely both to move 25. D extremities 29. D that
instead of the *after* understood

559

NOTES

480. 7. G—L nor halfe   27. I—M how she should deale   33. A—M of that beautie   35. CM the woman   39. D to be their

481. 5. M *omits* that *after* with   7. E—M no leasure   A—M turne it selfe into   9. D of the heart

482. 7. E—M *omit* so   17. KLM *omit* was   20. E—M uncertainty   32. A—M taking his woonted

483. 3. BD—M over her face   6. ABD—M borowed her beautie C borrow- (*end of line*) her beautie   9. D *omits* an *before* amazement   21. F—M caried by the   22. F nor having   31. A—M Revenge, Revenge unto him   35. KLM *omit* it   37. E—M destroying of himselfe   39. K *omits* to *after* accessarie

484. 5. D *omits* he   9. ABCE—M into all his D into his   10. F—M teares, nor with a   18. C Unpappie   21. AC unhappie hast, that haste   23. D to thy owne   28. I *omits* I *after* loved   31. A—M hast left thy love in me   32. KLM they revenge   35. M look on thee when he gave the

485. 3. E—M that I would willingly   5. D with her is al my hope   7. D can justice   12. KLM upon earth   13. BD all my misfortunes   C mis-fortune   28. M till I as it   30. A—M *omit* he   33. E—M death unto you

486. 6. KLM wayling   9. KLM in the despite of   12. BD—M dead on that condition   26. A—M building   31. E—M though I do bemone   32. F—M reason so to doe   34. F—M *omit* had   38. AC But that the speech

487. 8. D aske for thee   9. M whose from   26. A—M therefore bee comforted   33. A—M with teares of joy   37. BD chiefe part indeed of all

488. 1. E—M *omit* now   6. BD—M farthest   10. A—L into of cruelly tormenting our M into of cruelty termenting our   14. A—M indeede it was not my sister   27—28. M so they had set   31. I but when they   35. B neither to receive

489. 2. LM with that joy   6—7. KLM torment   7. F that of one of my   8. IM proceeds from   13. KLM *omit* the *before* imprecations D imprecation   14. M farther   15. D want of libertie   20. D of a abundance   25. CF—M prepare thy selfe for the   35. C well-come be all my miseries   36. D I pittie   37. D finde in mine

490. 10. M frame his mind   18. E—L contrarieties M contraries   19. KLM . but *instead of* both   23. A—M now they would have done it   25. M we might   32. BD—M who could lively   33. KLM should lively paint the lightsom   34. A—I finding then betweene   36. A—M his *instead of* with *after* sealed up

491. 1. BDEF moning lips   3. E—M *omit* had   9. E—M messengers   10. A—F brought answeres   11. M to in indite A—M unfortunate affection   15. M with the countenance   22. D mortall hatred   26. M to the possession   27. K their crueltie   28. C ungodly   31. LM with his speech   34. D *omits* most

NOTES

492. 7. LM of great punishment   11. A—M was upon the top   15. K with his matter   33. BD—GKLM murdered   39. KLM *transpose* enough *and* miserable

493. 3. HI *Philoxinus*   7. KLM *Ismenius*   9. KLM my *instead of* thy   10. D the *instead of* thy   32. M by that means D his double

494. 1. E—M *omit* a *before* good   9. M given me by other event   24. A—M *omit* there *before* giving   32. D in their destruction

495. 14. A—M *omit* up   15. I eyes levelled   A—M from top to toe   32—33. M difficulties   33. G—M valour

496. 24. A—M breathing nothing but   28. E—M all the former   34—35. KLM *transpose* yet *and* made   36. A—M strange disasters

497. 2. D *transposes* hast *and* thou   4. A—M but to weepe   9. LM thy faith to   12. BD—M wert disdained   25. E—M perfection

498. 23. A *commas in margin*

498. 30—502. 19. Among the rest...*hath made glorious. In all the folio editions this passage is to be found in the fourth Eclogues* C *omits division into stanzas*

498. 35. A—M *Who most the silly*   38. C *bark*

499. 1. A—M *braunches cleave*   14. M *all the Sun*   15. M *The bowels*   KLM *will all*   19. IM *Princes weare*   20. M *Tell these*   21. I *foretokens*   25. M *these words*   30. KLM *all words*   32. C *stars in constant constant*

500. 6. A—M *omit commas in margin*   C *Too well*   8. G *that thou no*   9. E—M *mourning night*   19. I *be full spent*   24. E *daily raving*   25. ACE *ô Sinne*   27. AC *set the triumph*   30. ACD *by the pompe*   34. M *it still*   35. LM *its self*

501. 14. F—M *his just*   17. F—M *all that life*   39. A—M *omit commas in margin*

502. 4. M *of her sight*   C *oj our fight*   12. BD *grow our*   14. F—M *For such deepe*   26. A—M consort of whose mourning   27. A—M naturall tunes of   29. F—M having before both their   31. G—M valour   32. A—M value

503. 6. M brothers   13—14. A—M *omit commas in margin*   19—20. E—M whom she most dearely   22. E—M by byding   24. I lost sound   33. ABCE *Pamela* steppes   38. D would not have

504. 6. BD—M in time past   11. M extremit   14. E—M *have no comma after* sadly *and put a semi-colon after* desperately   22. A—D them was   E—M then was   23. A—M bringing force   26. BD his brother   28. F—M with still intention   37. E—M upon his pride

505. 1. F—M already *instead of* ready   4. G—M *Fame* hath not   21—23. BD *omit* be tied...thou so much

506. 6. A—M overcome braver Knightes   8. HI *Evardes*   14. H—M *Evardes*   37. A—M much worse to skolde

NOTES

507. 6. E—M *omit* at   11. C courtesie, end put   16. DG—M more bragged   31. D had eyes   32. BD—M set it in her memorie

508. 15. F—M unexpected   18. *Between "Fortune" and* since A—M *insert* since our owne parents are content to be tyraunts over us 28—29. B—M *omit commas in margin*   35. B—M *omit commas in margin* A—M then will bee the time

509. 7. I gave consent   25. KLM the measure of that 40. KLM he hath found

510. 6. A—M therefore detaining   8. M to enquire   10. KLM was sufficient   13. BD—M prophecying   15. KL incrudelity 23. B—M *omit commas in margin*   24. KLM oblations   26. B—M *omit commas in margin*   29. KLM durst any one   33. C with noble arte

511. 2. F—M by *Amphialus*   5. G—M his desires, it   11. A—F *Anaxius* priviledge GKL *Anaxiu's* priviledge HIM *Anaxius's* priviledge   13. F—M daughter   26. BD—M take that away F—M runnings   27. F—M worthy men   28. E—M they went headlong   30. C were described

512. 18. BD—M have their beleefe   19. A—M servant 26. D *omits* if   27. C having hard all this   29. D these excellent   36. D either for

513. 19. D such a one   23. E—M *omit* but   32. KLM stronger nimbleness   37. D mistresse

514. 1. M *Proserpine*   18. B—M *omit commas in margin* E—M valour   26. A—M *insert* a *before* spoile   E—M *insert* a *before* fight   32. AC this whole globe   35. C looke one

515. 4. I on the inside   25. E—M *insert* the *before* humane 26. FGHKLM as if hee lifted

516. 7. LM But when Pity   10. KLM *omit* a *after* such 17—18. E—M therewith   18. KLM yet hee did   20. KLM and that in all the   29. BD—M remembring of what   40. KLM *omit* as *before* glorie

517. 3. F—L *semi-colon after* revenging   E—M injuries   C slaughter   18—19. I perchance such   20. A—M that great body 23. KLM so they did differ

518. 3. A—M So that consenting   20. BD—M more terrible 36. D sayings

519. 6. E—HKLM manly   9. A—M *omit* him   11. M as never having don so much

APPENDIX

The Eclogues being distributed in a different manner in all the folios, I append here an outline of the Eclogues as printed in 1593, giving the prose paragraphs which were then introduced. Such poems as appeared in 1593 for the first time will be printed in vol. II.

THE FIRST ECLOGES.

Basilius, because *Zelmane* so would have it *etc.* [*see* p. 126. l. 1—p. 132. l. 7 *incl.*].

Dorus did so well in answering *Thyrsis*, that every one desired to heare him sing something alone. Seing therfore a Lute lying under the Princesse *Pamelas* feete glad to have such an errand to approch her, he came, but came with a dismaied grace, all his bloud stirred betwixt feare and desire. And playing upon it with such sweetenes, as every bodie wondered to see such skill in a shepeheard, he sang unto it with a sorrowing voice these Elegiake verses :

Dorus.—*Fortune, Nature, Love, long have contended about me,*
Which etc. [*see* vol. II.].

Dorus when he had soong this, having had all the while a free beholding of the faire *Pamela* (who could well have spared such honor, and defended the assault he gave unto hir face with bringing a faire staine of shamefastnes unto it) let fall his armes, and remained so fastened in his thoughts, as if *Pamela* had graffed him there to growe in continuall imagination. But *Zelmane* espying it, and fearing he should too much forget himselfe, she came to him, and tooke out of his hand the Lute, and laying fast hold of *Philocleas* face with her eyes, she soong these *Sapphikes* speaking as it were to hir owne hope.

If mine eyes can speake to doo harty errande,
Or mine etc. [*see* p. 143. l. 15—p. 144. l. 8 *incl.*].

Great was the pleasure of *Basilius*, and greater would have bene *Gynæcias*, but that she found too well it was intended to her daughter, As for *Philoclea* she was swetely ravished withall. When *Dorus* desiring in a secret maner to speake of their cases, as perchance the parties intended might take some light of it, making lowe reverence to *Zelmane*, began this provoking song in hexameter verse unto her. Whereunto she soone finding whither his words were directed (in like tune and verse) answered as foloweth :

Dorus. Zelmane.

Dorus. *Lady reservd by the heav'ns to do pastors company honnor,*
Joyning etc. [*see* vol. II.].

APPENDIX

What exclaming praises *Basilius* gave to this Ecloge any man may ghesse, that knowes love is better then a paire of spectacles to make every thing seeme greater which is sene through it : and then is never tongue tied where fitt commendation (whereof womankinde is so likerouse) is offered unto it. But before any other came in to supplie the place, *Zelmane* having heard some of the shepheards by chaunce name *Strephon* and *Klaius*, supposing thereby they had bene present, was desirous both to heare them for the fame of their frindly love, and to know them, for their kindenesse towardes her best loved frinde. Much grieved was *Basilius*, that any desire of his mistresse should bee unsatisfied, and therefore to represent them unto hir (aswell as in their absence it might be) he commaunded on *Lamon*, who had at large sett down their country pastimes and first love to *Urania* to sing the whole discourse which he did in this manner.

A Shepheards tale no height of stile desires
To raise etc. [*see* vol. II.].

As *Lamon* would have proceded, *Basilius* knowing, by the wasting of the torches that the night also was farre wasted, and withall remembring *Zelmanes* hurt, asked hir whither she thought it not better to reserve the complaint of *Klaius* till an other day. Which she, perceiving the song had alreadie worne out much time, and not knowing when *Lamon* would ende, being even now stepping over to a new matter, though much delighted with what was spoken, willingly agreed unto. And so of all sides they went to recommend themselves to the elder brother of death.

The end of the first Booke.

THE SECOND ECLOGUES.

THE rude tumult of the *Enispians* gave occasion *etc.* [*see* p. 339. l. 1— p. 344. l. 9 *incl.*].

When they had ended to the good pleasing of the assistants, especiallie of *Zelmane*, who never forgat to give due cōmendatiōs to her friend *Dorus*, *Basilius* called for *Lamon* to end his discourse of *Strephon* & *Klaius*, wherwith the other day he marked *Zelmane* to have bene exceedingly delighted. But him sicknes had staied from that assemblie. which gave occasion to *Histor* and *Damon* two yonge shepheards, taking upō them the two frendly rivalles names, to present *Basilius* with some other of their complaints Ecloge-wise, and first with this double Sestine.

Strephon. Klaius.

Strephon.   *Yee Goteheard Gods, that love the grassie mountaines,*
Ye Nymphes etc. [*see* p. 141. l. 4—p. 143. l. 9 *incl.*].

But, as though all this had bene but the taking of a taste of their wailings, *Strephon* againe begā this Dizaine, which was answered unto him in that kind of verse which is called the crowne.

Strephon. Klaius.

Strephon.   *I Joy in griefe, and doo detest all joyes :*
Despise delight etc. [*see* p. 349. l. 5—p. 351. l. 34 *incl.*].

So well were these wailefull complaints accorded to the passions of all the princely hearers, while every one made what he heard of another the ballance of his owne fortune, that they stood a long while striken in a sad and silent

564

APPENDIX

consideration of them. Which the olde *Geron* no more marking then condemning in them, desirous to set foorth what counsailes the wisedome of age had layde up in store against such fancies (as he thought) follies of youth (yet so as it might not apeare that his wordes respected them) bending himselfe to a young shepheard named *Philisides*, (who neither had daunced nor song with them, and had all this time layne upon the ground at the foote of a *Cypresse* tree, leaning upon his elbowe with so deepe a melancoly that his sences caried to his minde no delight from any of their objects) he strake him upon the shoulder, with a right old mans grace, that will seeme livelier then his age will afford him, And thus began unto him his Ecloge.

Geron. Philisides.

Geron. *Up, up* Philisides, *let sorrowes goe,*
Who yelds etc. [*see* vol. II.].

Geron was even out of countenance, finding the words he thought were so wise, winne so little reputation at this young mans hands; and therefore sometimes looking upon an old acquaintance of his called *Mastix*, one of the repiningest fellows in the world, and that beheld no body but with a minde of mislike (saying still the world was amisse, but how it should be amended, he knew not) sometimes casting his eyes to the ground, even ashamed to see his gray haires despised, at last he spied his two dogges, whereof the elder was called *Melampus*, and the younger *Lælaps* (in deede the jewells he ever had with him) one brawling with another; which occasion he tooke to restore himselfe to his countenance, and rating *Melampus*, he began to speake to his doggs, as if in them a man should finde more obedience then in unbridled young men.

Geron. Mastix.

Geron. *Downe, downe* Melampus; *what? your fellow bite?*
I set you etc. [*see* vol. II.].

And away with his doggs streight he went as if he would be sure to have the laste worde: all the assemblie laughing at the lustines of the olde fellowe who departed muttering to himselfe he had sene more in his daies then twentie of them. But *Basilius*, who never before had heard *Philisides* (though having seldome failed to be at these metings) desired him hee woulde begin some Ecloge with some other of the shepheardes according to the accustomed guise. *Philisides* though very unwilling, at the Kings cōmaundmēt offred to sing with *Thyrsis*. But he directly refused him, seing, he should within few dayes be maried to the faire *Kala*; and since he had gotten his desire he would sing no more. Then the king willed *Philisides* to declare the discourse of his owne fortunes unknowen to them as being a stranger in that countrie but hee praied the King to pardon him, the time being farre to joyfull to suffer the rehearsall of his miseries. But to satisfie *Basilius* someway, hee began an Eclogue betwixt himselfe and the *Echo*, framing his voice so in those desert places as what wordes he would have the Echo replie unto, those he woulde sing higher then the rest; and so, kindelie framed a disputation betwixt himselfe and it, which with these hexameters in the following order he uttered.

Philisides.   Echo.

Faire Rocks, goodly rivers, sweet woods, when shall I see peace? Peace,
Peace? etc. [*see* p. 352. l. 12—p. 353. l. 24 *incl.*].

Philisides was commended for the placing of his Echo, but little did he regarde their praises, who had sett the foundation of his honour there, wher hee was most despisde: and therefore retorning againe to the traine of h

APPENDIX

desolate pensivenes, *Zelmanes* seing no body offer to fill the stage, as if her long restrayned conceates did now burst out of prison : she thus desiring her voice should be accorded to nothing, but to *Philocleas* eares, threw downe the burden of her minde in *Anacreous* kinde of verses.

> *My muse what ail's this ardour*
> *To blase etc. [see* vol. II.].

Basilius when shee had fully ended her song, fell prostrate upon the ground, and thanked the Gods they had preserved his life so longe, as to heare the very musicke they themselves used, in an earthly body. And then with like grace to *Zelmane* never left intreating her till she had (taking a *Lyra Basilius* helde for her) song these *Phaleuciakes*

> *Reason, tell me thy mind, if here be reason*
> *In this strange etc. [see* vol. II.].

Dorus had long he thought kept silence from saying, somwhat which might tend to the glorie of her in whom all glory to his seeming was included, but nowe hee brake it, singing these verses called *Asclepiadikes.*

> *O sweet woods the delight of solitarines!*
> *O how much etc. [see* vol. II.].

The other Shepeheards were offring themselves to have continued the sportes, but the night had so quietlie spent the most parte of herselfe among them that the king for that time licēsed thē. And so bringing *Zelmane* to her lodging, who would much rather have done the same for *Philoclea*, of all sides they went to counterfett a sleepe in their bedd, for a trewe one there agonies could not aforde them. Yet there they Lay (so might they be moste solitarie for the foode of their thoughts) til it was neere noone the next day, after which *Basilius* was to continue his *Appollo* devotions, and the other to meditate upon their private desires.

> *The end of the second Eclogues.*

The following variations have been noted between the text printed above from A and the other folios:

563. 17. KLM had sung thus   18. M *transposes* well *and* have 29. E maner so to

564. 4. E mankind is so   LM liquorish   39. LM state of their wailings   47. F—M a good while   KLM in sad & silent

565. 10. LM this Eclogue   33. C to the customed guise 48. KLM the place of his   49. HI *omit* sett *after* had   LM foundations

566. 1. C *Zelmane*   2. KLM long constrained conceits 4. BD—M *Anacreons*   8. KLM as hear the   16. KLM *Asclepiades*   21. KLM licensed them to depart   23. I beds DF their agonies   26. I to mediate   28. F—I *print* Eclogues *in Roman type* KLM *have* "Book" *instead of* "Eclogues"

ALPHABETICAL TABLE OF THE
PERSONAGES IN *ARCADIA*

*[The following Table does not contain the Personages
introduced in the Eclogues.]*

Aeschylus, Bk. III, Ch. 7
Agenor, brother of Philanax, Bk. III, Ch. 7, 8
Amiclas, King of Lacedæmon, Bk. I, Ch. 5, 7, 8
Amphialus, nephew of Basilius, Bk. I, Ch. 10, 11, 15, Bk. II, Ch. 11, 15,
     18, 27, Bk. III, Ch. 2—9, 11—18, 23, 24, 25
Anaxius, nephew of Euardes, Bk. II, Ch. 18, 19, 24, Bk. III, Ch. 15, 19,
     25—29
Andromana, Queen of Iberia, Bk. I, Ch. 16, Bk. II, Ch. 15, 20, 21
Antiphilus, Bk. II, Ch. 13, 14, 23, 24, 29
Arcadia, King of, *see* Basilius
Argalus, Bk. I, Ch. 5—8, 16, Bk. III, Ch. 12, 16
Argos, King of, Bk. III, Ch. 4
Armenia, King of, *see* Tiridates
Armenia, Queen of, *see* Artaxia
Artaxia, Queen of Armenia, Bk. I, Ch. 16, Bk. II, Ch. 13, 15, 19, 23, 29
Artesia, Bk. I, Ch. 15—17, Bk. III, Ch. 2, 14, 21, 23

Baccha, Bk. I, Ch. 16, Bk. II, Ch. 22
Barzanes, King of Hyrcania, Bk. II, Ch. 10, 13
Basilius, King of Arcadia, Bk. I, Ch. 3, 4, 13—17, 19, Bk. II, Ch. 1, 4, 11,
     12, 15, 16, 25—28, Bk. III, Ch. 2, 4, 8, 9, 11—13, 15, 16, 18—20, 25, 27
Bithynia, King of, Bk. II, Ch. 22, 23

Cecropia, mother of Amphialus, Bk. I, Ch. 11, 15, 19, Bk. II, Ch. 27, 28,
     Bk. III, Ch. 2—6, 9—12, 14, 17—24
Chremes, father of Dido, Bk. II, Ch. 19
Claius, Bk. I, Ch. 1, 2
Clinias, Bk. II, Ch. 26—28, Bk. III, Ch. 2, 4, 7, 11, 13, 14
Clitophon, son of Kalander, Bk. I, Ch. 4—6, 8, 10, 11, 17
Codrus, Bk. III, Ch. 8
Corinth, Queen of, *see* Helen
Crete, King of, Bk. II, Ch. 6
Ctesiphon, Bk. III, Ch. 8

TABLE OF PERSONAGES

Daiphantus, *see* Pyrocles
Daiphantus, *see* Zelmane, daughter of Plexirtus
Dametas, Bk. I, Ch. 3, 4, 13, 19, Bk. II, Ch. 2—5, 25, 28, Bk. III, Ch. 13
Demagoras, Bk. I, Ch. 5
Dido, Bk. II, Ch. 18, 19
Dorilaus, Prince of Thessalia, father of Musidorus, Bk. II, Ch. 6
Dorus, *see* Musidorus
Drialus, Bk. III, Ch. 7

Elis, Princess of, Bk. I, Ch. 16
Elpine, Bk. I. Ch. 17
Erona, Queen of Lycia, Bk. I, Ch. 16, Bk. II, Ch. 10, 12, 13, 18, 29
Euarchus, King of Macedonia, father of Pyrocles, Bk. II, Ch. 3, 6, 7, 9, 29
Euardes, King of Bithynia, Bk. II, Ch. 10, 13, 18
Eurileon, nephew of Amiclas, Bk. I, Ch. 5, 7, 8
Eurimelon, Bk. I, Ch. 17

Galatia, King of, *see* Leonatus
Giants, the two, and their sons, Bk. II, Ch. 9, 23
Gynecia, wife of Basilius, Bk. I, Ch. 3, 13—15, 17—19, Bk. II, Ch. 1, 4, 16, 25, Bk. III, Ch. 2, 9, 16, 19

Helen, Queen of Corinth, Bk. I, Ch. 7, 10, 11, 16, 17, Bk. II, Ch. 21, Bk. III, Ch. 25, 26
Helots, the, Bk. I, Ch. 2, 5—7
Hippolitus, Bk. III, Ch. 8

Iberia, King of, Bk. II, Ch. 15, 19, 20
Iberia, Queen of, *see* Andromana
Ismenus, brother of Artesia, Bk. I, Ch. 11, 15, Bk. III, Ch. 8

Kalander, Bk. I, Ch. 2—10, Bk. III, Ch. 19
Knight, the Black, *see* Musidorus
Knight, the Forsaken, *see* Musidorus
Knight, the Green, Bk. III, Ch. 15, 18
Knight, the Ill-apparelled, *see* Pyrocles
Knight, the White, Bk. III, Ch. 15, 18

Lacedæmon, King of, *see* Amiclas
Lacemon, Bk. I, Ch. 16
Lalus, Bk. I, Ch. 17
Lelius, Bk. II, Ch. 21
Leon, Bk. I, Ch. 17
Leonatus, King of Galatia, brother of Plexirtus, Bk. II, Ch. 10, 22—24
Leontius, Bk. III, Ch. 7
Leucippe, Bk. I, Ch. 16, Bk. II, Ch. 22
Leucippus & Nelsus, Bk. II, Ch. 7, 9
Lycia, Queen of, *see* Erona
Lycurgus, brother of Anaxius, Bk. III, Ch. 15, 18—20, 25—28
Lydia, King of, Bk. II, Ch. 6

Macedonia, King of, *see* Euarchus
Megalus, Bk. III, Ch. 8
Memnon, Bk. III, Ch. 7

568

TABLE OF PERSONAGES

Menalcas, Bk. I, Ch. 18, 19

Milo, Bk. III, Ch. 8

Miso, wife of Dametas, Bk. I, Ch. 3, Bk. II, Ch. 2, 5, 6, 11, 14—16, 24, 25,
    Bk. III, Ch. 2, 9

Mopsa, daughter of Dametas, Bk. I, Ch. 3, Bk. II, Ch. 2, 5, 6, 11, 14, 25,
    Bk. III, Ch. 1, 2

Musidorus, Prince of Thessalia, sometimes called Palladius, Dorus, the Black
    Knight, the Forsaken Knight, Bk. I, Ch. 1—6, 8—12, 14, 15, 17—19,
    Bk. II, Ch. 2, 3, 5—11, 13, 18—27, 29, Bk. III, Ch. 1, 8, 15, 18, 26

Nelsus, *see* Leucippus

Nestor, Bk. I, Ch. 17

Nisus, Bk. III, Ch. 7

Otaves, brother of Barzanes, Bk. II, Ch. 23

Palemon, Bk. III, Ch. 8

Palladius, son of Andromana, Bk. II, Ch. 15, 20, 21

Palladius, *see* Musidorus

Pamela, daughter of Basilius, Bk. I, Ch. 3, 13, 15, 17—19, Bk. II, Ch. 2, 3,
    5, 6, 11, 12, 14, 25, 28, Bk. III, Ch. 1, 2, 6, 9, 10, 11, 14, 19—21, 23, 24,
    26—28

Pamphilus, Bk. II, Ch. 18, 19, 22

Pannonia, King of, Bk. II, Ch. 6

Paphlagonia, King of, Bk. II, Ch. 10

Parthenia, Bk. I, Ch. 5, 7, 8, 16, Bk. III, Ch. 12, 16

Phalantus, brother of Helen, Queen of Corinth, Bk. I, Ch. 15—17, Bk. III,
    Ch. 11

Phebilus, Bk. I, Ch. 17, Bk. III, Ch. 7

Philanax, Bk. I, Ch. 4, Bk. II, Ch. 28, Bk. III, Ch. 2, 4, 8, 9, 13, 15, 16, 18,
    19, 26, 27

Philisides, Bk. II, Ch. 21

Philoclea, daughter of Basilius, Bk. I, Ch. 3, 13—14, 17, 19, Bk. II, Ch. 4, 5,
    11, 12, 14, 16, 17, 21, 24—26, 28, Bk. III, Ch. 2, 3, 5, 6, 9, 11, 12, 14,
    19—24, 26—28

Philoxenus, Bk. I, Ch. 11

Phrygia, King of, Bk. II, Ch. 7, 8

Phrygia, the new King of, Bk. II, Ch. 8, 23

Plangus, son of the King of Iberia, Bk. II, Ch. 10, 12, 13, 15, 29

Plexirtus, brother of Leonatus, Bk. II, Ch. 10, 22—24, 29

Plistonax, Bk. III, Ch. 8

Policrates, Bk. III, Ch. 7

Polixena, Bk. I, Ch. 17

Polycetes, Bk. I, Ch. 17

Pontus, King of, Bk. II, Ch. 9

Pontus, the new King of, Bk. II, Ch. 9, 10, 22—24

Pyrocles, Prince of Macedonia, sometimes called Daiphantus, Zelmane, the Ill-
    apparelled Knight, Bk. I, Ch. 1, 5—10, 12—19, Bk. II, Ch. 1—4, 6—29,
    Bk. III, Ch. 2, 14, 19—24, 26—29

Sarpedon, Bk. III, Ch. 8

Strephon, Bk. I, Ch. 1, 2

Strophilus, Bk. III, Ch. 8

TABLE OF PERSONAGES

Telamon, Bk. I, Ch. 17
Telenor, *see* Tydeus
Thessalia, Prince of, *see* Dorilaus *and* Musidorus
Thrace, King of, Bk. II, Ch. 6
Timotheus, father of Philoxenus, Bk. I, Ch. 11
Tiridates, King of Armenia, Bk. II, Ch. 10, 13, 15
Tressennius, Bk. III, Ch. 15
Tydeus & Telenor, Bk. II, Ch. 10, 22, 23

Urania, Bk. I, Ch. 1, 2, 16, 17

Zelmane, *see* Pyrocles
Zelmane, Plexirtus' daughter, sometimes called Daiphantus, Bk. I, Ch. 16,
    Bk. II, Ch. 20—23
Zoana, Bk. I, Ch. 17
Zoilus, brother of Anaxius, Bk. III, Ch. 15, 18—20, 25—28

INDEX OF FIRST LINES OF POEMS

A hatefull cure with hate to heale   325
Alas how long this pilgrimage doth last   227
And are you there old Pas? in troth I ever thought   344
Apollo great, whose beames the greater world do light   328
As I my little flocke on Ister banke   132

Come Dorus, come, let songs thy sorowes signifie   127
Come shepheards weedes, become your masters minde   113

Dorus, tell me, where is thy wonted motion   340

Faire rocks, goodly rivers, sweet woods, when shall I see peace? Peace   352

His being was in her alone   557

I Joye in griefe, and doo detest all joyes   349
If mine eyes can speake to doo harty errande   143
In faith, good Histor, long is your delay   137
In vaine, mine Eyes, you labour to amende   147

Let not old age disgrace my high desire   149
Loved I am, and yet complaine of Love   253

Me thought some staves he mist: if so, not much amisse   285
My sheepe are thoughts, which I both guide and serve   163
My words, in hope to blaze my stedfast minde   173

Now thanked be the great God Pan   122
Now was our heav'nly vaulte deprived of the light   394

Over these brookes trusting to ease mine eyes   257

Poore Painters oft with silly Poets joyne   239

Since so mine eyes are subject to your sight   155
Since that to death is gone the shepheard hie   498

The Fire to see my woes for anger burneth   442
Thou Rebell vile, come, to thy master yelde   339
Thy elder care shall from thy carefull face   327
Transformd in shew, but more transformd in minde   76

Unto a caitife wretch, whom long affliction holdeth   357

We love, and have our loves rewarded   126
What length of verse can serve brave Mopsas good to show   21
What toong can her perfections tell   218
Wyth two strange fires of equall heate possest   310

You Gote-heard Gods, that love the grassie mountaines   141
You living powres enclosed in stately shrine   172